SELECTED WORKS OF

Stephen Vincent BENÉT

VOLUME ONE
POETRY

VOLUME TWO
PROSE

HOLT, RINEHART AND WINSTON
New York · Chicago · San Francisco

The works included in this volume are covered by separate copyrights
as stated below:

VOLUME ONE

VOLUME TWO

STEPHEN VINCENT BENÉT

Of Mark Sabre, the hero of *If Winter Comes*, we are told that Byron's poems was "the first book he had ever bought 'specially'— not, that is, as one buys a bun, but as one buys a dog." I have a similar feeling for Stephen Vincent Benét's *Heavens and Earth* (his third volume of poems, following *Young Adventure*, and *Five Men and Pompey*, published while he was still at school). For that was the first book I ever bought on the strength of a review—and I wish my own reviews were always as reliable as that one proved to be. It appeared in *The Yale Literary Magazine;* I was a schoolboy at Taft at the time, and read the *Lit* much more religiously than I did when I got to Yale. What chiefly struck me in it was a comparison to William Morris, a current idol of mine, and a number of quotations, excellently chosen, which showed me that here was one of my predestined books. I bought it the first day of the following vacation (it was one of the curious features of secondary education as then practiced that while at school it was made as difficult as possible to read any books) and found all that I had been looking for and more besides. The resemblance to William Morris in certain poems was plain enough; in his first novel, *The Beginning of Wisdom*, which belongs to what he has elsewhere described as "the required project in those days, a school and college novel," Benét says of the boy who is not quite himself that one of his first outpourings was "a long and bloodily bad ballad stewed from the bones of William Morris"; but it was resemblance to Morris where he is least dangerous as an influence, in the mood of mediaevalism combined with brutal realism of "Shameful Death" or "The Haystack in the Floods"—and, making allowance for some youthful romanticism, the mood, here, of "Three Days' Ride."

But there was of course a great deal more than that. Even in that one poem, there was also, for instance, a technical device to take your breath away—literally, the way the *pnigos* in Aristophanes took away the breath of the actor—if (as you should) you read it aloud. It is that innocent refrain,

vii

> From Belton Castle to Solway side,
> Hard by the bridge, is three days' ride,

which, at each repetition, becomes more menacing, until in its final form,

> From Belton Castle to Solway side,
> Though great hearts break, is three days' ride,

the beating stresses give you a feeling in the chest which you will recognize from the last time you ran five miles.

There were other matters of technique, too, to fascinate a school-boy who had recently discovered the subject. There is the dirge in "The First Vision of Helen"—which he would not let me include here, with the oversevere judgment of a creator who has gone on to something else. God, I suppose, admires the dinosaurs less than we do. The poem is in various metres; one section begins:

> Close his eyes with the coins; bind his chin with the shroud.

That line, you will notice, is made of the musical phrase *tum ti tum ti ti tum* twice repeated; and that, with what the books call anacrusis and anaclasis, is the metrical unit of the entire lament. It was not until freshman year at Yale when I read *Prometheus Bound* that I learned to call it a dochmiac; but I was able to recognize it as a single foot, and a complete and rare one. (Gilbert Murray and another have used it to render Greek choruses; as far as I know it occurs nowhere else in English.) A good deal later I was able to ask Steve Benét, "M. Jourdain, did you know that in that passage you were writing in dochmiacs?" He replied honestly that he did not know whether he had ever encountered the foot or not, but he believed he had just felt that anapaests were "too curly."

Whether he found or invented it, it is the perfect measure for the sway of the bearers ("Slow as the stream and strong, answering knee to knee"); and the accommodation of the line to the breath in these two poems is the promise of what he achieves in *John Brown's Body* when he attacks one of the primary problems of verse in our day, the finding of a form which may bear the same relation to our easygoing talk that, presumably, blank verse did to the more formal speech of an earlier generation. Half a dozen poets are attempting it; Benét was one of the first in the field, and I think is the most successful, with the long, loose, five- or six-beat line that carries the bulk of *John Brown's Body*. It will be improved in the later poems; in *John Brown's Body* it is sometimes a little too loose, coming perilously near prose; yet it can carry casual conversations without incongruity, or at need can deepen without any sense of abrupt transition into blank verse for the nobility of Lincoln or Lee, or even slip into rhyme for the romantics of the Wingates. And it passes the great test for existence as a metre: single lines of it stay in your memory, existing by themselves.

It is over now, but they will not let it be over.

Professor Procrustes could explain that as an iambic or an anapaestic line, and name its variations; but to plain common sense it is neither. It is in a metre of its own; one of our time; one which Benét has given us.

There was more, too, in that thin purple book with a gilt demi-Pegasus on the cover, to meet one halfway and lead one out of the Pre-Raphaelite dreamland. There was an impish humor, which appeared not only in the openly grotesque poems, but was likely to crop up anywhere—in the tempting quotation, for instance, which begins "Young Blood," and which, when you catch him with the question, Steve will blandly tell you that he invented. It is this quality, by the way, which is most readily apparent when you know him. He is given a puckish air by his habit of twisting his legs round his chair, by his round glasses, and his squeaky voice—which I always hear, in "Nightmare with Angels," giving his own peculiarly emphatic intonation to the conclusion "In fact, you will not be saved." In talk he seems to "make fun" of everything, not in the sense of ridicule, but with the humor that comes from looking at anything with a really original mind. His talk ranges over everything he has read (and he has read everything) building pyramids in the air, and, like his own "Innovator," turning them upside down to see how they look; while from time to time his wife Rosemary puts in a wise and charming word as she sits serenely sewing—looking like an unusually humorous version of the housewifely Athena, as Steve behind his spectacles looks like an unusually humorous version of Athena's owl.

That is the Benét of the dry comments in *John Brown's Body*, upon McClellan—

He looked the part—he could have acted the part

ix

Word perfectly. He looked like an empire-builder.
But so few empire-builders have looked the part—

or upon Wendell Phillips—

He did his part,
Being strong and active, in all ways shaped like a man,
And the cause being one to which he professed devotion,
He spoke. He spoke well, with conviction, and frequently.

It is the Benét of the fantasies and fables, of the extraordinary
"Nightmares," which deepen from the fantastic-amusing to the
fantastic-terrifying. It's the author who can rewrite an old fairy
tale for today in the much-reprinted "King of the Cats," or can
write a new legend so perfect that it seems to have been always
a part of our folklore—for the Devil and Daniel Webster ought
forever to haunt New Hampshire as solidly as Rip Van Winkle
and his gnomes haunt the Hudson. And the Benét who turns
pyramids upside down in talk is the one who writes with imagination. The popular magazines are filled with stories that have invention, and ingenuity, and even a sort of conjurer's illusion; but
the rarest thing in the world there or anywhere else is real imagination, which is real magic—such as you find in that astonishing
piece of what-if, "The Curfew Tolls," or that haunting evocation
of the feeling of certain quiet city backwaters, "Glamour." It is
also one of the marks of imaginative insight that it can have an
Einsteinian view of both sides of a solid at once; can see Napoleon
as a good deal of a scoundrel and also as a great man; can destroy
all the traditional witchery of the traditional Southern belle, and
yet leave her, somehow, mistress of a more undeniable spell than
before.

And then, of course, in *Heavens and Earth* there was a section,
The Tall Town, which showed that there was poetry in New
York; and in Benét's previous volume, *Young Adventure*, to which
Heavens and Earth sent me back, there was "The Hemp," a ballad
laid in Virginia. He was to write finer celebrations of New York,
in prose and in verse, in "All Around the Town," and his city
poems, in visions of its decay and resurrection; and he was to write
greater ballads about America; but he had already declared that
delight in his city and country which was to be a major theme
in his work.

Americanism is so much in fashion now that Benét's Americanism, for all its brilliance of technical achievement, its breadth of sympathy, and its depth of feeling, is apt, now that the intellectual climate of the day has caught up with it, to seem less remarkable than it is. It is worth remembering that when other young men of his age were writing rondeaux and villanelles and tales of far away and long ago, Benét was already turning the ballad to American themes; and that at the end of the tinsel twenties, when it was the fashion to say that American life was rootless, drab, and everywhere the same, Benét was already writing *John Brown's Body*, with its sensitive feeling for half a dozen countrysides and racial strains, and for the American wilderness and the old English songs that frame the exquisite idyll of Jack Ellyat and Melora Vilas. (That story always reminds me somewhat of another idyll in the midst of a martial epic, the episode of Angelica and Medoro in the *Orlando Furioso*, and sets me to wondering about what the unconscious mind may do. I once asked Steve whether the line in *John Brown's Body*,

He danced with me. He could dance rather well. He is dead.

was intended to translate, as it so perfectly does, the epitaph on a Roman dancing boy: *Saltavit. Placuit. Mortuus est.* He replied that he had not intended it, but he knew the Latin line well—it was a favorite with Monty Woolley, who gave delight and a supply of anecdotes to generations of Yale actors—and, said Steve, "the unconscious does queer things." I have often wondered if his unconscious brought him the name of Melora, altered from Ariosto. Melora—Medoro: it might be.) And from the crowd of novels which try to add realism to historical fiction by getting up all the details of a campaign and not letting you off a single one of them, it is a pleasure to turn back to *Spanish Bayonet*, a historical novel which attains reality by the simple and difficult device of making the hero a real person.

There is no one to touch Benét in the variety and skill of his treatment of American themes; yet even his Americanism is only the outcome of something deeper. If he says, "Dear city of Cecrops," it is because that is the nearest earthly approach to the dear city of God. He loves New York as the communal achievement of the spirit of man; he loves America because there every man can most freely become what God meant him to be. One can perceive his feeling, in reverse, in his two grotesque nightmares, the ones which express a horror of insects and of machines; for they are the two things that have no right to be so intelligent—and so inhuman. And because he loves man he loves man's life. Life, one feels as one reads here, is too good to waste in holding a grudge like the Die-Hard, or in philandering, like the man to whom everybody was very nice, and too good to waste in being rich and proper, like the magnificent sheep who were Schooner Fairchild's classmates; and eternity is too good, as Doc Mellhorn found, to waste playing a harp.

When the free life of man is threatened by the cult of death, by those who deliberately make their souls eunuchs for the sake of the kingdoms of this earth, it is such a man who has both the surest guard against ultimate despair, and the most tragic sense of immediate peril. The spirit of man, he knows, is indestructible; the last of the legions goes, and Britain falls, but England rises; the savage by the waters of Babylon begins the hazardous mountaineering toward civilization; the refugee going into Egypt says, "We have been in exile before." But between there lies gaping the gulf of the Dark Ages; and the man who feels the tragedy of the waste of one Napoleon Bonaparte will be the one who can feel and make us feel the horror of the waste of whole generationsful of lives. If (in spite of the angel in the nightmare) we are to be saved, it will be in great part by the writings that show us all what we have to live for, and the good life that we could make.

BASIL DAVENPORT

SELECTED WORKS OF *Stephen Vincent Benét*

VOLUME ONE: POETRY

CONTENTS VOLUME ONE

TO ROSEMARY

JOHN BROWN'S BODY

John Brown's Body

INVOCATION

AMERICAN muse, whose strong and diverse heart
So many men have tried to understand
But only made it smaller with their art,
Because you are as various as your land,

As mountainous-deep, as flowered with blue rivers,
Thirsty with deserts, buried under snows,
As native as the shape of Navajo quivers,
And native, too, as the sea-voyaged rose.

Swift runner, never captured or subdued,
Seven-branched elk beside the mountain stream,
That half a hundred hunters have pursued
But never matched their bullets with the dream,

Where the great huntsmen failed, I set my sorry
And mortal snare for your immortal quarry.

You are the buffalo-ghost, the broncho-ghost
With dollar-silver in your saddle-horn,
The cowboys riding in from Painted Post,
The Indian arrow in the Indian corn,

And you are the clipped velvet of the lawns
Where Shropshire grows from Massachusetts sods,
The grey Maine rocks—and the war-painted dawns
That break above the Garden of the Gods.

The prairie-schooners crawling toward the ore
And the cheap car, parked by the station-door.

Where the skyscrapers lift their foggy plumes
Of stranded smoke out of a stony mouth
You are that high stone and its arrogant fumes,
And you are ruined gardens in the South

And bleak New England farms, so winter-white
Even their roofs look lonely, and the deep
The middle grainland where the wind of night
Is like all blind earth sighing in her sleep.

A friend, an enemy, a sacred hag
With two tied oceans in her medicine-bag.

They tried to fit you with an English song
And clip your speech into the English tale.
But, even from the first, the words went wrong,
The catbird pecked away the nightingale.

The homesick men begot high-cheekboned things
Whose wit was whittled with a different sound
And Thames and all the rivers of the kings
Ran into Mississippi and were drowned.

They planted England with a stubborn trust.
But the cleft dust was never English dust.

Stepchild of every exile from content
And all the disavouched, hard-bitten pack
Shipped overseas to steal a continent
With neither shirts nor honor to their back.

Pimping grandee and rump-faced regicide,
Apple-cheeked younkers from a windmill-square,
Puritans stubborn as the nails of Pride,
Rakes from Versailles and thieves from County Clare,

The black-robed priests who broke their hearts in vain
To make you God and France or God and Spain.

These were your lovers in your buckskin-youth.
And each one married with a dream so proud
He never knew it could not be the truth
And that he coupled with a girl of cloud.

4

And now to see you is more difficult yet
Except as an immensity of wheel
Made up of wheels, oiled with inhuman sweat
And glittering with the heat of ladled steel.

All these you are, and each is partly you,
And none is false, and none is wholly true.

So how to see you as you really are,
So how to suck the pure, distillate, stored
Essence of essence from the hidden star
And make it pierce like a riposting sword.

For, as we hunt you down, you must escape
And we pursue a shadow of our own
That can be caught in a magician's cape
But has the flatness of a painted stone.

Never the running stag, the gull at wing,
The pure elixir, the American thing.

And yet, at moments when the mind was hot
With something fierier than joy or grief,
When each known spot was an eternal spot
And every leaf was an immortal leaf,

I think that I have seen you, not as one,
But clad in diverse semblances and powers,
Always the same, as light falls from the sun,
And always different, as the differing hours.

Yet, through each altered garment that you wore
The naked body, shaking the heart's core.

All day the snow fell on that Eastern town
With its soft, pelting, little, endless sigh
Of infinite flakes that brought the tall sky down
Till I could put my hands in the white sky

And taste cold scraps of heaven on my tongue
And walk in such a changed and luminous light
As gods inhabit when the gods are young.
All day it fell. And when the gathered night

Was a blue shadow cast by a pale glow
I saw you then, snow-image, bird of the snow.

And I have seen and heard you in the dry
Close-huddled furnace of the city street
When the parched moon was planted in the sky
And the limp air hung dead against the heat.

I saw you rise, red as that rusty plant,
Dizzied with lights, half-mad with senseless sound,
Enormous metal, shaking to the chant
Of a triphammer striking iron ground.

Enormous power, ugly to the fool,
And beautiful as a well-handled tool.

These, and the memory of that windy day
On the bare hills, beyond the last barbed wire,
When all the orange poppies bloomed one way
As if a breath would blow them into fire,

I keep forever, like the sea-lion's tusk
The broken sailor brings away to land,
But when he touches it, he smells the musk,
And the whole sea lies hollow in his hand.

So, from a hundred visions, I make one,
And out of darkness build my mocking sun.

And should that task seem fruitless in the eyes
Of those a different magic sets apart
To see through the ice-crystal of the wise
No nation but the nation that is Art,

Their words are just. But when the birchbark-call
Is shaken with the sound that hunters make
The moose comes plunging through the forest-wall
Although the rifle waits beside the lake.

Art has no nations—but the mortal sky
Lingers like gold in immortality.

This flesh was seeded from no foreign grain
But Pennsylvania and Kentucky wheat,
And it has soaked in California rain
And five years tempered in New England sleet

To strive at last, against an alien proof
And by the changes of an alien moon,
To build again that blue, American roof
Over a half-forgotten battle-tune

And call unsurely, from a haunted ground,
Armies of shadows and the shadow-sound.

In your Long House there is an attic-place
Full of dead epics and machines that rust,
And there, occasionally, with casual face,
You come awhile to stir the sleepy dust;

Neither in pride nor mercy, but in vast
Indifference at so many gifts unsought,
The yellowed satins, smelling of the past,
And all the loot the lucky pirates brought.

I only bring a cup of silver air,
Yet, in your casualness, receive it there.

Receive the dream too haughty for the breast,
Receive the words that should have walked as bold
As the storm walks along the mountain-crest
And are like beggars whining in the cold.

The maimed presumption, the unskilful skill,
The patchwork colors, fading from the first,
And all the fire that fretted at the will
With such a barren ecstasy of thirst.

Receive them all—and should you choose to touch them
With one slant ray of quick, American light,
Even the dust will have no power to smutch them,
Even the worst will glitter in the night.

If not—the dry bones littered by the way
May still point giants toward their golden prey.

PRELUDE—THE SLAVER

He closed the Bible carefully, putting it down
As if his fingers loved it.
                              Then he turned.
"Mr. Mate."
              "Yes, sir."
                          The captain's eyes held a shadow.
"I think, while this weather lasts," he said, after a pause,
"We'd better get them on deck as much as we can.
They keep better that way. Besides," he added, unsmiling,
"She's begun to stink already. You've noticed it?"

The mate nodded, a boyish nod of half-apology,
"And only a week out, too, sir."
                                  "Yes," said the skipper.
His eyes looked into themselves. "Well. The trade," he said,
"The trade's no damn perfume-shop." He drummed with his
    fingers.
"Seem to be quiet tonight," he murmured, at last.
"Oh yes sir, quiet enough." The mate flushed. "Not
What you'd call quiet at home but—quiet enough."

"Um," said the skipper. "What about the big fellow?"

"Tarbarrel, sir? The man who says he's a king?
He was praying to something—it made the others restless.
Mr. Olsen stopped it."
                        "I don't like that," said the skipper.

"It was only an idol, sir."
                            "Oh."
                                    "A stone or something."
"Oh."

"But he's a bad one, sir—a regular sullen one—
He—eyes in the dark—like a cat's—enough to give you—"
The mate was young. He shivered. "The creeps," he said.

"We've had that kind," said the skipper. His mouth was hard
Then it relaxed. "Damn cheating Arabs!" he said,
"I told them I'd take no more of their pennyweight kings,
Worth pounds to look at, and then when you get them aboard

8

Go crazy so they have to be knocked on the head
Or else just eat up their hearts and die in a week
Taking up room for nothing."

The mate hardly heard him, thinking of something else.
"I'm afraid we'll lose some more of the women," he said.
"Well, they're a scratch lot," said the skipper, "Any sickness?"

"Just the usual, sir."
                        "But nothing like plague or—"
                                                    "No sir."
"The Lord is merciful," said the skipper.
His voice was wholly sincere—an old ship's bell
Hung in the steeple of a meeting-house
With all New England and the sea's noise in it.
"Well, you'd better take another look-see, Mr. Mate."
The mate felt his lips go dry. "Aye aye, sir," he said,
Wetting his lips with his tongue. As he left the cabin
He heard the Bible being opened again.

Lantern in hand, he went down to the hold.
Each time he went he had a trick of trying
To shut the pores of his body against the stench
By force of will, by thinking of salt and flowers,
But it was always useless.
                        He kept thinking:
When I get home, when I get a bath and clean food,
When I've gone swimming out beyond the Point
In that cold green, so cold it must be pure
Beyond the purity of a dissolved star,
When I get my shore-clothes on, and one of those shirts
Out of the linen-closet that smells of lavender,
Will my skin smell black even then, will my skin smell black?

The lantern shook in his hand.
                        This was black, here,
This was black to see and feel and smell and taste,
The blackness of black, with one weak lamp to light it
As ineffectually as a firefly in Hell,
And, being so, should be silent.
                        But the hold
Was never silent.

9

There was always that breathing.
Always that thick breathing, always those shivering cries.

A few of the slaves
Knew English—at least the English for water and Jesus.
"I'm dying." "Sick." "My name Caesar."
Those who knew
These things, said these things now when they saw the lantern
Mechanically, as tamed beasts answer the whipcrack.
Their voices beat at the light like heavy moths.
But most made merely liquid or guttural sounds
Meaningless to the mate, but horribly like
The sounds of palateless men or animals trying
To talk through a human throat.
The mate was used
To the confusion of limbs and bodies by now.
At first it had made him think of the perturbed
Blind coil of blacksnakes thawing on a rock
In the bleak sun of Spring, or Judgment Day
Just after the first sounding of the trump
When all earth seethes and crumbles with the slow
Vast, mouldy resurrection of the dead.
But he had passed such fancies.
He must see
As much as he could. He couldn't see very much.
They were too tightly packed but—no plague yet,
And all the chains were fast. Then he saw something.
The woman was asleep but her baby was dead.
He wondered whether to take it from her now.
No, it would only rouse the others. Tomorrow.
He turned away with a shiver.
His glance fell
On the man who said he had been a king, the man
Called Tarbarrel, the image of black stone
Whose eyes were savage gods.
The huge suave muscles
Rippled like stretching cats as he changed posture,
Magnificence in chains that yet was ease.
The smolder in those eyes. The steady hate.

The mate made himself stare till the eyes dropped.
Then he turned back to the companionway.

His forehead was hot and sweaty. He wiped it off,
But then the rough cloth of his sleeve smelt black.

The captain shut the Bible as he came in.
"Well, Mister Mate?"
                              "All quiet, sir."
                                            The captain
Looked at him sharply. "Sit down," he said in a bark.
The mate's knees gave as he sat. "It's—hot down there,"
He said, a little weakly, wanting to wipe
His face again, but knowing he'd smell that blackness
Again, if he did.
                    "Takes you that way, sometimes,"
Said the captain, not unkindly, "I remember
Back in the twenties."
                        Something hot and strong
Bit the mate's throat. He coughed.
                                    "There," said the captain,
Putting the cup down. "You'll feel better now.
You're young for this trade, Mister, and that's a fact."

The mate coughed and didn't answer, much too glad
To see the captain change back to himself
From something made of steam, to want to talk.
But, after a while, he heard the captain talking,
Half to himself.
                  "It's a fact, that," he was saying,
"They've even made a song of me—ever heard it?"
The mate shook his head, quickly, "Oh yes you have.
You know how it goes." He cleared his throat and hummed:

   *"Captain Ball was a Yankee slaver,
   Blow, blow, blow the man down!
   He traded in niggers and loved his Saviour,
   Give me some time to blow the man down."*

The droning chanty filled the narrow cabin
An instant with grey Massachusetts sea,
Wave of the North, wave of the melted ice,
The hard salt-sparkles on the harder rock.
The stony islands.
                    Then it died away.

"Well," said the captain, "if that's how it strikes them—
They mean it bad but I don't take it bad.
I get my sailing-orders from the Lord."
He touched the Bible. "And it's down there, Mister,
Down there in black and white—the sons of Ham—
Bondservants—sweat of their brows." His voice trailed off
Into texts. "I tell you, Mister," he said fiercely,
"The pay's good pay, but it's the Lord's work, too.
We're spreading the Lord's seed—spreading his seed—"

His hand made the outflung motion of a sower
And the mate, staring, seemed to hear the slight
Patter of fallen seeds on fertile ground,
Black, shining seeds, robbed from a black king's storehouse,
Falling and falling on American earth
With light, inexorable patter and fall,
To strike, lie silent, quicken.
                              Till the Spring
Came with its weeping rains, and the ground bore
A blade, a shadow-sapling, a tree of shadow,
A black-leaved tree whose trunk and roots were shadow,
A tree shaped like a yoke, growing and growing
Until it blotted all the seamen's stars.

Horses of anger trampling, horses of anger,
Trampling behind the sky in ominous cadence,
Beat of the heavy hooves like metal on metal,
Trampling something down. . . .
                              Was it they, was it they?
Or was it cold wind in the leaves of the shadow-tree
That made such grievous music?

                    Oh Lordy Je-sus
                    Won't you come and find me?
                    They put me in jail, Lord,
                    Way down in the jail.
                    Won't you send me a pro-phet
                    Just one of your prophets
                    Like Moses and Aaron
                    To get me some bail?

12

I'm feeling poorly
Yes, mighty poorly,
I ain't got no strength, Lord,
I'm all trampled down.
So send me an angel
Just any old angel
To give me a robe, Lord,
And give me a crown.

Oh Lordy Je-sus
It's a long time comin'
It's a long time co-o-min'
That Jubilee time.
We'll wait and we'll pray, Lord,
We'll wait and we'll pray, Lord,
But it's a long time, Lord,
Yes, it's a long time.

The dark sobbing ebbed away.
The captain was still talking. "Yes," he said,
"And yet we treat 'em well enough. There's no one
From Salem to the Guinea Coast can say
They lose as few as I do." He stopped.

"Well, Mister?"

The mate arose. "Good night sir and—"

"Good night."

The mate went up on deck. The breeze was fresh.
There were the stars, steady. He shook himself
Like a dog coming out of water and felt better.
Six weeks, with luck, and they'd be back in port
And he could draw his pay and see his girl.
Meanwhile, it wasn't his watch, so he could sleep.
The captain still below, reading that Bible. . . .
Forget it—and the noises, still half-heard—
He'd have to go below to sleep, this time,
But after, if the weather held like this,
He'd have them sling a hammock up on deck.
You couldn't smell the black so much on deck
And so you didn't dream it when you slept.

13

BOOK ONE

Jack Ellyat had been out all day alone,
Except for his new gun and Ned, the setter,
The old wise dog with Autumn in his eyes,
Who stepped the fallen leaves so delicately
They barely rustled. Ellyat trampled them down
Crackling, like cast-off skins of fairy snakes.
He'd meant to hunt, but he had let the gun
Rest on his shoulder.

               It was enough to feel
The cool air of the last of Indian summer
Blowing continually across his cheek
And watch the light distill its water of gold
As the sun dropped.

             Here was October, here
Was ruddy October, the old harvester,
Wrapped like a beggared sachem in a coat
Of tattered tanager and partridge feathers,
Scattering jack-o-lanterns everywhere
To give the field-mice pumpkin-colored moons.
His red clay pipe had trailed across the land
Staining the trees with colors of the sumach:
East, West, South, North, the ceremonial fume
Blue and enchanted as the soul of air
Drifted its incense.

             Incense of the wild,
Incense of earth fulfilled, ready to sleep
The stupefied dark slumber of the bear
All winter, underneath a frozen star.

Jack Ellyat felt that turning of the year
Stir in his blood like drowsy fiddle-music
And knew he was glad to be Connecticut-born
And young enough to find Connecticut winter
Was a black pond to cut with silver skates
And not a scalping-knife against the throat.
He thought the thoughts of youth, idle and proud.

        Since I was begotten
        My father's grown wise

14

But he has forgotten
The wind in the skies.
I shall not grow wise.

Since I have been growing
My uncle's got rich.
He spends his time sowing
A bottomless ditch.
I will not grow rich.

For money is sullen
And wisdom is sly,
But youth is the pollen
That blows through the sky
And does not ask why.

O wisdom and money
How can you requite
The honey of honey
That flies in that flight?
The useless delight?

So, with his back against a tree, he stared
At the pure, golden feathers in the West
Until the sunset flowed into his heart
Like a slow wave of honey-dropping dew
Murmuring from the other side of Sleep.
There was a fairy hush
Everywhere. Even the setter at his feet
Lay there as if the twilight had bewitched
His russet paws into two russet leaves,
A dog of russet leaves who did not stir a hair.

Then something broke the peace.
Like wind it was, the flutter of rising wind,
But then it grew until it was the rushing
Of winged stallions, distant and terrible,
Trampling beyond the sky.
                        The hissing charge
Of lightless armies of angelic horse
Galloping down the stars.
                        There were no words

In that implacable and feathery thunder,
And yet there must have been, or Ellyat's mind
Caught them like broken arrows out of the air.

Thirteen sisters beside the sea,
(Have a care, my son.)
Builded a house called Liberty
And locked the doors with a stately key.
None should enter it but the free.
(Have a care, my son.)

The walls are solid as Plymouth Rock.
(Rock can crumble, my son.)
The door of seasoned New England stock.
Before it a Yankee fighting-cock
Pecks redcoat kings away from the lock.
(Fighters can die, my son.)

The hearth is a corner where sages sit.
(Sages pass, my son.)
Washington's heart lies under it.
And the long roof-beams are chiseled and split
From hickory tough as Jackson's wit.
(Bones in the dust, my son.)

The trees in the garden are fair and fine.
(Trees blow down, my son.)
Connecticut elm and Georgia pine.
The warehouse groans with cotton and swine.
The cellar is full of scuppernong-wine.
(Wine turns sour, my son.)

Surely a house so strong and bold,
(The wind is rising, my son,)
Will last till Time is a pinch of mould!
There is a ghost, when the night is old.
There is a ghost who walks in the cold.
(The trees are shaking, my son.)

The sisters sleep on Liberty's breast,
(The thunder thunders, my son,)
Like thirteen swans in a single nest.

But the ghost is naked and will not rest
Until the sun rise out of the West.
(The lightning lightens, my son.)

All night long like a moving stain,
(The trees are breaking, my son,)
The black ghost wanders his house of pain.
There is blood where his hand has lain.
It is wrong he should wear a chain.
(The sky is falling, my son.)

The warning beat at his mind like a bird and passed.
Ellyat roused. He thought: they are going South.
He stared at the sky, confused. It was empty and bleak.
But still he felt the shock of the hooves on his heart.
—The riderless horses never bridled or tamed—
He heard them screaming like eagles loosed from a cloud
As they drove South to trample the indolent sun,
And darkness sat in his mind like a shadow enthroned.
He could not read the riddle their flight had set
But he felt wretched, and glad for the dog's cold nose
That now came nuzzling his hand.
                              Who has set you free?
Who has driven you out in the sky with an iron whip
Like blind, old thunders stubbornly marching abreast
To carry a portent high on shoulders of stone
The length and breadth of the Union?
The North and South are at peace and the East and West,
The tomahawk is buried in prairie-sod.
The great frontier rolls westward with the sun,
And the new States are crowding at the door,
The buckskin-States, the buffalo-horned, the wild
Mustangs with coats the color of crude gold.
Their bodies, naked as the hunter's moon,
Smell of new grass and the sweet milk of the corn.
Defiant virgins, fiercely unpossessed
As the bird-stars that walk the night untrodden.
They drag their skies and sunsets after them
Like calico ponies on a rawhide rope,
And who would ride them must have iron thighs
And a lean heart, bright as a bowie-knife.

Were they not foaled with treasure in their eyes
Between the rattlesnake and the painted rock?
Are they not matches for vaquero gods?
Are they not occupation for the strength
Of a whole ruffian world of pioneers?
And must they wait like spayed mares in the rain,
While Carolina and Connecticut
Fight an old quarrel out before a ghost?

So Ellyat talked to his young indignation,
Walking back home with the October moon.
But, even as he mused, he tried to picture
The South, that languorous land where Uncle Toms
Groaned Biblically underneath the lash,
And grinning Topsies mopped and mowed behind
Each honeysuckle vine.
                    They called them niggers
And cut their ears off when they ran away,
But then they loved their mammies—there was that—
Although they sometimes sold them down the river—
And when the niggers were not getting licked
Or quoting Scripture, they sang funny songs,
By the Swanee river, on the old plantation.

The girls were always beautiful. The men
Wore varnished boots, raced horses and played cards
And drank mint-juleps till the time came round
For fighting duels with their second cousins
Or tar-and-feathering some God-damn Yankee. . . .
The South . . . the honeysuckle . . . the hot sun . . .
The taste of ripe persimmons and sugar-cane . . .
The cloyed and waxy sweetness of magnolias . . .
White cotton, blowing like a fallen cloud,
And foxhounds belling the Virginia hills . . .

And then the fugitive slave he'd seen in Boston,
The black man with the eyes of a tortured horse. . . .

He whistled Ned. What do you think of it, Ned?
We're abolitionists, I suppose, and Father
Talks about Wendell Phillips and John Brown
But, even so, that doesn't have to mean

18

We'll break the Union up for abolition,
And they can't want to break it up for slavery—
It won't come to real fighting, will it, Ned?
But Ned was busy with a rabbit-track.
There was the town—the yellow window of home.

Meanwhile, in Concord, Emerson and Thoreau
Talked of an ideal state, so purely framed
It never could exist.
                    Meanwhile, in Boston
Minister Higginson and Dr. Howe
Waited for news about a certain project
That had to do with pikes and Harper's Ferry.

Meanwhile, in Georgia, Clay Wingate dreamed.

Settled more than a hundred year
By the river and county of St. Savier,
The Wingates held their ancestry
As high as Taliaferro or Huger,
Maryland Carroll, Virginia Lee.
They had ill-spelt letters of Albemarle's
And their first grant ran from the second Charles,
Clerkly inscribed upon parchmentries
"To our well-beloved John Wingate, these,"
Though envy hinted the royal mood
Held more of humor than gratitude
And the well-beloved had less applied
To honest John than his tall young bride,
At least their eldest to John's surprise,
Was very like Monmouth about the eyes,
Till his father wondered if every loyalty
Was always so richly repaid by royalty,
But, having long found that the principal question
In a happy life is a good digestion
And the worst stomachic of all is jealousy
He gave up the riddle, and settled zealously
To farming his acres, begetting daughters,
And making a study of cordial waters
Till he died at ninety of pure senility
And was greatly mourned by the local gentility.

John the Second was different cloth.
He had wings—but the wings of the moth.
Courtly, unlucky, clever and wise,
There was a Stuart in his eyes,
A gambler that played against loaded dice.
He could harrow the water and plough the sand,
But he could not do the thing at hand.
A fencing-foil too supple for use,
A racing colt that must run at loose.
And the Wingate acres had slipped away
If it had not been for Elspeth Mackay.
She was his wife, and her heart was bold
As a broad, bright guinea of Border gold.
Her wit was a tartan of colored weather.
Her walk was gallant as Highland heather.
And whatever she had, she held together.

It was she who established on Georgia soil
Wingate honor and Wingate toil
When John and his father's neighbors stood
At swords' points over a county feud
And only ill-fortune and he were friends.
—They prophesied her a dozen ends,
Seeking new ground for a broken man
Where only the deer and the rabbit ran
And the Indian arrow harried both,
But she held her word and she kept her troth,
Cleared the forest and tamed the wild
And gave the breast to the new-born child
While the painted Death went whooping by
—To die at last as she wished to die
In the fief built out of her blood and bone
With her heart for the Hall's foundation-stone.

Deep in her sons, and the Wingate blood,
She stamped her sigil of fortitude.
Thrift and love for the house and the chief
And a scone on the hob for the son of grief.
But a knife in the ribs for the pleasant thief.
And deep in her sons, when she was gone,
Her words took root, and her ghost lived on.
The slow voice haunting the ocean-shell

To counsel the sons of her sons as well.
And it was well for the Wingate line
To have that stiffening set in its spine.
For once in each breeding of Wingate kin
There came a child with an olive skin
And the mouth of Charles, the merry and sad,
And the bright, spoilt charm that Monmouth had.
Luckily seldom the oldest born
To sow the nettle in Wingate corn
And let the cotton blight on its stalk
While he wasted his time in witty talk,
Or worse, in love with no minister handy,
Or feeding a spaniel on nuts and brandy
And taking a melancholy pride
In never choosing the winning side.

Clay Wingate was the last to feel
The prick of that spur of tarnished steel,
Gilt, but crossed with the dubious bar
Of arms won under the bastard's star,
Rowel his mind, at that time or this,
With thoughts and visions that were not his.
A sorrow of laughter, a mournful glamor
And the ghostly stroke of an airy hammer
Shaking his heart with pity and pride
That had nothing to do with the things he eyed.
He was happy and young, he was strong and stout,
His body was hard to weary out.
When he thought of life, he thought of a shout.
But—there was a sword in a blackened sheath,
There was a shape with a mourning wreath:
And a place in his mind was a wrestling-ring
Where the crownless form of an outlawed king
Fought with a shadow too like his own,
And, late or early, was overthrown.

It is not lucky to dream such stuff—
Dreaming men are haunted men.
Though Wingate's face looked lucky enough
To any eye that had seen him then,
Riding back through the Georgia Fall
To the white-pillared porch of Wingate Hall.

Fall of the possum, fall of the 'coon,
And the lop-eared hound-dog baying the moon.
Fall that is neither bitter nor swift
But a brown girl bearing an idle gift,
A brown seed-kernel that splits apart
And shows the Summer yet in its heart,
A smokiness so vague in the air
You feel it rather than see it there,
A brief, white rime on the red clay road
And slow mules creaking a lazy load
Through endless acres of afternoon,
A pine-cone fire and a banjo-tune,
And a julep mixed with a silver spoon.

Your noons are hot, your nights deep-starred,
There is honeysuckle still in the yard,
Fall of the quail and the firefly-glows
And the pot-pourri of the rambler-rose,
Fall that brings no promise of snows . . .

Wingate checked on his horse's rein
With a hand as light as a butterfly
And drank content in body and brain
As he gazed for a moment at the sky.
This was his Georgia, this his share
Of pine and river and sleepy air,
Of summer thunder and winter rain
That spills bright tears on the window-pane
With the slight, fierce passion of young men's grief,
Of the mockingbird and the mulberry-leaf.
For, wherever the winds of Georgia run,
It smells of peaches long in the sun,
And the white wolf-winter, hungry and frore,
Can prowl the North by a frozen door
But here we have fed him on bacon-fat
And he sleeps by the stove like a lazy cat.
Here Christmas stops at everyone's house
With a jug of molasses and green, young boughs,
And the little New Year, the weakling one,
Can lie outdoors in the noonday sun,
Blowing the fluff from a turkey-wing
At skies already haunted with Spring—

Oh, Georgia . . . Georgia . . . the careless yield!
The watermelons ripe in the field!
The mist in the bottoms that tastes of fever
And the yellow river rolling forever. . . !

So Wingate saw it, vision or truth,
Through the colored window of his own youth,
Building an image out of his mind
To live or die for, as Fate inclined.

He drank his fill of the air, and then,
Was just about to ride on again
When—what was that noise beyond the sky,
That harry of unseen cavalry
Riding the wind?
              His own horse stirred,
Neighing. He listened. There was a word.
He could not hear it—and yet he heard.
It was an arrow from ambush flung,
It was a bell with a leaden tongue
Striking an hour.
            He was young
No longer. He and his horse were old,
And both were bound with an iron band.
He slipped from the saddle and tried to stand.
He struck one hand with the other hand.
But both were cold.

———————

The horses, burning-hooved, drove on toward the sea,
But, where they had passed, the air was troubled and sick
Like earth that the shoulder of earthquake heavily stirs.
There was a whisper moving that air all night,
A whisper that cried and whimpered about the house
Where John Brown prayed to his God, by his narrow bed.

———————

JOHN BROWN'S PRAYER

Omnipotent and steadfast God,
Who, in Thy mercy, hath
Upheaved in me Jehovah's rod
And his chastising wrath,

For fifty-nine unsparing years
Thy Grace hath worked apart
To mould a man of iron tears
With a bullet for a heart.

Yet, since this body may be weak
With all it has to bear,
Once more, before Thy thunders speak,
Almighty, hear my prayer.

I saw Thee when Thou did display
The black man and his lord
To bid me free the one, and slay
The other with the sword.

I heard Thee when Thou bade me spurn
Destruction from my hand
And, though all Kansas bleed and burn,
It was at Thy command.

I hear the rolling of the wheels,
The chariots of war!
I hear the breaking of the seals
And the opening of the door!

The glorious beasts with many eyes
Exult before the Crowned.
The buried saints arise, arise
Like incense from the ground!

Before them march the martyr-kings,
In bloody sunsets drest,
O, Kansas, bleeding Kansas,
You will not let me rest!

I hear your sighing corn again,
I smell your prairie-sky,
And I remember five dead men
By Pottawattomie.

Lord God it was a work of Thine,
And how might I refrain?

But Kansas, bleeding Kansas,
I hear her in her pain.

Her corn is rustling in the ground,
An arrow in my flesh.
And all night long I staunch a wound
That ever bleeds afresh.

Get up, get up, my hardy sons,
From this time forth we are
No longer men, but pikes and guns
In God's advancing war.

And if we live, we free the slave,
And if we die, we die.
But God has digged His saints a grave
Beyond the western sky.

Oh, fairer than the bugle-call
Its walls of jasper shine!
And Joshua's sword is on the wall
With space beside for mine.

And should the Philistine defend
His strength against our blows,
The God who doth not spare His friend,
Will not forget His foes.

———————

They reached the Maryland bridge of Harper's Ferry
That Sunday night. There were twenty-two in all,
Nineteen were under thirty, three not twenty-one,
Kagi, the self-taught scholar, quiet and cool,
Stevens, the cashiered soldier, Puritan-fathered,
A singing giant, gunpowder-tempered and rash.
Dauphin Thompson, the pippin-cheeked country-boy,
More like a girl than a warrior; Oliver Brown,
Married last year when he was barely nineteen;
Dangerfield Newby, colored and born a slave,
Freeman now, but married to one not free
Who, with their seven children, waited him South,
The youngest baby just beginning to crawl;

25

Watson Brown, the steady lieutenant, who wrote
Back to his wife,
                    "Oh, Bell, I want to see you
And the little fellow very much but must wait.
There was a slave near here whose wife was sold South.
They found him hanging in Kennedy's orchard next morning.
I cannot come home as long as such things are done here.
I sometimes think that we shall not meet again."

These were some of the band. For better or worse
They were all strong men.
                         The bearded faces look strange
In the old daguerreotypes: they should be the faces
Of prosperous, small-town people, good sons and fathers,
Good horse-shoe pitchers, good at plowing a field,
Good at swapping stories and good at praying,
American wheat, firm-rooted, good in the ear.
There is only one whose air seems out of the common,
Oliver Brown. That face has a masculine beauty
Somewhat like the face of Keats.
                                 They were all strong men.

They tied up the watchmen and took the rifleworks.
Then John Brown sent a raiding party away
To fetch in Colonel Washington from his farm.
The Colonel was George Washington's great-grand-nephew,
Slave-owner, gentleman-farmer, but, more than these,
Possessor of a certain fabulous sword
Given to Washington by Frederick the Great.
They captured him and his sword and brought them along
Processionally.
                 The act has a touch of drama,
Half costume-romance, half unmerited farce.
On the way, they told the Washington slaves they were free,
Or free to fight for their freedom.
                                    The slaves heard the news
With the dazed, scared eyes of cattle before a storm.
A few came back with the band and were given pikes,
And, when John Brown was watching, pretended to mount
A slipshod guard over the prisoners.
But, when he had walked away, they put down their pikes
And huddled together, talking in mourning voices.

It didn't seem right to play at guarding the Colonel
But they were afraid of the bearded patriarch
With the Old Testament eyes.
                              A little later
It was Patrick Higgins' turn. He was the night-watchman
Of the Maryland bridge, a tough little Irishman
With a canny, humorous face, and a twist in his speech.
He came humming his way to his job.
                              "Halt!" ordered a voice.
He stopped a minute, perplexed. As he told men later,
"Now I didn't know what 'Halt!' mint, any more
Than a hog knows about a holiday."
                              There was a scuffle.
He got away with a bullet-crease in his scalp
And warned the incoming train. It was half-past-one.
A moment later, a man named Shepherd Heyward,
Free negro, baggage-master of the small station,
Well-known in the town, hardworking, thrifty and fated,
Came looking for Higgins.
                              "Halt!" called the voice again,
But he kept on, not hearing or understanding,
Whichever it may have been.
                              A rifle cracked.
He fell by the station-platform, gripping his belly,
And lay for twelve hours of torment, asking for water
Until he was able to die.
                              There is no stone,
No image of bronze or marble green with the rain
To Shepherd Heyward, free negro of Harper's Ferry,
And even the books, the careful, ponderous histories,
That turn live men into dummies with smiles of wax
Thoughtfully posed against a photographer's background
In the act of signing a treaty or drawing a sword,
Tell little of what he was.
                              And yet his face
Grey with pain and puzzled at sudden death
Stares out at us through the bookworm-dust of the years
With an uncomprehending wonder, a blind surprise.
"I was getting along," it says, "I was doing well.
I had six thousand dollars saved in the bank.
It was a good town, a nice town, I liked the folks
And they liked me. I had a good job there, too.

On Sundays I used to dress myself up slick enough
To pass the plate in church, but I wasn't proud
Not even when trashy niggers called me Mister,
Though I could hear the old grannies over their snuff
Mumbling along, 'Look, chile, there goes Shepherd Heyward.
Ain't him fine in he Sunday clo'es—ain't him sassy and fine?
You grow up decent and don't play ball in the street,
And maybe you'll get like him, with a gold watch and chain.'
And then, suddenly—and what was it all about?
Why should anyone want to kill me? Why was it done?"

So the grey lips. And so the hurt in the eyes.
A hurt like a child's, at punishment unexplained
That makes the whole child-universe fall to pieces.
At the time of death, most men turn back toward the child.

Brown did not know at first that the first man dead
By the sword he thought of so often as Gideon's sword
Was one of the race he had drawn that sword to free.
It had been dark on the bridge. A man had come
And had not halted when ordered. Then the shot
And the scrape of the hurt man dragging himself away.
That was all. The next man ordered to halt would halt.
His mind was too full of the burning judgments of God
To wonder who it had been. He was cool and at peace.
He dreamt of a lamb, lying down by a rushing stream.

So the night wore away, indecisive and strange.
The raiders stuck by the arsenal, waiting perhaps
For a great bell of jubilation to toll in the sky,
And the slaves to rush from the hills with pikes in their hands,
A host redeemed, black rescue-armies of God.
It did not happen.
                    Meanwhile, there was casual firing.
A townsman named Boerley was killed. Meanwhile, the train
Passed over the bridge to carry its wild news
Of abolition-devils sprung from the ground
A hundred and fifty, three hundred, a thousand strong
To pillage Harper's Ferry, with fire and sword.
Meanwhile the whole countryside was springing to arms.
The alarm-bell in Charlestown clanged "Nat Turner has come.
Nat Turner has come again, all smoky from Hell,

Setting the slave to murder and massacre!"
The Jefferson Guards fell in. There were boys and men.
They had no uniforms but they had weapons.
Old squirrel-rifles, taken down from the wall,
Shot guns loaded with spikes and scraps of iron.
A boy dragged a blunderbuss as big as himself.
They started for the Ferry.
                              In a dozen
A score of other sleepy, neighboring towns
The same bell clanged, the same militia assembled.

The Ferry itself was roused and stirring with dawn.
And the firing began again.
                              A queer, harsh sound
In the ordinary streets of that clean, small town,
A desultory, vapid, meaningless sound.

God knows why John Brown lingered! Kagi, the scholar,
Who, with two others, held the rifle-works,
All morning sent him messages urging retreat.
They had the inexorable weight of common sense
Behind them, but John Brown neither replied
Nor heeded, brooding in the patriarch-calm
Of a lean, solitary pine that hangs
On the cliff's edge, and sees the world below
A tiny pattern of toy fields and trees,
And only feels its roots gripping the rock
And the almighty wind that shakes its boughs,
Blowing from eagle-heaven to eagle-heaven.

Of course they were cut off. The whole attempt
Was fated from the first.
                              Just about noon
The Jefferson Guards took the Potomac Bridge
And drove away the men Brown posted there.

There were three doors of possible escape
Open to Brown. With this the first slammed shut.
The second followed it a little later
With the recapture of the other bridge
That cut Brown off from Kagi and the arsenal
And penned the larger body of the raiders
In the armory.

29

Again the firing rolled,
And now the first of the raiders fell and died,
Dangerfield Newby, the freed Scotch-mulatto
Whose wife and seven children, slaves in Virginia,
Waited for him to bring them incredible freedom.
They were sold South instead, after the raid.
His body lay where the townspeople could reach it.
They cut off his ears for trophies.
                              If there are souls,
As many think that there are or wish that there might be,
Crystalline things that rise on light wings exulting
Out of the spoilt and broken cocoon of the body,
Knowing no sorrow or pain but only deliverance,
And yet with the flame of speech, the patterns of memory,
One wonders what the soul of Dangerfield Newby
Said, in what terms, to the soul of Shepherd Heyward,
Both born slave, both freed, both dead the same day.
What do the souls that bleed from the corpse of battle
Say to the tattered night?
                              Perhaps it is better
We have no power to visage what they might say.

The firing now was constant, like the heavy
And drumming rains of summer. Twice Brown sent
Asking a truce. The second time there went
Stevens and Watson Brown with a white flag.
But things had gone beyond the symbol of flags.
Stevens, shot from a window, fell in the gutter
Horribly wounded. Watson Brown crawled back
To the engine house that was the final fort
Of Brown's last stand, torn through and through with slugs.

A Mr. Brua, one of Brown's prisoners,
Strolled out from the unguarded prison-room
Into the bullets, lifted Stevens up,
Carried him over to the old hotel
They called the Wager House, got a doctor for him,
And then strolled back to take his prisoner's place
With Colonel Washington and the scared rest.
I know no more than this of Mr. Brua
But he seems curiously American,
And I imagine him a tall, stooped man

A little yellow with the Southern sun,
With slow, brown eyes and a slow way of talking,
Shifting the quid of tobacco in his cheek
Mechanically, as he lifted up
The dirty, bloody body of the man
Who stood for everything he most detested
And slowly carrying him through casual wasps
Of death to the flyspecked but sunny room
In the old hotel, wiping the blood and grime
Mechanically from his Sunday coat,
Settling his black string-tie with big, tanned hands,
And, then, incredibly, going back to jail.
He did not think much about what he'd done
But sat himself as comfortably as might be
On the cold bricks of that dejected guard-room
And slowly started cutting another quid
With a worn knife that had a brown bone-handle.

He lived all through the war and died long after,
This Mr. Brua I see. His last advice
To numerous nephews was "Keep out of trouble,
But if you're in it, chew and don't be hasty,
Just do whatever's likeliest at hand."

I like your way of talking, Mr. Brua,
And if there still are people interested
In cutting literary clothes for heroes
They might do worse than mention your string-tie.

There were other killings that day. On the one side, this,
Leeman, a boy of eighteen and the youngest raider,
Trying to flee from the death-trap of the engine-house
And caught and killed on an islet in the Potomac.
The body lay on a tiny shelf of rock
For hours, a sack of clothes still stung by bullets.

On the other side—Fontaine Beckham, mayor of the town,
Went to look at Heyward's body with Patrick Higgins.
The slow tears crept to his eyes. He was getting old.
He had thought a lot of Heyward. He had no gun
But he had been mayor of the town for a dozen years,
A peaceful, orderly place full of decent people,
And now they were killing people, here in his town,

He had to do something to stop it, somehow or other.
He wandered out on the railroad, half-distraught
And peeped from behind a water-tank at the raiders.
"Squire, don't go any farther," said Higgins, "It ain't safe."
He hardly heard him, he had to look out again.
Who were these devils with horns who were shooting his people?
They didn't look like devils. One was a boy
Smooth-cheeked, with a bright half-dreamy face, a little
Like Sally's eldest.
               Suddenly, the air struck him
A stiff, breath-taking blow. "Oh," he said, astonished.
Took a step and fell on his face, shot through the heart.
Higgins watched him for twenty minutes, wanting to lift him
But not quite daring. Then he turned away
And went back to the town.
               The bars had been open all day,
Never to better business.
When the news of Beckham's death spread from bar to bar,
It was like putting loco-weed in the whiskey,
The mob came together at once, the American mob,
They mightn't be able to take Brown's last little fort
But there were two prisoners penned in the Wager House.
One was hurt already, Stevens, no fun killing him.
But the other was William Thompson, whole and unwounded,
Caught when Brown tried to send his first flag of truce.

They stormed the hotel and dragged him out to the bridge,
Where two men shot him, unarmed, then threw the body
Over the trestle. It splashed in the shallow water,
But the slayers kept on firing at the dead face.
The carcass was there for days, a riven target,
Barbarously misused.
               Meanwhile the armory yard
Was taken by a new band of Beckham's avengers,
The most of Brown's prisoners freed and his last escape cut off.

What need to tell of the killing of Kagi the scholar,
The wounding of Oliver Brown and the other deaths?
Only this remains to be told. When the drunken day
Reeled into night, there were left in the engine-house
Five men, alive and unwounded, of all the raiders.
Watson and Oliver Brown

Both of them hurt to the death, were stretched on the floor
Beside the corpse of Taylor, the young Canadian.
There was no light, there. It was bitterly cold.
A cold chain of lightless hours that slowly fell
In leaden beads between two fingers of stone.
Outside, the fools and the drunkards yelled in the streets,
And, now and then, there were shots. The prisoners talked
And tried to sleep.
                    John Brown did not try to sleep,
The live coals of his eyes severed the darkness;
Now and then he heard his young son Oliver calling
In the thirsty agony of his wounds, "Oh, kill me!
Kill me and put me out of this suffering!"
John Brown's jaw tightened. "If you must die," he said,
"Die like a man." Toward morning the crying ceased.
John Brown called out to the boy but he did not answer.
"I guess he's dead," said John Brown.
                                      If his soul wept
They were the incredible tears of the squeezed stone.
He had not slept for two days, but he would not sleep.
The night was a chained, black leopard that he stared down,
Erect, on his feet. One wonders what sights he saw
In the cloudy mirror of his most cloudy heart,
Perhaps God clothed in a glory, perhaps himself
The little boy who had stolen three brass pins
And been well whipped for it.
                              When he was six years old
An Indian boy had given him a great wonder,
A yellow marble, the first he had ever seen.
He treasured it for months but lost it at last,
Boylike. The hurt of the loss took years to heal.
He never quite forgot.
                       He could see it now,
Smooth, hard and lovely, a yellow, glistening ball,
But it kept rolling away through cracks of darkness
Whenever he tried to catch it and hold it fast.
If he could only touch it, he would be safe,
But it trickled away and away, just out of reach,
There by the wall . . .
                        Outside the blackened East
Began to tarnish with a faint, grey stain
That caught on the fixed bayonets of the marines.

33

Lee of Virginia, Light Horse Harry's son,
Observed it broaden, thinking of many things,
But chiefly wanting to get his business done,
A curious, wry, distasteful piece of work
For regular soldiers.
                    Therefore to be finished
As swiftly and summarily as possible
Before this yelling mob of drunk civilians
And green militia once got out of hand.
His mouth set. Once already he had offered
The honor of the attack to the militia,
Such honor as it was.
                    Their Colonel had
Declined with a bright nervousness of haste.
"Your men are paid for doing this kind of work.
Mine have their wives and children." Lee smiled briefly,
Remembering that. The smile had a sharp edge.
Well, it was time.
                    The whooping crowd fell silent
And scattered, as a single man walked out
Toward the engine-house, a letter in his hand.
Lee watched him musingly. A good man, Stuart.
Now he was by the door and calling out.
The door opened a crack.
                    Brown's eyes were there
Over the cold muzzle of a cocked carbine.
The parleying began, went on and on,
While the crowd shivered and Lee watched it all
With the strict commonsense of a Greek sword
And with the same sure readiness.
                    Unperceived,
The dawn ran down the valleys of the wind,
Coral-footed dove, tracking the sky with coral . . .
Then, sudden as powder flashing in a pan,
The parleying was done.
                    The door slammed shut.
The little figure of Stuart jumped aside
Waving its cap.
                    And the marines came on.

Brown watched them come. One hand was on his carbine.
The other felt the pulse of his dying son.

34

"Sell your lives dear," he said. The rifle-shots
Rattled within the bricked-in engine-room
Like firecrackers set off in a stone jug,
And there was a harsh stink of sweat and powder.
There was a moment when the door held firm.
Then it was cracked with sun.
                            Brown fired and missed.
A shadow with a sword leaped through the sun.
"That's Ossawattomie," said the tired voice
Of Colonel Washington.
                    The shadow lunged
And Brown fell to his knees.
                        The sword bent double,
A light sword, better for parades than fighting,
The shadow had to take it in both hands
And fairly rain his blows with it on Brown
Before he sank.
                Now two marines were down,
The rest rushed in over their comrades' bodies,
Pinning one man of Brown's against the wall
With bayonets, another to the floor.

Lee, on his rise of ground, shut up his watch.
It had been just a quarter of an hour
Since Stuart gave the signal for the storm,
And now it was over.
                    All but the long dying.

──────────

Cudjo, the negro, watched from the pantry
The smooth glissades of the dancing gentry,
His splay-feet tapping in time to the tune
While his broad face beamed like a drunken moon
At candles weeping in crystal sconces,
Waxed floors glowing like polished bronzes,
Sparkles glinting on Royal Worcester
And all the stir and color and luster
Where Miss Louisa and Miss Amanda,
Proud dolls scissored from silver paper,
With hoopskirts wide as the front veranda
And the gypsy eyes of a caged frivolity,
Pointed their toes in a satin caper
To the nonchalant glory of the Quality.

35

And there were the gentlemen, one and all,
Friends and neighbors of Wingate Hall—
Old Judge Brooke from Little Vermilion
With the rusty voice of a cracked horse-pistol
And manners as stiff as a French cotillion.
Huger Shepley and Wainscott Bristol,
Hawky arrogant sons of anger
Who rode like devils and fought like cocks
And watched, with an ineffable languor
Their spoilt youth tarnish a dicing-box.
The Cazenove boys and the Cotter brothers,
Pepperalls from Pepperall Ride.
Cummings and Crowls and a dozen others,
Every one with a name and a pride.
Sallow young dandies in shirts with ruffles,
Each could dance like a blowing feather,
And each had the voice that Georgia muffles
In the lazy honey of her May weather.

Cudjo watched and measured and knew them,
Seeing behind and around and through them
With the shrewd, dispassionate, smiling eye
Of the old-time servant in days gone by.
He couldn't read and he couldn't write,
But he knew Quality, black or white,
And even his master could not find
The secret place in the back of his mind
Where witch-bones talked to a scarlet rag
And a child's voice spoke from a conjur-bag.
For he belonged to the hidden nation,
The mute, enormous confederation
Of the planted earth and the burden borne
And the horse that is ridden and given corn.
The wind from the brier-patch brought him news
That never went walking in white men's shoes
And the grapevine whispered its message faster
Than a horse could gallop across a grave,
Till, long ere the letter could tell the master,
The doomsday rabbits had told the slave.

He was faithful as bread or salt,
A flawless servant without a fault,

Major-domo of Wingate Hall,
Proud of his white folks, proud of it all.
They might scold him, they might let him scold them,
And he might know things that he never told them,
But there was a bond, and the bond would hold,
On either side until both were cold.

So he didn't judge, though he knew, he knew,
How the yellow babies down by the Slough,
Had a fourth of their blood from old Judge Brooke,
And where Sue Crowl got her Wingate look,
And the whole, mad business of Shepley's Wager,
And why Miss Harriet married the Major.
And he could trace with unerring ease
A hundred devious pedigrees
Of man and horse, from the Squire's Rapscallion
Back to the stock of the Arab stallion,
And the Bristol line through its baffling dozens
Of doubly-removed half-second-cousins,
And found a creed and a whole theology
On the accidents of human geology.

He looked for Clay in the dancing whirl,
There he was, coming down the line,
Hand in hand with a dark, slim girl
Whose dress was the color of light in wine
Sally Dupré from Appleton
Where the blackshawled ladies rock in the sun
And young things labor and old things rule,
A proud girl, taught in a humbling school
That the only daughters of misalliance
Must harden their hearts against defiance
Of all the uncles and all the aunts
Who succour such offspring of mischance
And wash them clean from each sinful intention
With the kindliest sort of incomprehension.

She had the Appleton mouth, it seemed,
And the Appleton way of riding,
But when she sorrowed and if she dreamed,
Something came out from hiding.
She could sew all day on an Appleton hem

And look like a saint in plaster,
But when the fiddles began to play
And her feet beat fast but her heart beat faster
An alien grace inhabited them
And she looked like her father, the dancing-master,
The scapegrace elegant, "French" Dupré,
Come to the South on a luckless day,
With bright paste buckles sewn on his pumps.
A habit of holding the ace of trumps,
And a manner of kissing a lady's hand
Which the county failed to understand.
He stole Sue Appleton's heart away
With eyes that were neither black nor grey,
And broke the heart of the Brookes' best mare
To marry her safely with time to spare
While the horsewhip uncles toiled behind—
He knew his need and she knew her mind.
And the love they had was as bright and brief
As the dance of the gilded maple-leaf,
Till she died in Charleston of childbed fever
Before her looks or his heart could leave her.
It took the flavor out of his drinking
And left him thoughts he didn't like thinking,
So he wrapped his child in the dead girl's shawl
And sent her politely to Uncle Paul
With a black-edged note full of grief and scruples
And half the money he owed his pupils,
Saw that Sue had the finest hearse
That I. O. U.'s could possibly drape her
And elegized her in vile French verse
While his hot tears spotted the borrowed paper.

He still had manners, he tried to recover,
But something went when he buried his lover.
No women with eyes could ever scold him
But he would make places too hot to hold him,
He shrugged his shoulders and kept descending—
Life was a farce, but it needed ending.
The tag-line found him too tired to dread it
And he died as he lived, with an air, on credit,
In his host's best shirt and a Richmond garret,
Talking to shadows and drinking claret.

He passed when Sally was barely four
And the Appleton kindred breathed once more
And, with some fervor, began to try
To bury the bone of his memory
And strictly expunge from his daughter's semblance
All possible traces of a resemblance.
Which system succeeded, to outward view,
As well as most of such systems do
And resulted in mixing a martyr's potions
For "French" Dupré in his daughter's notions.

And slander is sinful and gossip wrong,
But country memories are long,
The Appleton clan is a worthy clan
But we remember the dancing-man.
The girl is pretty, the girl seems wise,
The girl was born with her father's eyes.
She will play with our daughters and know our sons,
We cannot offend the Appletons.
Bristols and Wingates, Shepleys and Crowls,
We wouldn't hurt her to save our souls.
But after all—and nevertheless—
For one has to think—and one must confess—
And one should admit—but one never knows—
So it has gone, and so it goes,
Through the sun and the wind and the rainy weather
Whenever ladies are gathered together,
Till, little by little and stitch by stitch,
The girl is put in her proper niche
With all the virtues that we can draw
For someone else's daughter-in-law,
A girl to be kind to, a girl we're lucky in,
A girl to marry some nice Kentuckian,
Some Alabaman, some Carolinian—
In fact, if you ask me for my opinion,
There are lots of boys in the Northern sections
And some of them have quite good connections—
She looks charming this evening, doesn't she?
If she danced just a little less *dashingly!*

Cudjo watched her as she went by,
"She's got a light foot," thought Cudjo, "Hi!

A light, swif' foot and a talkin' eye!
But you'll need more'n dat, Miss Sally Dupré
Before you proposals with young Marse Clay.
And as soon as de fiddles finish slewin'
Dey's sixteen things I ought to be doin'.
The Major's sure to be wantin' his dram,
We'll have to be cuttin' a second ham,
And dat trashy high-yaller, Parker's Guinea,
Was sayin' some Yankee name Old John Brown
Has raised de Debil back in Virginny
And freed de niggers all over town,
He's friends with de ha'nts and steel won't touch him
But the paterollers is sure to cotch him.
How come he want to kick up such a dizziness!
Nigger-business ain't white-folks' business."

———————

There was no real moon in all the soft, clouded night,
The rats of night had eaten the silver cheese,
Though here and there a forgotten crumb of old brightness
Gleamed and was blotted.
                            But there was no real moon,
No bowl of nacre, dripping an old delusive
Stain on the changed, strange grass, making faces strange;
There was only a taste of warm rain not yet fallen,
A wine-colored dress, turned black because of no moon,
—It would have been spangled in moon—and a broadcloth coat,
And two voices talking together, quite softly, quite calmly.
The dance. Such a lovely dance. But you dance so lightly.
Amanda dances so well. But you dance so lightly.
Louisa looks so pretty in pink, don't you think?
Are you fond of Scott? Yes, I'm very fond of Scott.
Elegant extracts from gilt-edged volumes called Keepsakes
And Godey's Lady's Book words.
                            If I were a girl,
A girl in a Godey's Lady's Book steel-engraving,
I would have no body or legs, no aches or delusions.
I would know what to do. I would marry a man called Mister.
We would live in a steel-engraving, in various costumes
Designed in the more respectable Paris modes,
With two little boys in little plush hats like muffins,

And two little girls with pantalettes to their chins.
I must do that, I think.
                         But now my light feet know
That they will be tired and burning with all my dancing
Before I cool them in the exquisite coolness
Of water or the cool virginal sheets of virgins,
And a face comes swimming toward me out of black broadcloth
And my heart knocks.
                         Who are you, why are you here?
Why should you trouble my eyes?
                         No, Mr. Wingate,
I cannot agree with you on the beauties of Byron.
But why should something melt in the stuff of my hand,
And my voice sound thin in my ears?
                         This face is a face
Like any other face. Did my mother once
Hear thin blood sing in her ears at a voice called Mister?
And wish for—and not wish for—and when the strange thing
Was consummate, then, and she lay in a coil of darkness,
Did she feel so much changed? What is it to be
A woman?
          No, I must live in a steel-engraving.

His voice said. But there was other than his voice.
Something that heard warm rain on unopened flowers
And spoke or tried to speak across swimming blackness
To the slight profile and the wine-colored dress.
Her hair was black. Her eyes might be black or grey.
He could not remember, it irked him not to remember.
But she was just Sally Dupré from Appleton
Only she was not. Only she was a shadow
And a white face—a terrible, white shut face
That looked through windows of inflexible glass
Disdainfully upon the beauties of Byron
And every puppy that ever howled for the moon
To brush warm raindrops across the unopened flower
And so quiet the heart with—what?
                         But you speak to her aunts.
You are Wingate of Wingate Hall. You are not caught
Like a bee drunk with the smell of honey, the smell of sleep,
In a slight flower of glass whose every petal
Shows eyes one cannot remember as black or grey.

You converse easily on elegant subjects
Suitable for young ladies.
                                        You do not feel
The inexorable stairs of the flesh ascended
By an armed enemy with a naked torch.
This has been felt before, this has been quenched
With fitting casualness in flesh that has
A secret stain of the sun.
                                        It is not a subject
Suitable for the converse of young ladies.

"My God, My God, why will she not answer the aching?
My God, My God, to lie at her side through the darkness!"

And yet—is it real—do I really—
                                        The wine-colored dress
Rose. Broadcloth rose and took her back to the dance.

———————

The nickeled lamp threw a wide yellow disk
On the red tablecloth with the tasseled fringes.
Jack Ellyat put his book down with a slight
Impatient gesture.
                                There was mother, knitting
The same grey end of scarf while Father read
The same unaltered paper through the same
Old-fashioned spectacles with the worn bows.

Jane with one apple-cheek and one enshadowed,
Soundlessly conjugated Latin verbs,
"Amo, amas, amat," through sober lips,
"Amamus, amatis, amant," and still no sound.
He glanced at the clock. On top of it was Phaëton
Driving bronze, snarling horses down the sharp,
Quicksilver, void, careening gulfs of air.
Until they smashed upon a black-marble sea.
The round spiked trophy of the brazen sun
Weighed down his chariot with its heavy load
Of ponderous fire.
                                To be like Phaëton
And drive the trophy-sun!
                                        But he and his horses

Were frozen in their attitude of snarling,
Frozen forever to the tick of a clock.
Not all the broomstick witches of New England
Could break that congealed motion and cast down
The huge sun thundering on the black marble
Of the mantelpiece, streaked with white veins of foam.
If once such things could happen, all could happen,
The snug, safe world crack up like broken candy
And the young rivers, roaring, rush to the sea;
White bulls that caught the morning on their horns
And shook the secure earth until they found

Some better recompense for life than life,
The untamed ghost, the undiminished star.

But it would not happen. Nothing would ever happen.
He had been here, like this, ten thousand times,
He would be here, like this, ten thousand more,
Until at last the little ticks of the clock
Had cooled what had been hot, and changed the thin,
Blue, forking veins across the back of his hand
Into the big, soft veins on Father's hand.
And the world would be snug.
                              And he would sit
Reading the same newspaper, after dinner,
Through spectacles whose bows were getting worn
While a wife knitted on an endless scarf
And a child slowly formed with quiet lips
"Amo, amas, amat," and still no sound.
And it would be over. Over without having been.

His father turned a creaking page of paper
And cleared his throat. "The *Tribune* calls," he said,
"Brown's raid the work of a madman. Well, they're right,
But—"
            Mrs. Ellyat put her knitting down.
"Are they going to hang him, Will?"
                                    "It looks that way."
"But, Father, when—"
                    "They have the right, my son,
He broke the law."
                  "But, Will! You don't believe—"

43

A little spark lit Mr. Ellyat's eyes.
"I didn't say I thought that he was wrong.
I said they had the right to hang the man,
But they'll hang slavery with him."
                                A quick pulse
Beat in Jack Ellyat's wrist. Behind his eyes
A bearded puppet creaked upon a rope
And the sky darkened because he was there.
Now it was Mother talking in a strange
Iron-bound voice he'd never heard before.
"I prayed for him in church last Sunday, Will.
I pray for him at home here every night.
I don't know—I don't care—what laws he broke.
I know that he was right. I pray to God
To show the world somehow that he was right
And break these Southern people into knowing!
And I know this—in every house and church,
All through the North—women are praying for him,
Praying for him. And God will hear those prayers."

"He will, my dear," said Mr. Ellyat gently,
"But what will be His answer?"
                                He took her hand,
Smoothing it for a moment. Then she sighed
And turned back to the interminable scarf.
Jack Ellyat's pulse beat faster.
                                Women praying,
Praying at night, in every house in the North,
Praying for old John Brown until their knees
Ached with stiff cold.
                                Innumerable prayers
Inexorably rising, till the dark
Vault of the midnight was so thronged and packed
The wild geese could not arrow through the storm
Of terrible, ascendant, women's prayers. . . .

The clock struck nine, and Phaëton still stood
Frozenly urging on his frozen horses,
But, for a moment, to Jack Ellyat's eyes,
The congealed hoofs had seemed to paw the air
And the bronze car roll forward.

On Saturday, in Southern market towns,
When I was a boy with twenty cents to spend,
The carts began to drift in with the morning,
And, by the afternoon, the slipshod Square
And all broad Center Street were lined with them;
Moth-eaten mules that whickered at each other
Between the mended shafts of rattletrap wagons,
Mud-spattered buggies, mouldy phaetons,
And, here and there, an ox-cart from the hills
Whose solemn team had shoulders of rough, white rock,
Innocent noses, black and wet as snailshells,
And that inordinate patience in their eyes.

There always was a Courthouse in the Square,
A cupolaed Courthouse, drowsing Time away
Behind the grey-white pillars of its porch
Like an old sleepy judge in a spotted gown;
And, down the Square, always a languid jail
Of worn, uneven brick with moss in the cracks
Or stone weathered the grey of weathered pine.
The plump jail-master wore a linen duster
In summer, and you used to see him sit
Tilted against the wall in a pine-chair,
Spitting reflectively in the warm dust
While endless afternoons slowly dissolved
Into the longer shadow, the dust-blue twilight.
Higgledy-piggledy days—days that are gone—
The trotters are dead, all the yellow-painted sulkies
Broken for firewood—the old Courthouse grins
Through new false-teeth of Alabama limestone—
The haircloth lap-robe weeps on a Ford radiator—

But I have seen the old Courthouse. I have seen
The flyspecked windows and the faded flag
Over the judge's chair, touched the scuffed walls,
Spat in the monumental brass spittoons
And smelt the smell that never could be aired,
Although one opened windows for a year,
The unforgettable, intangible
Mixture of cheap cigars, worm-eaten books,
Sweat, poverty, negro hair-oil, grief and law.
I have seen the long room packed with quiet men,

45

Fit to turn mob, if need were, in a flash—
Cocked-pistol men, so lazily attentive
Their easy languor knocked against your ribs
As, hour by hour, the lawyers droned along,
And minute on creeping minute, your cold necknape
Waited the bursting of the firecracker,
The flare of fury.
                        And yet, that composed fury
Burnt itself out, unflaring—was held down
By a dry, droning voice, a faded flag.
The kettle never boiled, the pistol stayed
At cock but the snake-head hammer never fell. . . .
The little boys climbed down beyond the windows. . . .

So, in the cupolaed Courthouse there in Charlestown,
When the jail-guards had carried in the cot
Where Brown lay like a hawk with a broken back,
I hear the rustle of the moving crowd,
The buzz outside, taste the dull, heavy air,
Smell the stale smell and see the country carts
Hitched in the streets.
                        For a long, dragging week
Of market-Saturdays the trial went on.
The droning voices rise and fall and rise.
Stevens lies quiet on his mattress, breathing
The harsh and difficult breath of a dying man,
Although not dying then.
                        Beyond the Square
The trees are dry, but all the dry leaves not fallen—
Yellow leaves falling through a grey-blue dusk,
The first winds of November whirl and scatter them. . . .

Read as you will in any of the books,
The details of the thing, the questions and answers,
How sometimes Brown would walk, sometimes was carried,
At first would hardly plead, half-refused counsel,
Accepted later, made up witness-lists,
Grew fitfully absorbed in his defense,
Only to flare in temper at his first lawyers
And drive them from the case.
                        Questions and answers,
Wheels creaking in a void.

46

                    Sometimes he lay
Quiet upon his cot, the hawk-eyes staring.
Sometimes his fingers moved mechanically
As if at their old task of sorting wool,
Fingertips that could tell him in the dark
Whether the wool they touched was from Ohio
Or from Vermont. They had the shepherd's gift.
It was his one sure talent.
                    Questions creaking
Uselessly back and forth.
                    No one can say
That the trial was not fair. The trial was fair,
Painfully fair by every rule of law,
And that it was made not the slightest difference.
The law's our yardstick, and it measures well
Or well enough when there are yards to measure.
Measure a wave with it, measure a fire,
Cut sorrow up in inches, weigh content.
You can weigh John Brown's body well enough,
But how and in what balance weigh John Brown?

He had the shepherd's gift, but that was all.
He had no other single gift for life.
Some men are pasture Death turns back to pasture,
Some are fire-opals on that iron wrist,
Some the deep roots of wisdoms not yet born.
John Brown was none of these,
He was a stone,
A stone eroded to a cutting edge
By obstinacy, failure and cold prayers.
Discredited farmer, dubiously involved
In lawsuit after lawsuit, Shubel Morgan
Fantastic bandit of the Kansas border,
Red-handed murderer at Pottawattomie,
Cloudy apostle, whooped along to death
By those who do no violence themselves
But only buy the guns to have it done,
Sincere of course, as all fanatics are,
And with a certain minor-prophet air,
That fooled the world to thinking him half-great
When all he did consistently was fail.

47

So far one advocate.
                    But there is this.

Sometimes there comes a crack in Time itself.
Sometimes the earth is torn by something blind.
Sometimes an image that has stood so long
It seems implanted as the polar star
Is moved against an unfathomed force
That suddenly will not have it any more.
Call it the *mores*, call it God or Fate,
Call it Mansoul or economic law,
That force exists and moves.
                         And when it moves
It will employ a hard and actual stone
To batter into bits an actual wall
And change the actual scheme of things.
                              John Brown
Was such a stone—unreasoning as the stone,
Destructive as the stone, and, if you like,
Heroic and devoted as such a stone.
He had no gift for life, no gift to bring
Life but his body and a cutting edge,
But he knew how to die.
                       And yardstick law
Gave him six weeks to burn that hoarded knowledge
In one swift fire whose sparks fell like live coals
On every State in the Union.
                           Listen now,
Listen, the bearded lips are speaking now,
There are no more guerilla-raids to plan,
There are no more hard questions to be solved
Of right and wrong, no need to beg for peace,
Here is the peace unbegged, here is the end,
Here is the insolence of the sun cast off,
Here is the voice already fixed with night.

JOHN BROWN'S SPEECH

I have, may it please the Court, a few words to say.
    In the first place I deny everything but what I have all along
admitted: of a design on my part to free slaves. . . .
    Had I interfered in the matter which I admit, and which I

admit has been fairly proved . . . had I so interfered in behalf of the rich, the powerful, the intelligent, or the so-called great . . . and suffered and sacrificed, what I have in this interference, it would have been all right. Every man in this Court would have deemed it an act worthy of reward rather than punishment.

I see a book kissed which I suppose to be the Bible, or at least the New Testament, which teaches me that all things whatsoever I would that men should do unto me, I should do even so to them. It teaches me further to remember them that are in bonds as bound with them. I endeavored to act up to that instruction. I say I am yet too young to understand that God is any respecter of persons. I believe that to have interfered as I have done, as I have always freely admitted I have done in behalf of His despised poor, I did no wrong, but right. Now, if it is deemed necessary that I should forfeit my life for the furtherance of the ends of justice and mingle my blood further with the blood of my children and with the blood of millions in this slave country whose rights are disregarded by wicked, cruel and unjust enactments, I say, let it be done.

Let me say one word further. I feel entirely satisfied with the treatment I have received on my trial. Considering all the circumstances, it has been more generous than I expected. But I feel no consciousness of guilt. I have stated from the first what was my intention and what was not. I never had any design against the liberty of any person, nor any disposition to commit treason or incite slaves to rebel or make any general insurrection. I never encouraged any man to do so but always discouraged any idea of that kind.

Let me say also, in regard to the statements made by some of those connected with me, I hear it has been stated by some of them that I have induced them to join with me. But the contrary is true. I do not say this to injure them, but as regretting their weakness. Not one but joined me of his own accord, and the greater part at their own expense. A number of them I never saw, and never had a word of conversation with, till the day they came to me, and that was for the purpose I have stated.

Now I have done.

———————

The voice ceased. There was a deep, brief pause.
The judge pronounced the formal words of death.

49

One man, a stranger, tried to clap his hands.
The foolish sound was stopped.
There was nothing but silence then.
                                 No cries in the court,
No roar, no slightest murmur from the thronged street,
As Brown went back to jail between his guards.
The heavy door shut behind them.
There was a noise of chairs scraped back in the court-room,
And that huge sigh of a crowd turning back into men.

A month between the sentence and the hanging.
A month of endless visitors, endless letters.
A Mrs. Russell came to clean his coat.
A sculptor sketched him.
                        In the anxious North,
The anxious Dr. Howe most anxiously
Denied all godly connection with the raid,
And Gerrit Smith conveniently went mad
For long enough to sponge his mind of all
Memory of such an unsuccessful deed.
Only the tough, swart-minded Higginson
Kept a grim decency, would not deny.
Pity the portly men, pity the pious,
Pity the fool who lights the powder-mine,
They need your counterfeit penny, they will live long.

In Charlestown meanwhile, there were whispers of rescue.
Brown told them,
"I am worth now infinitely more to die than to live."
And lived his month so, busily.
A month of trifles building up a legend
And letters in a pinched, firm handwriting
Courageous, scriptural, misspelt and terse,
Sowing a fable everywhere they fell
While the town filled with troops.
                                 The Governor came,
Enemies, friends, militia-cavaliers,
Old Border Foes.
                  The month ebbed into days,
The wife and husband met for the last time,
The last letter was written:

50

"To be inscribed on the old family Monument at North Elba,
Oliver Brown born 1839 was killed at Harpers Ferry, Va. Nov.
   17th 1859
Watson Brown born 1835 was wounded at Harpers Ferry Nov.
   17th and died Nov. 19th 1859
(My Wife can) supply *blank* dates to above
John Brown born May 9th 1800 was executed at Charlestown
   Va. December 2nd 1859."

At last the clear warm day, so slow to come.

The North that had already now begun
To mold his body into crucified Christ's,
Hung fables about those hours—saw him move
Symbolically, kiss a negro child,
Do this and that, say things he never said,
To swell the sparse, hard outlines of the event
With sentimental omen.
                    It was not so.
He stood on the jail-porch in carpet-slippers,
Clad in a loose ill-fitting suit of black,
Tired farmer waiting for his team to come.
He left one last written message:

   "I, John Brown, am now quite *certain* that the crimes of this
guilty land: will never be purged *away:* but with Blood. I had
as I now think: vainly flattered myself that without *very much*
bloodshed; it might be done."

They did not hang him in the jail or the Square.
The two white horses dragged the rattling cart
Out of the town. Brown sat upon his coffin.
Beyond the soldiers lay the open fields
Earth-colored, sleepy with unfallen frost.
The farmer's eye took in the bountiful land.
"This *is* a beautiful country," said John Brown.

The gallows-stairs were climbed, the death-cap fitted.
Behind the gallows,
Before a line of red-and-grey cadets,
A certain odd Professor T. J. Jackson
Watched disapprovingly the ragged militia

Deploy for twelve long minutes ere they reached
Their destined places.
The Presbyterian sabre of his soul
Was moved by a fey breath.
                                        He saw John Brown,
A tiny blackened scrap of paper-soul
Fluttering above the Pit that Calvin barred
With bolts of iron on the unelect;
He heard the just, implacable Voice speak out
"Depart ye wicked to eternal fire."
And sternly prayed that God might yet be moved
To save the predestined cinder from the flame.

Brown did not hear the prayer. The rough black cloth
Of the death-cap hid his eyes now. He had seen
The Blue Ridge Mountains couched in their blue haze.
Perhaps he saw them still, behind his eyes—
Perhaps just cloth, perhaps nothing any more.
"I shall look unto the hills from whence cometh my help."

The hatchet cut the cord. The greased trap fell.

Colonel Preston:

"So perish all such enemies of Virginia,
    All such enemies of the Union,
    All such foes of the human race."

————————

John Brown's body lies a-mouldering in the grave.
He will not come again with foolish pikes
And a pack of desperate boys to shadow the sun.
He has gone back North. The slaves have forgotten his eyes.
John Brown's body lies a-mouldering in the grave.
John Brown's body lies a-mouldering in the grave.
Already the corpse is changed, under the stone,
The strong flesh rotten, the bones dropping away.
Cotton will grow next year, in spite of the skull.
Slaves will be slaves next year, in spite of the bones.
Nothing is changed, John Brown, nothing is changed.

*"There is a song in my bones. There is a song
In my white bones."*

I hear no song. I hear
Only the blunt seeds growing secretly
In the dark entrails of the preparate earth,
The rustle of the cricket under the leaf,
The creaking of the cold wheel of the stars.

"Bind my white bones together—hollow them
To skeleton pipes of music. When the wind
Blows from the budded Spring, the song will blow."

I hear no song. I only hear the roar
Of the Spring freshets, and the gushing voice
Of mountain-brooks that overflow their banks,
Swollen with melting ice and crumbled earth.

"That is my song.
It is made of water and wind. It marches on."

No, John Brown's body lies a-mouldering,
A-mouldering.

"My bones have been washed clean
And God blows through them with a hollow sound,
And God has shut his wildfire in my dead heart."

I hear it now,
Faint, faint as the first droning flies of March,
Faint as the multitudinous, tiny sigh
Of grasses underneath a windy scythe.

"It will grow stronger."

It has grown stronger. It is marching on.
It is a throbbing pulse, a pouring surf,
It is the rainy gong of the Spring sky
Echoing,
John Brown's body,
John Brown's body.
But still it is not fierce. I find it still
More sorrowful than fierce.

"You have not heard it yet. You have not heard
The ghosts that walk in it, the shaking sound."

Strong medicine,
Bitter medicine of the dead,
I drink you now. I hear the unloosed thing,
The anger of the ripe wheat—the ripened earth
Sullenly quaking like a beaten drum
From Kansas to Vermont. I hear the stamp
Of the ghost-feet. I hear the ascending sea.

"Glory, Glory, Hallelujah,
Glory, Glory, Hallelujah,
Glory, Glory, Hallelujah!"

What is this agony of the marching dust?
What are these years ground into hatchet blades?

"Ask the tide why it rises with the moon,
My bones and I have risen like that tide
And an immortal anguish plucks us up
And will not hide us till our song is done."

The phantom drum diminishes—the year
Rolls back. It is only winter still, not spring,
The snow still flings its white on the new grave,
Nothing is changed, John Brown, nothing is changed
John . . . Brown . . .

BOOK TWO

A smoke-stained Stars-and-Stripes droops from a broken tooth-pick and ninety tired men march out of fallen Sumter to their ships, drums rattling and colors flying.

Their faces are worn and angry, their bellies empty and cold, but the stubborn salute of a gun, fifty times repeated, keeps their backs straight as they march out, and answers something stubborn and mute in their flesh.

Beauregard, *beau sabreur,* hussar-sword with the gilded hilt, the gilded metal of the guard twisted into lovelocks and roses, vain as Murat, dashing as Murat, Pierre Gustave Toutant Beauregard is a pose of conquering courtesy under a palmetto-banner.

The lugubrious little march goes grimly by his courtesy,
watches it unsmiling, a light half-real, half that of invisible fo
lights on his French, dark, handsome face.

———————

The stone falls in the pool, the ripples spread.
The colt in the Long Meadow kicked up his heels.
"That was a fly," he thought, "It's early for flies."
But being alive, in April, was too fine
For flies or anything else to bother a colt.
He kicked up his heels again, this time in pure joy,
And started to run a race with the wind and his shadow.
After the stable stuffiness, the sun.
After the straw-littered boards, the squelch of the turf.
His little hoofs felt lighter than dancing-shoes,
He scared himself with a blue-jay, his heart was a leaf.
He was pure joy in action, he was the unvexed
Delight of all moving lightness and swift-footed pace,
The pride of the flesh, the young Spring neighing and rearing.
Sally Dupré called to him from the fence.
He came like a charge in a spatter of clean-cut clods,
Ears back, eyes wide and wild with folly and youth.
He drew up snorting.
                    She laughed and brushed at her skirt
Where the mud had splashed it.
                    "There, Star—there, silly boy!
Why won't you ever learn sense?"
                    But her eyes were hot,
Her hands were shaking as she offered the sugar
—Long-fingered, appleblossom-shadow hands—
Star blew at the sugar once, then mumbled it up.
She patted the pink nose. "There, silly Star!
That's for Fort Sumter, Star!" How hot her eyes were!
"Star, do you know you're a Confederate horse?
Do you know I'm going to call you Beauregard?"

Star whinnied, and asked for more sugar. She put her hand
On his neck for a moment that matched the new green leaves
And sticky buds of April.
                    You would have said
They were grace in quietness, seen so, woman and horse. . . .

The widened ripple breaks against a stone
The heavy noon walks over Chancellorsville
On brazen shoes, but where the squadron rode
Into the ambush, the blue flies are coming
To blow on the dead meat.

Carter, the telegraph-operator, sighed
And propped his eyes awake again.
                                        He was tired.
Dog-tired, stone-tired, body and mind burnt up
With too much poker last night and too little sleep.
He hated the Sunday trick. It was Riley's turn
To take it, but Riley's wife was having a child.
He cursed the child and the wife and Sunday and Riley.
Nothing ever happened at Stroudsburg Siding
And yet he had to be here and keep awake
With the flat, stale taste of too little sleep in his mouth
And wait for nothing to happen.
                                        His bulky body
Lusted for sleep with every muscle and nerve.
He'd rather have sleep than a woman or whiskey or money.
He'd give up the next three women that might occur
For ten minutes' sleep, he'd never play poker again,
He'd—battered face beginning to droop on his hands—
Sleep—women—whiskey—eyelids too heavy to lift—
"Yes, Ma, I said, 'Now I lay me.' "—
                                        The sounder chattered
And his head snapped back with a sharp, neck-breaking jerk.
By God, he'd nearly— *chat—chitter-chatter-chat-chat—*
For a moment he took it in without understanding
And then the vein in his forehead began to swell
And his eyes bulged wide awake.
                                        "By Jesus!" he said,
And stared at the sounder as if it had turned to a snake.
"By Jesus!" he said, "By Jesus, they've done it!" he said.

The cruelty of cold trumpets wounds the air.
The ponderous princes draw their gauntlets on.
The captains fit their coal-black armor on.

Judah P. Benjamin, the dapper Jew,
Seal-sleek, black-eyed, lawyer and epicure,

Able, well-hated, face alive with life,
Looked round the council-chamber with the slight
Perpetual smile he held before himself
Continually like a silk-ribbed fan.
Behind the fan, his quick, shrewd, fluid mind
Weighed Gentiles in an old balance.
                                    There they were.
Toombs, the tall, laughing, restless Georgian,
As fine to look at as a yearling bull,
As hard to manage.
                        Stephens, sickly and pale,
Sweet-voiced, weak-bodied, ailingly austere,
The mind's thin steel wearing the body out,
The racked intelligence, the crippled charm.
Mallory—Reagan—Walker—at the head
Davis.
        The mind behind the silk-ribbed fan
Was a dark prince, clothed in an Eastern stuff,
Whose brown hands cupped about a crystal egg
That filmed with colored cloud. The eyes stared, searching.

"I am the Jew. What am I doing here?
The Jew is in my blood and in my hands,
The lonely, bitter and quicksilver drop,
The stain of myrrh that dyes no Gentile mind
With tinctures out of the East and the sad blare
Of the curled ramshorn on Atonement Day.
A river runs between these men and me,
A river of blood and time and liquid gold,
—Oh white rivers of Canaan, running the night!—
And we are colleagues. And we speak to each other
Across the roar of that river, but no more.
I hide myself behind a smiling fan.
They hide themselves behind a Gentile mask
And, if they fall, they will be lifted up,
Being the people, but if I once fall
I fall forever, like the rejected stone.
That is the Jew of it, my Gentile friends,
To see too far ahead and yet go on
And I can smile at it behind my fan
With a drowned mirth that you would find uncouth.
For here we are, the makeshift Cabinet

Of a new nation, gravely setting down
Rules, precedents and cautions, never once
Admitting aloud the cold, plain Franklin sense
That if we do not hang together now
We shall undoubtedly hang separately.
It is the Jew, to see too far ahead—

I wonder what they're doing in the North,
And how their Cabinet shapes, and how they take
Their railsplitter, and if they waste their time
As we waste ours and Mr. Davis's.

Jefferson Davis, pride of Mississippi,
First President of the Confederate States,
What are you thinking now?
       Your eyes look tired.
Your face looks more and more like John Calhoun.
And that is just, because you are his son
In everything but blood, the austere child
Of his ideas, the flower of states-rights.
I will not gird against you, Jefferson Davis.
I sent you a challenge once, but that's forgotten,
And though your blood runs differently from mine,
The Jew salutes you from behind his fan,
Because you are the South he fell in love with
When that young black-haired girl with the Gentile-eyes,
Proud, and a Catholic, and with honey-lips,
First dinted her French heels upon his heart. . . .
We have changed since, but the remembered Spring
Can change no more, even in the Autumn smokes.
We cannot help that havoc of the heart
But my changed mind remembers half the spring
And shall till winter falls.
       No, Jefferson Davis,
You are not she—you are not the warm night
On the bayou, or the New Orleans lamps,
The white-wine bubbles in the crystal cup,
The almond blossoms, sleepy with the sun:
But, nevertheless, you are the South in word,
Deed, thought and temper, the cut cameo
Brittle but durable, refined but fine,
The hands well-shaped, not subtle, but not weak,

The mind set in tradition but not unjust,
The generous slaveholder, the gentleman
Who neither forces his gentility
Nor lets it be held lightly—
                        and yet, and yet
I think you look too much like John Calhoun,
I think your temper is too brittly-poised,
I think your hands too scholar-sensitive,
And though they say you mingle in your voice
The trumpet and the harp, I think it lacks
That gift of warming men which coarser voices
Draw from the common dirt you tread upon
But do not take in your hands. I think you are
All things except success, all honesty
Except the ultimate honesty of the earth,
All talents but the genius of the sun.
And yet I would not have you otherwise,
Although I see too clearly what you are.

Except—except—oh honeydropping Spring,
Oh black-haired woman with the Gentile eyes!
Tell me, you Gentiles, when your Gentile wives
Pray in the church for you and for the South,
How do they pray?—not in that lulling voice
Where some drowned bell of France makes undertones
To the warm river washing the levee.
You do not have so good a prayer as mine.
You cannot have so good a prayer as mine."

———————

Lincoln, six feet one in his stocking feet,
The lank man, knotty and tough as a hickory rail,
Whose hands were always too big for white-kid gloves,
Whose wit was a coonskin sack of dry, tall tales,
Whose weathered face was homely as a plowed field—
Abraham Lincoln, who padded up and down
The sacred White House in nightshirt and carpet-slippers,
And yet could strike young hero-worshipping Hay
As dignified past any neat, balanced, fine
Plutarchan sentences carved in a Latin bronze;
The low clown out of the prairies, the ape-buffoon,

The small-town lawyer, the crude small-time politician,
State-character but comparative failure at forty
In spite of ambition enough for twenty Caesars,
Honesty rare as a man without self-pity,
Kindness as large and plain as a prairie wind,
And a self-confidence like an iron bar:
This Lincoln, President now by the grace of luck,
Disunion, politics, Douglas and a few speeches
Which make the monumental booming of Webster
Sound empty as the belly of a burst drum,
Lincoln shambled in to the Cabinet meeting
And sat, ungainly and awkward. Seated so
He did not seem so tall nor quite so strange
Though he was strange enough. His new broadcloth suit
Felt tight and formal across his big shoulders still
And his new shiny top-hat was not yet battered
To the bulging shape of the old familiar hat
He'd worn at Springfield, stuffed with its hoard of papers.
He was pretty tired. All week the office-seekers
Had plagued him as the flies in fly-time plague
A gaunt-headed, patient horse. The children weren't well
And Mollie was worried about them so sharp with her tongue.
But he knew Mollie and tried to let it go by.
Men tracked dirt in the house and women liked carpets.
Each had a piece of the right, that was all most people could stand.

Look at his Cabinet here. There were Seward and Chase,
Both of them good men, couldn't afford to lose them,
But Chase hates Seward like poison and Seward hates Chase
And both of 'em think they ought to be President
Instead of me. When Seward wrote me that letter
The other day, he practically told me so.
I suppose a man who was touchy about his pride
Would send them both to the dickens when he found out,
But I can't do that as long as they do their work.
The Union's too big a horse to keep changing the saddle
Each time it pinches you. As long as you're sure
The saddle fits, you're bound to put up with the pinches
And not keep fussing the horse.
                                    When I was a boy
I remember figuring out when I went to town
That if I had just one pumpkin to bump in a sack

It was hard to carry, but once you could get two pumpkins,
One in each end of the sack, it balanced things up.
Seward and Chase'll do for my pair of pumpkins.
And as for me—if anyone else comes by
Who shows me that he can manage this job of mine
Better than I can—well, he can have the job.
It's harder sweating than driving six cross mules,
But I haven't run into that other fellow yet
And till or supposing I meet him, the job's my job
And nobody else's.
                        Seward and Chase don't know that.
They'll learn it, in time.
                        Wonder how Jefferson Davis
Feels, down there in Montgomery, about Sumter.
He must be thinking pretty hard and fast,
For he's an able man, no doubt of that.
We were born less than forty miles apart,
Less than a year apart—he got the start
Of me in age, and raising too, I guess,
In fact, from all you hear about the man,
If you set out to pick one of us two
For President, by birth and folks and schooling,
General raising, training up in office,
I guess you'd pick him, nine times out of ten
And yet, somehow, I've got to last him out.

These thoughts passed through the mind in a moment's flash.
Then that mind turned to business.
                        It was the calling
Of seventy-five thousand volunteers.

————————

Shake out the long line of verse like a lanyard of woven steel
And let us praise while we can what things no praise can deface,
The corn that hurried so fast to be ground in an iron wheel
The obdurate, bloody dream that slept before it grew base.

Not the silk flag and the shouts, the catchword patrioteers,
The screaming noise of the press, the preachers who howled for
    blood,
But a certain and stubborn pith in the hearts of the cannoneers
Who hardly knew their guns before they died in the mud.

They came like a run of salmon where the ice-fed Kennebec flings
Its death at the arrow-silver of the packed and mounting host,
They came like the young deer trooping to the ford by Eutaw
    Springs,
Their new horns fuzzy with velvet, their coats still rough with
    the frost.

North and South they assembled, one cry and the other cry,
And both are ghosts to us now, old drums hung up on a wall,
But they were the first hot wave of youth too-ready to die,
And they went to war with an air, as if they went to a ball.

Dress-uniform boys who rubbed their buttons brighter than gold,
And gave them to girls for flowers and raspberry-lemonade,
Unused to the sick fatigue, the route-march made in the cold,
The stink of the fever camps, the tarnish rotting the blade.

We in our time have seen that impulse going to war
And how that impulse is dealt with. We have seen the circle
    complete.
The ripe wheat wasted like trash between the fool and the whore.
We cannot praise again that anger of the ripe wheat.

This we have seen as well, distorted and half-forgotten
In what came before and after, where the blind went leading the
    blind,
The first swift rising of youth before the symbols were rotten,
The price too much to pay, the payment haughty in kind.

So with these men and then. They were much like the men you
    know,
Under the beards and the strangeness of clothes with a different
    fit.
They wrote mush-notes to their girls and wondered how it would
    go,
Half-scared, half-fierce at the thought, but none yet ready to
    quit.

Georgia, New York, Virginia, Rhode Island, Florida, Maine,
Piney-woods squirrel-hunter and clerk with the brand-new gun,
Thus they were marshalled and drilled, while Spring turned
    Summer again,

Until they could stumble toward death at gartersnake-crooked
    Bull Run.

Wingate sat in his room at night
Between the moon and the candle-light,
Reading his Byron with knitted brows,
While his mind drank in the peace of his house,
It was long past twelve, and the night was deep
With moonlight and silence and wind and sleep,
And the small, dim noises, thousand-fold,
That all old houses and forests hold.
The boards that creak for nothing at all,
The leaf that rustles, the bough that sighs,
The nibble of mice in the wainscot-wall,
And the slow clock ticking the time that dies
All distilled in a single sound
Like a giant breathing underground,
A sound more sleepy than sleep itself.
Wingate put his book on the shelf
And went to the window. It was good
To walk in the ghost through a silver wood
And set one's mettle against the far
Bayonet-point of the fixed North Star.
He stood there a moment, wondering.
North Star, wasp with the silver sting
Blue-nosed star on the Yankee banners,
We are coming against you to teach you manners!
With crumbs of thunder and wreaths of myrtle
And cannon that dance to a Dixie chorus,
With a song that bites like a snapping-turtle
And the tiger-lily of Summer before us,
To pull you down like a torn bandanna,
And drown you deeper than the Savannah!

And still, while his arrogance made its cry,
He shivered a little, wondering why.

There was his uniform, grey as ash,
The boots that shone like a well-rubbed table,
The tassels of silk on the colored sash
And sleek Black Whistle down in the stable,
The housewife, stitched from a beauty's fan,

The pocket-Bible with Mother's writing,
The sabre never yet fleshed in man,
And all the crisp new toys of fighting.
He gloated at them with a boyish pride,
But still he wondered, Monmouth-eyed.
The Black Horse Troop was a cavalier
And gallant name for a lady's ear.
He liked the sound and the ringing brag
And the girls who stitched on the county flag,
The smell of horses and saddle-leather
And the feel of the squadron riding together,
From the loose-reined canter of colts at large,
To the crammed, tense second before the charge:
He liked it all with the young, keen zest
Of a hound unleashed and a hawk unjessed.

And yet—what happened to men in war?
Why were they all going out to war?

He brooded a moment. It wasn't slavery,
That stale red-herring of Yankee knavery
Nor even states-rights, at least not solely,
But something so dim that it must be holy.
A voice, a fragrance, a taste of wine,
A face half-seen in old candleshine,
A yellow river, a blowing dust,
Something beyond you that you must trust,
Something so shrouded it must be great,
The dead men building the living State
From 'simmon-seed on a sandy bottom,
The woman South in her rivers laving
That body whiter than new-blown cotton
And savage and sweet as wild-orange-blossom,
The dark hair streams on the barbarous bosom,
If there ever has been a land worth saving—
In Dixie land, I'll take my stand,
And live and die for Dixie! . . .

And yet—and yet—in some cold Northern room,
Does anyone else stare out the obdurate moon
With doubtful passion, seeing his toys of fighting
Scribbled all over with such silver writing

From such a heart of peace, they seem the stale
Cast properties of a dead and childish tale?
And does he see, too soon,
Over the horse, over the horse and rider,
The grey, soft swathing shadowness of the spider,
Spinning his quiet loom?
No—no other man is cursed
With such doubleness of eye,
They can hunger, they can thirst,
But they know for what and why.

I can drink the midnight out,
And rise empty, having dined.
For my courage and my doubt
Are a double strand of mind,
And too subtly intertwined.
They are my flesh, they are my bone,
My shame and my foundation-stone.
I was born alone, to live alone.

Sally Dupré, Sally Dupré,
Eyes that are neither black nor grey,
Why do you haunt me, night and day?

Sea-changing eyes, with the deep, drowned glimmer
Of bar-gold crumbling from sunken ships,
Where the sea-dwarfs creep through the streaked, green shimmer
To press the gold to their glass-cold lips.
They sculpture the gold for a precious ring,
In the caverns under the under-skies,
They would marry the sea to a sailor-king!
You have taken my heart from me, sea-born eyes.
You have taken it, yes, but I do not know.
There are too many roads where I must go.
There are too many beds where I have slept
For a night unweeping, to quit unwept,
And it needs a king to marry the sea.

Why have you taken my heart from me?
I am not justice nor loyalty.
I am the shape of the weathercock,
That all winds come to and all winds mock.
You are the image of sea-carved stone,

The silent thing that can suffer alone,
The little women are easier,
The easy women make lighter love,
I will not take your face to the war,
I will not carry your cast-off glove.

Sally Dupré, Sally Dupré,
Heart and body like sea-blown spray,
I cannot forget you, night or day.

So Wingate pondered in Wingate Hall,
And hated and loved in a single breath,
As he tried to unriddle the doubtful scrawl
Of war and courage and love and death,
And then was suddenly nothing but sleep—
And tomorrow they marched—to a two-months chasing
Of Yankees running away like sheep
And peace in time for the Macon racing.

He got in his bed. Where the moonlight poured,
It lay like frost on a sleeping sword.

———————————

It was stuffy at night in the cabins, stuffy but warm.
And smells are a matter of habit. So, if the air
Was thick as black butter with the commingled smells
Of greens and fried fat and field-sweat and heavy sleep,
The walls were well-chinked, the low roof kept out the rain.
Not like the tumble-down cabins at Zachary's place
Where the field-hands lived all year on hominy-grits
And a piece of spoiled pork at Christmas.
                                        But Zachary
Was a mean man out of the Bottoms, no quality to him.
Wingate was quality. Wingate cared for its own.
A Wingate cabin was better than most such cabins,
You might have called it a sty, had they set you there;
A Middle Age serf might have envied the well-chinked walls.
While as for its tenants then, being folk unversed
In any law but the law of the Wingate name,
They were glad to have it, glad for fire on the hearth,
A roof from the dark-veined wind.
                                Their bellies were warm

66

And full of food. They were heavy in love with each other.
They liked their cabin and lying next to each other,
Long nights of winter when the slow-burning pine-knots
Danced ghosts and witches over the low, near ceiling,
Short nights of summer, after the work of the fields,
When the hot body aches with the ripened sweetness
And the children and the new tunes are begotten together.

"What you so wakeful for, black boy?"
                                        "Thinkin', woman."
"You got no call to be thinkin', little black boy,
Thinkin's a trouble, a h'ant lookin' over de shoulder,
Set yo' head on my breas' and forget about thinkin'."

"I got my head on yo' breas', and it's sof' dere, woman,
Sof' and sweet as a mournin' out of de Scriptures,
Sof' as two Solomon doves. But I can't help thinkin'."

"Ain't I good enough for you no more, black boy?
Don' you love me no more dat you mus' keep thinkin'?"

"You's better'n good to me and I loves you, woman,
Till I feels like Meshuck down in de fiery furnace,
Till I feels like God's own chile. But I keeps on thinkin',
Wonderin' what I'd feel like if I was free."

"Hush, black boy, hush for de Lord's sake!"
                                        "But listen, woman——"

"Hush yo'self, black boy, lean yo'self on my breas',
Talk like that and paterollers'll git you,
Swinge you all to bits with a blacksnake whip,
Squinch-owl carry yo' talk to de paterollers,
It ain't safe to talk like that."
                              "I got to, woman,
I got a feelin' in my heart."
                              "Den you sot on dat feelin'!
Never heard you talk so in all my born days!
Ain't we got a good cabin here?"
                              "Sho', we got a good cabin."

"Ain't we got good vittles, ain't old Mistis kind to us?"

"Sho' we got good vittles, and ole Mistis she's kind.
I'se mighty fond of ole Mistis."
                              "Den what you talkin',
You brash fool-nigger?"
                              "I just got a feelin', woman.
Ole Marse Billy, he's goin' away tomorrow,
Marse Clay, he's goin' with him to fight de Yankees,
All of 'em goin', yes suh."
                              "And what if dey is?"

"Well, sposin' de Yankees beats?"
                              "Ain't you got *no* sense,
    nigger?
Like to see any ole Yankees lick ole Marse Billy
And young Marse Clay!"
                              "Hi, woman, ain't dat de trufe!"
"Well, den——"
                              "But I sees 'em all, jus' goin' and goin',
Goin' to war like Joshua, goin' like David,
And it makes me want to be free. Ain't you never thought
At all about bein' free?"
                              "Sho', co'se I thought of it.
I always reckoned when ole Marse Billy died,
Old Mistis mebbe gwine to set some of us free,
Mebbe she will."
                              "But we-uns gwine to be old den,
We won't be young and have the use of our hands,
We won't see our young 'uns growin' up free around us,
We won't have the strength to hoe our own co'n ourselves,
I want to be free, like me, while I got my strength."

"You might be a lot worse off and not be free,
What'd you do if ole man Zachary owned us?"

"Kill him, I reckon."
                              "Hush, black boy, for God's sake hush!"

"I can't help it, woman. Dey ain't so many like him
But what dey is is too pizen-mean to live.
Can't you hear dat feelin' I got, woman? I ain't scared
Of talk and de paterollers, and I ain't mean.

I'se mighty fond of ole Mistis and ole Marse Billy,
I'se mighty fond of 'em all at de Big House,
I wouldn't be nobody else's nigger for nothin'.
But I hears 'em goin' away, all goin' away,
With horses and guns and things, all stompin' and wavin',
And I hears de chariot-wheels and de Jordan River,
Rollin' and rollin' and rollin' thu' my sleep,
And I wants to be free. I wants to see my chillun
Growin' up free, and all bust out of Egypt!
I wants to be free like an eagle in de air,
Like an eagle in de air."

Iron-filings scattered over a dusty
Map of crook-cornered States in yellow and blue.
Little, grouped male and female iron-filings,
Scattered over a patchwork-quilt whose patches
Are the red-earth stuff of Georgia, the pine-bough green of Vermont.
Here you are clustered as thick as a clump of bees
In swarming time. The clumps make cities and towns.
Here you are strewn at random, like single seeds
Lost out of the wind's pocket.
                              But now, but now,
The thunderstone has fallen on your map
And all the iron-filings shiver and move
Under the grippings of that blinded force,
The cold pull of the ash-and-cinder star.

The map is vexed with the long battle-worms
Of filings, clustered and moving.
                                  If it is
An enemy of the sun who has so stolen
Power from a burnt star to do this work,
Let the bleak essence of the utter cold
Beyond the last gleam of the most outpost light
Freeze in his veins forever.
                            But if it is
A fault in the very metal of the heart,
We and our children must acquit that fault
With the old bloody wastage, or give up
Playing the father to it.

O vexed and strange,
Salt-bitter, apple-sweet, strong-handed life!
Your million lovers cast themselves like sea
Against your mountainy breast, with a clashing noise
And a proud clamor—and like sea recoil,
Sucked down beneath the forefoot of the new
Advancing surf. They feed the battle-worms,
Not only War's, but in the second's pause
Between the assaulting and the broken wave,
The voices of the lovers can be heard,
The sea-gull cry.

———————

Jake Diefer, the barrel-chested Pennsylvanian,
Hand like a ham and arms that could wrestle a bull,
A roast of a man, all solid meat and good fat,
A slow-thought-chewing Clydesdale horse of a man,
Roused out of his wife's arms. The dawn outside
Was ruddy as his big cheeks. He yawned and stretched
Gigantically, hawking and clearing his throat.
His wife, hair tousled around her like tousled corn,
Stared at him with sleep-blind eyes.
                              "Jake, it ain't come morning,
Already yet?"
              He nodded and started to dress.
She burrowed deeper into the bed for a minute
And then threw off the covers.
                         They didn't say much
Then, or at breakfast. Eating was something serious.
But he looked around the big kitchen once or twice
In a puzzled way, as if trying hard to remember it.
She too, when she was busy with the first batch
Of pancakes, burnt one or two, because she was staring
At the "SALT" on the salt-box, for no particular reason.
The boy ate with them and didn't say a word,
Being too sleepy.
                  Afterwards, when the team
Was hitched up and waiting, with the boy on the seat,
Holding the reins till Jake was ready to take them,
Jake didn't take them at once.
                          The sun was up now,
The spilt-milk-mist of first morning lay on the farm,

Jake looked at it all with those same mildly-puzzled eyes,
The red barn, the fat rich fields just done with the winter,
Just beginning the work of another year.
The boy would have to do the rest of the planting.

He blew on his hands and stared at his wife dumbly.
He cleared his throat.
        "Well, good-by, Minnie," he said,
"Don't you hire any feller for harvest without you write me,
And if any more of those lightning-rodders come around,
We don't want no more dum lightning-rods."
                        He tried
To think if there was anything else, but there wasn't.
She suddenly threw her big, red arms around his neck,
He kissed her with clumsy force.
             Then he got on the wagon
And clucked to the horses as she started to cry.

Up in the mountains where the hogs are thin
And razorbacked, wild Indians of hogs,
The laurel's green in April—and if the nights
Are cold as the cold cloud of watersmoke
Above a mountain-spring, the midday sun
Has heat enough in it to make you sweat.

They are a curious and most native stock,
The lanky men, the lost, forgotten seeds
Spilled from the first great wave-march toward the West
And set to sprout by chance in the deep cracks
Of that hill-billy world of laurel-hells.
They keep the beechwood-fiddle and the salt
Old-fashioned ballad-English of our first
Rowdy, corn-liquor-drinking, ignorant youth;
Also the rifle and the frying-pan,
The old feud-temper and the old feud-way
Of thinking strangers better shot on sight
But treating strangers that one leaves unshot
With border-hospitality.
                The girls
Have the brief-blooming, rhododendron-youth

71

Of pioneer women, and the black-toothed age.
And if you yearn to meet your pioneers,
You'll find them there, the same men, inbred sons
Of inbred sires perhaps, but still the same;
A pioneer-island in a world that has
No use for pioneers—the unsplit rock
Of Fundamentalism, calomel,
Clan-virtues, clannish vices, fiddle-tunes
And a hard God.
                    They are our last frontier.
They shot the railway-train when it first came,
And when the Fords first came, they shot the Fords.
It could not save them. They are dying now
Or being educated, which is the same.
One need not weep romantic tears for them,
But when the last moonshiner buys his radio,
And the last, lost, wild-rabbit of a girl
Is civilized with a mail-order dress,
Something will pass that was American
And all the movies will not bring it back.

They are misfit and strange in our new day,
In Sixty-One they were not quite so strange,
Before the Fords, before the day of the Fords . . .

Luke Breckinridge, his rifle on his shoulder,
Slipped through green forest alleys toward the town,
A gawky boy with smoldering eyes, whose feet
Whispered the crooked paths like moccasins.
He wasn't looking for trouble, going down,
But he was on guard, as always. When he stopped
To scoop some water in the palm of his hand
From a sweet trickle between moss-grown rocks,
You might have thought him careless for a minute,
But when the snapped stick cracked six feet behind him
He was all sudden rifle and hard eyes.
The pause endured a long death-quiet instant,
Then he knew who it was.
                              "Hi, Jim," he said,
Lowering his rifle. The green laurel-screen
Hardly had moved, but Jim was there beside him.
The cousins looked at each other. Their rifles seemed
To look as well, with much the same taut silentness.

72

"Goin' to town, Luke?"
"Uh-huh, goin' to town,
You goin'?"
"Looks as if I was goin'."
"Looks
As if you was after squirrels."
"I might be.
You goin' after squirrels?" "I might be, too."
"Not so many squirrels near town."
"No, reckon there's not."

Jim hesitated. His gaunt hands caressed
The smooth guard of his rifle. His eyes were sharp.
"Might go along a piece together," he said.
Luke didn't move. Their eyes clashed for a moment,
Then Luke spoke, casually.
"I hear the Kelceys
Air goin' to fight in this here war," he said.
Jim nodded slowly, "Yuh, I heerd that too."
He watched Luke's trigger-hand.
"I might be goin'
Myself sometime," he said reflectively
Sliding his own hand down. Luke saw the movement.
"We-uns don't like the Kelceys much," he said
With his eyes down to pinpoints.
Then Jim smiled.
"We-uns neither," he said.
His hand slid back.

They went along together after that
But neither of them spoke for half-a-mile,
Then finally, Jim said, half-diffidently,
"You know who we air goin' to fight outside?
I heard it was the British. Air that so?"
"Hell, no," said Luke, with scorn. He puckered his brows.
"Dunno's I rightly know just who they air."
He admitted finally, "But 'tain't the British.
It's some trash-lot of furriners, that's shore.
They call 'em Yankees near as I kin make it,
But they ain't Injuns neither."
"Well," said Jim

73

Soothingly, "Reckon it don't rightly matter
Long as the Kelceys take the other side."

It was noon when the company marched to the railroad-station.
The town was ready for them. The streets were packed.
There were flags and streamers and pictures of Lincoln and
    Hamlin.
The bad little boys climbed up on the trees and yelled,
The good little boys had clean paper-collars on,
And swung big-eyed on white-painted wicket-gates,
Wanting to yell, and feeling like Fourth of July.
Somebody fastened a tin can full of firecrackers
To a yellow dog's tail and sent him howling and racketing
The length of the street.
                        "There goes Jeff Davis!" said somebody,
And everybody laughed, and the little boys
Punched each other and squealed between fits of laughing
"There goes Jeff Davis—lookit ole yellow Jeff Davis!"
And then the laugh died and rose again in a strange
Half-shrill, half-strangled unexpected shout
As they heard the Hillsboro' Silver Cornet Band
Swinging "John Brown's Body" ahead of the soldiers.
I have heard that soul of crowd go out in the queer
Groan between laughter and tears that baffles the wise.
I have heard that whanging band.

"We'll hang Jeff Davis on a sour-apple tree."
Double-roll on the snare-drums, double squeal of the fife,
"We'll hang Jeff Davis on a sour-apple tree!"
Clash of the cymbals zinging, throaty blare of cornets,
"We'll hang Jeff Davis on a sour-apple tree!"
"On to Richmond! On to Richmond! On to Richmond!"
"Yeah! There they come! Yeah! Yeah!"
And they came, the bearskin drum-major leading the band,
Twirling his silver-balled baton with turkey-cock pomp,
The cornet-blowers, the ranks. The drum-major was fine,
But the little boys thought the captain was even finer,
He looked just like a captain out of a book
With his sword and his shoulder-straps and his discipline-face.
He wasn't just Henry Fairfield, he was a captain,
—Henry Fairfield worried about his sword,
Hoping to God that he wouldn't drop his sword,

And wondering hotly whether his discipline-face
Really looked disciplined or only peevish—
"*Yeah!* There they come! There's Jack! There's Charlie! Yeah!
   Yeah!"
The color-guard with the stiff, new flapping flag,
And the ranks and the ranks and the ranks, the amateur
Blue, wavering ranks, in their ill-fitting tight coats,
Shoulders galled already by their new guns,
—They were three-months' men, they had drilled in civilian
   clothes
Till a week ago—"There's Charlie! There's Hank, yeah, yeah!"
"On to Richmond, boys! Three cheers for Abe Lincoln!
Three cheers for the boys! Three groans for old Jeff Davis
And the dirty Rebs!"
"*We'll hang Jeff Davis on a sour-apple tree!*"

Jack Ellyat, marching, saw between blue shoulders
A blur of faces. They all were faces he knew,
Old Mrs. Cobb with her wart and her Paisley shawl,
Little George Freeman, the slim Tucker girls,
All of them cheering and shouting—and all of them strange
Suddenly, different, faces he'd never seen.
Faces somehow turned into one crowd-face.
His legs went marching along all right but they felt
Like somebody else's legs, his mind was sucked dry.
It was real, they were going away, the town was cheering them.
Henry Fairfield was marching ahead with his sword.
Just as he'd thought about it a thousand times,
These months—but it wasn't the way that he'd thought about it.
"On to Richmond! On to Richmond! On to Richmond!"
There were Mother and Father and Jane and the house.
Jane was waving a flag. He laughed and called to them.
But his voice was stiff in his throat, not like his real voice.
This, everything, it was too quick, too crowded, not Phaëton
Charging his snarling horses at a black sea,
But a numb, hurried minute with legs that marched
Mechanically, feeling nothing at all.
The white crowd-face—the sweat on the red seamed neck
Of the man ahead—"On to Richmond!"—blue shoulders bobbing—
Flags—cheering—somebody kissed him—Ellen Baker—
She was crying—wet mouth of tears—didn't want her to kiss him—
Why did she want to—the station—*halt*—Mother and Jane.

75

The engineer wore a flag in his coat-lapel.
The engine had "On to Richmond!" chalked all over it.
Nothing to say now—Mother looks tired to death—
I wish I weren't going—no, I'm glad that I am—
The damn band's playing "John Brown's Body" again,
I wish they'd stop it!—I wish to God we could start—
There—*close up, men!*—oh my God, they've let Ned out!
I told them for God's sake to lock him up in the cellar,
But they've let him out—maybe he got out by himself—
He's got too much sense—"No, down, Ned! Down, good dog!
Down, I tell you!—"

"*Good-by, boys! Good-by! We'll hang Jeff
Davis!*"

The engine squealed, the packed train started to move.
Ned wanted to come, but they wouldn't let him come.
They had to kick him away, he couldn't see why.

In another column, footsore Curly Hatton
Groaned at the thought of marching any more.
His legs weren't built for marching and they knew it,
Butterball-legs under a butterball-body.
The plump good-tempered face with its round eyes
Blue and astonished as a china-doll's,
Stared at the road ahead and hated it
Because there was so much of it ahead
And all of it so dry.
                    He didn't mind
The rest so much. He didn't even mind
Being the one sure necessary joke
Of the whole regiment. He'd always been
A necessary joke—fat people were.
Fat babies always were supposed to laugh.
Fat little boys had fingers poked at them.
And, even with the road, and being fat,
You had a good time in this funny war,
Considering everything, and one thing most.

His mind slipped back two months. He saw himself
In the cool room at Weatherby's Retreat
Where all the girls were sewing the new star
In the new flag for the first volunteers.

He hadn't thought of fighting much before,
He was too easy-going. If Virginia
Wanted secession, that was her affair.
It seemed too bad to break the Union up
After some seventy years of housekeeping.
But he could understand the way you'd feel
If you were thin and angry at the Yanks.
He knew a lot of Yankees that he liked,
But then he liked most people, on the whole
Although most girls and women made him shy.
He loved the look of them and the way they walked,
He loved their voices and their little sweet mouths,
But something always seemed to hold him back,
When he was near them.
                              He was too fat, too friendly,
Too comfortable for dreams, too easy-shy.
The porcelain dolls stood on the mantelpiece,
Waiting such slim and arrant cavaliers
As porcelain dolls must have to make them proud,
They had no mercy for fat Cupidons,
Not even Lucy, all the years before,
And Lucy was the porcelain belle of the world!
And so when she said.
                              And he couldn't believe
At first.
          But she was silver and fire and steel
That day of the new stars and the new flag,
Fire and bright steel for the invading horde
And silver for the men who drove them off,
And so she sewed him in her flag and heart:
Though even now, he couldn't believe she had
In spite of all the letters and the socks
And kissing him before he went away.
But it was so—the necessary joke
Made into a man at last, a man in love
And loved by the most porcelain belle of the world.
And he was ready to march to the world's end
And fight ten million Yanks to keep it so.

"Oh God, after we're married—the cool night
Over the garden—and Lucy sitting there
In her blue dress while the big stars come out."

His face was funny with love and footsore pride,
The man beside him saw it, gave a laugh,
"Curly's thinking it's time for a julep, boys!
Hot work for fat men, Curly!"

The crows fly over the Henry House, through the red sky of
  evening, cawing,
Judith Henry, bedridden, watches them through the clouded
  glass of old sight.
(July is hot in Virginia—a parched, sun-leathered farmer sawing
Dry sticks with a cicada-saw that creaks all the lukewarm night.)

But Judith Henry's hands are cool in spite of all midsummer's
  burning,
Cool, muted and frail with age like the smoothness of old yellow
  linen, the cool touch of old, dulled rings.
Her years go past her in bed like falling waters and the waters
  of a millwheel turning,
And she is not ill content to lie there, dozing and calm, remembering youth, to the gushing of those watersprings.

She has known Time like the cock of red dawn and Time like a
  tired clock slowing;
She has seen so many faces and bodies, young and then old, so
  much life, so many patterns of death and birth.
She knows that she must leave them soon. She is not afraid to
  flow with that river's flowing.
But the wrinkled earth still hangs at her sufficed breast like a
  weary child, she is unwilling to go while she still has milk for
  the earth.

She will go in her sleep, most likely, she has the sunk death-sleep
  of the old already,
(War-bugles by the Potomac, you cannot reach her ears with
  your brass lyric, piercing the crowded dark.)
It does not matter, the farm will go on, the farm and the children
  bury her in her best dress, the plow cut its furrow, steady,
(War-horses of the Shenandoah, why should you hurry so fast
  to tramp the last ashy fire from so feeble and retired a spark?)

78

There is nothing here but a creek and a house called the Henry
House, a farm and a bedridden woman and people with country faces.
There is nothing for you here. And La Haye Sainte was a quiet
farm and the mile by it a quiet mile.
And Lexington was a place to work in like any one of a dozen
dull, little places.
And they raised good crops at Blenheim till the soldiers came
and spoiled the crops for a while.

The red evening fades into twilight, the crows have gone to
their trees, the slow, hot stars are emerging.
It is cooler now on the hill—and in the camps it is cooler, where
the untried soldiers find their bivouac hard.
Where, from North and South, the blind wrestlers of armies
converge on the forgotten house like the double pincers of an
iron claw converging.
And Johnston hurries his tired brigades from the Valley, to
bring them up in time before McDowell can fall on Beauregard.

———————

The congressmen came out to see Bull Run,
The congressmen who like free shows and spectacles.
They brought their wives and carriages along,
They brought their speeches and their picnic-lunch,
Their black constituent-hats and their devotion:
Some even brought a little whiskey, too,
(A little whiskey is a comforting thing
For congressmen in the sun, in the heat of the sun.)
The bearded congressmen with orator's mouths,
The fine, clean-shaved, Websterian congressmen,
Come out to see the gladiator's show
Like Iliad gods, wrapped in the sacred cloud
Of Florida-water, wisdom and bay-rum,
Of free cigars, democracy and votes,
That lends such portliness to congressmen.
(The gates fly wide, the bronze troop marches out
Into the stripped and deadly circus-ring,
"*Ave, Caesar!*" the cry goes up, and shakes
The purple awning over Caesar's seat.)
"*Ave, Caesar! Ave,* O congressmen,
We who are about to die,
Salute you, congressmen!"

79

Eleven States,
New York, Rhode Island, Maine,
Connecticut, Michigan and the gathered West,
Salute you, congressmen!
The red-fezzed Fire-Zouaves, flamingo-bright,
Salute you, congressmen!
The raw boys still in their civilian clothes,
Salute you, congressmen!
The second Wisconsin in its homespun grey,
Salutes you, congressmen!
The Garibaldi Guards in cocksfeather hats,
Salute you, congressmen!
The Second Ohio with their Bedouin-caps,
Salutes you, congressmen!
Sherman's brigade, grey-headed Heintzelman,
Ricketts' and Griffin's doomed and valiant guns,
The tough, hard-bitten regulars of Sykes
Who covered the retreat with the Marines,
Burnside and Porter, Willcox and McDowell,
All the vast, unprepared, militia-mass
Of boys in red and yellow Zouave pants,
Who carried peach-preserves inside their kits
And dreamt of being generals overnight;
The straggling companies where every man
Was a sovereign and a voter—the slack regiments
Where every company marched a different step;
The clumsy and unwieldy-new brigades
Not yet distempered into battle-worms;
The whole, huge, innocent army, ready to fight
But only half-taught in the tricks of fighting,
Ready to die like picture-postcard boys
While fighting still had banners and a sword
And just as ready to run in blind mob-panic,
Salutes you with a vast and thunderous cry,
Ave, Caesar, ave, O congressmen,
Ave, O Iliad gods who forced the fight!
You bring your carriages and your picnic-lunch
To cheer us in our need.
                              You come with speeches,
Your togas smell of heroism and bay-rum.
You are the people and the voice of the people
And, when the fight is done, your carriages

Will bear you safely, through the streaming rout
Of broken troops, throwing their guns away.
You come to see the gladiator's show,
But from a high place, as befits the wise:
You will not see the long windrows of men
Strewn like dead pears before the Henry House
Or the stone-wall of Jackson breathe its parched
Devouring breath upon the failing charge,
Ave, Caesar, ave, O congressmen,
Cigar-smoke wraps you in a godlike cloud,
And if you are not to depart from us
As easily and divinely as you came,
It hardly matters.
                    Fighting Joe Hooker once
Said with that tart, unbridled tongue of his
That made so many needless enemies,
"Who ever saw a dead cavalryman?"
                              The phrase
Stings with a needle sharpness, just or not,
But even he was never heard to say,
"Who ever saw a dead congressman?"
And yet, he was a man with a sharp tongue.

The day broke, hot and calm. In the little farm-houses
That are scattered here and there in that rolling country
Of oak and rail-fence, crooked creeks and second-growth pine,
The early-risers stand looking out of the door
At the long dawn-shadows for a minute or two
—Shadows are always cool—but the blue-glass sky
Is fusing with heat even now, heat that prickles the hairs
On the back of your hand.
                    They sigh and turn back to the house.
"Looks like a scorcher today, boys!"
                              They think already
Of the cool jug of vinegar-water down by the hedge.

Judith Henry wakened with the first light,
She had the short sleep of age, and the long patience.
She waited for breakfast in vague, half-drowsy wonderment
At various things. Yesterday some men had gone by
And stopped for a drink of water. She'd heard they were soldiers.

She couldn't be sure. It had seemed to worry the folks
But it took more than soldiers and such to worry her now.
Young people always worried a lot too much.
No soldiers that had any sense would fight around here.
She'd had a good night. Today would be a good day.

———————

A mile and a half away, before the Stone Bridge,
A Union gun opened fire.

———————

Six miles away, McDowell had planned his battle
And planned it well, as far as such things can be planned—
A feint at one point, a flanking march at another
To circle Beauregard's left and crumple it up.
There were Johnston's eight thousand men to be reckoned with
But Patterson should be holding them, miles away,
And even if they slipped loose from Patterson's fingers
The thing might still be done.
                                    If you take a flat map
And move wooden blocks upon it strategically,
The thing looks well, the blocks behave as they should.
The science of war is moving live men like blocks.
And getting the blocks into place at a fixed moment.
But it takes time to mold your men into blocks
And flat maps turn into country where creeks and gullies
Hamper your wooden squares. They stick in the brush,
They are tired and rest, they straggle after ripe blackberries,
And you cannot lift them up in your hand and move them.
—A string of blocks curling smoothly around the left
Of another string of blocks and crunching it up—
It is all so clear in the maps, so clear in the mind,
But the orders are slow, the men in the blocks are slow
To move, when they start they take too long on the way—
The General loses his stars and the block-men die
In unstrategic defiance of martial law
Because still used to just being men, not block-parts.
McDowell was neither a fool nor a fighting fool;
He knew his dice, he knew both armies unready,
But congressmen and nation wanted a battle
And he felt their hands on his shoulders, forcing his play.

He knew well enough when he played that he played for his head
As Beauregard and Johnston were playing for theirs,
So he played with the skill he had—and does not lie
Under a cupolaed gloom on Riverside Drive.
Put Grant in his place that day and with those same dice,
Grant might have done little better.
                                    Wherefore, now,
Irvin McDowell, half-forgotten general,
Who tried the game and found no luck in the game
And never got the chance to try it again
But did not backbite the gamblers who found more luck in it
Then or later in double-edged reminiscences;
If any laurel can grow in the sad-colored fields
Between Bull Run and Cub Run and Cat Hairpin Bend
You should have a share of it for your hardworking ghost
Because you played as you could with your cold, forced dice
And neither wasted your men like the fighting fools
Nor posed as an injured Napoleon twenty years later.
Meanwhile, McDowell watched his long flanking column
File by, on the Warrentown pike, in the first dawn-freshness.
"Gentlemen, that's a big force," he said to his staff.

A full rifled battery begins to talk spitefully to Evans' Carolinians. The grey skirmish-line, thrown forward on the other
side of Bull Run, ducks its head involuntarily as a locomotive
noise goes by in the air above it, and waits for a flicker of blue
in the scrub-oaks ahead.

Beauregard, eager *sabreur*, whose heart was a French
Print of a sabretasche-War with "La Gloire" written under it,
Lovable, fiery, bizarre, picturesque as his name,
Galloped toward Mitchell's Ford with bald, quiet Joe Johnston,
The little precise Scotch-dominie of a general,
Stubborn as flint, in advance not always so lucky,
In retreat more dangerous than a running wolf—
Slant shadow, sniffing the traps and the poisoned meat,
And going on to pause and slash at the first
Unwary dogs before the hunters came up.
Grant said of him once,

"I was always anxious with Joe Johnston in front of me,
I was never half so anxious in front of Lee."
He kissed his friends in the Nelson-way we've forgotten,
He could make men cheer him after six-weeks retreating.
Another man said of him, after the war was done,
Still with that puzzled comparison we find
When Lee, the reticent sword, comes into the question,
"Yes, Lee was a great general, a good man;
But I never wanted to put my arms round his neck
As I used to want to with Johnston."
       The two sayings
Make a good epitaph for so Scotch a ghost,
Or would if they were all.
      They are not quite all,
He had to write his reminiscences, too,
And tell what he would have done if it had not been
For Davis and chance and a dozen turns of the wheel.
That was the thistle in him—the other strain—
But he was older then.
     I'd like to have seen him
That day as he galloped along beside Beauregard,
Sabreur and dominie planning the battle-lines.
They'd ordered Jackson up to the threatened left
But Beauregard was sure that the main assault
Would come on the right. He'd planned it so—a good plan—
But once the blocks start moving, they keep on moving.

The hands of the scuffed brown clock in the kitchen of the
 Henry House point to nine-forty-five.
Judith Henry does not hear the clock, she hears in the sky a
 vast dim roar like piles of heavy lumber crashingly falling.
They are carrying her in her bed to a ravine below the Sudley
 Road, maybe she will be safe there, maybe the battle will go
 by and leave her alive.
The crows have been scared from their nests by the strange
 crashing, they circle in the sky like a flight of blackened leaves,
 wheeling and calling.

Back at Centerville, there are three-months' men,
A Pennsylvania regiment, a New York Battery.

84

They hear the spent wave of the roar of the opening guns,
But they are three-months' men, their time is up today.
They would have fought yesterday or a week ago,
But then they were still enlisted—today they are not—
Their time is up, and there can't be much use or sense
In fighting longer than you've promised to fight.
They pack up their things and decide they'd better go home,
And quietly march away from that gathering roar.

Luke Breckinridge, crouched by the Warrentown pike,
Saw stuffed dolls in blue coats and baggy trousers
Go down like squirrels under the rifle-cracks.
His eyes glowed as a bullet ripped his sleeve
And he felt well. Armies weren't such a much,
Too damn many orders, too damn much saluting,
Too many damn officers you weren't allowed
To shoot when they talked mean to you because
They were your officers, which didn't make sense.
But this was something he could understand,
Except for those dirty stinkers of big guns,
It wasn't right to shoot you with big guns
But it was a good scrap except for that—
Carried a little high, then . . . change it . . . good . . .
Though men were hard to miss when you were used
To squirrels. His eyes were narrow. He hardly heard
The officer's voice. The woods in front of him
Were full of Kelceys he was going to kill,
Blue-coated Kelcey dolls in baggy trousers.
It was a beautiful and sufficing sight.

The first blue wave of Burnside is beaten back from the pike to
stumble a little way and rally against Porter's fresh brigade.
Bee and Bartow move down from the Henry House plateau—
grey and butternut lines trampling the bullet-cut oak-leaves,
splashing across Young's Branch.
Tall, black-bearded Bee rides by on his strong horse, his long
black hair fluttering.
Imboden's red-shirted gunners unlimber by the Henry House

to answer the Parrotts and howitzers of Ricketts and Griffin.
The air is a sheet of iron, continually and dully shaken.

———————

Shippy, the little man with the sharp rat-eyes,
Saw someone run in front of them waving a sword;
Then they were going along toward a whining sound
That ran like cold spring-water along his spine.
God, he was in for it now! His sharp rat-eyes
Flickered around and about him hopelessly.
If a fellow could only drop out, if a fellow could only
Pretend he was hurt a little and then drop out
Behind a big, safe oak-tree—no use—no use—
He was in for it, now. He couldn't get away.
*"Come on, boys—come on, men—clean them out with the
     bayonet!"*
He saw a rail-fence ahead, a quiet rail-fence,
But men were back of it—grey lumps—a million bees
Stinging the air—Oh Jesus, the corporal's got it—
He couldn't shoot, even—he was too scared to shoot—
His legs took him on—he couldn't stop his legs
Or the weak urine suddenly trickling down them.

———————

Curly Hatton, toiling along the slow
Crest of the Henry Hill, over slippery ground,
Glanced at the still-blue sky that lay so deep
Above the little pines, so pooled, so calm.
He thought, with the slow drowsiness of fatigue,
Of Lucy feeding the white, greedy swans
On the blue pool by Weatherby's Retreat.
They stretched their necks, and clattered with their wings.
There was a fragrance sleeping in her hair.
"Close up, folks—don't straggle—we're going into action!"
His butterball-legs moved faster—Lucy—Lucy—

———————

Bee and Bartow's brigades are broken in their turn—it is fight
and run away—fight and run away, all day—the day will go to

whichever of the untried wrestlers can bear the pain of the grips
an instant longer than the other.

Beauregard and Johnston hurry toward the firing—McDowell
has already gone—

The chessplayers have gone back to little pieces on the shaken
board—little pieces that cannot see the board as a whole.

The block-plan is lost—there is no plan any more—only the
bloodstained, fighting blocks, the bloodstained and blackened
men.

Jack Ellyat heard the guns with a knock at his heart
When he first heard them. They were going to be in it, soon.
He wondered how it would feel. They would win, of course,
But how would it feel? He'd never killed anything much.
Ducks and rabbits, but ducks and rabbits weren't men.
He'd never even seen a man killed, a man die,
Except Uncle Amos, and Uncle Amos was old.
He saw a red sop spreading across the close
Feathers of a duck's breast—it had been all right,
But now it made him feel sick for a while, somehow.
Then they were down on the ground, and they were firing,
And that was all right—just fire as you fired at drill.
Was anyone firing at them? He couldn't tell.
There was a stone bridge. Were there rebels beyond the bridge?
The shot he was firing now might go and kill rebels
But it didn't feel like it.
                    A man down the line
Fell and rolled flat, with a minor coughing sound
And then was quiet. Ellyat felt the cough
In the pit of his stomach a minute.
But, after that, it was just like a man falling down.
It was all so calm except for their guns and the distant
Shake in the air of cannon. No more men were hit,
And, after a while, they all got up and marched on.
If Rebels had been by the bridge, the rebels were gone,
And they were going on somewhere, you couldn't say where,
Just marching along the way that they always did.
The only funny thing was, leaving the man
Who had made that cough, back there in the trampied grass
With the red stain sopping through the blue of his coat

87

Like the stain on a duck's breast. He hardly knew the man
But it felt funny to leave him just lying there.

The wreckage of Bee, Bartow and Evans' commands streams
back into a shallow ravine below a little wood—broken blocks
hammered into splinters by war—two thousand confused men
reeling past their staggering flags and the hoarse curses and
rallying cries of their officers, like sheep in a narrow run.
Bee tries to halt them furiously—he stands up in his stirrups,
tree-tall, while the blue flood of the North trickles over the
stream and pours on and on.
He waves his sword—the toyish glitter sparkles—he points to
a grey dyke at the top of the ravine—a grey dyke of musket-
holding Virginians, silent and ready.
"Look, men, there's Jackson's brigade! It stands there like a
stone wall. Rally behind the Virginians!"
They rally behind them—Johnston and Beauregard are there
—the Scotch dominie plucks a flag and carries it forward to
rally the Fourth Alabama—the French hussar-sword rallies them
with bursting rockets of oratory—his horse is shot under him,
but he mounts again.
And the grey stone wall holds like a stiff dyke while the tired
men get their breath behind it—and the odd, lemon-sucking,
ex-professor of tactics who saw John Brown hung in his carpet-
slippers and prayed a Presbyterian prayer for his damned soul,
has a new name that will last as long as the face they cut for
him on Stone Mountain, and has the same clang of rock against
the chisel-blade.

Judith Henry, Judith Henry, they have moved you back at
    last, in doubt and confusion, to the little house where
    you know every knothole by heart.
It is not safe, but now there is no place safe, you are between the
    artillery and the artillery, and the incessant noise comes
    to your dim ears like the sea-roar within a shell where
    you are lying.
The walls of the house are riddled, the brown clock in the kitchen
    gouged by a bullet, a jar leaks red preserves on the cup-
    board shelf where the shell-splinter came and tore the
    cupboard apart.

The casual guns do not look for you, Judith Henry, they find
  you in passing merely and touch you only a little, but the
  touch is enough to give your helpless body five sudden
  wounds and leave you helplessly dying.

———————

Wingate gentled Black Whistle's pawing
With hand and wisdom and horseman's play
And listened anew to the bulldogs gnawing
Their bone of iron, a mile away.
There was a wood that a bonfire crowned
With thick dark smoke without flame for neighbor,
And the dull, monotonous, heavy sound
Of a hill or a woman in too-long labor,
But that was all for the Black Horse Troop
And had been all since the day's beginning,
That stray boy beating his metal hoop
And the tight-lipped wonder if they were winning.
Wainscott Bristol, behind his eyes,
Was getting in bed with a sweet-toothed wench,
Huger Shepley felt for his dice
And Stuart Cazenove swore in French
"Mille diables and Yankee blood!
How long are we going to stick in the mud?"
While a Cotter hummed with a mocking sigh,
" 'If you want a good time, jine the cavalry!' "
"Stuart's in it, Wade Hampton's in it."
"The Yanks'll quit in another minute!"
"General Beau's just lost us!"
                              "Steady!"
"And he won't find us until he's ready!"
"It must be two—we've been here since six."
"It's Virginia up to her old-time tricks!
They never did trust a Georgia man,
But Georgia'll fight while Virginia can!"

The restless talk was a simmering brew
That made the horses restless too;
They stamped and snuffled and pricked their ears—
There were cheers, off somewhere—but which side's cheers?
Had the Yankees whipped? Were the Yankees breaking?

The whole troop grumbled and wondered, aching
For fighting or fleeing or fornicating
Or anything else except this bored waiting.

An aide rode up on a sweating mare
And they glowered at him with hostile stare.
He had been in it and they had not.
He had smelt the powder and heard the shot,
And they hated his soul and his martial noise
With the envious hate of little boys.
Then "Yaaih! Yaaih!"
                        —and Wingate felt
The whole troop lift like a lifted dart
And loosened the sabre at his belt,
And felt his chest too small for his heart.

Curly Hatton was nothing any more
But a dry throat and a pair of burnt black hands
That held a hot gun he was always firing
Though he no longer remembered why he fired.
They ran up a cluttered hill and took hacked ground
And held it for a while and fired for a while,
And then the blue men came and they ran away,
To go back, after a while, when the blue men ran.
There was a riddled house and a crow in a tree,
There was uneven ground. It was hard to run.
The gun was heavy and hot. There once had been
A person named Lucy and a flag and a star
And a cane chair beside wistarias
Where a nigger brought you a drink. These had ceased to exist.
There was only very hot sun and being thirsty.
Yells—crashings—screams from black lips—a dead, tattered crow
In a tattered tree. There had once been a person named Lucy
Who had had an importance. There was none of her now.

Up the hill again. Damn tired of running up hill.
And then he found he couldn't run any more,
He had to fall down and be sick. Even that was hard,
Because somebody near kept making a squealing noise—
The dolefully nasty noise of a badly-hurt dog.

It got on his nerves and he tried to say something to it,
But it was he who made it, so he couldn't stop it.

Jack Ellyat, going toward the battle again,
Saw the other side of the hill where Curly was lying,
Saw, for a little while, the two battered houses,
The stuffed dead stretched in numb, disorderly postures,
And heard for a while again that whining sound
That made you want to duck, and feel queer if you did.

To him it was noise and smoke and the powder-taste
And, once and again, through the smoke, for a moment seen,
Small, monstrous pictures, gone through the brain like light,
And yet forever bitten into the brain;
A marsh, a monstrous arras of live and dead
Still shaking under the thrust of the weaver's hand,
The crowd of a deadly fair.
                                        Then, orders again.
And they were going away from the smoke once more.

The books say "Keyes' brigade made a late and weak
Demonstration in front of the Robinson house
And then withdrew to the left, by flank, down Young's Branch,
Taking no further part in the day."
                                        To Jack Ellyat
It was a deadly fair in a burning field
Where strange crowds rushed to and fro and strange drunkards
    lay
Sprawled in a stupor deeper than wine or sleep,
A whining noise you shrank from and wanted to duck at,
And one dead cough left behind them in the tall grass
With the slow blood sopping its clothes like the blood on a shot
    duck's breast.

Imboden is wounded, Jackson is shot through the hand, the
guns of Ricketts and Griffin, on the Henry House plateau, are
taken and retaken; the gunners shot down at their guns while
they hold their fire, thinking the advancing Thirty-Third Virginia is one of their own regiments, in the dimness of the battle-
cloud.

It is nearly three o'clock—the South gathers for a final charge —on the left, Elzey's brigade, new-come from the Shenandoah, defiles through the oaks near the Sudley Road to reinforce the grey wrestler—the blue wrestler staggers and goes back, on unsteady heels.

The charge sweeps the plateau—Bartow is killed, black-haired Bee mortally wounded, but the charge goes on.

For a moment, the Union line is a solid crescent again—a crescent with porcupine-pricks of steel—and then a crescent of sand—and then spilt sand, streaming away.

There is no panic at first. There is merely a moment when men have borne enough and begin to go home. The panic comes later, when they start to jostle each other.

Jefferson Davis, riding from Manassas, reaches the back-wash of the battle. A calm grey-bearded stranger tells him calmly that the battle is lost and the South defeated. But he keeps on, his weak eyes stung with the dust, a picture, perhaps, of a Plutarch death on a shield in his schooled mind—and is in time to see the last blue troops disappear beyond Bull Run, and hear the last sour grumble of their guns.

———————

Judith Henry, Judith Henry, your body has born its ghost at last, there are no more pictures of peace or terror left in the broken machine of the brain that was such a cunning picture-maker:

Terrified ghost, so rudely dishoused by such casual violence, be at rest; there are others dishoused in this falling night, the falling night is a sack of darkness, indifferent as Saturn to wars or generals, indifferent to shame or victory.

War is a while but peace is a while and soon enough the earth-colored hands of the earth-workers will scoop the last buried shells and the last clotted bullet-slag from the racked embittered acre,

And the rustling visitors drive out fair Sundays to look at the monument near the rebuilt house, buy picture postcards and wonder dimly what you were like when you lived and what you thought when you knew you were going to die.

———————

Wingate felt a frog in his throat
As he patted Black Whistle's reeking coat

And reined him in for a minute's breath.
He was hot as the devil and tired to death,
And both were glad for the sun in the West
And a panting second of utter rest,
While Wingate's mind went patching together
Like a cobbler piecing out scraps of leather
The broken glimmers of what they'd done
Since the sun in the West was a rising sun,
The long, bored hours of shiftless waiting
And that single instant of pure, fierce hating
When the charge came down like a cataract
On a long blue beach of broken sand
And Thought was nothing but all was Act
And the sabre seemed to master the hand.
Wainscott Bristol, a raging terrier
Killing the Yankee that shot Phil Ferrier
With a cut that spattered the bloody brains
Over his saddle and bridle-reins,
One Cotter cursing, the other praying,
And both of them slashing like scythes of slaying,
Stuart Cazenove singing "Lord Randall"
And Howard Brooke as white as a candle,
While Father fought like a fiend in satin,
And killed as he quoted tag-ends of Latin,
The prisoners with their sick, dazed wonder
And the mouths of children caught in a blunder
And over it all, the guns, the thunder,
The pace, the being willing to die,
The stinging color of victory.

He remembered it all like a harsh, tense dream.
It had a color. It had a gleam.
But he had outridden and lost the rest
And he was alone with the bloody West
And a trampled road, and a black hill-crest.

The road and the bushes all about
Were cluttered with relics of Yankee rout,
Haversacks spilling their shirts and socks,
A burst canteen and a cartridge-box.
Rifles and cups trampled underfoot,
A woman's locket, a slashed black boot

Stained and oozing along the slash
And a ripe pear crushed to a yellow mash.
Who had carried the locket and munched the pear,
And why was a dead cat lying there,
Stark and grinning, a furry sack,
With a red flannel tongue and a broken back?
You didn't fight wars with a tabby-cat. . . .
He found he was telling the Yankees that,
They couldn't hear him of course, but still . . .
He shut his eyes for a minute until
He felt less dizzy. There, that was better,
And the evening wind was chilly and keen—
—He'd have to write Mother some sort of letter—
—He'd promised Amanda a Yank canteen,
But he didn't feel like getting it here,
Where that dead cat snickered from ear to ear—

Back in the pinewoods, clear and far,
A bugle sang like a falling star.
He shivered, turned Black Whistle around
And galloped hastily toward the sound.

_____

Curly Hatton opened his eyes again.
A minute ago he had been marching, marching,
Forever up and down enormous hills
While his throat scratched with thirst and something howled—
But then there was a clear minute—and he was lying
In a long, crowded, strangely-churchly gloom
Where lanterns bobbed like marshlights in a swamp
And there was a perpetual rustling noise
Of dry leaves stirred by a complaining wind.
No, they were only voices of wounded men.
"Water. Water. Water. Water. Water."
He heard the rain on the roof and sucked his lips.
"Water. Water. Water. Water. Water."
Oh, heavy sluices of dark, sweet, Summer rain,
Pour down on me and wash me free again,
Cleanse me of battles, make my flesh smell sweet,
I am so sick of thirst, so tired of pain,
So stale with wounds and the heat!
Somebody went by, a doctor with red sleeves;

He stared at the red sleeves and tried to speak
But when he spoke, he whispered. This was a church.
He could see a dim altar now and a shadow-pulpit.
He was wounded. They had put the wounded men in a church.
Lucy's face came to him a minute and then dissolved,
A drowned face, ebbing away with a smile on its mouth.
He had meant to marry that face in another church.
But he was dying instead. It was strange to die.

All night from the hour of three, the dead man's hour, the rain
  falls in heavy gusts, in black irresistible streams as if the whole
  sky were falling in one wet huddle.
All night, living and dead sleep under it, without moving, on
  the field; the surgeons work in the church; the wounded moan;
  the dissevered fragments of companies and regiments look
  for each other, trying to come together.
In the morning, when the burial-parties go out, the rain is still
  falling, damping the powder of the three rounds fired over the
  grave; before the grave is well-dug, the bottom of the grave
  is a puddle.
All day long the Southern armies bury their dead to the sodden
  drums of the rain; all day the bugle calls a hoarse-throated
  "Taps"; the bugler lets the water run from his bugle-
  mouth and wipes it clean again and curses the rainy
  weather.

All night the Union army fled in retreat
Like horses scared by a shadow—a stumbling flood
Of panicky men who had been brave for a while
And might be brave again on another day
But now were merely children chased by the night
And each man tainting his neighbor with the same
Blind fear.
          When men or horses begin to run
Like that, they keep on running till they tire out
Unless a strong hand masters a bridle-rein.
Here there was no hand to master, no rein to clutch,
Where the riderless horses kicked their way through the crowd
And the congressmen's carriages choked Cat Hairpin Bend.
Sykes and the regulars covered the retreat,
And a few brigades were kept in some sort of order,
But the rest—They tried to stop them at Centerville.

McDowell and his tired staff held a haggard conference.
But before the officers could order retreat
The men were walking away.
                                        They had fought and lost.
They were going to Washington, they were going back
To their tents and their cooking-fires and their letters from Susie.
They were going back home to Maine or Vermont or Ohio,
And they didn't care who knew it, and that was that.

Meanwhile, on the battlefield, Johnston and Beauregard,
Now joined by the dusty Davis, found themselves
As dazed by their victory as their foes by defeat.
They had beaten one armed mob with another armed mob
And Washington was theirs for the simple act
Of stretching a hand to the apple up on the bough,
If they had known. But they could not know it then.
They too saw spectres—unbroken Union reserves
Moving to cut their supply-line near Manassas.
They called back the pursuit, such scattered pursuit as it was.
Their men were tired and disordered. The chance went by
While only the stiff-necked Jackson saw it clear
As a fighting-psalm or a phrase in Napoleon's tactics.
He said to the surgeon who was binding his wound,
With a taciturn snap, "Give me ten thousand fresh troops
And I will be in Washington by tomorrow."
But they could not give him the troops while there yet was time.
He had three days' rations cooked for the Stonewall Brigade
And dourly awaited the order that never came.
He had always been at God's orders, and God had used him
As an instrument in winning a certain fight.
Now, if God saw fit to give him the men and guns,
He would take Washington for the glory of God.
If He didn't, it was God's will and not to be questioned.

Meanwhile he could while the hours of waiting away
By seeing the Stonewall Brigade was properly fed,
Endeavoring, with that rigid kindness of his
To show Imboden his error in using profanity
—In the heat of battle many things might be excused,
But nothing excused profanity, even then—
And writing his Pastor at Lexington a letter
Enclosing that check for the colored Sunday-school

Which he'd promised, and, being busy, had failed to send.
There is not one word of Bull Run in all that letter
Except the mention of "a fatiguing day's service."
It would not have occurred to Jackson there might have been.

Walt Whitman, unofficial observer to the cosmos, reads of the defeat in a Brooklyn room. The scene rises before him, more real than the paper he stares upon. He sees the defeated army pouring along Pennsylvania Avenue in the drizzling rain, a few regiments in good order, marching in silence, with lowering faces—the rest a drenched, hungry mob that plods along on blistered feet and falls asleep on the stoops of houses, in vacant lots, in basement-areas huddled, too tired to remember battle or be ashamed of flight.

Nothing said—no cries or cheers from the windows, no jeers from the secessionists in the watching crowd—half the crowd is secessionist at heart, even now, more than ever now.

Two old women, white-haired, stand all day in the rain, giving coffee and soup and bread to the passing men. The tears stream down their faces as they cut the bread and pour out the coffee.

Whitman sees it all in his mind's eye—the tears of the two women—the strange look on the men's faces, awake or asleep— the dripping, smoke-colored rain. Perplexed and deep in his heart, something stirs and moves—he is each one of them in turn—the beaten men, the tired women, the boy who sleeps there quietly with his musket still clutched tightly to him. The long lines of a poem begin to lash themselves against his mind, with the lashing surge and long thunder of Montauk surf.

Horace Greeley has written Lincoln an hysterical letter—he has not slept for seven nights—in New York, "on every brow sits sullen, scorching, black despair."

He was trumpeting "On to Richmond!" two weeks ago. But then the war was a thing for an editorial—a triumphal parade of Unionists over rebels. Now there has been a battle and a defeat. He pleads for an armistice—a national convention—anything on almost any terms to end this war.

Many think as he does; many fine words ring hollow as the skull of an orator, the skull of a maker of war. They have raised the Devil with slogans and editorials, but where is the charm that will lay him? Who will bind the Devil aroused?

Only Lincoln, awkwardly enduring, confused by a thousand counsels, is neither overwhelmed nor touched to folly by the madness that runs along the streets like a dog in August scared of itself, scaring everyone who crosses its path.

Defeat is a fact and victory can be a fact. If the idea is good, it will survive defeat, it may even survive the victory.

His huge, patient, laborious hands start kneading the stuff of the Union together again; he gathers up the scraps and puts them together; he sweeps the corners and the cracks and patches together the lost courage and the rags of belief.

The dough didn't rise that time—maybe it will next time. God must have tried and discarded a lot of experiment-worlds before he got one even good enough to whirl for a minute—it is the same with a belief, with a cause.

It is wrong to talk of Lincoln and a star together—that old rubbed image is a scrap of tinsel, a scrap of dead poetry—it dries up and blows away when it touches a man. And yet Lincoln had a star, if you will have it so—and was haunted by a prairie-star.

Down in the South another man, most unlike him but as steadfast, is haunted by another star that has little to do with tinsel, and the man they call "Evacuation" Lee begins to grow taller and to cast a longer shadow.

BOOK THREE

By Pittsburg Landing, the turbid Tennessee
Sucks against black, soaked spiles with soil-colored waters.
That country is huge and disorderly, even now.
—This is Ellyat's tune, this is no tune but his—
Country of muddy rivers, sombre and swollen,
Country of bronze wild turkeys and catfish-fries
And brushpile landings going back to the brush.
A province of mush and milk, a half-cleared forest,
A speckled guinea-cock that never was cooped
But ran away to grow his spurs by himself.
Neither North nor South, but crunching a root of its own
Between strong teeth—perhaps a wild-onion-root,
Perhaps a white stalk of arbutus, hardier there,
Than any phantom-arbutus of Eastern Springs.
A mudsill man with the river-wash in his ears,
Munching the coarse, good meal of a johnny-cake

Hot from the hob—even now it tastes of the brush,
The wilderness, the big lost star in the pines,
The brown river-dirt, the perpetual river-sound,
In spite of the sidewalks, in spite of the trolley-cars.
No trolley-car-bell can drown that river-sound,
Or take the loneliness out of the lost moon,
The night too big for a man, too lonesome and wide.
The vastness has been netted in railroad tracks
But it is still vast, uneasy.
                                        And when the brief
Screech of the railway-whistle stabs at the trees
That grow so thick, so unplanned, so untidily strong
On either side of the two planned ribs of steel,
Ghost-steamboats answer it from the sucking brown water.
In Sixty-two, it was shaggy with wilderness still
For stretches and stretches of close-packed undergrowth,
Wild as a muskrat, ignorant of the axe;
Stretches and stretches where roughly-chinked log-cabins,
Two shouts and a holler away from the nearest neighbors,
Stood in a wisp of open. All night long
The cabin-people heard the chant of the trees,
The forest, hewn away from the painful clearing
For a day or a year, with sweat and back-breaking toil,
But waiting to come back, to crush the crude house
And the planted space with vines and trailers of green,
To quench the fire on the hearth with running green saps,
With a chant of green, with tiny green tendrils curling,
—This is Ellyat's tune, this is no tune but his—
The railway-train goes by with a shrill, proud scream
And the woman comes to the door in a butternut dress
Hair tousled up in a knot on the back of her head,
A barefoot child at her skirt.
                                    The train goes by.
They watch it with a slow wonder that is not pathos
Nor heroism but merely a slow wonder.

———————

Jack Ellyat, in camp above Pittsburg Landing,
Speck in Grant's Army of the Tennessee,
Thought of old fences in Connecticut
With a homesick mind.
                            This country was too new,

Too stragglingly-unplanned, too muddy with great,
Uncomfortable floods, too roughly cut
With a broad hatchet out of a hard tree.

It had seemed fine when he was mustered out
After Bull Run, to wear a veteran air,
And tell pink Ellen Baker about war
And how, as soon as he could re-enlist
He'd do it where he got a chance to fight—
Wet mouth of tears—he hadn't wanted to kiss her
At first, but it was easier later on.
Why had he ever gone out to Chicago?
Why had he ever heard that shallow band
Whanging its brass along a Western street
And run to sign the muster-roll again?
Why had he ever talked about Bull Run
To these green, husky boys from Illinois
And Iowa, whose slang was different slang,
Who called suspenders galluses and swore
In the sharp pops of a mule-driver's whip?
Bull Run—it had impressed them for a week
But then they started to call him "Bull Run Jack." . . .

Henry Fairfield marching along with his sword,
All the old company marching after him
Back in McClellan's army, back by the known
Potomac, back in the safe and friendly East;
All the papers telling how brave they were
And how, as soon as the roads dried up in the spring,
"The little Napoleon" would hammer the South to bits
With a blue thunderbolt.
                              And here he was
A lost pea, spilt at random in a lost war;
A Tennessee war that had no *Tribunes* or polish
Where he was the only Easterner in the whole
Strange-swearing regiment of Illinois farmers,
Alien as Rebels, and rough as all outdoors.

He wanted to get transferred, he wanted to be
Back with the company, back with the Eastern voices,
Back where nobody called him "Bull Run Jack"
And snickered at him for shaving every two days.

100

He'd written about it and Father knew a congressman
But nothing would happen—he'd never get away,
He'd stay being Bull Run Jack till the end of the war
And march through acres of hostile Tennessee mud
Till his legs dropped off, and never get to be Corporal.
He was sick of the war and the mud and the Western faces.
He hated the sight of his Illinois uniform.
He was sorry for himself. He felt with a vague
Soft blur of self-pity that he was really quite brave,
And if people only knew, they'd do something about it.

This is Ellyat's tune, this is no tune but his.
Nine months have passed since McDowell reddened Bull Run,
Nine strong-hoofed months, but they have meant little to Ellyat.
What means the noise of the wind to the dust in the wind?
But the wind calls strange things out, calls strange men out,
A dozen pictures flash in front of the eyes
And are gone in a flash—
                          rough-bearded Tecumseh Sherman,
Who had tried most things, but being cursed with a taste
For honesty, had found small luck in his stars;
Ex-soldier, banker, lawyer, each in its turn,
Ex-head of a Southern military-school,
Untidy ex-president of a little horse-railroad;
Talkative, nervous, salty, Scotch-Irish fighter,
High-strung, quick-tempered, essentially modern-minded,
Stamping the length of the dusty corridors
Of a Western hotel with a dead cigar in his teeth,
Talking the war to himself, till the word goes round
The new general is crazy—
                          neat, handsome McClellan,
Ex-railroad president too, but a better railroad;
The fortunate youth, the highly-modern boy-wonder,
The snapping-eyed, brisk banner-salesman of war
With all the salesman's gifts and the salesman's ego;
Great organizer, with that magnetic spark
That pulls the heart from the crowd—and all of it spoiled
By the Napoleon-complex that haunts such men.
There never has been a young banner-salesman yet
That did not dream of a certain little cocked-hat
And feel it fit. McClellan felt that it fitted.
—After a year and a day, the auditors come,

Dry auditors, going over the books of the company,
Sad auditors, with groups of red and black figures
That are not moved by a dream of precious cocked hats.
And after the auditors go, the board of directors
Decides, with a sigh, to do without banner-salesmen—
It is safer to dream of a rusty Lincoln stovepipe.
That dream has more patience in it.
                                        And yet, years later,
Meeting the banner-salesman in some cheap street
With the faded clippings of old success in his pocket,
One cannot help feeling sorry for the cocked hat
So briefly worn in a dream of luck and the ego.
One cannot help feeling sorry for George McClellan,
He should have been a hero by every rule.
He looked the part—he could have acted the part
Word perfectly. He looked like an empire-maker.
But so few empire-makers have looked the part.

Fate has a way of picking unlikely material,
Greasy-haired second lieutenants of French artillery,
And bald-headed, dubious, Roman rake-politicians.
Her stiff hands were busy now with an odd piece of wood,
Sometime Westpointer, by accident more than choice,
Sometime brevet-captain in the old Fourth Infantry,
Mentioned in Mexican orders for gallant service
And, six years later, forced to resign from the Army
Without enough money to pay for a stateroom home.
Turned farmer on Hardscrabble Farm, turned bill-collector,
Turned clerk in the country-store that his brothers ran,
The eldest-born of the lot, but the family-failure,
Unloading frozen hides from a farmer's sleigh
With stoop-shouldered strength, whittling beside the stove,
And now and then turning to whiskey to take the sting
From winter and certain memories.
                                        It didn't take much.
A glass or two would thicken the dogged tongue
And flush the fair skin beneath the ragged brown beard.
Poor and shabby—old "Cap" Grant of Galena,
Who should have amounted to something but hadn't so far
Though he worked hard and was honest.
                                        A middle-aged clerk,
A stumpy, mute man in a faded army overcoat,

Who wrote the War Department after Fort Sumter,
Offering them such service as he could give
And saying he thought that he was fit to command
As much as a regiment, but getting no answer.
So many letters come to a War Department,
One can hardly bother the clerks to answer them all—
Then a Volunteer colonel, drilling recruits with a stick,
A red bandanna instead of an officer's sash;
A brigadier-general, one of thirty-seven,
Snubbed by Halleck and slighted by fussy Frémont;
And then the frozen February gale
Over Fort Henry and Fort Donelson,
The gunboats on the cold river—the brief siege—
"Unconditional surrender"—and the newspapers.

Major-General Grant, with his new twin-stars,
Who, oddly, cared so little for reading newspapers,
Though Jesse Grant wrote dozens of letters to them
Pointing out all the wonders his son had done
And wringing one dogged letter from that same son
That should have squelched anybody but Jesse Grant.
It did not squelch him. He was a business man,
And now Ulysses had astonished Galena
By turning out to be somebody after all;
Ulysses' old father was going to see him respected
And, incidentally, try to wangle a contract
For army-harness and boom the family tannery.
It was a great surprise when Ulysses refused,
The boy was so stubborn about it.
                              And everywhere
Were business-people, picking up contraband cotton,
Picking up army-contracts, picking up shoddy,
Picking up shoes and blankets, picking up wagons,
Businesslike robins, picking up juicy earthworms,
Picking up gold all over Tom-Tiddler's Ground,
And Ulysses wouldn't see it.
                              Few people have been
More purely Yankee, in essence, than Jesse Grant.

More pictures—Jefferson Davis, in dripping Spring rain,
Reading a chilly inauguration-address
To an unstirred crowd. He is really President now.

103

His eyes are more tired, his temper beginning to fray.
A British steamer in the Bahama Channel
Stopped by a Captain Wilkes and a Union cruiser.
They take two men, and let the steamer puff on
—And light a long hissing fuse that for a month
Nearly brings war with England. Lincoln and Seward
Stamp out the fuse, and let the Confederates go—
Wooden frigates at anchor in Hampton Roads
Burning and sinking with tattered banners apeak
Under the strange new, armadillo-bite
Of something plated with iron that yet can float,
The *Merrimac*—and all Washington and the North
In a twenty-four-hours' panic—then, next day—
As Lincoln stares from the window of the White House
For the sooty sign in the sky that means defeat—
The armadillo, smoking back in her pride
To crunch up another meal of weak wooden ships,
Is beaten off by another leaky prodigy
A tin-can cylinder on a floating shingle,
The *Monitor*—the first fight of iron-clads,
The sinking of all the world's old sea-bitten names,
Temeraire, *Victory*, and *Constellation*,
Serapis, *Bon Homme Richard*, *Golden Hind*,
Galleys of Antony, galleys of Carthage,
Galleons with gilded Virgins, galleasses,
Viking long-serpents, siren-haunted galliots,
Argos and argosies and the Achæan pride,
Moving to sea in one long wooden wall
Behind the huge ghost-flagship of the Ark
In such a swelling cloud of phantom sail
They whitened Ocean—going down by the head,
Green water seeping through the battened ports,
Spreading along the scrubbed and famous decks,
Going down—going down—going down—to mermaid-pools,
To Fiddler's Green—to the dim barnacle-thrones,
Where Davy Jones drinks everlasting rum
With the sea-horses of his sunken dreams.

But this is Ellyat's tune—and if the new
Army of the Potomac stands astrain
To end Secession with its "little Napoleon."
If Lee is just about to find his hour;

If, among many mirrors and gilt chairs,
Under the flare of the gas-chandeliers
A sallow-faced and puffy Emperor
With waxed mustachios and a slick goatee
Gave various Southern accents, talking French,
Evasive answers and no definite help,
Ready enough to recognize the South
If he were sure of profit in the scheme
But not yet finding such a profit sure;
If in the foggy streets of Westminster,
The salty streets of Liverpool and Hull,
The same mole-struggle in the dark went on
Between Confederate and Unionist—
The *Times* raved at the North—Mr. Gladstone thought
England might recognize the South next year,
While Palmerston played such a tangled game
It is illegible yet—and Henry Adams
Added one more doubt to his education
By writing propaganda for the North,
It is all mist to Ellyat.
                    And when he sleeps,
He does not dream of Grant or Lee or Lincoln.
He only dreams that he is back at home
With a heroic wound that does not hurt,
A uniform that never stings with lice,
And a sword like Henry Fairfield's to show Ellen Baker.

————————

As far as the maps and the blocks on the maps have meaning
The situation is this.
                    A wide Western river,
A little lost landing, with a steamboat-store,
A post office where the roads from the landings meet,
A plank church three miles inland called Shiloh Chapel,
An undulating and broken table-land
Roughed into a triangle by bordering creeks.
Each side of the triangle runs about four miles long
And, scattered in camps from the tip of the triangle
To the base at the landing, are thirty-three thousand men,
Some fairly seasoned in war, but many green sticks,
Grant's Army of the Tennessee.
                    Down the river

Don Carlos Buell has twenty-five thousand more
In the Army of the Ohio.
                    Opposing these
Are Albert Sidney Johnston and Beauregard
With something like forty thousand butternut fighters,
Including a martial bishop.
                    Johnston plans
To smash Grant's army to bits, before Buell can join it,
And water his wagon-trains in the Tennessee.
He has sneaked his army along through wilderness roads
Till now they are only a mile and a half away
Tonight from the Union lines.
                    He is tall and active.
Light brown hair streaked with grey feathers, blue claymore eyes
That get steel shadows in battle, a face like Hamilton's,
Old Westpointer, old cavalry-colonel, well-schooled in war.
Lincoln offered to make him a major-general
And rumor says that he could have had the command
Of the Union armies, once.
                    But he resigned
And later, went with his State. It is hard to say
What he might have been.
                    They called him the *"preux chevalier"*
At times, as they called and were to call many others
With that Waverley-streak that was so strong in the South.
They also called him one of Davis's pets,
One of the tin Westpointers that Davis favored
Above good politicians and courtesy colonels.
The Richmond *Enquirer* didn't think so much of him,
His soldiers thought rather more.
                    Only this can be said.
He caught Grant napping in some strange flaw of skill
Which happened once and did not happen again.
And drove his unprepared, unwatchful brigades
Back almost into the river.
                    And in the heat
Of seeing his lines go forward, he bled to death
From a wound that should not have been mortal.
                    After which,
While the broken Union stragglers under the bluff
Were still howling that they were beaten, Buell came up,
Lew Wallace came up, the knife half-sunk in the wound

106

Was not thrust home, the night fell, the battle lagged.
The bulldog got the bone in his teeth again
And next day, reinforced, beat Beauregard back
And counted a Union victory.
                              In the books
Both sides claim victory on one day or the other
And both claims seem valid enough.
                              It only remains
To take the verdict of the various dead
In this somewhat indecisive meeting of blocks.
There were thirty-five hundred dead when the blocks had met.
But, being dead, their verdict is out of court.
They cannot puzzle the books with their testimony.

Now, though, it is only the evening before the day.
Johnston and Beauregard meet with their corps-commanders
By the wagon-cut Pittsburg road. The march has been slow.
The marching men have been noisy and hard to manage.
By every rule of war, Grant must have been warned
Long before now, and is planning an ambush for them.
They are being marched into an open Union trap.
So Beauregard thinks and says—and is perfectly right
According to rules. There is only one difficulty.
There is no ambush.
                        Sherman has just reported
The presence of enemy troops in front of his lines
But says he expects nothing more than some picket-firing
And Grant that evening telegraphs General Halleck,
"I have scarcely the faintest idea of an attack."

So much for the generals. Beauregard makes his point
And is overruled.
                    The April night comes down.
The butternut men try to get some sleep while they can.
They are to be up and fighting by five in the morning.

———————

Jack Ellyat, least of any, expected attack.
He woke about five with a dazzle struck in his eyes
Where a long dawn-ray slid through a crack in the tent.
He cursed at the ray and tried to go back to sleep
But he couldn't do it, although he was tired enough,

Something ate at his mind as soon as he wakened
And kept on eating.
                    This morning was Sunday morning.
The bells would be jangling for church back home, pretty soon,
The girls would be going to church in white Sunday dresses,
No, it was too early for that—they'd be muffled up
In coats and galoshes. Their cheeks would be pink as apples.
He wanted to see a girl who washed her hair,
Not a flat old woman sucking a yellow snuffstick
Or one of the girls in the dirty blue silk wrappers
With flags on their garters. He wanted to see a girl.

He wondered idly about the flags on the garters.
Did they change them to Rebel flags when the Rebels came?
Some poor whore down the river had had herself
Tattooed with a Secesh flag. She was patriotic.
She cried so hard when the Union troops were landed
That the madam had to hide her down in the cellar.
He must be bad to be thinking of things like that
On Sunday morning. He'd better go to church
If they had any kind of church, and make up for it—
O frosty churchbells jangling across the thin
Crust of packed frost, under Connecticut sky,
Put snow on my tongue, and the grey, cool flower of rain--
He had to get up. He couldn't lie here and listen
To Bailey and the rest of them, snoring away.
His throat was dry. He needed a drink of water
But not from a muddy river—put rain on my tongue!
Souse me with chilly, sweet flaws of Puritan rain—
He started to put on his boots, looking over at Bailey.
Bailey was bearded, Bailey was thirty-two,
Bailey had been a teamster and was a corporal.
The waking Bailey looked like a stupid horse,
The sleeping Bailey looked like a dirty sack,
Bailey called him "Colonel" and didn't mean it,
Bailey had had him tossed in a blanket once,
Bailey had told the tale of the tattooed whore,
Somehow he hated Bailey worse than the rest.
He managed to leave the tent without waking Bailey.
It was very early still. The sun was just up.
A fair sky, a very fair day. The air still held
That bloom which is not the bloom on apple or peach

But the bloom on a fruit made up of pure water and light,
The freshness of dawn, still trembling, being new-born.
He sucked at it gratefully.
                        The camp was asleep.
All that length of tents still asleep. He could see through the tents.
He could see all those sleeping, rough, lousy, detested men
Laden with sleep as with soft leaden burdens laden,
Movelessly lying between the brown fawns of sleep
Like infants nuzzled against the flanks of a doe,
In quietness slumbering, in a warm quietness,
While sleep looked at them with her fawn's agate eyes
And would not wake them yet.
                        And he was alone,
And for a moment, could see this, and see them so
And, being free, stand alone, and so being free
To love or hate, do neither, but merely stand
Above them like sleep and see them with untouched eyes.
In a while they would wake, and he would hate them again.
But now he was sleep. He was the sun on the coat
Of the halted fawn at the green edge of the wood
Staring at morning.
                        He could not hate them yet.

Somebody near by, in the woods, took a heap of dry sticks,
And began to break them quickly, first one by one,
Then a dozen together, then hard-cracking axe-helves breaking.
Ellyat was running. His mouth felt stiff with loud words
Though he heard no sound from his mouth. He could see the white
Fine pine-splinters flying from those invisible axe-helves. . . .

For a minute all of them were tangled together
In the bucking tent like fish in a canvas scoop,
Then they were out of it somehow—falling in line—
Bailey's hair looked angry and sleepy. The officers
Were yelling the usual things that officers yelled.
It was a surprise. They were going to be licked again.
It did not matter yet. It would matter soon.
Bailey had lost his blouse and his pants weren't buttoned.
He meant to tell Bailey about it. There wasn't time.
His eyes felt bald as glass but that was because
He kept looking for flying pine-splinters in the air.

Now they were setting off firecrackers under a boiler
And a man ran past with one hand dripping red paint,
Holding the hand with his other hand and talking
As if the hurt hand were a doll.
                                    An officer hit him
With the flat of a sword. It spanked some dust from his coat
And the man's face changed from a badly-fitting mask
Of terror, cut into ridges of sallow wax,
To something pink and annoyed, but he kept on running.
All this happened at once as they were moving.
The dawn had been hit to pieces with a hard mallet.
There were no fawns. There was an increasing noise
Through which he heard the lugubrious voice of Bailey
Singing off-key, like a hymn,
        "When I was a weaver, I lived by myself,
            And I worked at the weaver's tra-a-de—"

The officers were barking like foxes now.

As the last tent dropped behind them, Ellyat saw
A red, puzzled face, looking out from under a tent-flap,
Like a bear from a cave. The face had been drunk last night,
And it stared at the end of the column with a huge and stupid
    wisdom.

"When I was a weaver, I lived by myself,
And I worked at the weaver's trade—"

Jack Ellyat found himself back behind somebody's tent
After a while. He had been out in the woods.
He remembered scrouging against a too-porous tree
For a day or a number of minutes while he jerked
A rattling ramrod up and down in a gun.
But they couldn't stay in the woods—they had to come back.
They had called him "Bull Run Jack" but they had to come back,
Bailey and all the rest. He had come back with them,
But that was different—that was all right for him.
This red-colored clang of haste was different for him.
Bailey and all the rest could run where they liked.
He was an old soldier. He would stay here and fight.

Running, he tripped on a rope, and began to fall,
Bailey picked him back on his feet. "Did they get you, Bud?"
"No, they didn't get me."
                            Ellyat's voice was a snarl.
What business had Bailey steadying him like that?
He hadn't been running.
                            Suddenly he saw
Grey shouting strangers bursting into the tents
And his heart shrank up in a pea.
                            "Oh hell," he said,
Hopelessly ramming a cartridge. He was an old soldier.
He wasn't going to run. He was going to act
Vast fictive heroisms in front of Bailey,
If they only gave him time, just a little time.

A huge horse rose above the wall of the tent
And hung there a second like a bad prodigy,
A frozen scream full of hoofs.
                            He struck at its head
And tried to get out from under as it lunged down
But he wasn't quite quick enough.
                            As he slipped and fell
He saw the laughter pasted on Bailey's face
But before he could hear the laugh, the horse had fallen,
Jarring the world.
                            After blunt, sickly time
A fat young man with a little pink moustache
Was bawling "Hey, Yank, surrender!" into his ear
And nervously waving a pistol in front of his eyes.
He nodded weakly. "Hey, boys," called the fat young man,
"I got two Yanks!" His mouth was childish with pleasure.
He was going to tell everybody he had two Yanks.
"Here, Yank, come and pull the horse off the other Yank."

The prisoner's column straggled along the road
All afternoon. Jack Ellyat marched in it numbly.
He was stiff and sore. They were going away from the battle
But they could still hear it, quaking,
The giant stones rolled over the grumbling bridge.

Some of the prisoners tried to joke with the guards,
Some walked in silence, some spoke out now and then,
As if to explain to the world why they were there.

One man said, "I got a sore heel." Another said,
"All the same the Tenth Missouri's a damn good regiment."
Another said, "Listen, boys, don't it beat all hell?
I left my tobacco behind me, back in the tent,
Don't it beat all hell to lose your tobacco like that?"

Bailey kept humming the "Weaver," but now and then
He broke it off, to say, with a queer satisfaction,
"Well, we surely did skedaddle—we surely did."
Jack Ellyat had said nothing for a long time.
This was war, this was Phaëton, this was the bronze chariot
Rolling the sky. If he had a soul any more
It felt scrawny and thin as a sick turkey-poult.
It was not worth the trouble to fatten. He tried to fatten it
With various thoughts, now and then, but the thoughts were
   spoilt
Corn. They had damn well skedaddled. They damn well had.
That was all. The rest of the army could win or lose
They had surely skedaddled. They had been whipped again.
He had been whipped again.
                            He was no longer
The old soldier—no longer even "Bull Run Jack."
He had lost a piece of himself. It had ragged edges
That piece. He could see it left behind in the tents
Under a dirty coat and a slab of tobacco.

After a while he knocked against Bailey's arm.
"Where are we going?" he said, in a shy voice.
Bailey laughed, not badly, "Well, Colonel, Corinth I guess,
Corinth first—and then some damn prison-camp."
He spat in the road. "It won't be good grub," he said.
"Bacon and hominy-grits. They don't eat right.
They don't eat nothing but bacon and hominy-grits.
God, I'm goin' to get tired of bacon and hominy-grits!"

Ellyat looked. There was something different about him.
He stated a fact. "You've buttoned your pants," he said.
"I remember you didn't have 'em buttoned this morning."

"That's so," said Bailey, impressed, "Now when did I button
   'em?"

They chewed at the question, trying to puzzle it out.
It seemed very important to both for quite a long time.

It was night now. The column still marched. But Bailey and
    Ellyat
Had dropped to the rear of the column, planning escape.
There were few guards and the guards were as tired as they.
Two men could fall in a ditch by the side of the road
And get away, perhaps, if they picked a good time.
They talked it over in stupid whispers of weariness.
The next bend—no, the guard was coming along.
The next bend after—no, there was light for a moment
From a brief star, then clouded—the top of the hill—
The bottom of the hill—and they still were marching.
Rain began to fall, a drizzle at first, then faster.
Ellyat's eyes were thick. He walked in a dream,
A heavy dream, cut from leaden foil with blunt shears.
Then Bailey touched him—he felt the tired bones of his skull
Click with a sudden spark—his feet stopped walking—
He held his breath for an instant,
And then wearily slumped in the ditch with enormous noise,
Hunching his shoulders against a phantom bayonet.

But when he could raise his head, the column had gone.
He felt fantastic. They couldn't escape like this.
You had to escape like a drawing in *Harper's Weekly*
With stiff little men on horses like sickle-pears
Firing round frozen cream-puffs into your back.
But they had escaped.
                  Life came back to him in a huge
Wave of burnt stars. He wanted to sing and yell.
He crackled out of the ditch and stood beside Bailey.
Had he ever hated Bailey? It could not have been.
He loved Bailey better than anything else in the world.

They moved slyly toward the woods, they were foxes escaped.
Wise foxes sliding away to a hidden earth
To a sandy floor, to the warm fawn-flanks of sweet sleep. . . .
And then an awful molasses-taffy voice
Behind them yelled "Halt!" and "Halt!" and—sudden explosion
Of desultory popcorn in iron poppers—

Wild running at random—a crash among broken boughs—
A fighting sound—Bailey's voice, half-strangled but clear,
"Run like hell, Jack, they'll never catch you!"
                                        He ran like hell.

Time passed like the rain. Time passed and was one with the
    rain.

———————————

Ellyat woke from a nightmare and put out his hand
To touch the wall by his bed, but there was no wall.
Then he listened for Bailey's snoring.
                                    And he heard
The gorged, sweet pouring of water through infinite boughs,
The hiss of the big spilt drop on the beaten leaf,
The bird-voiced and innumerable rain,
A wet quail piping, a thousand soaked black flutes
Building a lonely castle of sliding tears,
Strange and half-cruel as a dryad's bright grief.

Ellyat huddled closer under the tree,
Remembering what he could. He had run for years,
He had slept for years—and yet it was still not dawn.
It seemed cruel to him that it should never be dawn.
It seemed cruel that Bailey was lost. He had meant to show
Some fictive heroisms in front of Bailey.
He had not. Bailey had saved his skin instead,
And Bailey was lost. And in him something was lost,
Something worse than defeat or this rain—some piece of himself.
Some piece of courage.
                        Now the slant rain began
To creep through his sodden heart. He thought, with wild awe,
"This is Nibelung Hall. I am lying in Nibelung Hall.
I am long dead. I fell there out of the sky
In a wreck of horses, spilling the ball of the sun,
And they shut my eyes with stone runes and put me to sleep
On a bier where the living stream perpetually flows
Past Ygdrasil and waters the roots of the world.
I can hear the ravens scream from the cloudy roof.
I can hear the bubbles rising in the clear stream.
I can hear the old gods shout in the heathen sky
As the hawk-Valkyrie carry the stiffened lumps

Of corpse-faced heroes shriekingly to Valhalla.
This is Nibelung Hall. I must break the runes from my eyes.
I must escape it or die."
                          He slept. The rain fell.

———————

Melora Vilas, rising by candlelight,
Looked at herself in the bottom of the tin basin
And wished that she had a mirror.
                          Now Spring was here,
She could kneel above the well of a forest pool
And see the shadow hidden under the water,
The intent brown eyes, the small face cut like a heart.
She looked at the eyes and the eyes looked back at her,
But just when it seemed they could start to talk to each other—
"What are you like? Who are you?"—
                          a ripple flawed
The deep glass and the shadow trembled away.

If she only had a mirror, maybe she'd know
Something, she didn't know what, but something important,
Something like knowing your skin and you were alive
On a good day, something as drenched as sleep,
As wise as sleep, as piercing as the bee's dagger.
But she'd never know it unless she could get a mirror
And they'd never get a mirror while they were hiders.
They were bound to be hiders as long as the war kept on.
Pop was that way. She remembered roads and places.
She was seventeen. She had seen a lot of places,
A lot of roads. Pop was always moving along.
Everybody she'd ever known was moving along.
—Dusty wagons full of chickens and children,
Full of tools and quilts, Rising Sun and Roses of Sharon,
Mahogany dressers out of Grandmother's house,
Tin plates, cracked china, a couple of silver spoons,
Moving from State to State behind tired, scuffed horses
Because the land was always better elsewhere.

Next time they'd quit. Next stop they'd settle right down.
Next year they'd have time to rub up the mahogany dresser.

115

Next place, Mom could raise the flowers she wanted to raise.
But it never began. They were always moving along.

She liked Kansas best. She wished they'd go back to Kansas.
She liked the smell of the wind there.
But Pop hadn't wanted to join with the Free-Soilers
And then the slavery men had shot up the town
And killed the best horse they had. That had settled Pop.
He said something about a plague on both of your houses
And moved along. So now they were hiders here
And whenever you wanted to ask Pop about the war
All he said was that same old thing about the plague.
She mustn't call him Pop—that was movers'-talk.
She must call him Father, the way Mom, Mother wanted.
But it was hard to remember. Mom talked a lot
About old times back in the East and Grandmother's house.
She couldn't remember an East. The East wasn't real.
There was only the dusty road and moving along.
Although she knew that Mom had worn a silk dress
And gone to a ball, once. There was a picture of Pop
And Mom, looking Eastern, in queer old Eastern clothes.
They weren't white trash. She knew how to read and figure.
She'd read *Macbeth* and *Beulah* and *Oliver Twist*.
She liked *Beulah* best but *Macbeth* would have suited Pop.
Sometimes she wondered what had happened to them,
When Mother used to live in Grandmother's house
And wear silk dresses, and Father used to read Latin—
When had they started to go just moving along,
And how would it feel to live in Grandmother's house?

But it was so long ago, so hard to work out
And she liked it this way—she even liked being hiders.
It was exciting, especially when the guns
Coughed in the sky as they had all yesterday,
When Bent hid out in the woods to keep from recruiters,
And you knew there were armies stumbling all around you,
Big, blundering cows of armies, snuffling and tramping
The whole scuffed world with their muddy, lumbering hoofs,
Except the little lost brushpile where you were safe.
There were guns in the sky again today. Big armies.
An army must be fine to look at.
                              But Pop
Would never let her do it or understand.

116

An army or a mirror. She didn't know
Which she'd rather find, but whenever she thought of it
The mirror generally won. You could keep a mirror yourself.

She had to call the hogs that afternoon.
You had to call them once or twice a month
And give them food or else they ran too wild
And never came for butchering in the Fall,
Though they lived well enough without your calling,
Fat in the forest, feeding on beech mast,
Wild muscadines and forest provender
That made their flesh taste sweet as hazelnuts.

She liked the hogs, they weren't tame, sleepy hogs
Grunting in a black wallow, they were proud
Rapid and harsh and savage as Macbeth.
There was a young boar that she called Macbeth,
She'd seen him fight grey-bristled, drowsy Duncan
And drive him from the trough.
                                    Fagin was there,
Bill Sikes was there and Beulah the black sow,
And Lady Macduff whose grunt was half a whine.
You could learn lots about a book from hogs.
She poured the swill and cupped her hands to call.
Sometimes they'd help her with it, Pop or Bent,
But Pop was off with Bent this afternoon
And Mom was always busy.
                                    Slim and straight
She stood before the snake-rail pen that kept
Macbeths on their own proper side of the fence.
"Piggy," she called, "Here, piggy, piggy, piggy!"
It wasn't the proper call, but the hogs knew
That sweet clear loudness with its sleepy silver
Trembling against a chanter of white ash.
"Here, piggy, piggy, piggy, piggy, piggy!
Here, piggy, piggy!" There was a scrambling noise
At the edge of the woods. "Here, piggy!"
                                    It was Banquo.
Greedy, but hesitant.
                          The Artful Dodger
Slim, black and wicked, had two feet in the trough

Before that obese indecision moved.
"Here, piggy! Here, piggy, piggy!"
                                        The gleaming call
Floated the air like a bright glassy bubble,
Far, far, with its clean silver and white ash.
And Ellyat, lost and desperate in the wood,
Heard it, desirous as the elvish blast
Wound on a tiny horn of magic grass
To witch steel riders into a green hill.
He stumbled toward its music.
                                        "Piggy, piggy,
Here, piggy, piggy!"
                                        The swine grunted and jostled.
Melora watched them, trying to count them up
With grave eyes, brown as nuts in rainwater.
They were all there, she thought—she must be sure.
She called again. No, something moved in the woods.
She stared past the clearing, puzzled. So Ellyat saw her
Beyond the swine, head lifted like a dark foal
That listens softly for strangeness.
                                        And she saw
An incoherent scarecrow in blue clothes
Stagger on wooden feet from the deep wood.
She called to him to keep away from the hogs,
Half-frightenedly.
                                        He did not hear or obey.
He was out of Nibelung Hall.
                                        She put one hand
On the rail of the fence to steady herself and waited.
"You can't come in here," she said, fiercely. "The hogs'll kill
    you."
But he was past the fed hogs and over the fence.
She saw a queer look on his face. "You're hungry," she said.
He grinned, made a noise in his throat, and fell, trying to touch
    her.

_____

        Now that I am clean again,
        Now I've slept and fed,
        How shall I remember when
        I was someone dead?

Now the balm has worked its art
And the gashes dry,
And the lizard at my heart
Has a sleepy eye,

How shall I remember yet
Freezing underground,
With the wakened lizard set
To the living wound?

Do not ponder the offence
Nor reject the sore,
Do not tear the cerements
Flesh may need once more.

Cold comes back and pain comes back
And the lizard, too.
And the burden in the sack
May be meant for you.

Do not play the risen dunce
With unrisen men.
Lazarus was risen once
But earth gaped again.

————————

So Ellyat swam back to life, swam back to warmth
And the smell of cooking food. It was night. He heard
Impenetrable rain shake a low roof
And hiss stray, scattering drops on an open fire.
But he was safe. That rain was caged in the sky.
It could not fall on him.
                    He lay in a lax
Idleness, warm and hungry, not wanting to move.
A grub in a close cocoon neither bold nor wise, but content.

A tall woman was cooking mush in an iron pot.
The smell of the mush was beautiful, the shape of the pot
More beautiful than an urn by sea-nymphs carved
From sunken marbles stained with the cold sea-rose.
The woman was a great Norn, in her pot she cooked a new world,

Made of pure vapors and the juices of unspoilt light,
A new globe of sulliless amber and grains of white corn,
An orbed perfection. All life was beautiful now.

A girl came into the room upon light, quick feet.
He stared at her, solemnly. She was young and thin.
The small, just head was set on the slender neck
With a clean sureness. The heavy hair was a helm
Of bronze cooled under a ripple, marked by that flowing.
It was not slight but it could not weight her down.
Her hands and feet were well made and her body had
That effortless ease, that blood that flies with the bird.
She saw his open eyes and came over to him,
Not shyly but not concernedly.
                                    Their eyes met.
The older woman kept stirring her melted world.
"Well," said the girl, "You look better." He nodded, "Yes."
Their eyes said, "I have seen a new thing. In the deep cells
Below the paltry clockwork of the ticked heart,
I have seen something neither light nor night,
A new thing, a new picture. It may mean
The lifting of a shut latch. It may mean nothing."

She made an escaping gesture with her right hand.
"You didn't say who you were," she said. "You just fell.
You better tell who you are, Pop'll want to know."
A shadow crossed her. "Pop won't want to keep you," she said.
"But I reckon we'll have to keep you here for a piece,
You're not fit to travel yet and that's a fact.
You look a little bit like Young Seward," she said
Reflectively, "But sometimes you look more like Oliver.
I dunno. What's your name?"
                                    Ellyat put forth his hand
Toward being alive again, slowly, hauling it down.
He remembered. He was Jack Ellyat. He had been lost.
He had lain with hel-shoes on in Nibelung Hall
For twenty years. This was the girl with the swine
Whose loud sweet calling had come to him in the wood
And lifted him back to warmth and a cooking world.
He had lost a piece of himself, a piece of life,
He must find it, but now—
                                    "What's your name?" he said in a whisper.

This is the hidden place that hiders know.
This is where hiders go.
Step softly, the snow that falls here is different snow,
The rain has a different sting.
Step softly, step like a cloud, step softly as the least
Whisper of air against the beating wing,
And let your eyes be sealed
With two blue muscadines
Stolen from secret vines,
Or you will never find in the lost field
The table spread, the signs of the hidden feast.

This is where hiders live.
This is the tentative
And outcast corner where hiders steal away
To bake their hedgehogs in a lump of clay,
To raise their crops and children wild and shy,
And let the world go by
In accidental marches of armed wrath
That stumble blindly past the buried path.
Step softly, step like a whisper, but do not speak
Or you will never see
The furriness curled within the hollow tree,
The shadow-dance upon the wilderness-creek.

This is the hiders' house.
This is the ark of pine-and-willow-boughs.
This is the quiet place.
You may call now, but let your call be sweet
As clover-honey strained through silver sieves
And delicate as the dust upon the moth
Or you will never find your fugitives.
Call once, and call again,
Then, if the lifted strain
Has the true color and substance of the wild,
You may perceive, if you have lucky eyes,
Something that ran away from being wise
And changed silk ribbons for a greener cloth,
Some budding-horned and deer-milk-suckled child
Some lightness, moving toward you on light feet,
Some girl with indolent passion in her face.

Jack Ellyat wondered about things, six days later.
The world had come back to its shape. He was well and strong.
He had seen the old man with the burnt dreams in his eyes,
Who had fallen from something years ago in his youth
Or risen from something with an effort too stark;
The runaway who had broken the pasture-bars
To test the figments of life on a wild stone.
You could see the ultimate hardness of that strange stone
Cut in his face—but then, there was something else,
That came at moments and went, and answered no questions.
Had the feel of the stone been worth it, after all?
It puzzled Ellyat.
                    He couldn't figure it out.
Going West to get fat acres was common enough,
But, once you got the acres, you settled down,
You sent your children to school. You put up a fence.
When a war came along, you fought on your proper side;
You didn't blast both sides with Mercutio's curse
And hide in a wilderness.
                    The man was all wrong,
And yet the man was not weak. It was very strange.
If the man had been weak, you could understand him all right.

The woman was more easy to understand.
He liked the woman—he liked the rough shaggy boy
Who had lived so much in the woods to keep from the armies
That his ears were sharp as a squirrel's, and all his movements
Had something untamed about them, something leafy and strange.
Of course he ought to be fighting for the North,
He was really a skulk—but things were different here.
You couldn't reason about the difference in words
But you felt it inside your skin.
                    Things were different here.
Like Nibelung Hall in the rain of his fever-dream,
But with no terror, with an indolent peace.

He'd have to get back to the regiment pretty soon.
He couldn't stay here. They none of them wanted him here.
He'd have to get back. But he didn't know where to go.
They could tell him how to get back to Pittsburg Landing
But how did he know if the army was there or not?
He didn't even know who'd won in the battle,

And, if the Rebs had won, he'd be captured again
As soon as he got on a road.
                              Well, he'd have to chance it.
He couldn't stay here and fall in love with Melora.
Melora came walking down the crooked path
With a long shadow before her. It was the hour
When the heat is out of the gold of afternoon
And the cooled gold has not yet turned into grey,
The hour of the paused tide, neither flow nor ebb,
The flower beginning to close but not yet closed.

He saw her carry her fairy head aloft
Against that descending gold,
He saw the long shadow that her slight body made.

When she came near enough to him, she heard him humming
A tune he had thought forgotten, the weaver's tune.
"And the only harm that I've ever done,
Was to love a pretty maid."

She halted, trying to listen. He stopped the tune.
"What's that you were singing?" she said.
                              "Oh, just trash," he said.
"I liked it. Sing it some more."
                              But he would not sing it.

They regarded each other a foot or so apart.
Their shadows blotted together into one shadow.

She put her hand to both cheeks, and touched them lightly,
As if to cool them from something.
                              A soft, smooth shock
Inexplicable as the birth of a star
And terrible as the last cry of the flesh
Ran through his cords and struck.
                              He stared at the shadows.
Then she took her shadow into the house with her
But he still stood looking where the shadows had touched.

——————

John Vilas watched them go off through the wood
To get the water from the other spring,

The big pail clanking between them.
His hard mouth
Was wry with an old nursery-rhyme, but his eyes
Looked somewhere beyond hardness.
Let them go.
Harriet said and Harriet always said
And Harriet was right, but let them go.
Men who go looking for the wilderness-stone
And find it, should not marry or beget,
But, having done so, they must take the odds
As the odds are.
Faustus and I are old.
We creep about among the hollow trees
Where the bright devils of our youth have gone
Like a dissolving magic, back to earth.
But in our tarnished and our antique wands
And in the rusty metal of our spells
There still remain such stubbornness and pith
As may express elixirs from a rock
Or pick a further quarrel with the gods
Should we find cause enough.
I know this girl,
This boy, this youth, this honey in the blood,
This kingly danger, this immediate fire.
I know what comes of it and how it lies
And how, long afterwards, at the split core
Of the prodigious and self-eaten lie,
A little grain of truth lies undissolved
By all the acids of philosophy.
Therefore, I will not seek a remedy
Against a sword but in the sword itself
Nor medicine life with anything but life.
I am too old to try the peddler's tricks,
Too wise, too foolish, too long strayed in the wood,
The custom of the world is not my custom,
Nor its employments mine.
I know this girl
As well as if I never lay with her mother.
I know her heart touched with that wilderness-stone
That turns good money into heaps of leaves
And builds an outcast house of apple-twigs
Beside a stream that never had a name.

124

She will forget what I cannot forget,
And she may learn what I shall never learn,
But, while the wilderness-stone is strong in her,
I'd have her use it for a touchstone yet
And see the double face called good and bad
With her own eyes. So, if she stares it down,
She is released, and if it conquers her,
She was not weighted with a borrowed shield.

We are no chafferers, my daughter and I.
We give what pleases us and when we choose,
And, having given, we do not take back.
But once we shut our fists upon a star
It will take portents to unloose that grip
And even then the stuff will keep the print.
It is a habit of living.
                        For the boy
I do not know but will not stand between.
He has more toughness in him than he thinks.
—I took my wife out of a pretty house.
—I took my wife out of a pleasant place.
—I stripped my wife of comfortable things.
—I drove my wife to wander with the wind.
—And we are old now, Faustus.
                        Let it be so.
There was one man who might have understood,
Because he was half-oriole and half-fox,
Not Emerson, but the man by Walden Pond.
But he was given to the birds in youth
And never had a woman or a daughter.

The filled pail stood on a stone by the lip of the spring,
But they had forgotten the pail.
                        The spring was a cool
Wavering mirror that showed them their white, blurred faces
And made them wonder to see the faces so like
And yet so silent and distant.
                        Melora turned.
"We ought to go back," she said in a commonplace voice.
"Not yet, Melora."
                        Something, as from the spring

Rising, in silver smoke, in arras of silvers,
Drifting around them, pushed by a light, slow wind.
"Not yet Melora."
                        They sat on a log above.
Melora's eyes were still looking down at the spring.
Her knees were hunched in her arms.
                                    "You'll be going," she said,
Staring at the dimmed glass. "You'll be going soon."
The silver came closer, soaking into his body,
Soaking his flesh with bright, impalpable dust.
He could smell her hair. It smelt of leaves and the wind.
He could smell the untaken whiteness of her clean flesh,
The deep, implacable fragrance, fiercer than sleep,
Sweeter than long sleep in the sun.
                        He touched her shoulder.
She let the hand stay but still she gazed at the spring.
Then, after a while, she turned.
                        The mirrored mouths
Fused in one mouth that trembled with the slow waters.

———————

Melora, in the room she had to herself
Because they weren't white-trash and used to be Eastern,
Let the rain of her hair fall down,
In a stream, in a flood, on the white birch of her body.
She was changed, then. She was not a girl any more.
She was the white heart of the birch,
Half hidden by a fleece that a South wind spun
Out of bronze air and light, on a wheel of light.
Her sharp clear breasts
Were two young victories in the hollow darkness
And when she stretched her hands above her head
And let the spun fleece ripple to her loins,
Her body glowed like deep springs under the sun.

She had no song to sing herself asleep
Tonight, but she would need no song to sing.
A thousand thoughts ran past her in a brief
Unhurrying minute, on small, quiet feet
But did not change her. Nothing could change her now.
—Black winter night against the windowpane
And she, a child, singing her fear to sleep

With nursery-rhymes and broken scraps of tunes.
How well she could remember those old songs.
But this night she would sleep without a song
Except the song the earth knows in the night
After the huge embrace of the bright day,
And that was better.
                    She thought to herself.
"I don't know. I can't think. I ought to be scared.
I ought to have lots of maybes. I can't find them.
It's funny. It's different. It's a big pair of hands
Pushing you somewhere—but you've got to go.
Maybe you're crazy but you've got to go.
That's why Mom went. I know about Mom now.
I know how she used to be. It's pretty sweet.
It's rhymes, it's hurting, it's feeling a bird's heart
Beat in your hand, it's children growing up,
It's being cut to death with bits of light,
It's wanting silver bullets in your heart,
It's not so happy, but it's pretty sweet,
I've got to go."
                    She passed her narrow hands
Over her body once, half-wonderingly.

"Divide this transitory and temporal flesh
Into twelve ears of red and yellow corn
And plant each ear beside a different stream.
Yet, in the summer, when the harvesters
Come with their carts, the grain shall change again
And turn into a woman's body again
And walk across a heap of sickle-blades
To find the naked body of its love."

She slipped her dress back on and stole downstairs.
The bare feet, whispering, made little sound.
A sleeper breathed, a child turned in its sleep.
She heard the tiny breathings. She shut the door.

The moon rode a high heaven streaked with cloud.
She watched it for a moment. Then she drank
That moon from its high heaven with her mouth
And felt the immaculate burning of that frost
Run from her fingers in such corporal silver

Her whole slight body was a corposant
Of hollow light and the cold sap of the moon.

She knew the dark grass cool beneath her feet.
She knew the opening of the stable door.
It shut behind her. She was in darkness now.

———————

Jack Ellyat, lying in a warm nest of hay,
Stared at the sweet-smelling darkness with troubled eyes.
He was going tomorrow. He couldn't skulk any more.
—Oh, reasonless thirst in the night, what can slake your thirst,
Reasonless heart, why will you not let me rest?
I have seen a woman wrapped in the grace of leaves,
I have kissed her mouth with my mouth, but I must go—
He was going back to find a piece of himself
That he had lost in a tent, in a red loud noise,
Under a sack of tobacco. Until he found it
He could never be whole again
                                    —but the hunger creeps
Like a vine about me, crushing my narrow wisdom,
Crushing my thoughts—
                            He couldn't stay with Melora.
He couldn't take her back home. If he were Bailey
He would know what to do. He would follow the weaver's tune.
He would keep Melora a night from the foggy dew
And then go off with the sunrise to tell the tale
Sometime for a campfire yarn. But he wasn't Bailey.
He saw himself dead without ever having Melora
And he didn't like it.
                            Maybe, after the war.
Maybe he could come back to the hider's place,
Maybe—it is a long time till after the war
And this is now—you took a girl when you found her—
A girl with flags on her garters or a new girl—
It didn't matter—it made a good campfire yarn—
It was men and women—Bailey—the weaver's tune—

He heard something move and rustle in the close darkness
"What's that?" he said. He got no answering voice
But he knew what it was. He saw a light-footed shadow

128

Come toward the nest where he lay. For a moment then
He felt weak, half-sickened almost.
                        Then his heart began
To pound to a marching rhythm that was not harsh
Nor sweet, but enormous cadence.
                        "Melora," he said.
His hand went out and touched the cup of her breast.

What things shall be said of you,
Terrible beauty in armor?
What things shall be said of you,
Horses riding the sky?
The fleetness, the molten speed,
The rhythm rising like beaten
Drums of barbaric gold
Until fire mixes with fire?

The night is a sparkling pit
Where Time no longer has power
But only vast cadence surging
Toward an instant of tiny death.
Then, with the slow withdrawal
Of seas from a rock of moonlight,
The clasping bodies unlock
And the lovers have little words.

What is this spear, this burnished
Arrow in the deep waters
That is not quenched by them
Until it has found its mark?
What is this beating of wings
In the formless heart of the tempest?
This wakening of a sun
That was not wakened before?

They have dragged you down from the sky
And broken you with an ocean
Because you carried the day,
Phaëton, charioteer.
But still you loose from the cloud

The matched desires of your horses
And sow on the ripened earth
The quickened, the piercing flame.

What things shall be said of you,
Terrible beauty in armor?
Dance that is not a dance,
Brief instant of welded swords.
For a moment we strike the black
Door with a fist of brightness.
And then it is over and spent,
And we sink back into life.

Back to the known, the sure,
The river of sleep and waking,
The dreams floating the river,
The nearness, the conquered peace.
You have come and smitten and passed,
Poniard, poniard of sharpness.
The child sleeps in the planet.
The blood sleeps again.

———————

He wasn't going away when he went to the wood.
He told himself that. They had broken the dime together.
They had cut the heart on the tree.
                          The jack-knife cut
Two pinched half-circles of white on the green bark.
The tree-gum bled from the cuts in sticky, clear drops,
And there you were.
                          And shortly the bark would dry
Dead on the living wood and leave the white heart
All through the winter, all through the rain and snow,
A phantom-blaze to guide a tall phantom-hunter
Who came in lightness along a leaf-buried path.
All through the snowing winter it would be white.
It would take many springs to cover that white again.
What have I done in idleness, in sweet idleness,
What have I done to the forest?
                          I have marked
A tree to be my own with a jack-knife blade

In idleness, in sweet idleness. I have loosed
A dryad out of the tree to chain me with wild
Grapevines and forest trailers forever and ever
To the hider's place, to the outcast house of the lost,
And now, when I would be free, I am free no more.
He thought of practical matters. There ought to be
A preacher and a gold ring and a wedding-dress,
Only how could there be?
                              He rolled hard words
Over his tongue. "A shotgun wedding," he said.
It wasn't like that, it never could be like that,
But there was a deadly likeness.
                              He saw the bored
Shamefaced seducer in the clean Sunday collar,
The whining, pregnant slut in the cheesecloth veil.
They weren't like that—but the picture colored his mind.

If he only could go away without going away
And have everything turn out just as it ought to be
Without rings or hiding!
                              He told himself "I'm all right.
I'm not like Bailey. I wouldn't sleep with a girl
Who never slept with anybody before
And then just go off and leave her."
                              But it was Melora.
It wasn't seducing a girl. It was all mixed up.
All real where it ought to be something told in a sermon,
And all unreal when you had to do something about it,
His thoughts went round and round like rats in a cage,
But all he knew was—
                    he was sick for a room
And a red tablecloth with tasselled fringes,
Where a wife knitted on an end of a scarf,
A father read his paper through the same
Unchanging spectacles with the worn bows
And a young girl beneath a nickeled lamp
Soundlessly conjugated Latin verbs,
"Amo, amas, amat," and still no sound—

Slight dryad, trailing the green, curled vines of the Spring,
I hate you for this moment, I hate your white breast
And idleness, sweet, hidden idleness—

121

He started awake. He had been walking through dreams.
How far had he come? He studied the sun and the trees.
Was he lost? No, there was the way.

                                He turned back slowly,
To the dryad, the idleness—to the cheesecloth veil,
The incredible preacher, the falling out of life.
He'd ask her this evening where you could find such preachers.
The old man mustn't know till the thing was done
Or he would turn to a father out of a cheap
Play, a cheap shotgun father with a wool beard
Roaring gilt rhetoric—and loading a musket.
He got the dry grins.

                       If the property-father shot him
Would they carve his name on the soldiers' monument
After the war?

                   There should be a special tablet.
"Here lies John Ellyat Junior, shot and killed
By an angry father for the great cause of Union.
'How sleep the brave.' "

                    He stumbled and looked around him.
"Well, I might go on as far as the road," he said.

A little while later he burst through the screen of brush.
And saw the highroad below him.

                      He wiped his face.
The road dipped down a hill to a little bridge.
He was safe enough now.

                  What was it Melora had said?
The highroad was six miles away from the farm,
Due west, and he could tell the west by the sun.
He must have covered a dozen, finding the road,
But getting back would be easy.

                    The sun was high.
He ought to be starting soon. But he lay down
And stared for a while at the road. It was good to see
A road in the open again, a dust-bitten road
Where people and horses went along to a town.
—Dryad, deep in the woods, your trails are small,
Winding and faint—they run between grass and flowers—
But it is good once more to come on a road
That is not drowsy with your idleness—

He looked down toward the bridge. There were moving blobs
    of dust
Crossing it—men on horses. His heart gave a strange
Throb of desire. What were they? They looked like soldiers.
Blue coats or grey? He could not tell for the dust.
He'd have to get back in the woods before they passed,
He was a hider now. But he kept on staring
A long two minutes, trying to make them out,
Till his eyes stung. One man had a yellow beard
And carried his rifle slung the Missouri way
But there were Missouri troops on either side.
In a minute he could tell—and wriggle away—

A round stick jabbed in his back.
                                A slow voice said
"Reach for the sky, Yank, or I'll nachully drill yuh."
His hands flew up.
                "Yuh're the hell of a scout," said the voice
With drawling scorn. "Yuh h'ain't even got a gun.
I could have picked yuh off ten minutes ago,
Yuh made more noise than a bear, bustin thru' that bresh.
What'd yuh ust to work at—wrappin' up corsets?
Yeah—yuh kin turn around."
                            Jack Ellyat turned
Incredulously.
            "Well, I'll be damned," said the boy
In butternut clothes with the wrinkled face of a leaf.
"Yuh're a young 'un all right—aw, well, don't take it so hard.
Our boys get captured, too. Hey, Billy!" he called,
"Got a Yankee scout."
                    The horse-hoofs stopped in the road.
"Well, bring him along," said a voice.
                                      Jack Ellyat slid
Down a little bank and stood in front of the horses.
He was dazed. This was not happening. But the horses
Were there, the butternut men on the horses were there.

A gaunt old man with a sour, dry mouth was talking,
"He's no scout," he said, "He's one of their lousy spies.
Don't he look like a spy? Let's string him up to a tree."
His eye roved, looking for a suitable branch,

133

His mouth seemed pleased.

Ellyat saw two little scooped dishes,
Hung on a balance, wavering in the air.
One was bright tin and carried his life and breath,
The other was black. They were balanced with dreadful even-
ness.
But now the black dish trembled, starting to fall.

"Hell, no," said the boy with the face like a wrinkled leaf.
"He's a scout all right. What makes yuh so savage, Ben?
Yuh're always hankerin' after a necktie-party.
Who captured the bugger anyhow?"

"Oh, well,"
Said the other man. "Oh, well." He spat in the dust.
"Anyhow," he said, with a hungry look at Ellyat,
"He's got good boots."

The boy with the wrinkled face
Remarked that, as for the boots, no Arkansaw catfish
Was going to take them away from their lawful captor.

The rest sat their horses loosely and looked at him
With mild curiosity, ruminating tobacco.
Ellyat tried to think. He could not think.

He was free,
These stuffless men on stuffless horses had freed him
From dryads and fathers, from cheesecloth veils and Melora.
He began to talk fast. He didn't hear what he said.
"But I've got to get back," he said. Then he stopped. They
laughed.
"Oh, yuh'll get over it, Bub," said the wrinkled boy,
"It ain't so bad. You won't have to fight no more.
Maybe yuh'll git exchanged. Git up on that horse.
No, take off them boots first, thanks."

He slung the boots
Around his neck. "Now I got some good boots," he said.
And grinned at the gaunt man with the sour mouth.
"Now, Bub, I'll just tie yuh a little with this yere rope
And then you won't be bustin' loose from the gang.
Grab the pommel as well as yuh kin."

The gaunt man coughed.
"I tell you," he said, in a disappointed voice,
"If we just strung him up it'd make things a hull lot easier.

134

He's a spy for sure, and everyone strings up spies.
We got a long piece to go yet and he's a nuisance."

"Aw, shut yore face," said Jim Breckinridge in a drawl,
"Yuh kin hang any Yanks yuh ketch on a piece uh dishrag,
Yuh ain't caught no armies yit."
                                    The gaunt man was silent.
Ellyat saw the little tin dish that carried the life
Slowly sink down, to safety, the black dish rise.
"Come on," said Billy. The horses started to move,
Stirring a dust that rose for a little while
In a faint cloud. But after the horses had gone,
The cloud settled, the road went to sleep again.

BOOK FOUR

Strike up, strike up for Wingate's tune,
Strike up for Sally Dupré!
Strike up, strike up for the April moon,
And the rain on the lilac spray!
For Wingate Hall in its pride once more,
For the branch of myrtle over the door,
Because the men are back from the war;
For the clean bed waiting the dusty rider
And the punchbowl cooling for thirsty throttles,
For the hot cooks boiling the hams in cider
And Cudjo grinning at cobwebbed bottles—
The last of the wine, the last of the wine,
The last of the '12 and the '29!
Three times voyaged around the Cape
Till old Judge Brooke, with an oath oracular,
Pronounced it the living soul of the grape,
And the veriest dregs to be supernacular!

Old Judge Brooke with his double chins
Sighing over his hoarded claret
And sending the last of his cherished bins
To the hospital-doctors with "I can spare it
But if you give it to some damned layman
Who doesn't know brandy from licorice-water

135

And sports a white ribbon, by fire and slaughter,
I'll hang the lot of you higher than Haman!"

The Wingate cellars are nearly bare
But Miss Louisa is doing her hair
In the latest style of Napoleon's court.
(A blockade-runner brought the report,
A blockade-runner carried the silk,
Heavy as bullion and white as milk,
That makes Amanda a gleaming moth.
For the coasts are staked with a Union net
But the dark fish slip through the meshes yet,
Shadows sliding without a light,
Through the dark of the moon, in the dead of night,
Carrying powder, carrying cloth,
Hoops for the belle and guns for the fighter,
Guncotton, opium, bombs and tea.
Fashionplates, quinine and history.
For Charleston's corked with a Northern fleet
And the Bayou City lies at the feet
Of a damn-the-torpedoes commodore;
The net draws tighter and ever tighter,
But the fish dart past till the end of the war,
From Wilmington to the Rio Grande,
And the sandy Bahamas are Dixie Land
Where the crammed, black shadows start for the trip
That, once clean-run, will pay for the ship.
They are caught, they are sunk with all aboard.
They scrape through safely and praise the Lord,
Ready to start with the next jammed hold
To pull Death's whiskers out in the cold,
The unrecorded skippers and mates
Whom even their legend expurgates,
The tough daredevils from twenty ports
Who thumbed their noses at floating forts
And gnawed through the bars of a giant's cage
For a cause or a laugh or a living-wage,
Who five long years on a sea of night,
Pumped new blood to the vein bled white
—And, incidentally, made the money
For the strangely rich of the after years—
For the flies will come to the open honey,

136

And, should war and hell have the same dimensions,
Both have been paved with the best intentions
And both are as full of profiteers.)

The slaves in the quarters are buzzing and talking.
—All through the winter the ha'nts went walking,
Ha'nts the size of a horse or bigger,
Ghost-patrollers, scaring a nigger,
But now the winter's over and broken,
And the sun shines out like a lovin' token,
There's goin' to be mixin's and mighty doin's,
Chicken-fixin's and barbecuin's,
Old Marse Billy's a-comin' home!
He's slewn a brigade with a ha'nts's jaw-bone,
He's slewn an army with one long sabre,
He's scared old Linkum 'most to death,
Now he's comin' home to rest from he labor,
Play on he fiddle and catch he breath!

The little black children with velvet eyes
Tell each other tremendous lies.
They play at Manassas with guns of peeled
Willow-stalks from the River Field,
Chasing the Yanks into Kingdom Come
While one of them beats on a catskin drum.
They are happy because they don't know why.
They scare themselves pretending to die,
But all through the scare, and before and after,
Their voices are rich with the ancient laughter,
The negro laughter, the blue-black rose,
The laughter that doesn't end with the lips
But shakes the belly and curls the toes
And prickles the end of the fingertips.

Up through the garden, in through the door,
That undercurrent of laughter floats,
It mounts like a sea from floor to floor,
A dark sea, covering painted boats,
A warm sea, smelling of earth and grass,
It seeps through the back of the cheval-glass
Where Amanda stares at her stately self
Till her eyes are bright with a different spark,

It sifts like a dye, where Louise's peering
In a shagreen-case for a garnet ear-ring
Till the little jewels shine in the dark,
It spills like a wave in the crowded kitchen
Where the last good sugar of Wingate Hall
Is frosting a cake like a Polar Highland
And fat Aunt Bess in her ice-wool shawl
Spends the hoarded knowledge her heart is rich in
On oceans of trifle and floating-island.

Fat Aunt Bess is older than Time
But her eyes still shine like a bright, new dime,
Though two generations have gone to rest
On the sleepy mountain of her breast.
Wingate children in Wingate Hall,
From the first weak cry in the bearing-bed
She has petted and punished them, one and all,
She has closed their eyes when they lay dead.
She raised Marse Billy when he was puny,
She cared for the Squire when he got loony,
Fed him and washed him and combed his head,
Nobody else would do instead.
The matriarch of the weak and the young,
The lazy crooning, comforting tongue.
She has had children of her own,
But the white-skinned ones are bone of her bone.
They may not be hers, but she is theirs,
And if the shares were unequal shares,
She does not know it, now she is old.
They will keep her out of the rain and cold.
And some were naughty, and some were good,
But she will be warm while they have wood,
Rule them and spoil them and play physician
With the vast, insensate force of tradition,
Half a nuisance and half a mother
And legally neither one nor the other,
Till at last they follow her to her grave,
The family-despot, and the slave.

—Curious blossom from bitter ground,
Master of masters who left you bound,
Who shall unravel the mingled strands

138

Or read the anomaly of your hands?
They have made you a shrine and a humorous fable,
But they kept you a slave while they were able,
And yet, there was something between the two
That you shared with them and they shared with you,
Brittle and dim, but a streak of gold,
A genuine kindness, unbought, unsold,
Graciousness founded on hopeless wrong
But queerly living and queerly strong. . . .

There were three stout pillars that held up all
The weight and tradition of Wingate Hall.
One was Cudjo and one was you
And the third was the mistress, Mary Lou.
Mary Lou Wingate, as slightly made
And as hard to break as a rapier-blade.
Bristol's daughter and Wingate's bride,
Never well since the last child died
But staring at pain with courteous eyes.
When the pain outwits it, the body dies,
Meanwhile the body bears the pain.
She loved her hands and they made her vain,
The tiny hands of her generation
That gathered the reins of the whole plantation;
The velvet sheathing the steel demurely
In the trained, light grip that holds so surely.

She was at work by candlelight,
She was at work in the dead of night,
Smoothing out troubles and healing schisms
And doctoring phthisics and rheumatisms,
Guiding the cooking and watching the baking,
The sewing, the soap-and-candle-making,
The brewing, the darning, the lady-daughters,
The births and deaths in the negro-quarters,
Seeing that Suke had some new, strong shoes
And Joe got a week in the calaboose,
While Dicey's Jacob escaped a whipping
And the jellybag dripped with its proper dripping,
And the shirts and estrangements were neatly mended,
And all of the tasks that never ended.

Her manner was gracious but hardly fervent
And she seldom raised her voice to a servant.
She was often mistaken, not often blind,
And she knew the whole duty of womankind,
To take the burden and have the power
And seem like the well-protected flower,
To manage a dozen industries
With a casual gesture in scraps of ease,
To hate the sin and to love the sinner
And to see that the gentlemen got their dinner
Ready and plenty and piping-hot
Whether you wanted to eat or not.
And always, always, to have the charm
That makes the gentlemen take your arm
But never the bright, unseemly spell
That makes strange gentlemen love too well,
Once you were married and settled down
With a suitable gentleman of your own.

And when that happened, and you had bred
The requisite children, living and dead,
To pity the fool and comfort the weak
And always let the gentlemen speak
To succor your love from deep-struck roots
When gentlemen went to bed in their boots,
And manage a gentleman's whole plantation
In the manner befitting your female station.

This was the creed that her mother taught her
And the creed that she taught to every daughter.
She knew her Bible—and how to flirt
With a swansdown fan and a brocade skirt.
For she trusted in God but she liked formalities
And the world and Heaven were both realities.
—In Heaven, of course, we should all be equal,
But, until we came to that golden sequel,
Gentility must keep to gentility
Where God and breeding had made things stable,
While the rest of the cosmos deserved civility
But dined in its boots at the second-table.
This view may be reckoned a trifle narrow,
But it had the driving force of an arrow,

And it helped Mary Lou to stand up straight,
For she was gentle, but she could hate
And she hated the North with the hate of Jael
When the dry hot hands went seeking the nail,
The terrible hate of women's ire,
The smoky, the long-consuming fire.
The Yankees were devils, and she could pray,
For devils, no doubt, upon Judgment Day,
But now in the world, she would hate them still
And send the gentlemen out to kill.

The gentlemen killed and the gentlemen died,
But she was the South's incarnate pride
That mended the broken gentlemen
And sent them out to the war again,
That kept the house with the men away
And baked the bricks where there was no clay,
Made courage from terror and bread from bran
And propped the South on a swansdown fan
Through four long years of ruin and stress,
The pride—and the deadly bitterness.

Let us look at her now, let us see her plain,
She will never be quite like this again.
Her house is rocking under the blast
And she hears it tremble, and still stands fast,
But this is the last, this is the last.
The last of the wine and the white corn meal,
The last high fiddle singing the reel,
The last of the silk with the Paris label,
The last blood-thoroughbred safe in the stable
—Yellow corn meal and a jackass colt,
A door that swings on a broken bolt,
Brittle old letters spotted with tears
And a wound that rankles for fifty years—
This is the last of Wingate Hall,
The last bright August before the Fall,
Death has been near, and Death has passed,
But this is the last, this is the last.
There will be hope, and a scratching pen,
There will be cooking for tired men,
The waiting for news with shut, hard fists,

And the blurred, strange names in the battle-lists,
The April sun and the April rain,
But never this day come back again.

But she is lucky, she does not see
The axe-blade sinking into the tree
Day after day, with a slow, sure stroke
Till it chops the mettle from Wingate oak.
The house is busy, the cups are filling
To welcome the gentlemen back from killing,
The hams are boiled and the chickens basting,
Fat Aunt Bess is smiling and tasting,
Cudjo's napkin is superfine,
He knows how the gentlemen like their wine,
Amanda is ready, Louisa near her,
Glistering girls from a silver mirror,
Everyone talking, everyone scurrying,
Upstairs and downstairs, laughing and hurrying,
Everyone giving and none denying,
There is only living, there is no dying.
War is a place but it is not here,
The peace and the victory are too near.
One more battle, and Washington taken,
The Yankees mastered, the South unshaken,
Fiddlers again, and the pairing season,
The old-time rhyme and the old-time reason,
The grandchildren, and the growing older
Till at last you need a gentleman's shoulder,
And the pain can stop, for the frayed threads sever,
But the house and the courtesy last forever.

So Wingate found it, riding at ease,
The cloud-edge lifting over the trees,
A white-sail glimmer beyond the rise,
A sugar-castle that strained the eyes,
Then mounting, mounting, the shining spectre
Risen at last from the drop of nectar,
The cloud expanding, the topsails swelling,
The doll's house grown to a giant's dwelling,
Porches and gardens and ells and wings
Linking together like puzzle-rings,

Till the parts dissolved in a steadfast whole,
And Wingate saw it, body and soul.

Saw it completely, and saw it gleam,
The full-rigged vessel, the sailing dream,
The brick and stone that were somehow quick
With a ghost not native to stone and brick,
The name held high and the gift passed on
From Wingate father to Wingate son,
No longer a house but a conjur-stone
That could hate and sorrow and hold its own
As long as the seed of Elspeth Mackay
Could mix its passion with Wingate clay
And the wind and the river had memories. . . .

Wingate saw it all—but with altered eyes.
He was not yet broken on any wheel,
He had no wound of the flesh to heal,
He had seen one battle, but he was still
The corn unground by the watermill,
He had ridden the rainy winter through
And he and Black Whistle were good as new,
The Black Horse Troop still carried its pride
And rode as the Yankees could not ride,
But, when he remembered a year-old dawn,
Something had come and something gone,
And even now, when he smelt the Spring,
And his heart was hot with his homecoming,
There was a whisper in his ear
That said what he did not wish to hear,
"This is the last, this is the last,
Hurry, hurry, this is the last,
Drink the wine before yours is spilled,
Kiss the sweetheart before you're killed,
She will be loving, and she will grieve,
And wear your heart on her golden sleeve
And marry your friend when he gets his leave.
It does not matter that you are still
The corn unground by the watermill,
The stones grind till they get their will.
Pluck the flower that hands can pluck,
Touch the walls of your house for luck,

Eat of the fat and drink the sweet,
There is little savor in dead men's meat.
It does not matter that you once knew
Future and past and a different you,
That went by when the wind first blew.
There is no future, there is no past,
There is only this hour and it goes fast,
Hurry, hurry, this is the last,
This is the last,
This is the last."

He heard it and faced it and let it talk.
The tired horses dropped to a walk.
And then Black Whistle lunged at the bit
And whinnied because he was alive,
And he saw the porch where the evenings sit
And the tall magnolias shading the drive,
He heard the bell of his father's mirth,
"Tallyho, Yanks—we've gone to earth!
Home, boy, home to Wingate Hall,
Home in spite of them, damn them all!"
He was stabbed by the rays of the setting sun,
He felt Black Whistle break to a run,
And then he was really there again,
Before he had time to think or check,
And a boy was holding his bridle-rein,
And Mary Lou's arms were around his neck.

Sally Dupré and Wingate talk with the music. . . .

The dance. Such a lovely dance. But you dance so lightly.
Amanda dances so well. But you dance so lightly.
(Do you remember the other dance?)
Phil Ferrier was here, remember, last year.
(He danced with me. He could dance rather well. He is dead.)
We were all so sorry when we heard about Phil.
(How long will you live and be able to dance with me?)
Yes. Phil was a fine fellow. We all liked Phil.
(Do not talk of the dead.
At first we talk of the dead, we write of the dead,
We send their things to their people when we can find them,

We write letters to you about them, we say we liked him,
He fought well, he died bravely, here is his sword,
Here is his pistol, his letters, his photograph case;
You will like to have these things, they will do instead.
But the war goes on too long.
After a while you still want to talk of the dead.
But we are too tired. We will send you the pistol still,
The photograph-case, the knickknacks, if we can find them,
But the war has gone on too long.
We cannot talk to you still, as we used to, about the dead.)
Nancy Huguenot's here tonight. Have you danced with her yet?
She didn't want to come. She was brave to come.
(Phil Ferrier was Nancy's lover.
She sent him off. She cut her hair for a keepsake.
They were going to be married as soon as he came back.
For a long time she dressed in black.
Then one morning she rose, and looked at the sun on the wall,
She put on a dress with red sleeves and a red, striped shawl,
She said "Phil was my beau. He wouldn't have liked me in black."
She used to cry quite a lot but she hasn't cried much since then.
I think she'll get well and marry somebody else.
I think she's right. If I had to wear grief for a lover,
I wouldn't wear black.
I would wear my best green silk and my Empire sacque
And walk in the garden at home and feel the wind
Blow through my rags of honor forever and ever.
And after that, when I married some other beau,
I would make a good wife and raise my children on sweet
Milk, not on poison, though it might have been so.
And my husband would never know
When he turned to me, when I kissed him, when we were kind,
When I cleaned his coat, when we talked about dresses and
    weather,
He had married something that belonged to the wind
And felt the blind
And always stream of that wind on her too-light bones,
Neither fast nor slow, but never checked or resigned,
Blowing through rags of honor forever and ever.)

They are calling for partners again. Shall we dance again?
(Why do we hate each other so well, when we
Are tied together by something that will not free us?

If I see you across a room, I will go to you,
If you see me across a room, you will come to me,
And yet we hate each other.)

Not yet, for a minute. I want to watch for a minute.
(I do not hate you. I love you. But you must take me.
I will not take your leavings nor you my pity.
I must break you first for a while and you must break me.
We are too strong to love the surrendered city.
So we hate each other.)

That's a pretty girl over there. Beautiful hair.
(She is the porcelain you play at being.)
Yes, isn't she. Her name is Lucy Weatherby.
(I hate her hair. I hate her porcelain air.)
She can't be from the county or I'd remember her.
(I know that kind of mouth. Your mouth is not that.
Your mouth is generous and bitter and sweet.
If I kissed your mouth, I would have to be yours forever.
Her mouth is pretty. You could kiss it awhile.)
No, they're kin to the Shepleys. Lucy comes from Virginia.
(I know that kind of mouth. I know that hair.
I know the dolls you like to take in your hands,
The dolls that all men like to take in their hands,
I will not fight with a doll for you or any one.)

We'd better dance now.
(Lucy Weatherby.
When this dance is done, I will leave you and dance with her.
I know that shallow but sufficient mouth.)
As you please.
(Lucy Weatherby.
I will make an image of you, a doll in wax.
I will pierce the little wax palms with silver bodkins.
No, I will not.)
That's good music. It beats in your head.
(It beats in the head, it beats in the head,
It ties the heart with a scarlet thread,
This is the last,
This is the last,
Hurry, hurry, this is the last.
We dance on a floor of polished sleet,

But the little cracks are beginning to meet,
Under the play of our dancing feet.
I do not care. I am Wingate still.
The corn unground by the watermill.
And I am yours while the fiddles spill,
But my will has a knife to cut your will,
My birds will never come to your hill.

You are my foe and my only friend,
You are the steel I cannot bend,
You are the water at the world's end.

But Wingate Hall must tumble down,
Tumble down, tumble down,
A dream dissolving, a ruined thing,
Before we can melt from the shattered crown
Gold enough for a wedding-ring.
And Wingate Hall must lie in the dust,
And the wood rot and the iron rust
And the vines grow over the broken bust,
Before we meet without hate or pride,
Before we talk as lover and bride,
Before the daggers of our offence
Have the color of innocence,
And nothing is said and all is said,
And we go looking for secret bread,
And lie together in the same bed.)

Yes, it's good music, hear it lift.
(It is too mellow, it is too swift,
I am dancing alone in my naked shift,
I am dancing alone in the snowdrift.
You are my lover and you my life,
My peace and my unending strife
And the edge of the knife against my knife.
I will not make you a porcelain wife.

We are linked together for good and all,
For the still pool and the waterfall,
But you are married to Wingate Hall.
And Wingate Hall must tumble down,

Tumble down, tumble down,
Wingate Hall must tumble down,
An idol broken apart,
Before I sew on a wedding gown
And stitch my name in your heart.
And Wingate Hall must lie in the grass,
And the silk stain and the rabbits pass
And the sparrows wash in the gilded glass,
Before the fire of our anger smothers,
And our sorrows can laugh at their lucky brothers,
Before the knives of our enmity
Are buried under the same green tree
And nothing is vowed and all is vowed
And we have forgotten how to be proud,
And we sleep like cherubs in the same cloud.)

———————

Lucy Weatherby, cuddled up in her bed,
Drifted along toward sleep with a smile on her mouth,
"I was pretty tonight," she thought, "I was pretty tonight.
Blue's my color—blue that matches my eyes.
I always ought to wear blue. I'm sorry for girls
Who can't wear that sort of blue. Her name is Sally
But she's too dark to wear the colors I can,
I'd like to give her my blue dress and see her wear it,
She'd look too gawky, poor thing.
                                    He danced with her
For a while at first but I hadn't danced with him then,
He danced with me after that. He's rather a dear.
I wonder how long he'll be here. I think I like him.
I think I'm going to be pretty while I am here.

Lucy Weatherby—Lucy Shepley—Lucy Wingate—
Huger's so jealous, nearly as jealous as Curly,
Poor Curly—I ought to answer his mother's letter
But it's so hard answering letters."
                                    She cried a little,
Thinking of Curly. The tears were fluent and warm,
They did not sting in her eyes. They made her feel brave.
She could hardly remember Curly any more
But it was right to cry for him, now and then,

148

Slight tears at night and a long, warm, dreamless sleep
That left you looking pretty.
                              She dried the tears
And thought to herself with a pleasant little awe,
"You really are mighty brave, dear. You really are.
Nobody would think your beau was killed at Manassas."
—She could hardly remember Curly any more—
She tried to make Curly's face come out of the darkness
But it was too hard—the other faces kept coming—
Huger Shepley and all the Virginia boys
And now this new boy's face with the dark, keen eyes.

Boys who were privates, boys who were majors and captains,
Nice old Generals who patted your shoulder,
Darling convalescents who called you an angel—
A whole, great lucky-bag of nice, thrilling boys,
Fighting for you—and the South and the Cause, of course.
You were a flame for the Cause. You sang songs about it.
You sent white feathers to boys who didn't enlist
And bunches of flowers to boys who were suitably wounded.
You wouldn't dream of making peace with the North
While a single boy was left to fight for the Cause
And they called you the Dixie Angel.
                              They fought for the Cause
But you couldn't help feeling, too, that they fought for you,
And when they died for you—and the Cause and the flag—
Your heart was tender enough. You were willing to say
You had been engaged to them, even when you hadn't
And answer their mothers' letters in a sweet way,
Though answering letters was hard.
                              She cuddled closer,
"Pillow, tell me I'm pretty, tell me I'm lovely,
Tell me I'm nicer than anybody you know,
Tell me that nice new boy is thinking about me,
Tell me that Sally girl couldn't wear my blue,
Tell me the war won't end till we've whipped the Yankees,
Tell me I'll never get wrinkles and always have beaus."

———————

The slave got away from Zachary's place that night.
He was a big fellow named Spade with one cropped ear.
He had splay feet and sometimes walked with a limp.

His back was scarred. He was black as a pine at night.
He'd tried to run away a couple of times
—That was how he got some of the marks you could tell him
    by—
But he'd been pretty quiet now for a year or so
And they thought he had settled down.
                            When he got away
He meant to kill Zachary first but the signs weren't right.
He talked to the knife but the knife didn't sweat or heat,
So he just got away instead.
                        When he reached the woods
And was all alone, he was pretty scared for a while,
But he kept on going all night by the big soft stars,
Loping as fast as he could on his long splay feet
And when morning broke, he knew he was safe for a time.

He came out on a cleared place, then. He saw the red
Sun spill over the trees.
                        He threw his pack
Down on the ground and started to laugh and laugh,
"Spade, boy, Spade, you's lucky to git dis far.
You never managed to git dis far before,
De Lawd's sho'ly with you, Spade."
                            He ate and drank.
He drew a circle for Zachary's face in the ground
And spat in the circle. Then he thought of his woman.
"She's sho'ly a grievin' woman dis mawnin', Spade."
The thought made him sad at first, but he soon cheered up.
"She'll do all right as soon as she's thu with grievin'.
Grievin' yaller gals always does all right.
Next time I'se gwine to git me a coal-black gal.
I'se tired of persimmon-skins.
                            I'se gwine to break loose.
De signs is right dis time. I'se gwine to be free,
Free in de Norf."
                    He saw himself in the North.
He had a stovepipe hat and a coal-black gal.
He had a white-folks' house and a regular mule.
He worked for money and nobody ever owned him.
He got religion and dollars and lucky dice
And everybody he passed in the white folks' street
Said "Good mawnin', Mr. Spade—Mr. Spade, good mawnin'."

He chuckled aloud. "Good mawnin', Mistuh Spade,
Gwine to be free, Mistuh Spade—yes, suh, Mistuh Spade!"
For a lazy moment, he was already there—
Then he stiffened, nostrils flaring, at a slight sound.
It couldn't be dogs already.
                                        "Jesus," he whispered,
"Sweet, lovin' Jesus, don't let 'em git me again,
Burn me up, but don't let 'em git me again,
Dey's gwine to cut me apart."
                                        The rabbit ran past.
He stared at it for a moment with wild, round eyes,
Started a yell of laughter—and choked it off.
"Dat ain't no nachul rabbit dere, Spade, boy.
Dat's a sign. Yes, suh. You better start makin' tracks.
Take your foot in your hand, Mistuh Spade."
                                        He swung the bundle
Up on his shoulders and slid along through the trees.
The bundle was light. He was going to be hungry soon
And the big splay feet would soon be bleeding and sore,
But, as he went, he shook with uncanny chuckles.
"Good mawnin', Mr. Spade—glad to see you dis mawnin'
How's Mrs. Spade, Mr. Spade?"

————————

Sally Dupré, from the high porch of her house
Stared at the road.
                        They would be here soon enough.
She had waved a flag the last time they went away.
This time she would wave her hand or her handkerchief.
That was what women did. The column passed by
And the women waved, and it came back and they waved,
And, in between, if you loved, you lived by a dull
Clock of long minutes that passed like sunbonneted women
Each with the same dry face and the same set hands.
I have read, they have told me that love is a pretty god
With light wings stuck to his shoulders.
                                        They did not tell me
That love is nursing a hawk with yellow eyes,
That love is feeding your heart to the beak of the hawk
Because an old woman, gossiping, uttered a name.

151

They were coming now.
She remembered the first time.
They were different now. They rode with a different rein.
They rode all together. They knew where they were going.
They were famous now, but she wondered about the fame.
And yet, as she wondered, she felt the tears in her blood
Because they could ride so easily.
                              He was there.
She fed her heart to the hawk and watched him ride.

She thought, "But they like this, too. They are like small boys
Going off to cook potatoes over a fire
Deep in the woods, where no women can ever come
To say how blackened and burnt the potatoes are
And how you could cook them better back in a house.
Oh, they like to come home. When they're sick they like to come
    home,
They dream about home—they write you they want to come
    back,
And they come back and live in the house for a while
And raise their sons to hear the same whistle-tune
Under the window, the whistle calling the boys
Out to the burnt potatoes.
                              O whistler Death,
What have we done to you in a barren month,
In a sterile hour, that our lovers should die before us?"
Then she thought. "No, no, I can't bear it. It cannot be borne."
And knowing this, bore it.
                              He saw her. He turned his horse.
"If he comes here, I can't keep it back, I can't keep it back,
I can't stand it, don't let him come." He was coming now.
He rides well, she thought, while her hands made each other cold.
I will have to remember how. And his face is sharper.
The moustache quite changes his face. The face that I saw
While he was away was clean-shaven and darker-eyed.
I must change that, now. I will have to remember that.
It is very important.
                              He swung from Black Whistle's back.
His spurs made a noise on the porch. She twisted her hands.
"If I shut my eyes, I can make him kiss me. I will not."

They were saying good-by, now. She heard polite voices say-
    ing it.

Then the voices ended. "No, no, it is not to be borne,
It is the last twist of the vise."
                              Her will snapped then.
When she looked at him, she knew that the knives were edgeless.
In an instant life would begin, life would be forever.

His eyes wavered. There was a thin noise in her ears,
A noise from the road.
                        The instant fell and lay dead
Between them like something broken.

She turned to see what had killed it.

Lucy Weatherby, reining a bright bay mare,
Played with the braided lash of a riding-whip
And talked to Wingate's father with smiling eyes,
While Huger Shepley tried to put in a word
And the whole troop clustered about her.
                                    Her habit was black
But she had a knot of bright ribbons pinned at her breast,
Red and blue—the Confederate colors.
                                They had cheered her.
They had cheered her, riding along with her colored ribbons.
It was that which had killed the instant.
                                    Sally looked
At the face with the new moustache she had to remember.
"Good-by," she said. The face bent over her hand
And kissed it acceptably.
                        Then the face had gone.
He was back with the others now. She watched for a minute.
Lucy was unpinning her knot of ribbons.
She saw a dozen hands go up for the knot
And Lucy laugh her sweet laugh and shake her bright head,
Glance once at Huger Shepley and once at Clay,
And then toss the colored knot to the guidon-bearer
Who grinned and tied the ribbons around the staff
While some of them cheered again.
                                Then the horses moved.
They went by Lucy. Lucy was waving her hand.
She had tears in her eyes and was saying brave words to the
    soldiers.
Sally watched a back and a horse go out of sight.
She was tired, then.

When the troop had quite disappeared
Lucy rode up to the house.
                              The two women kissed
And talked for a while about riding-habits and war.
"I just naturally love every boy in the Black Horse Troop,
Don't you, Sally darling? They're all so nice and polite,
Quite like our Virginia boys, and the Major's a dear,
And that nice little one with the guidon is perfectly sweet.
You ought to have heard what he said when I gave him the knot.
Though, of course, I can tell why you didn't come down to the
    road,
War's terrible, isn't it? All those nice boys going off—
I feel just the way you do, darling—we just have to show them
Whenever we can that we know they are fighting for us,
Fighting for God and the South and the cause of the right—
'Law, Chile, don't you fret about whether you's pretty or plain,
You just do what you kin, and the good Lawd'll brighten your
    tracks.'
That's what my old mammy would tell me when I was knee-high
And I always remember and just try to do what I can
For the boys and the wounded and—well, that's it, isn't it, dear?
We've all got to do what we can in this horrible war."
Sally agreed that we had, and drank from a cup.
She thought. "Lucy Weatherby. Yes. I must look for a doll.
I must make a doll with your face, an image of wax.
I must call that doll by your name."

————

Now the scene expands, we must look at the scene as a whole.
How are the gameboards chalked and the pieces set?
There is an Eastern game and a Western game.
In the West, blue armies try to strangle the long
Snake of the Mississippi with iron claws;
Buell and Grant against Bragg and Beauregard.
They have hold of the head of the snake where it touches the
    Gulf,
New Orleans is taken, the fangs of the forts drawn out,
The ambiguous Butler wins ambiguous fame
By issuing orders stating that any lady
Who insults a Union soldier in uniform
Shall be treated as a streetwalker plying her trade.
The orders are read and hated. The insults stop

But the ladies remember Butler for fifty years
And make a fabulous devil with pasteboard horns
—"Beast" Butler, the fiend who pilfered the silver spoons—
From a slightly-tarnished, crude-minded, vain politician
Who loved his wife and ached to be a great man.
You were not wise with the ladies, Benjamin Butler,
It has been disproved that you stole New Orleans spoons
But the story will chime at the ribs of your name and stain it,
Ghost-silver, clinking against the ribs of a ghost,
As long as the ladies have tongues.
                              Napoleon was wiser
But he could not silence one ugly, clever De Staël.
Make war on the men—the ladies have too-long memories.

The head of the snake is captured—the tail gripped fast—
But the body in between still writhes and resists,
Vicksburg is still unfallen—Grant not yet master—
Sheridan, Sherman, Thomas still in the shadow.
The eyes of the captains are fixed on the Eastern game,
The presidents—and the watchers oversea—
For there are the two defended kings of the board,
Muddy Washington, with its still-unfinished Capitol,
Sprawling, badly-paved, beset with sharp hogs
That come to the very doorsteps and grunt for crumbs,
Full of soldiers and clerks, full of all the baggage of war,
"Bombproof" officers, veterans back on leave,
Recruits, spies, spies on the spies, politicians, contractors,
Reporters, slackers, ambassadors, bands and harlots,
Negro-boys who organize butting-matches
To please the recruits, tattooers and fortune-tellers,
Rich man, poor man, soldier, beggarman, thief,
And one most lonely man in a drafty White House
Whose everlasting melancholy runs
Like a deep stream under the funny stories,
The parable-maker, humble in many things
But seldom humble with his fortitude,
The sorrowful man who cracked the sure-fire jokes,
Roared over Artemus Ward and Orpheus C. Kerr
And drove his six cross mules with a stubborn hand.
He has lost a son, but he has no time to grieve for him.
He studies tactics now till late in the night
With the same painful, hewing industry

He put on studying law.
                    McClellan comes,
McClellan goes, McClellan bustles and argues,
McClellan is too busy to see the President,
McClellan complains of this, complains of that,
The Government is not supporting him,
The Government cannot understand grand strategy,
The Government—
                    McClellan feels abused.
McClellan is quite sincere and sometimes right.
They come to the lonely man about McClellan
With various tales.
                    McClellan lacks respect,
McClellan dreams about a dictatorship,
McClellan does that and this.
                    The lonely man
Listens to all the stories and remarks,
"If McClellan wins, I will gladly hold his horse."

A hundred miles away in an arrow-line
Lies the other defended king of the giant chess,
Broad-streeted Richmond.
                    All the baggage of war
Is here as well, the politicians, the troops,
The editors who scream at the government,
The slackers, the good and the bad, but the flavor is different:
There is something older here, and smaller and courtlier,
The trees in the streets are old trees used to living with people,
Family-trees that remember your grandfather's name.
It is still a clan-city, a family-city, a city
That thinks of the war, on the whole, as a family-matter,
A woman city, devoted and fiercely jealous
As any of the swan-women who ruled it then—
Ready to give their lives and hearts for the South,
But already a little galled by Jefferson Davis
And finding him rather too much of a doctrinaire
With a certain comparative touch of the parvenu.
He is not from Virginia, we never knew his grandfather.

The South is its husband, the South is not quite its master.
It has a soul while Washington is a symbol,
Beautiful, witty, feminine, narrow and valiant,

Unwisely-chosen, perhaps, for a king of the game,
But playing the part with a definite air of royalty
Until, in the end, it stands for the South completely
And when it falls, the sword of the South snaps short.

At present, the war has not yet touched it home.
McClellan has landed, on the Peninsula,
But his guns are still far away.
                                    The ladies go
To Mrs. Davis's parties in last year's dresses.
Soon they are to cut the green and white chintz curtains
That shade their long drawing-rooms from the lazy sun
To bandage the stricken wounded of Seven Pines.

The lonely man with the chin like John Calhoun's
Works hard and is ill at ease in his Richmond White House.
His health was never too strong—it is tiring now
Under a mass of detail, under the strain
Of needless quarrels with secretaries and chiefs
And a Congress already beginning to criticize him.
He puts his trust in God with a charmed devotion
And his faith, too often, in men who can feed his vanity.
They mock him for it. He cannot understand mocking.
There is something in him that prickles the pride of men
Whom Lincoln could have used, and makes them his foes.
Joe Johnston and he have been at odds from the first,
Beauregard and he are at odds and will be at odds,
One could go through a list—
                                    He is quite as stubborn as Lincoln
In supporting the people he trusts through thick and thin,
But—except for Lee—the people he trusts so far
Seldom do the work that alone can repay the trust.
They fail in the end and his shoulders carry the failure,
And leave him, in spite of his wife, in spite of his God,
Lonely, beginning and end, with that other's loneliness.
The other man could have understood him and used him.
He could never have used or comprehended the other.
It is their measure.
                        And yet, a deep loneliness,
A deep devotion, a deep self-sacrifice,
Binds the strange two together.
                                    He, too, is to lose

A child in his White House, ere his term is accomplished.
He, too, is to be the scapegoat for all defeat.
And he is to know the ultimate bitterness,
The cause lost after every expense of mind,
And bear himself with decent fortitude
In the prison where the other would not have kept him.
One cannot balance tragedy in the scales
Unless one weighs it with the tragic heart.
The other man's tragedy was the greater one
Since the blind fury tore the huger heart,
But this man's tragedy is the more pitiful.
Thus the Eastern board and the two defended kings.
But why is the game so ordered, what crowns the kings?
They are cities of streets and houses like other cities.
Baltimore might be taken, and war go on,
Atlanta will be taken and war go on,
Why should these two near cities be otherwise?
We do not fight for the real but for shadows we make.
A flag is a piece of cloth and a word is a sound,
But we make them something neither cloth nor a sound,
Totems of love and hate, black sorcery-stones,
So with these cities.
                    And so the third game is played,
The intricate game of the watchers oversea,
The shadow that falls like the shadow of a hawk's wing
Over the double-chessboard until the end—
The shadow of Europe, the shadows of England and France,
The war of the cotton against the iron and wheat.
The shadows ponder and mutter, biding their time;
If the knights and bishops that play for the cotton-king
Can take the capital-city of wheat and iron,
The shadow-hands will turn into hands of steel
And intervene for the cotton that feeds the mills.
But if the fable throned on a cotton-bale
Is checkmated by the pawns of iron and wheat,
The shadows will pause, and cleave to iron and wheat,
They will go their ways and lift their eyes from the game,
For iron and wheat are not to be lightly held.
So the watchers, searching the board.
                    And so the game.
The blockade grips, the blockade-runners break through,
There are duels and valors, the Western game goes on

158

And the snake of the Mississippi is tamed at last,
But the fight in the East is the fight between the two kings.
If Richmond is threatened, we threaten Washington,
You check our king with McClellan or Hooker or Grant,
We will check your king with Jackson or Early or Lee
And you must draw back strong pieces to shield your king,
For we hold the chord of the circle and you the arc
And we can shift our pieces better than you.

So it runs for years until Jubal Early, riding,
A long twelve months after Gettysburg's high tide,
Sees the steeples of Washington prick the blue June sky
And the Northern king is threatened for the last time.
But, by then, the end is too near, the cotton is withered.
Now the game still hangs in the balance—the cotton in bloom—
The shadows of the watchers long on the board.
McClellan has moved his men from their camps at last
In a great sally.
                    There are many gates he can try.
The Valley gate and the old Manassas way,
But he has chosen to ferry his men by sea,
To the ragged half-island between the York and the James
And thrust up a long, slant arm from Fortress Monroe
Northwest toward Richmond.
                            The roads are sticky and soft,
There are forts at Yorktown and unmapped rivers to cross.
He has many more men than Johnston or John Magruder
But the country hinders him, and he hinders himself
By always thinking the odds on the other side
And that witches of ruin haunt each move he makes.
But even so—he has boarded that jutting deck
That is the Peninsula, and his forces creep
Slowly toward Richmond, slowly up to the high
Defended captain's cabin of the great ship.
—There was another force that came from its ships
To take a city set on a deck of land,
The cause unlike, but the fighting no more stark,
The doom no fiercer, the fame no harder to win.
There are no gods to come with a golden smoke
Here in the mud between the York and the James
And wrap some high-chinned hero away from death.
There are only Bibles and buckles and cartridge belts

That sometimes stop a bullet before it kills
But oftener let it pass.
                              And when Sarpedon
Falls and the heavy darkness stiffens his limbs
They will let him lie where he fell, they will not wash him
In the running streams of Scamander, the half-divine,
They will bury him in a shallow and cumbered pit.
But, if you would sing of fighters, sing of these men,
Sing of Fair Oaks and the battered Seven Days,
Not of the raging of Ajax, the cry of Hector,
These men were not gods nor shielded by any gods,
They were men of our shape: they fought as such men may fight
With a mortal skill: when they died it was as men die.

Army of the Potomac, advancing army,
Alloy of a dozen disparate, alien States,
City-boy, farm-hand, bounty-man, first volunteer,
Old regular, drafted recruit, paid substitute,
Men who fought through the war from First Bull Run,
And other men, nowise different in look or purpose,
Whom the first men greeted at first with a ribald cry
"Here they come! Two hundred dollars and a ka-ow!"
Rocks from New England and hickory-chunks from the West,
Bowery boy and clogging Irish adventurer,
Germans who learnt their English under the shells
Or didn't have time to learn it before they died.
Confused, huge weapon, forged from such different metals,
Misused by unlucky swordsmen till you were blunt
And then reforged with anguish and bloody sweat
To be blunted again by one more unlucky captain
Against the millstone of Lee.
                                Good stallion,
Ridden and ridden against a hurdle of thorns
By uncertain rider after uncertain rider.
The rider fails and you shiver and catch your breath,
They plaster your wounds and patch up your broken knees,
And then, just as you know the grip of your rider's hands
And begin to feel at home with his horseman's tricks,
Another rider comes with a different seat,
And lunges you at the bitter hurdle again,
And it beats you again—and it all begins from the first,
The patching of wounds, the freezing in winter camps,

The vain mud-marches, the diarrhea, the wastage,
The grand reviews, the talk in the newspapers,
The sour knowledge that you were wasted again,
Not as Napoleons waste for a victory
But blindly, unluckily—
                              until at last
After long years, at fish-hook Gettysburg,
The blade and the millstone meet and the blade holds fast.
And, after that, the chunky man from the West,
Stranger to you, not one of the men you loved
As you loved McClellan, a rider with a hard bit,
Takes you and uses you as you could be used,
Wasting you grimly but breaking the hurdle down.
You are never to worship him as you did McClellan,
But at the last you can trust him. He slaughters you
But he sees that you are fed. After sullen Cold Harbor
They call him a butcher and want him out of the saddle,
But you have had other butchers who did not win
And this man wins in the end.
                              You see him standing,
Reading a map, unperturbed, under heavy fire.
You do not cheer him as the recruits might cheer
But you say "Ulysses doesn't scare worth a darn.
Ulysses is all right. He can finish the job."
And at last your long lines go past in the Grand Review
And your legend and his begins and are mixed forever.

Now, though, he is still just one of the Western leaders,
And Little Mac is your darling.
                              You are unshaken
By the ruin of Fredericksburg, the wounds of Antietam,
Chancellorsville is a name in the Wilderness,
Your pickets, posted in front of the Chickahominy,
Hear the churchbells of Richmond, ringing;
Listen well to those bells, they are very near tonight,
But you will not hear them again for three harsh years.

Black months of war, hard-featured, defeated months
Between Fair Oaks and Gettysburg,
What is your tale for this army?
What do the men,
So differently gathered for your word to devour,

161

Say to your ears, deaf with cannon? What do they bring
In powder-pocked hands to the heart of the burst shell?
Let us read old letters awhile,
Let us try to hear
The thin, forgotten voices of men forgotten
Crying out of torn scraps of paper, notes scribbled and smudged
On aces, on envelope-backs, on gilt-edged cards stolen out of a
    dead man's haversack.

—Two brothers lay on the field of Fredericksburg
After the assault had failed.
They were unwounded but they could not move,
The sharpshooters covered that patch of ground too well.
They had a breastwork to hide them from the bullets,
A shelter of two dead men. One had lost his back,
Scooped out from waist to neck with a solid shot.
The other's legs were gone. They made a good breastwork.
The brothers lay behind them, flat in the mud,
All Sunday till night came down and they could creep off.
They did not dare move their hands for fourteen hours.
—A middle-aged person named Fletcher from Winchester
Enlisted in the Massachusetts Sharpshooters.
He was a crack-duckshooter, skilful and patient.
They gave him the wrong sort of rifle and twenty rounds
And told him to join his company.
It took him days to find it. He had no rations,
He begged bread and green corn and peaches and shot a hog;
So got there at last. He joined just before Antietam.
He'd never been drilled but he knew how to shoot,
Though at first his hands kept shaking.
"It was different kind of gunning from what I was used to,
I was mad with myself that I acted so like a coward."
But as soon as they let him lie down and fight on his own,
He felt all right. He had nineteen cartridges now.
The first five each killed a man—he was a good shot—
Then the rifle fouled. He began to get up and fix it,
Mechanically. A bullet went through his lung.
He lay on the field all day. At the end of the day
He was captured, sent to prison, paroled after weeks,
Died later, because of the wound.
That was his war—

162

Other voices, rising out of the scraps of paper,
Till they mix in a single voice that says over and over
"It is cold. It is wet. We marched till we couldn't stand up.
It is muddy here. I wish you could see us here.
I wish everybody at home could see us here.
They would know what war is like. We are still patriotic.
We are going to fight. We hope this general's good.
We hope he can make us win. We'll do all we can.
But I wish we could show everybody who stays at home
What this is like."
Voices of tired men,
Sick, convalescent, afraid of being sick.
"The diarrhea is bad. I hope I don't get it
But everybody seems to get it sometime.
I felt sick last night. I thought I was going to die,
But Jim rubbed me and I feel better. There's just one thing,
I hope I never get sent to the hospital,
You don't get well when you go to the hospital.
I'd rather be shot and killed quick."
(Nurses and doctors, savagely, tenderly working,
Trying to beat off death without enough knowledge,
Trying and failing.
Clara Barton, Old Mother Bickerdyke,
Overworked evangels of common sense,
Nursing, tending, clearing a ruthless path
Through the cant and red tape, through the petty jealousies
To the bitter front, bringing up the precious supplies
In spite of hell and high water and pompous fools,
To the deadly place where the surgeons' hands grew stiff
Under the load of anguish they had to deal,
Where they bound men's wounds and swabbed them with green
    corn leaves,
There being no other lint.
Whitman, with his sack of tobacco and comfits,
Passing along the terrible, crowded wards,
Listening, writing letters, trying to breathe
Strong life into lead-colored lips.
He does what he can. The doctors do what they can.
The nurses save a life here and another there,
But the sick men die like flies in the hospitals.)

Voices of boys and men,
Homesick, stubborn, talking of little things,
"We get better food. I'm getting to be a good cook.
The food's bad. The whole company yelled 'Hard Bread!' today.
There are only three professed Christians in my whole regiment,
I feel sad about that.
I wish you could see the way we have to live here,
I wish everybody at home could see what it's like.
It's muddy. It's cold. My shoes gave out on the march.
We lost the battle. The general was drunk.
This is the roughest life that you ever saw.
If I ever get back home—"
And, over and over, in stiff, patriotic phrases,
"I am resigned to die for the Union, mother.
If we die in this battle, we will have died for the right,
We will have died bravely—you can trust us for that.
It is only right to die for our noble Union.
We will save it or die for it. There's just one thing.
I hope I die quick. I hope I don't have to die
In the hospital.
There is one thought that to me is worse than death.
(This, they say over and over) it is the thought
Of being buried as they bury us here
After a battle. Sometimes they barely cover us.
I feel sick when I think of getting buried like that,
Though if nothing except our death will rescue our Union,
You can trust us to die for it."
And, through it all, the deep diapason swelling,
"It is cold. We are hungry. We marched all day in the mud.
We could barely stand when we got back into camp.
Don't believe a thing the newspapers say about us.
It's all damn lies.
We are willing to die for our Union,
But I wish you could all of you see what this is like,
Nobody at home can imagine what it is like.
We are ready to fight. We know we can fight and win.
But why will they waste us in fights that cannot be won?
When will we get a man that can really lead us?"
These are the articulate that write the letters.
The inarticulate merely undergo.
There are times of good food and times of campfire jokes,
Times of good weather, times of partial success

In those two years.
                    "The mail came. Thanks for the papers.
We had a good feed at Mrs. Wilson's place.
I feel fine today. We put on a show last night.
You ought to have seen Jim Wheeler in 'Box and Cox.'
Our little band of Christians meets often now
And the spirit moves in us strongly, praise be to God.
The President reviewed us two days ago.
You should have seen it, father, it was majestic.
I have never seen a more magnificent sight.
It makes me proud to be part of such an army.
We got the tobacco. The socks came. I'm feeling fine."
All that—but still the deep diapason throbs
Under the rest.
                    The cold. The mud. The bleak wonder.
The weakening sickness—the weevils tainting the bread—
We were beaten again in spite of all we could do.
We don't know what went wrong but something went wrong.
When will we find a man who can really lead us?
When will we not be wasted without success?

Army of the Potomac, army of brave men,
Beaten again and again but never quite broken,
You are to have the victory in the end
But these bleak months are your anguish.
                                        Your voice dies out.
Let us hear the voice of your steadfast enemy.

Army of Northern Virginia, fabulous army,
Strange army of ragged individualists,
The hunters, the riders, the walkers, the savage pastorals,
The unmachined, the men come out of the ground,
Still for the most part, living close to the ground
As the roots of the cow-pea, the roots of the jessamine,
The lazy scorners, the rebels against the wheels,
The rebels against the steel combustion-chamber
Of the half-born new age of engines and metal hands.
The fighters who fought for themselves in the old clan-fashion.
Army of planters' sons and rusty poor-whites,
Where one man came to war with a haircloth trunk
Full of fine shirts and a body-servant to mend them,
And another came with a rifle used at King's Mountain

And nothing else but his pants and his sun-cracked hands,
Aristo-democracy armed with a forlorn hope,
Where a scholar turned the leaves of an Arabic grammar
By the campfire-glow, and a drawling mountaineer
Told dirty stories old as the bawdy world,
Where one of Lee's sons worked a gun with the Rockbridge
    Battery
And two were cavalry generals.
                              Praying army,
Full of revivals, as full of salty jests,
Who debated on God and Darwin and Victor Hugo,
Decided that evolution might do for Yankees
But that Lee never came from anything with a tail,
And called yourselves "Lee's miserables faintin' "
When the book came out that tickled your sense of romance,
Army of improvisators of peanut-coffee
Who baked your bread on a ramrod stuck through the dough,
Swore and laughed and despaired and sang "Lorena,"
Suffered, died, deserted, fought to the end.
Sentimental army, touched by "Lorena,"
Touched by all lace-paper-valentines of sentiment,
Who wept for the mocking-bird on Hallie's grave
When you had better cause to weep for more private griefs,
Touched by women and your tradition-idea of them,
The old, book-fed, half-queen, half-servant idea,
False and true and expiring.
                              Starving army,
Who, after your best was spent and your Spring lay dead,
Yet held the intolerable lines of Petersburg
With deadly courage.
                      You too are a legend now
And the legend has made your fame and has dimmed that fame,
—The victor strikes and the beaten man goes down
But the years pass and the legend covers them both,
The beaten cause turns into the magic cause,
The victor has his victory for his pains—
So with you—and the legend has made a stainless host
Out of the dusty columns of footsore men
Who found life sweet and didn't want to be killed,
Grumbled at officers, grumbled at Governments.
That stainless host you were not. You had your cowards,
Your bullies, your fakers, your sneaks, your savages.

You got tired of marching. You cursed the cold and the rain.
You cursed the war and the food—and went on till the end.
And yet, there was something in you that matched your fable.
What was it? What do your dim, faint voices say?
"Will we ever get home? Will we ever lick them for good?
We've got to go on and fight till we lick them for good.
They've got the guns and the money and lots more men
But we've got to lick them now.
We're not fighting for slaves.
Most of us never owned slaves and never expect to,
It takes money to buy a slave and we're most of us poor,
But we won't lie down and let the North walk over us
About slaves or anything else.
                      We don't know how it started
But they've invaded us now and we're bound to fight
Till every last damn Yankee goes home and quits.
We used to think we could lick them in one hand's turn.
We don't think that any more.
                 They keep coming and coming.
We haven't got guns that shoot as well as their guns,
We can't get clothes that wear as well as their clothes,
But we've got to keep on till they're licked and we're independent,
It's the only thing we can do.
                Though some of us wonder—
Some of us try and puzzle the whole thing through,
Some of us hear about Richmond profiteers,
The bombproofs who get exempted and eat good dinners,
And the rest of it, and say, with a bitter tongue,
'This is the rich man's war and the poor man's fight.'
And more of us, maybe, say that, after a while,
But most of us just keep on till we're plumb worn out,
We just keep on.
             We've got the right men to lead us,
It doesn't matter how many the Yankees are,
Marse Robert and Old Jack will take care of that,
We'll have to march like Moses and fight like hell
But we're bound to win unless the two of them die
And God wouldn't be so mean as to take them both,
So we just keep on—and keep on—"
                   To the Wilderness,
To Appomattox, to the end of the dream.

Army of Northern Virginia, army of legend,
Who were your captains that you could trust them so surely?
Who were your battle-flags?
                              Call the shapes from the mist,
Call the dead men out of the mist and watch them ride.
Tall the first rider, tall with a laughing mouth,
His long black beard is combed like a beauty's hair,
His slouch hat plumed with a curled black ostrich-feather,
He wears gold spurs and sits his horse with the seat
Of a horseman born.
                    It is Stuart of Laurel Hill,
"Beauty" Stuart, the genius of cavalry,
Reckless, merry, religious, theatrical,
Lover of gesture, lover of panache,
With all the actor's grace and the quick, light charm
That makes the women adore him—a wild cavalier
Who worships as sober a God as Stonewall Jackson,
A Rupert who seldom drinks, very often prays,
Loves his children, singing, fighting, spurs, and his wife.
Sweeney his banjo-player follows him.
And after them troop the young Virginia counties,
Horses and men, Botetort, Halifax,
Dinwiddie, Prince Edward, Cumberland, Nottoway,
Mecklenburg, Berkeley, Augusta, the Marylanders,
The horsemen never matched till Sheridan came.
Now the phantom guns creak by. They are Pelham's guns.
That quiet boy with the veteran mouth is Pelham.
He is twenty-two. He is to fight sixty battles
And never lose a gun.
                      The cannon roll past,
The endless lines of the infantry begin.
A. P. Hill leads the van. He is small and spare,
His short, clipped beard is red as his battleshirt,
Jackson and Lee are to call him in their death-hours.
Dutch Longstreet follows, slow, pugnacious and stubborn,
Hard to beat and just as hard to convince,
Fine corps commander, good bulldog for holding on,
But dangerous when he tries to think for himself,
He thinks for himself too much at Gettysburg,
But before and after he grips with tenacious jaws.
There is D. H. Hill—there is Early and Fitzhugh Lee—
Yellow-haired Hood with his wounds and his empty sleeve,

168

Leading his Texans, a Viking shape of a man,
With the thrust and lack of craft of a berserk sword,
All lion, none of the fox.
                    When he supersedes
Joe Johnston, he is lost, and his army with him,
But he could lead forlorn hopes with the ghost of Ney.
His bigboned Texans follow him into the mist.
Who follows them?
                    These are the Virginia faces,
The Virginia speech. It is Jackson's foot-cavalry,
The Army of the Valley,
It is the Stonewall Brigade, it is the streams
Of the Shenandoah, marching.
                    Ewell goes by,
The little woodpecker, bald and quaint of speech,
With his wooden leg stuck stiffly out from his saddle,
He is muttering, "Sir, I'm a nervous Major-General,
And whenever an aide rides up from General Jackson
I fully expect an order to storm the North Pole."
He chuckles and passes, full of crotchets and courage,
Living on frumenty for imagined dyspepsia,
And ready to storm the North Pole at a Jackson phrase.
Then the staff—then little Sorrel—and the plain
Presbyterian figure in the flat cap,
Throwing his left hand out in the awkward gesture
That caught the bullet out of the air at Bull Run,
Awkward, rugged and dour, the belated Ironside
With the curious, brilliant streak of the cavalier
That made him quote Mercutio in staff instructions,
Love lancet windows, the color of passion-flowers,
Mexican sun and all fierce, taut-looking fine creatures;
Stonewall Jackson, wrapped in his beard and his silence,
Cromwell-eyed and ready with Cromwell's short
Bleak remedy for doubters and fools and enemies,
Hard on his followers, harder on his foes,
An iron sabre vowed to an iron Lord,
And yet the only man of those men who pass
With a strange, secretive grain of harsh poetry
Hidden so deep in the stony sides of his heart
That it shines by flashes only and then is gone.
It glitters in his last words.
                    He is deeply ambitious,

The skilled man, utterly sure of his own skill
And taking no nonsense about it from the unskilled,
But God is the giver of victory and defeat,
And Lee, on earth, vicegerent under the Lord.
Sometimes he differs about the mortal plans
But once the order is given, it is obeyed.
We know what he thought about God. One would like to know
What he thought of the two together, if he so mingled them.
He said two things about Lee it is well to recall.
When he first beheld the man that he served so well,
"I have never seen such a fine-looking human creature."
Then, afterwards, at the height of his own fame,
The skilled man talking of skill, and something more.
"General Lee is a phenomenon,
He is the only man I would follow blindfold."
Think of those two remarks and the man who made them
When you picture Lee as the rigid image in marble.
No man ever knew his own skill better than Jackson
Or was more ready to shatter an empty fame.
He passes now in his dusty uniform.
The Bible jostles a book of Napoleon's Maxims
And a magic lemon deep in his saddlebags.

And now at last,
Comes Traveller and his master. Look at them well.
The horse is an iron-grey, sixteen hands high,
Short back, deep chest, strong haunch, flat legs, small head,
Delicate ear, quick eye, black mane and tail,
Wise brain, obedient mouth.
                    Such horses are
The jewels of the horseman's hands and thighs,
They go by the word and hardly need the rein.
They bred such horses in Virginia then,
Horses that were remembered after death
And buried not so far from Christian ground
That if their sleeping riders should arise
They could not witch them from the earth again
And ride a printless course along the grass
With the old manage and light ease of hand.
The rider, now.
                    He too, is iron-grey,
Though the thick hair and thick, blunt-pointed beard

Have frost in them.
                    Broad-foreheaded, deep-eyed,
Straight-nosed, sweet-mouthed, firm-lipped, head cleanly set,
He and his horse are matches for the strong
Grace of proportion that inhabits both.
They carry nothing that is in excess
And nothing that is less than symmetry,
The strength of Jackson is a hammered strength,
Bearing the tool marks still. This strength was shaped
By as hard arts but does not show the toil
Except as justness, though the toil was there.
—And so we get the marble man again,
The head on the Greek coin, the idol-image,
The shape who stands at Washington's left hand,
Worshipped, uncomprehended and aloof,
A figure lost to flesh and blood and bones,
Frozen into a legend out of life,
A blank-verse statue—
                        How to humanize
That solitary gentleness and strength
Hidden behind the deadly oratory
Of twenty thousand Lee Memorial days,
How show, in spite of all the rhetoric,
All the sick honey of the speechifiers,
Proportion, not as something calm congealed
From lack of fire, but ruling such a fire
As only such proportion could contain?

The man was loved, the man was idolized,
The man had every just and noble gift.
He took great burdens and he bore them well,
Believed in God but did not preach too much,
Believed and followed duty first and last
With marvellous consistency and force,
Was a great victor, in defeat as great,
No more, no less, always himself in both,
Could make men die for him but saved his men
Whenever he could save them—was most kind
But was not disobeyed—was a good father,
A loving husband, a considerate friend:
Had little humor, but enough to play
Mild jokes that never wounded, but had charm,

Did not seek intimates, yet drew men to him,
Did not seek fame, did not protest against it,
Knew his own value without pomp or jealousy
And died as he preferred to live—sans phrase,
With commonsense, tenacity and courage,
A Greek proportion—and a riddle unread.
And everything that we have said is true
And nothing helps us yet to read the man,
Nor will he help us while he has the strength
To keep his heart his own.
                              For he will smile
And give you, with unflinching courtesy,
Prayers, trappings, letters, uniforms and orders,
Photographs, kindness, valor and advice,
And do it with such grace and gentleness
That you will know you have the whole of him
Pinned down, mapped out, easy to understand—
And so you have.
                    All things except the heart.
The heart he kept himself, that answers all.
For here was someone who lived all his life
In the most fierce and open light of the sun,
Wrote letters freely, did not guard his speech,
Listened and talked with every sort of man,
And kept his heart a secret to the end
From all the picklocks of biographers.

He was a man, and as a man he knew
Love, separation, sorrow, joy and death.
He was a master of the tricks of war,
He gave great strokes and warded strokes as great.
He was the prop and pillar of a State,
The incarnation of a national dream,
And when the State fell and the dream dissolved
He must have lived with bitterness itself—
But what his sorrow was and what his joy,
And how he felt in the expense of strength,
And how his heart contained its bitterness,
He will not tell us.
                      We can lie about him,
Dress up a dummy in his uniform
And put our words into the dummy's mouth,

Say "Here Lee must have thought," and "There, no doubt,
By what we know of him, we may suppose
He felt—this pang or that—" but he remains
Beyond our stagecraft, reticent as ice,
Reticent as the fire within the stone.

Yet—look at the face again—look at it well—
This man was not repose, this man was act.
This man who murmured "It is well that war
Should be so terrible, if it were not
We might become too fond of it—" and showed
Himself, for once, completely as he lived
In the laconic balance of that phrase;
This man could reason, but he was a fighter,
Skilful in every weapon of defence
But never defending when he could assault,
Taking enormous risks again and again,
Never retreating while he still could strike,
Dividing a weak force on dangerous ground
And joining it again to beat a strong,
Mocking at chance and all the odds of war
With acts that looked like hairbreadth recklessness
—We do not call them reckless, since they won.
We do not see him reckless for the calm
Proportion that controlled the recklessness—
But that attacking quality was there.
He was not mild with life or drugged with justice,
He gripped life like a wrestler with a bull,
Impetuously. It did not come to him
While he stood waiting in a famous cloud,
He went to it and took it by both horns
And threw it down.
                              Oh, he could bear the shifts
Of time and play the bitter loser's game,
The slow, unflinching chess of fortitude,
But while he had an opening for attack
He would attack with every ounce of strength.
His heart was not a stone but trumpet-shaped
And a long challenge blew an anger through it
That was more dread for being musical
First, last, and to the end.
                              Again he said

A curious thing to life.
"I'm always wanting something."
The brief phrase
Slides past us, hardly grasped in the smooth flow
Of the well-balanced, mildly-humorous prose
That goes along to talk of cats and duties,
Maxims of conduct, farming and poor bachelors,
But for a second there, the marble cracked
And a strange man we never saw before
Showed us the face he never showed the world
And wanted something—not the general
Who wanted shoes and food for ragged men,
Not the good father wanting for his children,
The patriot wanting victory—all the Lees
Whom all the world could see and recognize
And hang with gilded laurels—but the man
Who had, you'd say, all things that life can give
Except the last success—and had, for that,
Such glamor as can wear sheer triumph out,
Proportion's son and Duty's eldest sword
And the calm mask who—wanted something still,
Somewhere, somehow and always.
Picklock biographers,
What could he want that he had never had?

He only said it once—the marble closed—
There was a man enclosed within that image.
There was a force that tried Proportion's rule
And died without a legend or a cue
To bring it back. The shadow-Lees still live.
But the first-person and the singular Lee?

The ant finds kingdoms in a foot of ground
But earth's too small for something in our earth,
We'll make a new earth from the summer's cloud,
From the pure summer's cloud.
It was not that,
It was not God or love or mortal fame.
It was not anything he left undone.
—What does Proportion want that it can lack?
—What does the ultimate hunger of the flesh
Want from the sky more than a sky of air?

He wanted something. That must be enough.

Now he rides Traveller back into the mist.

———

Continual guns, be silent for a moment,
Be silent, now.
We know your thirst. We hear the roll of your wheels
Crushing down tangled June,
Virginia June,
With tires of iron, with heavy caissons creaking,
Crushing down maidenhair and wilderness-seal,
Scaring the rabbit and the possum-children,
Scaring the redbird and the mockingbird
As McClellan's army moves forward.
We know your bloody thirst so soon to be slaked
With the red burst-grape juices.
But now, we would have you silent, a little moment,
We would have you hold your peace and point at the moon
For when you speak, we can hear no sound but your sound,
And we would hear the voices of men and women
For a little while.

Jake Diefer, the barrel-chested Pennsylvanian,
Shippy, the little man with the sharp rat-eyes,
Luke Breckinridge, the gawky boy from the hills,
Clay Wingate, Melora Vilas, Sally Dupré,
The slaves in the cabins, ragged Spade in the woods,
We have lost these creatures under a falling hammer.
We must look for them now, again.

Jake Diefer is with the assault that comes from the ships,
He has marched, he has fought at Fair Oaks, but he looks the
      same:
A slow-thought-chewing Clydesdale horse of a man
Who doesn't think much of the way that they farm down here.
The sun may be good, if you like that sort of sun,
But the barns and the fields are different, they don't look right,
They don't look like Pennsylvania.
                              He spits and wonders.
Whenever he can, he reads a short, crumpled letter
And tries to puzzle out from the round, stiff writing

How things are back on the farm.
                                    The boy's a good boy
But the boy can't do it all, or the woman either.
He knows too much about weather and harvest-hands
—It's all right fighting the Rebels to save the Union
But they ought to get through with it quicker, now they've
    begun,
They don't take the way the crops are into account,
You can't go off and leave a farm like a store,
And you can't expect a boy to know everything,
Or a hired man. No, sir.
                              He walks along like an ox.
—He'd like to see the boy and the woman again,
Eat pancakes and sleep in a bed and look at the hay—
This business comes first but after it's finished up—
He can't say he's bothered exactly most of the time.
The weather bothers him more than anything.
He knows it's not the same sort of weather down here,
But every day when he wakes, he looks at the sky
And tries to figure out what it's like back home.

Shippy, the little man with the sharp rat-eyes,
Creeps into an old house in beleaguered Richmond
And meets a woman dressed in severe black silk
With a gentle voice, soft delicate useless hands,
A calm, smooth, faded, handsome mask of a face
And an incredible secret under her brooches.
You would picture her with ivory crochet-needles
Demurely tatting, demurely singing mild hymns
To an old melodeon before a blurred mirror.
She is to live in Richmond throughout the war,
A Union spy, never caught, never once suspected,
And when she dies, she dies with a shut prim mouth
Locked on her mystery.
                              Shippy is afraid.
She gives him instructions, he tries to remember them.
But his hands are sweating, his eyes creep around the floor.
He is afraid of the rustle of the black silk.
He wishes he were back in Pollet's Hotel
With Sophy, the chambermaid.
                                    The woman talks
And he listens, while the woman looks through and through him.

Melora Vilas, rising by crack of dawn,
Looked at herself in the bottom of her tin basin
And wished that she had a mirror.
                              She thought dully,
"He's been gone two months. I can't get used to it yet.
I've got to get used to it. Maybe I'll die instead.
No, I'd know if he'd died."

Sally Dupré was tired of scraping lint
But her hands kept on. The hours, sunbonneted women,
Passed and passed. "If he ever comes back to me!"
She finished her scraping and wondered how to make coffee
Out of willow-bark and life from a barren stick. . . .
Spade the fugitive stared at the bleak North Star. . . .
Luke Breckinridge, on picket out in the woods,
Remembered a chambermaid at Pollet's Hotel.
And wanted a fight. He hadn't been lucky, of late.
Jim, his cousin, was lucky, out in the West,
Riding a horse and capturing Yankee scouts.
But his winter here had been nothing but work and mud,
He'd nearly got courtmartialed a dozen times,
Though they knew how he could shoot.
                              The chambermaid's name
Was Sophy. She was little and scared and thin,
But he liked her looks and he liked the size of her eyes,
He'd like to feed her up and see how she looked,
If they ever got through with fighting the Yankees here.
The Yankees weren't all Kelceys. He knew that now,
But he always looked for Kelceys whenever he fought. . . .
Clay Wingate slept in his cloak and dreamed of a girl
With Sally's face and Lucy Weatherby's mouth
And waked again
To know today there would be continual guns.
Continual guns, silent so brief a moment,
Speak again, now,
For now your ignorance
Drowns out the little voices of human creatures.
Jackson slips from the Valley where he has played
A dazzling game against Banks and Shield and Frémont
And threatened the chess-game-king of Washington
Till strong pieces meant to join in McClellan's game
Are held to defend that king.

177

                                And now the two,
Jackson and Lee, strike hard for Seven Days
At the host come up from its ships, come up from the sea
To take the city set on a deck of land,
Till the deck is soaked and red with a bloody juice.
And the host goes back.
                            You can read in the histories
How the issue wavered, the fog of tiny events,
How here, at one dot, McClellan might have wrung
A victory, perhaps, with his larger force,
And there, on the other hand, played canny and well;
How Jackson, for once, moved slowly, how Porter held,
And the bitter, exhausted wrestling of Malvern Hill.
What we know is this.
                        The host from the ships went back,
Hurt but not broken, hammered but undestroyed,
To find a new base far up the crook of the James
And rest there, panting.
                         Lincoln and Halleck come.
The gaunt, plain face is deeper furrowed than ever,
The eyes are strained with looking at books of tactics
And trying to understand.
                          There is so much
For one man to understand, so many lies,
So much half-truth, so many counselling voices,
So much death to be sown and reaped and still no end.
The dead of the Seven Days. The four months dead
Boy who used to play with a doll named Jack,
Was a bright boy as boys are reckoned and now is dead.
The doll named Jack was sometimes a Union soldier,
Sometimes a spy.
                 The boy and his brother held
A funeral in the White House flower-beds
After suitably executing the doll named Jack
But then they thought of a different twist to the game.
The gaunt man signed a paper.
                               "The doll named Jack
Is pardoned. By order of the President.
A. Lincoln."
             So Jack was held in honor awhile
But next day the boy and his brother forgot the pardon
And the doll named Jack was shot and buried once more.

So much death to be sown and reaped.
                              So much death to be sown
By one no sower of deaths.
                    And still no end.

The council is held. The chiefs and captains debate.
McClellan clings to his plan of storming the deck
From the water ways. He is cool now. He argues well.
He has written Lincoln "From the brink of eternity"
—A strained, high-flown, remarkable speech of a letter
Of the sort so many have written and still will write—
Telling how well he has done in saving his army,
No thanks to the Government, or to anything else
But the pith of his fighting-men and his own craft.
Lincoln reads and pockets the speech and thanks him.
There had been craft and courage in that retreat
And much was due to McClellan.
                              The others speak.
Some corps commanders agree and some demur,
The Peninsula-stroke has failed and will fail again.
Elbow-rubbing Halleck, newly-made chief of staff,
Called "Old Brains," for reasons that history
Still tries to fathom, demurs. He urges withdrawal.
Washington must be defended first and last—
Withdraw the army and put it in front of Washington.
Lincoln listens to all as he tries to sift
The mustardseed from the twenty barrels of chaff
With patient hands.
                    There has been a growth in the man,
A tempering of will in these trotting months
Whose strong hoofs striking have scarred him again and again.
He still rules more by the rein than by whip or spur
But the reins are fast in his hands and the horses know it.
He no longer says "I think," but "I have decided."
And takes the strength and the burden of such decision
For good or bad on himself.
                          He will bear all things
But lack of faith in the Union and that not once.
Now at last he decides to recall McClellan's army
For right or wrong.
                  We see the completed thing,
Long afterward, knowing all that was still to come,

And say "He was wrong."
                    He saw the incomplete,
The difficult chance that might turn a dozen ways
And so decided.
                Be it so. He was wrong.

So the deck is cleared and the host goes back to its ships.
The bells in the Richmond churches, clanging for Sunday,
Clang as if silver were mixed in their sweet bell-metal,
The dark cloud lifts, the girls wear flowers again.
Virginia June,
Crushed under cannon, under the cannon ruts,
The trampled grass lifts up its little green guidons,
The honeysuckle and the eglantine
Blow on their tiny trumpets,
Blow out "Dixie,"
Blow out "Lorena," blow the "Bonnie Blue Flag"
—There are many dead, there are many too many dead,
The hospitals are crowded with broken dolls—
But cotton has won again, cotton is haughty,
Cotton is mounting again to a sleepy throne,
Wheat and iron recoil from the fields of cotton,
The sweet grass grows over them, the cotton blows over them,
One more battle and free, free, free forever.
Cotton moves North in a wave, in a white-crested
Wave of puff-blossoms—in a long grey coil
Of marching men with tongues as dry as cotton.
Cotton and honeysuckle and eglantine
Move North in a drenching wave of blossom and guns
To wash out wheat and iron forever and ever.
There will be other waves that set toward the North,
There will be a high tide,
But this is the high hour.
Jackson has still three hammerstrokes to strike,
Lee is still master of the attacking sword,
Stuart still carries his black feather high.
Put silver in your bell-metal, Richmond bells,
The wave of the cotton goes North to your sweet ringing,
The first great raiding wave of the Southern dream.

———

Jack Ellyat, in prison deep in the South,
Gaunt, bearded, dirty old man with the captive eyes,

Lay on his back and stared at the flies on the wall
And tried to remember, through an indifferent mist,
A green place lost in the woods and a herd of black swine.
They came and went and the mist moved round them again.
The mist was not death. He was used to death by now,
But the mist still puzzled him, sometimes.
It was curious—being so weak and yet used to death.
When you were strong, you thought of death as a strong
Rider on a black horse, perhaps, or at least
As some strong creature, dreadful because so strong.
But when you were weak and lived in a place like this,
Things changed. There was nothing strong about death any more.
He was only the gnawed rat-bone on the dirty floor,
That you stumbled across and hardly bothered to curse.
That was all.
        The two Michigan men had died last night.
The Ohio brothers were going to die this week,
You got pretty soon so you knew when people would die,
It passed the time as well as carving bone-rings,
Playing checkers with straws or learning Italian nouns
From the lanky schoolteacher-sergeant from Vermont.
Somewhere, sometime, in a tent, by a red loud noise,
Under a dirty coat and a slab of tobacco,
He had lost a piece of himself, a piece of life.
He couldn't die till he got that piece of him back
And felt its ragged edges fit in his heart.
Or so he thought. Sometimes, when he slept, he felt
As if he were getting it back—but most of the time
It was only the mist and counting the flies that bothered him.
He heard a footstep near him and turned his head.
"Hello, Charley," he said, "Where you been?"
                        Bailey's face looked strange,
The red, hot face of a hurt and angry boy,
"Out hearing the Rebs," he said. He spat on the floor
And broke into long, blue curses. When he was through,
"Did you hear them?" he asked. Jack Ellyat tried to remember
A gnat-noise buzzing the mist. "I guess so," he said.
"What was it? Two-bottle Ed on another tear?"
"Hell," said Bailey. "They cheered. They've licked us again.
The news just come. It happened back at Bull Run."
"You're crazy," said Ellyat. "That was the start of the war.
"I was in that one."

181

"Oh, don't be a fool," said Bailey,
"They licked us again, I tell you, the same old place.
Pope's army's ruined."
                         "Who's he?" said Ellyat wearily.
"Aw, we had him out West—he's God Almighty's pet horse,
He came East and told all the papers how good he was,
'Headquarters in the saddle'!" Bailey snickered.
"Well, they snaffled his saddle and blame near snaffled him,
Jackson and Lee—anyhow they licked us again."

"What about Little Mac?"
                         "Well, Gawd knows what's happened to *him*,"
Said Bailey, flatly, "Maybe he's captured, too,
Maybe they captured Old Abe and everyone else.
I don't know—you can't tell from those lyin' Rebs."

There was a silence. Ellyat lay on his back
And watched the flies on the wall for quite a long time.
"I wish I had a real newspaper," said Bailey,
"Not one of your Richmond wipers. By God, you know, Jack,
When we get back home, I'll read a newspaper, sometimes.
I never was much at readin' the newspaper
But I'd like to read one now, say once in a while."
Ellyat laughed.
               "You know, Charley," he said at last.
"We've got to get out of this place."
                         Bailey joined in the laugh.
Then he stopped and stared at the other with anxious eyes.
"You don't look crazy," he said, "Stop countin' those flies."
Ellyat raised himself on one arm.
                         "No, honest, Charley,
I mean it, damn it. We've got to get out of here.
I know we can't but we've got to. . . ."
                         He swallowed dryly.
"Look here—" he said, "It just came over me then.
I've got a girl and she doesn't know where I am.
I left her back in a tent—no, that wasn't a girl—
And you say we got licked again. But that's just it, Charley.
We get licked too much. We've got to get out of here."

He sank back to the floor and shut his ghost-ridden eyes.
Bailey regarded him for a long, numb moment.

"You couldn't walk a mile and a half," he muttered,
"And, by God, I couldn't carry you twenty feet,
And, by God, if we could, there ain't no way to get out,
But all the same—"
                              "If there was any use tryin',"
He said, half-pleadingly, half-defiantly,
"I tell you, Jack, if there was any use tryin'—"
He stopped. Ellyat's eyes were shut. He rose with great care.
"I'll get you some water," he muttered. "No, let you sleep."
He sat down again and stared at the sleeping face.
"He looks bad," he thought. "I guess I look bad myself.
I guess the kid's goin' to die if we don't get out.
I guess we're both goin' to die. I don't see why not."
He looked up at the flies on the ceiling and shook his fist.
"Listen, you dirty Rebs," he said, under his breath,
"Flap your goddam wings—we're goin' to get out of here!"

———————

John Brown lies dead in his grave and does not stir,
It is nearly three years since he died and he does not stir,
There is no sound in his bones but the sound of armies
And that is an old sound.

He walks, you will say, he walks in front of the armies,
A straggler met him, going along to Manassas,
With his gun on his shoulder, his phantom-sons at heel,
His eyes like misty coals.

A dead man saw him striding at Seven Pines,
The bullets whistling through him like a torn flag,
A madman saw him whetting a sword on a Bible,
A cloud above Malvern Hill.

But these are all lies. He slumbers. He does not stir.
The spring rains and the winter snows on his slumber
And the bones of his flesh breed armies and yet more armies
But he himself does not stir.

It will take more than cannon to shake his fortress,
His song is alive and throbs in the tramp of the columns,
His song is smoke blown out of the mouth of a cannon,
But his song and he are two.

The South goes ever forward, the slave is not free,
The great stone gate of the Union crumbles and totters,
The cotton-blossoms are pushing the blocks apart,
The roots of cotton grow in the crevices,
(John Brown's body lies a-mouldering in the grave.)
Soon the fight will be over, the slaves will be slaves forever.
(John Brown's body lies a-mouldering in the grave.)
You did not fight for the Union or wish it well,
You fought for the single dream of a man unchained
And God's great chariot rolling. You fought like the thrown
Stone, but the fighters have forgotten your dream.
(John Brown's body lies a-mouldering in the grave.)
You fought for a people you did not comprehend,
For a symbol chained by a symbol in your own mind,
But, unless you arise, that people will not be free.
Are there no seeds of thunder left in your bones
Except to breed useless armies?
(John Brown's body lies a-mouldering in the grave.)
Arise, John Brown,
Call up your sons from the ground,
In smoky wreaths, call up your sons to heel,
Call up the clumsy country boys you armed
With crazy pikes and a fantastic mind.
Call up the American names,
Kagi, the self-taught scholar, quiet and cool,
Stevens, the cashiered soldier, bawling his song,
Dangerfield Newby, the freed Scotch-mulatto,
Watson and Oliver Brown and all the hard-dying.
Call up the slug-riddled dead of Harper's Ferry
And cast them down the wind on a raid again.
This is the dark hour,
This is the ebb-tide,
This is the sunset, this is the defeat.
The cotton-blossoms are growing up to the sky,
The great stone gate of the Union sinks beneath them,
And under the giant blossoms lies Egypt's land,
The dark river,
The ground of bondage,
The chained men.
If the great gate falls, the cotton grows over your dream.
Find your heart, John Brown,
(A-mouldering in the grave.)

Call your sons and get your pikes,
(A-mouldering in the grave.)
Your song goes on, but the slave is still a slave,
And all Egypt's land rides Northward while you moulder in the
    grave!
Rise up, John Brown,
(A-mouldering in the grave.)
Go down, John Brown,
(Against all Egypt's land)
Go down, John Brown,
Go down, John Brown,
Go down, John Brown, and set that people free!

BOOK FIVE

It was still hot in Washington, that September,
Hot in the city, hot in the White House rooms,
Desiccate heat, dry as a palm-leaf fan,
That makes hot men tuck cotton handkerchiefs
Between their collars and their sweaty necks,
And Northern girls look limp at half-past-four,
Waiting the first cool breath that will not come
For hours yet.
                    The sentinel on post
Clicks back and forth, stuffed in his sweltering coat,
And dreams about brown bottles of cold beer
Deep in a cellar.
                    In the crowded Bureaus
The pens move slow, the damp clerks watch the clock.
Women in houses take their corsets off
And stifle in loose gowns.
                              They could lie down
But when they touch the bed, the bed feels hot,
And there are things to do.
                              The men will want
Hot food when they come back from work.
                                           They sigh
And turn, with dragging feet, to the hot kitchens.

Sometimes they pause, and push a window up
To feel the blunt, dry buffet of the heat

185

Strike in the face and hear the locust-cry
Of shrilling newsboy-voices down the street,
"News from the army—extra—ter-ble battle—
Terr-r-ble vic'try—ter-r-ble defeat—
Lee's army trapped invading Maryland—
McClellan—Sharpsburg—fightin'—news from the front—"
The women at the windows sigh and wonder
"I ought to buy a paper—No, I'll wait
Till Tom gets home—I wonder if it's true—
Terrible victory—terrible defeat—
They're always saying that—when Tom gets home
He'll have some news—I wonder if the army—
No, it's too hot to buy a paper now—"

A hot, spare day of waiting languidly
For contradictory bits of dubious news.

It was a little cooler, three miles out,
Where the tall trees shaded the Soldiers' Home.
The lank man, Abraham Lincoln, found it so,
Glad for it, doubtless, though his cavernous eyes
Had stared all day into a distant fog
Trying to pierce it.
                    "General McClellan
Is now in touch with Lee in front of Sharpsburg
And will attack as soon as the fog clears."

It's cleared by now. They must be fighting now.

We can't expect much from the first reports.
Stanton and Halleck think they're pretty good
But you can't tell. Nobody here can tell.
We're all too far away.
                        You get sometimes
Feeling as if you heard the guns yourself
Here in the room and felt them shake the house
When you keep waiting for the news all day.
I wish we'd get some news.
                            Bull Run was first.
We got the news of Bull Run soon enough.
First that we'd won, hands down, which was a lie,
And then the truth.
                    It may be that to-day.

186

I told McClellan not to let them go,
Destroy them if he could—but you can't tell.
He's a good man in lots of different ways,
But he can't seem to finish what he starts
And then, he's jealous, like the rest of them,
Lets Pope get beaten, wanted him to fail,
Because he don't like Pope.
                                    I put him back
Into command. What else was there to do?
Nobody else could lick those troops in shape.
But, if he wins, and lets Lee get away,
I'm done with him.
                            Bull Run—the Seven Days—
Bull Run again—and eighteen months of war—
And still no end to it.
                                What is God's will?

They come to me and talk about God's will
In righteous deputations and platoons,
Day after day, laymen and ministers.
They write me Prayers From Twenty Million Souls
Defining me God's will and Horace Greeley's.
God's will is General This and Senator That,
God's will is those poor colored fellows' will,
It is the will of the Chicago churches,
It is this man's and his worst enemy's.
But all of them are sure they know God's will.
I am the only man who does not know it.

And, yet, if it is probable that God
Should, and so very clearly, state His will
To others, on a point of my own duty,
It might be thought He would reveal it me
Directly, more especially as I
So earnestly desire to know His will.

The will of God prevails. No doubt, no doubt—
Yet, in great contests, each side claims to act
In strict accordance with the will of God.
Both may, one must be wrong.
                                        God could have saved
This Union or destroyed it without war

187

If He so wished. And yet this war began,
And, once begun, goes on, though He could give
Victory, at any time, to either side.
It is unfathomable. Yet I know
This, and this only. While I live and breathe,
I mean to save the Union if I can,
And by whatever means my hands can find
Under the Constitution.
                        If God reads
The hearts of men as clearly as He must
To be Himself, then He can read in mine
And has, for twenty years, the old, scarred wish
That the last slave should be forever free
Here, in this country.
                        I do not go back
From that scarred wish and have not.
                                    But I put
The Union, first and last, before the slave.
If freeing slaves will bring the Union back
Then I will free them; if by freeing some
And leaving some enslaved I help my cause,
I will do that—but should such freedom mean
The wreckage of the Union that I serve
I would not free a slave.
                        O Will of God,
I am a patient man, and I can wait
Like an old gunflint buried in the ground
While the slow years pile up like moldering leaves
Above me, underneath the rake of Time,
And turn, in time, to the dark, fruitful mold
That smells of Sangamon apples, till at last
There's no sleep left there, and the steel event
Descends to strike the live coal out of me
And light the powder that was always there.

That is my only virtue as I see it,
Ability to wait and hold my own
And keep my own resolves once they are made
In spite of what the smarter people say.
I can't be smart the way that they are smart.
I've known that since I was an ugly child.
It teaches you—to be an ugly child.

188

It teaches you—to lose a thing you love.
It sticks your roots down into Sangamon ground
And makes you grow when you don't want to grow
And makes you tough enough to wait life out,
Wait like the fields, under the rain and snow.

I have not thought for years of that lost grave
That was my first hard lesson in the queer
Thing between men and women we call love.
But when I think of it, and when I hear
The rain and snow fall on it, as they must,
It fills me with unutterable grief.

We've come a good long way, my hat and I,
Since then, a pretty lengthy piece of road,
Uphill and down but mostly with a pack.
Years of law-business, years of cracking jokes,
And watching Billy Herndon do his best
To make me out, which seemed to be a job;
Years trying how to learn to handle men,
Which can be done, if you've got heart enough,
And how to deal with women or a woman
And that's about the hardest task I know.
For, when you get a man, you've got the man
Like a good big axehandle in your fist,
But you can't catch a woman like an axe.
She'll run like mercury between your hands
And leave you wondering which road she went,
The minute when you thought you knew her ways.

I understand the uses of the earth,
And I have burned my hands at certain fires
Often enough to know a use for fire,
But when the genius of the water moves,
And that's the woman's genius, I'm at sea
In every sense and meaning of the word,
With nothing but old patience for my chart,
And patience doesn't always please a woman.

Bright streams of water, watering the world,
Deep seas of water that all men must sail
Or rest half-men and fill the narrow graves,

When will I understand or comprehend
Your salt, sweet taste, so different from the taste
Of Sangamon russets, weighing down the bough?
You can live with the water twenty years
And never understand it like the earth
But that's the lesson I can't seem to learn.

"Abraham Lincoln, his hand and pen,
He will be good, but God knows when."
He will be wise, but God knows when.

It doesn't matter. If I had some news—
News from that fog—
           I'll get the hypo, sure,
Unless I watch myself, waiting for news.
I can't afford to get the hypo now,
I've got too much to do.
              Political years,
Housekeeping years of marrying and begetting
And losing, too, the children and the town,
The wife, the house, the life, the joy and grief,
The profound wonder still behind it all.

I had a friend who married and was happy.
But something haunted him that haunted me
Before he did, till he could hardly tell
What his own mind was, for the brooding veil
And immaterial horror of the soul
Which colors the whole world for men like that.

I do not know from whence that horror comes
Or why it hangs between us and the sun
For some few men, at certain times and days,
But I have known it closer than my flesh,
Got up with it, lain down and walked with it,
Scotched it awhile, but never killed it quite,
And yet lived on.
           I wrote him good advice,
The way you do, and told him this, for part,
"Again you fear that that Elysium
Of which you've dreamed so much is not to be.
Well, I dare swear it will not be the fault

Of that same black-eyed Fanny, now your wife.
And I have now no doubt that you and I,
To our particular misfortune, dream
Dreams of Elysium far exceeding all
That any earthly thing can realize."

I wrote that more than twenty years ago,
At thirty-three, and now I'm fifty-three,
And the slow days have brought me up at last
Through water, earth and fire, to where I stand,
To where I stand—and no Elysiums still.

No, no Elysiums—for that personal dream
I dreamt of for myself and in my youth
Has been abolished by the falling sledge
Of chance and an ambition so fulfilled
That the fulfillment killed its personal part.

My old ambition was an iron ring
Loose-hooped around the live trunk of a tree.
If the tree grows till bark and iron touch
And then stops growing, ring and tree are matched
And the fulfillment fits.
                    But, if by some
Unlikely chance, the growing still keeps on,
The tree must burst the binding-ring or die.

I have not once controlled the circumstances.
They have controlled me. But with that control
They made me grow or die. And I have grown.
The iron ring is burst.
                    Three elements,
Earth, water and fire. I have passed through them all,
Still to find no Elysium for my hands,
Still to find no Elysium but growth,
And the slow will to grow to match my task.

Three elements. I have not sought the fourth
Deeply, till now—the element of air,
The everlasting element of God,
Who must be there in spite of all we see,
Who must be there in spite of all we bear,
Who must exist where all Elysiums

Are less than shadows of a hunter's fire
Lighted at night to scare a wolf away.

I know that wolf—his scars are in my hide
And no Elysiums can rub them out.
Therefore at last, I lift my hands to You
Who Were and Are and Must Be, if our world
Is anything but a lost ironclad
Shipped with a crew of fools and mutineers
To drift between the cold forts of the stars.

I've never found a church that I could join
Although I've prayed in churches in my time
And listened to all sorts of ministers
Well, they were good men, most of them, and yet—
The thing behind the words—it's hard to find.
I used to think it wasn't there at all
Couldn't be there. I cannot say that, now.
And now I pray to You and You alone.
Teach me to know Your will. Teach me to read
Your difficult purpose here, which must be plain
If I had eyes to see it. Make me just.

There was a man I knew near Pigeon Creek
Who kept a kennel full of hunting dogs,
Young dogs and old, smart hounds and silly hounds.
He'd sell the young ones every now and then,
Smart as they were and slick as they could run.
But the one dog he'd never sell or lend
Was an old half-deaf foolish-looking hound
You wouldn't think had sense to scratch a flea
Unless the flea were old and sickly too.
Most days he used to lie beside the stove
Or sleeping in a piece of sun outside.
Folks used to plague the man about that dog
And he'd agree to everything they said,
"No—he ain't much on looks—or much on speed—
A young dog can outrun him any time,
Outlook him and outeat him and outleap him,
But, Mister, that dog's hell on a cold scent
And, once he gets his teeth in what he's after,
He don't let go until he knows he's dead."

192

I am that old, deaf hunting-dog, O Lord,
And the world's kennel holds ten thousand hounds
Smarter and faster and with finer coats
To hunt your hidden purpose up the wind
And bell upon the trace you leave behind.
But, when even they fail and lose the scent,
I will keep on because I must keep on
Until You utterly reveal Yourself
And sink my teeth in justice soon or late.
There is no more to ask of earth or fire
And water only runs between my hands,
But in the air, I'll look, in the blue air,
The old dog, muzzle down to the cold scent,
Day after day, until the tired years
Crackle beneath his feet like broken sticks
And the last barren bush consumes with peace.

I should have tried the course with younger legs,
This hunting-ground is stiff enough to pull
The metal heart out of a dog of steel;
I should have started back at Pigeon Creek
From scratch, not forty years behind the mark.
But you can't change yourself, and, if you could,
You might fetch the wrong jack-knife in the swap.
It's up to you to whittle what you can
With what you've got—and what I am, I am
For what it's worth, hypo and legs and all.
I can't complain. I'm ready to admit
You could have made a better-looking dog
From the same raw material, no doubt,
But, since You didn't, this'll have to do.

Therefore I utterly lift up my hands
To You, and here and now beseech Your aid.
I have held back when others tugged me on,
I have gone on when others pulled me back
Striving to read Your will, striving to find
The justice and expedience of this case,
Hunting an arrow down the chilly airs
Until my eyes are blind with the great wind
And my heart sick with running after peace.
And now, I stand and tremble on the last

Edge of the last blue cliff, a hound beat out,
Tail down and belly flattened to the ground,
My lungs are breathless and my legs are whipped,
Everything in me's whipped except my will.
I can't go on. And yet, I must go on.

I will say this. Two months ago I read
My proclamation setting these men free
To Seward and the rest. I told them then
I was not calling on them for advice
But to hear something that I meant to do.
We talked about it. Most of them approved
The thing, if not the time. Then Seward said
Something I hadn't thought of, "I approve
The proclamation—but, if issued now
With our defeats in everybody's mouth
It may be viewed as a last shriek for help
From an exhausted, beaten government.
Put it aside until a victory comes,
Then issue it with victory."
                                    He was right.
I put the thing aside—and ever since
There has been nothing for us but defeat,
Up to this battle now—and still no news.

If I had eyes to look to Maryland!
If I could move that battle with my hands!
No, it don't work. I'm not a general.
All I can do is trust the men who are.

I'm not a general, but I promise this,
Here at the end of every ounce of strength
That I can muster, here in the dark pit
Of ignorance that is not quite despair
And doubt that does but must not break the mind!
The pit I have inhabited so long
At various times and seasons, that my soul
Has taken color in its very grains
From the blind darkness, from the lonely cave
That never hears a footstep but my own
Nor ever will, while I'm a man alive
To keep my prison locked from visitors.

What if I heard another footstep there,
What if, some day—there is no one but God,
No one but God who could descend that stair
And ring his heavy footfalls on the stone.
And if He came, what would we say to Him?

That prison is ourselves that we have built,
And, being so, its loneliness is just,
And, being so, its loneliness endures.
But, if another came,
                        What would we say?
What can the blind say, given back their eyes?

No, it must be as it has always been.
We are all prisoners in that degree
And will remain so, but I think I know
This—God is not a jailor . . . .
                        And I make
A promise now to You and to myself.
If this last battle is a victory
And they can drive the Rebel army back
From Maryland, back over the Potomac,
My proclamation shall go out at last
To set those other prisoners and slaves
From this next year, then and forever free.

So much for my will. Show me what is Yours!

That must be news, those footsteps in the hall,
Good news, or else they wouldn't come so fast.

What is it, now? Yes, yes, I'm glad of that.
I'm very glad. There's no mistake this time?
We have the best of them? They're in retreat?
This is a great day, Stanton. . . . .
. . . . .If McClellan
Can only follow up the victory now!

Lord, I will keep my promise and go on,
Your will, in much, still being dark to me,
But, in this one thing, as I see it, plain.

And yet—if Lee slips from our hands again
As he well may from all those last reports
And the war still goes on—and still no end—
Even after this Antietam—not for years—

I cannot read it but I will go on,
Old dog, old dog, but settled to the scent
And with fresh breath now from this breathing space,
Almighty God.
    At best we never seem
To know You wholly, but there's something left,
A strange, last courage.
      We can fail and fail,
But, deep against the failure, something wars,
Something goes forward, something lights a match,
Something gets up from Sangamon County ground
Armed with a bitten and a blunted axe
And after twenty thousand wasted strokes
Brings the tall hemlock crashing to the ground.

Spade saw the yellow river rolling ahead
His sore, cracked lips curled back in a death's head grin
And his empty belly ceased to stick to his sides.
He sat on the bank a minute to rest his legs
And catch his breath. He had lived for the last three days
On a yam, two ears of horse-corn and the lame rabbit
That couldn't run away when he threw the stick.

He was still a big man but the ribs stuck into his skin
And the hard, dry muscles were wasted to leather thongs.
"Boy, I wisht we had a good meal," he thought with a dull
Fatigue. "Dat's Freedom's lan' ovah dere fer sho',
But how we gwine to swim it without a good meal?
I wisht we had even a spoonful of good hot pot-licker
Or a smidgin' of barbecued shote.
      Dat river's cold.
Colder'n Jordan. I wisht we had a good meal."

He went down to the river and tested it with his hand.
The cold jumped up his arm and into his heart,
Sharp as the toothache. His mouth wried up in a queer

196

Grimace. He felt like crying. "I'se tired," he said.
"Flow easy, river," he said.
                              Then he tumbled in.
The hard shock of the plunge took his breath away.
So stinging at first that his arms and legs moved fast,
But then the cold crept into his creaking bones
And he rolled wild eyes.
                         "Oh, God," he thought as he struggled,
"I'se weak as a cat. I ust to be a strong man."

The yellow flood sucked round him, pulling him down,
The yellow foam had a taste like death in his mouth,
"We ought to of had a good meal," he thought with a weak
Wonder, as he fought weakly. "A good hot meal.
Dis current, she's too strong for a hungry mouth.
We'se done our best, but she fights like a angel would
Like wrestlin' with a death-angel."
                                    He choked and sank
To come up gasping and staring with bloodshot eyes.
His brain had a last, clear flash. "You're drowned," said the brain.
Then it stopped working.
                         But the black, thrashing hands
Caught hold of something solid and hard and rough
And hung to it with a last exhausted grip.
—He had been fighting an angel for seven nights
And now he hung by his hands to the angel's neck,
Lost in an iron darkness of beating wings.
If he once let go, the angel would push him off
And touch him across the loins with a stony hand
In the last death-trick of the wrestle.
                                        He moaned a little.
The blackness began to lighten. He saw the river
Rolling and rolling. He was clutched to a log
Like a treetoad set afloat on a chip of wood,
And the log and he were rushing downstream together,
But the current pulled them both toward the freedom side.

He hunched up a little higher. An eddy took
The log and him and spun them both like a top
While he prayed and sickened.
                              Then they were out of the eddy
And drifting along more slowly, straight for the shore.

He hauled himself up the bank with enormous care,
Vomited and lay down.
                        When he could arise
He looked at his hands. They were still hooked into a curve.
It took quite a time to straighten them back again.

He said a prayer as he tried to dry his clothes,
Then he looked for a stone and threw it into the river.
"You'se a mean and hungry river," he said. "You is.
Heah's a present for you. I hope it busts up your teef.
Heah's a present fum Mistah Spade."
                        He felt better then,
But his belly started to ache. "Act patient," he said,
Rubbing it gently, "We'se loose in Freedom's land,
Crossed old Jordan—bound to get vittles now."

He started out for the town. The town wasn't far
But he had to go slow. Sometimes he fell on the way.
The last time he fell was in front of a little yard
With a white, well-painted fence. A woman came out.
"Get along," she said. "You can't get sick around here.
I'm tired of you nigger tramps. You're all of you thieves."
Spade rose and said something vague about swimming rivers
And vittles. She stamped her foot. "Get along!" she said,
"Get along or I'll call the dog and——"
                        Spade got along.

The next house, the dog was barking out in the yard,
He went by as fast as he could, but when he looked back
A man had come out with a hostile stick in his hand.
Spade shook his head. "Freedom's land," he thought to himself,
"They's some mighty quick-actin' people in Freedom's land,
Some mighty rash-tempered dogs."
                        He swayed as he walked.
Here was another house. He looked for the dog
With fright in his eyes. Then a swimming qualm came over him,
A deathly faintness. His hands went out to the fence.
He gripped two palings, hung, and stared at his shoes.
Somebody was talking to him. He tried to move on
But his legs wouldn't walk. The voice was a woman's voice.

She'd be calling the dog in a minute. He shivered hard.
"Excuse me ma'am, but I'se feelin' poorly," he said.

"I just crossed over—I'll go as soon as I kin."
A man's voice now. They were taking him under the arms.
He didn't care what they did. He let himself walk.

Then he was sitting up in a bentwood chair
In a tidy kitchen that smelt of frying and ham;
The thick, good smell made him strangely sick at first
But it soon passed off. They fed him little by little
Till at last he could tell his tale and ask about them.

They were churchgoing people and kind to runaway slaves.
She wore a blue dress. They had two sons in the war.
That was all that he knew and all that he ever knew.
But they let him sleep in the garret and gave him some shoes
And fifty cents when he left.
                              He wanted to stay
But times were bad and they couldn't afford to keep him.
The town was tired of runaway negroes now.

All the same, when he left, he walked with a different step.
He went down town. He was free. He was Mister Spade.
The President had written a letter about it
And the mule and the coal-black gal might come any day.

He hummed a tuneless whistle between his teeth
And fished a piece of paper out of his pants,
They'd written him down a boss's name and address
But he'd have to get somebody to read it again.
He approached a group of three white men on a corner
Holding the paper.
                   " 'Scuse me, boss, can you tell me——"
The white men looked at him with hard, vacant eyes.
At last one of them took the paper. "Oh, Hell," he said,
Spitting, and gave Spade a stare. Then he seemed to think
Of something funny. He nudged the other two men.
"Listen, nigger," he said. "You want Mr. Braid.
You'll find him two blocks down at the Marshal's office,
Tell him Mr. Clarke sent you there—Mr. William Clarke–
He'll fix you up all right."
                            The other men grinned,
Adding directions. Spade thanked them and went away.
He heard them laugh as he went.

                                    Another man took him
To a red-faced person who sat in a tilted chair,
Reading a paper, his feet cocked up on his desk.
He looked at Spade and his feet came down with a slam.
"Take that God damn smile off," he said. "Who let you come in?
You contraband niggers think that you own this town
And that all you've got to do is cross over here
For people to feed you free the rest of your lives.
Well it don't go down with me—just understand that."

Spade brought out his paper, dumbly. The man looked at it.
"Hell, this ain't for me," he said.
                              Spade started to go.

"Come back here, nigger," ordered the red-faced man.
"Hey, Mike!" he yelled, "Here's another of Lincoln's pets.
Send him out with the rest of the gang."
                                    "But, boss——" said Spade.
"Don't get lippy with me," said the man, "Mike, take him along."
The pimply boy named Mike jerked a sallow thumb.
"Come on, black beauty," he said. "We got you a job."
Spade followed him, dazed.
                              When they were out in the street
The boy turned to him. "Now, nigger, watch out," he said,
Patting a heavy pistol swung at his belt,
With puppy-fierceness, "You don't get away from me.
I'm a special deputy, see?"
                              "All right, boss," said Spade.
"I ain't aimin' to get away from nobody now,
I just aims to work till I gets myself a good mule."
The boy laughed briefly. The conversation dropped.
They walked out of the town till they came to a torn-up road
Where a gang of negroes was working.
                                    "Say, boss—" said Spade.
The boy cut him off. "Hey, Jerry," he called to the foreman,
"Here's another one."
                        The foreman looked up and spat.
"Judas!" he said, "Can't they keep the bastards at home?
I'd put a gun on that river if I was Braid.
Well, come along, nig, get a move on and find a shovel.
Don't stand lookin' at me all day."
                                    The boy went away.

200

Spade found a shovel and started work on the road.
The foreman watched him awhile with sarcastic eyes,
Spade saw that he, too, wore a pistol.
                                            "Christ," said the foreman,
Disgustedly, "Try and put some guts in it there.
You're big enough. That shovel'll cost five dollars.
Remember that—it comes out of your first week's pay.
You're a free nigger now."
                                            He chuckled. Spade didn't answer
And, after a while, the foreman moved away.

Spade turned to the gingerskinned negro who worked beside him.
"You fum de Souf?" he mouthed at him.
                                            Ginger nodded.
"I been here a month now. They fotched me here the first day.
Got any money?"
                                            "Nuthin' but fifty cents."
"You better give it to him," said Ginger, stealing
A glance at the foreman. "He'll treat you bad if you don't.
He's a cranky man."
                                            Spade's heart sank into his boots.
"Don't we uns get paid? We ain't none of us slaves no more,
The President said so. Why we wuhkin' like dis?"
Ginger snickered. "Sho' we uns get paid," he said,
"But we got to buy our stuff at de company sto'
And he sells his old shovels a dozen times what dey's wuth.
I only been here a month but I owes twelve dollars.
Dey ain't no way to pay it except by wuhk,
And de more you wuhk de more you owe at the sto.'
I kain't figure it out exactly but it's dat way."
Spade worked for a while, revolving these things in his mind.
"I reckoned I sho' was gwine to be sassy and free
When I swum dat river," he said.
                                            Ginger grinned like a monkey,
"Swing your shubbel, boy, and forget what you ain't.
You mought be out on de chain-gang, bustin' up rocks,
Or agin, you mought be enlisted."
                                            "Huh?" said Spade.

"Sho', dey's gwine to enlist us all when we finish dis road.
All excep' me. I got bad sight in my eyes
And dey knows about it."

                                        "Dey kain't enlist me," said Spade.
"I ain't honin' to go an' fight in no white-folks war,
I ain't bust loose into Freedom's land fer dat,
All I want is a chance to git me a gal and a mule.
If I'se free, how kin dey enlist me, lessen I want?"

"You watch 'em," said Ginger. They worked on for a time.
The foreman stood on the bank and watched them work,
Now and then he drank from a bottle.
                                        Spade felt hungry.

          Autumn is filling his harvest-bins
              With red and yellow grain,
          Fire begins and frost begins
              And the floors are cold again.

          Summer went when the crop was sold,
              Summer is piled away,
          Dry as a faded marigold
              In the dry, long-gathered hay.

          It is time to walk to the cider-mill
              Through air like apple wine
          And watch the moon rise over the hill,
              Stinging and hard and fine.

          It is time to cover your seed-pods deep
              And let them wait and be warm,
          It is time to sleep the heavy sleep
              That does not wake for the storm.

          Winter walks from the green, streaked West
              With a bag of Northern Spies,
          The skins are red as a robin's breast,
              The honey chill as the skies.

Melora Vilas walked in the woods that autumn
And heard the dry leaves crackle under her feet,
Feeling, below the leaves, the blunt heavy earth.

"It's getting-in time," she thought. "It's getting-in time,
Time to put things in barns and sit by the stove,
Time to watch the long snow and remember your lover.

He isn't dead. I know that he isn't dead.
Maybe they've changed his body into a tree,
Maybe they've changed his body into a cloud
Or something that sleeps through the Winter.
                                        But I'll remember.
I'll sleep through the Winter, too. We all sleep then
And when the Spring freshet drums in the narrow brooks
And fills them with a fresh water, they'll let him come
Out of the cloud and the tree and the Winter-sleep.

The Winter falls and we lie like beleaguered stones
In the black, cramped ground.
                            And then you wake in the morning
And the air's got soft and you plant the narrow-edged seeds,
They grow all Summer and now we've put them in barns
To sleep again for a while.
I am the seed and the husk. I have sown and reaped.
My heart is a barn full of grain that my work has harvested.
My body holds the ripe grain. I can wait my time."

She walked on farther and came to the lip of the spring,
The brown leaves drifted the water. She watched them drift.

"I am satisfied," she thought, "I am satisfied.
I can wait my time in spite of Mom being sad
And Pop looking fierce and sad when he sees me walk
So heavy and knows I'll have to walk heavier still
Before my time comes. I'm sorry to make them sad,
I'm sorry I did a bad thing if it was a bad thing;
But I'm satisfied.
                  We cut the heart on the tree.
I've got my half of the dime and he's got his,
He'll come back when Winter's over or else I'll find him,
When you can push up the windows, when the new colts
Come out in the Spring, when the snake sheds his winter coat,
When the old, shed coat of Winter lies on the ground
Grey as wasp-paper under the green, slow rain,
When the big barn door rolls open.

I was worried to death at first and I couldn't tell.
But as soon as I knew what it was—it was different then—
It made things all right.
                    I can't tell why it did that."

She awkwardly stooped and put her hand on the ground,
Under the brittle leaves the soil was alive,
Torn with its harvest, turned on its side toward sleep,
But stripped for battle, too, for the unending
Battle with Winters till the Spring is born
Like a tight green leaf uncurling, so slightly, so gently,
Out of the husk of ice and the blank, white snows.

The wind moved over it, blowing the leaves away,
Leaving the bare, indomitable breast.
She felt a wind move over her heavy body,
Stripping it clean for war.
                    She felt the blind-featured
Mystery move, the harmonics of the quick grain,
The battle and the awakening for battle,
And the salt taste of peace.

A flight of geese passed by in a narrow V,
Honking their cry.
                    That cry was stuck in her heart
Like a bright knife.
                    She could have laughed or wept
Because of that cry flung down from a moving wing,
But she stood silent.
                    She had touched the life in the ground.

———————

Love came by from the riversmoke,
    When the leaves were fresh on the tree,
But I cut my heart on the blackjack oak
    Before they fell on me.

The leaves are green in the early Spring,
    They are brown as linsey now,
I did not ask for a wedding-ring
    From the wind in the bending bough.

Fall lightly, lightly, leaves of the wild,
  Fall lightly on my care,
I am not the first to go with child
  Because of the blowing air.

I am not the first nor yet the last
  To watch a goosefeather sky,
And wonder what will come of the blast
  And the name to call it by.

Snow down, snow down, you whitefeather bird,
  Snow down, you winter storm,
Where the good girls sleep with a gospel word
  To keep their honor warm.

The good girls sleep in their modesty,
  The bad girls sleep in their shame,
But I must sleep in the hollow tree
  Till my child can have a name.

I will not ask for the wheel and thread
  To spin the labor plain,
Or the scissors hidden under the bed
  To cut the bearing-pain.

I will not ask for the prayer in church
  Or the preacher saying the prayer,
But I will ask the shivering birch
  To hold its arms in the air.

Cold and cold and cold again,
  Cold in the blackjack limb
The winds of the sky for his sponsor-men
  And a bird to christen him.

Now listen to me, you Tennessee corn,
  And listen to my word,
This is the first child ever born
  That was christened by a bird.

He's going to act like a hound let loose
  When he comes from the blackjack tree,

And he's going to walk in proud shoes
All over Tennessee.

I'll feed him milk out of my own breast
And call him Whistling Jack.
And his dad'll bring him a partridge nest,
As soon as his dad comes back.

———————

John Brown's raid has gone forward, the definite thing is done,
Not as we see it done when we read the books,
A clear light burning suddenly in the sky,
But dimly, obscurely, a flame half-strangled by smoke,
A thing come to pass from a victory not a victory,
A dubious doctrine dubiously received.
The papers praise, but the recruiting is slow,
The bonds sell badly, the grind of the war goes on—
There is no sudden casting off of a chain,
Only a slow thought working its way through the ground,
A slow root growing, touching a hundred soils,
A thousand minds—no blossom or flower yet

It takes a long time to bring a thought into act
And when it blossoms at last, the gardeners wonder—
There have been so many to labor this patch of ground,
Garrison, Beecher, a dozen New England names,
Courageous, insulting Sumner, narrow and strong,
With his tongue of silver and venom and his wrecked body,
Wendell Phillips, Antinous of Harvard—
But now that the thought has arisen, they are not sure
It was their thought after all—it is good enough—
The best one could expect from a man like Lincoln,
But this and that are wrong, are unshrewdly planned,
We could have ordered it better, we knew the ground,
It should have been done before, in a different way,
And our praise is grudging.
                                    Pity the gardeners,
Pity Boston, pity the pure in heart,
Pity the men whom Time goes past in the night,
Without their knowledge. They worked through the heat of the
    day.

206

Let us even pity
Wendell Phillips, Antinous of Harvard,
For he was a model man and such men deserve
A definite pity at times.
                        He too did his best.
Secure in his own impenetrable self-knowledge,
He seldom agreed with Lincoln or thought him wise;
He sometimes thought that a stunning defeat would give
A needed lesson to the soul of the nation,
And, before, would have broken the Union as blithely as Yancey
For his own side of abolition, speaking about it
In many public meetings where he was heckled
But usually silenced the hecklers sooner or later
With his mellifluous, masculine, well-trained accents.
War could hardly come too soon for a man like that
And when it came, he was busy. He did his part,
Being strong and active, blessed with a ready mind,
And the cause being one to which he professed devotion,
He spoke. He spoke well, with conviction, and frequently.

So much for the banner-bearers of abolition,
The men who carried the lonely flag for years
And could bear defeat with the strength of the pure in heart
But could not understand the face of success.

The other dissenters are simpler to understand.
They are ready to fight for the Union but not for niggers,
They don't give a damn for niggers and say so now
With a grievous cry.
                        And yet the slow root-thought works
Gradually through men's minds.
                        The Lancashire spinners,
Thrown out of work because no cotton can come
To feed their mills through the choking Union blockade,
Yet hold starvation meetings and praise the Union.
The tide has begun to turn in some English minds,
The watchers overseas feel their hands grow numb,
Slidell and Mason and Huse still burrow and argue,
But a cold breath blows through the rooms with the chandeliers.
A door is beginning to close.
                        Few men perceive
The turn of the tide, the closing of the door.

Lincoln does not perceive it. He sees alone
The grind of the war, the lagging of the recruits,
Election after election going against him,
And Lee back safe in Virginia after Antietam
While McClellan sticks for five weeks and will not move.
He loses patience at last and removes McClellan.
Burnside succeeds him—
                    and the grimly bewildered
Army of the Potomac has a new rider,
Affable, portly, whiskered and self-distrusting,
Who did not wish the command and tried to decline it,
Took it at last and almost wept when he did.
A worried man who passes like a sad ghost
Across November, looking for confidence,
And beats his army at last against stone walls
At Fredericksburg in the expected defeat
With frightful slaughter.
                    The news of the thing comes back.
There are tears in his eyes. He never wanted command.
"Those men over there," he groans, "Those men over there"
—They are piled like cordwood in front of the stone wall—

He wants to lead a last desperate charge himself,
But he is restrained.
                    The sullen army draws back,
Licking its wounds. The night falls. The newspapers rave.
There are sixty-three hundred dead in that doomed attack
That never should have been made.
                              His shoulders are bowed.
He tries a vain march in the mud and resigns at last
The weapon he could not wield.
                    Joe Hooker succeeds him.
The winter clamps down, cold winter of doubt and grief.

          The sun shines, the wind goes by,
          The prisoners and captives lie
          In a cell without an eye.

          Winter will not touch them more
          Than the cold upon a sore
          That was frozen long before.

208

Summer will not make them sweet
Nor the rainy Springs refresh
That extremity of heat
In the self-corrupting flesh.

The band blares, the bugles snort,
They lose the fort or take the fort,
Someone writes a wise report.

Someone's name is Victory.
The prisoners and captives lie
Too long dead before they die.

––––––––––

For all prisoners and captives now,
For the dark legion,
The Andersonvillers, the Castle Thunder men,
The men who froze at Camp Morton and came from the dun-
    geons
With blood burst out on their faces.
The men who died at Salisbury and Belle Isle,
Elmira, St. Louis, Camp Douglas—the Libby tunnellers—
The men in the fetid air.

There are charges back and forth upon either side,
Some true, some false.
                    You can read the official reports,
The dozen thick black-bound volumes of oaths and statements,
A desert of type, a dozen black mummy-cases
Embalming the long-forgotten, building again
The cumbrous machine of guards and reports and orders,
"Respectfully submitted" . . . "I beg to state" . . .
"State of kitchen—good." . . . "Food, quality of—quite good." . . .
"Police of hospital—good except Ward 7" . . .
"Remarks—we have ninety-five cases of smallpox now." . . .
"Remarks—as to general health of prisoners, fair." . . .
"Remarks" . . . "Remarks" . . . "Respectfully submitted" . . .
Under this type are men who used to have hands
But the creaking wheels have respectfully submitted them
Into a void, embalmed them in mummy-cases,
With their chills and fever, their looks and plans of escape.

209

They called one "Shorty," they called another "The Judge,"
One man wore the Virgin's medal around his neck,
One had a broken nose and one was a liar,
"Respectfully submitted—"
                              But, now and then,
A man or a scene escapes from the mummy-cases,
Like smoke escaping, blue smoke coiling into pictures,
Stare at those coils—
                        and see in the hardened smoke,
The triple stockade of Andersonville the damned,
Where men corrupted like flies in their own dung
And the gangrened sick were black with smoke and their filth.
There were thirty thousand Federal soldiers there
Before the end of the war.
                              A man called Wirtz,
A Swiss, half brute, half fool, and wholly a clod,
Commanded that camp of spectres.
                                    One reads what he did
And longs to hang him higher than Haman hung,
And then one reads what he said when he was tried
After the war—and sees the long, heavy face,
The dull fly buzzing stupidly in the trap,
The ignorant lead of the voice, saying and saying,
"Why, I did what I could, I was ordered to keep the jail.
Yes, I set up deadlines, sometimes chased men with dogs,
Put men in torturing stocks, killed this one and that,
Let the camp corrupt till it tainted the very guards
Who came there with mortal sickness.
But they were prisoners, they were dangerous men,
If a hundred died a day—how was it my fault?
I did my duty. I always reported the deaths.
I don't see what I did different from other people.
I fought well at Seven Pines and was badly wounded.
I have witnesses here to tell you I'm a good man
And that I was really kind. I don't understand.
I'm old. I'm sick. You're going to hang me. Why?"

Crush out the fly with your thumb and wipe your hand,
You cannot crush the leaden, creaking machine,
The first endorsement, the paper on the desk
Referred by Adjutant Feeble to Captain Dull
For further information and his report.

Some men wish evil and accomplish it
But most men, when they work in that machine,
Just let it happen somewhere in the wheels.
The fault is no decisive, villainous knife
But the dull saw that is the routine mind.

Why, if a man lay dying on their desk
They'd do their best to help him, friend or foe,
But this is merely a respectfully
Submitted paper, properly endorsed
To be sent on and on, and gather blood.

Stare at the smoke again for a moment's space
And see another live man in another prison.

A colored trooper named Woodson was on guard
In the prison at Newport News, one night around nine.
There was a gallery there, where the privy was,
But prisoners weren't allowed in it after dark.

The colored soldier talked with the prisoners
At first, in a casual, more or less friendly way;
They tried to sell him breastpins and rings they had
And bothered him by wanting to go to the privy.

At last, he fired on a man
Who went in the gallery, but happened to miss him.
A lieutenant came down to ask the cause of the shot.
Woodson told him.
           A second prisoner went
On the same errand, a shadow slipping through shadows.
Woodson halted him twice but he kept on moving.
"There's a man in the gallery now," said the young lieutenant.
"Well, I reckon it's one of the men makin' water again,"
Said Woodson, uneasily. The lieutenant stiffened.
He was officer of the guard and orders were orders.
"Why don't you use the bayonet on him?" he said.
Woodson jumped forward. The bayonet hunched and struck.
The man ran into the privy and fell like a log. . . . .
A prisoner said "You've killed him dead," in a voice.
"Yes, by God!" said Woodson, cleaning his bayonet,
"They buried us alive at Fort Pillow."

                                    The court
Found the sentry a trifle hasty, but on the whole
Within his instructions, the officer's orders lawful;
One cannot dispute the court.
                              And yet the man
Who went to the privy is inconveniently dead.
It seems an excessive judgment for going there.

The little pictures wreathe into smoke again.
The mummy-cases close upon the dark legion.
The papers are filed away.
                           If they once were sent
To another court for some last woid of review,
They are back again. It seems strange that such tidy files
Of correspondence respectfully submitted
Should be returned from God with no final endorsement.

                    ————————

The slow carts hitched along toward the place of exchange
Through a bleak wind.
                      It was not a long wagon train,
Wagons and horses were too important to waste
On prisoners for exchange, if the men could march.
Many did march and some few died on the way
But more died up in the wagons, which was not odd.
If a man was too sick to walk, he was pretty sick.

They had been two days on the road.
                                   Jack Ellyat lay
Between a perishing giant from Illinois
Who raved that he was bailing a leaky boat
Out on the Lakes, and a slight, tubercular Jew
Who muttered like a sick duck when the wagon jounced.
Bailey marched. He still was able to march
But his skin hung on him. He hummed to the Weaver's tune.

They got to the river at last.
                              Jack Ellyat saw
A yellow stream and slow boats crossing the stream.
Bailey had helped him out. He was walking now
With his arm around Bailey's neck. Their course was a crab's.

The Jew was up and staring with shoe-button eyes
While his cough took him. The giant lay on a plank,
Some men were trying to lift him.
                              The wind blew
Over a knife of frost and shook their rags.
The air was a thawing ice of most pure, clear gold.
They stared across the river and saw the flag
And the tall, blue soldiers walking in thick, warm coats
Like strong, big men who fed well. And then they cheered,
A dry thin cheer, pumped up from exhausted lungs
And yet with a metal vibrance.
                              The bright flag flapped.
"I can smell 'em frying meat," said the coughing Jew.
He sniffed, "Oh God, I hope it ain't ham," he said
With his mouth puckered. A number of scarecrows laughed.
And then they heard the echo of their own cheer
Flung back at them, it seemed, in a high, shrill wail
With that tongue of metal pulsing its feebleness.
But it did not end like an echo, it gathered and rose,
It was the Confederate sick on the other side,
Cheering their own.
                    The two weak crowd-voices met
In one piping, gull-like cry.
                              Then the boats began
To take the weak men on board.
                              Jack Ellyat walked
To his boat on stuffless legs. "Keep quiet," he thought,
"You're not through yet—you won't be through till you land.
They can jerk you back, even now, if you look too pleased.
Look like a soldier, damn you, and show them how."
The thought was childish but it stiffened his back
And got him into the boat.
                          In the midst of the stream
They passed a boat with Confederate prisoners
So near they could yell at each other.
                                      "Hello there, Yank."
"Hello Reb" . . . "You look pretty sick—don't we feed you
    good?" . . .
"You don't look so damn pretty, yourself" . . . "My, ain't that a
    shame!" . . .
"You'll look a lot sicker when Hooker gets after you." . . .
"Hell, old Jack'll take Hooker apart like a coffee-pot" . . .

"Well, good-by, Yank" . . . "Good-by, Reb" . . . "Get fat if you
  kin."

So might meet and pass, perhaps, on a weedier stream
Other boats, no more heavily charged, to a wet, black oar.
Bailey watched the boat move away with its sick grey men
Still yelling stingless insults through tired lips.
He cupped his hands to his mouth. "Oh——" he roared,
Then he sank back, coughing.
                                    "They look pretty bad," he said,
"They look glad to get back. They ain't such bad Rebs at that."

The boat's nose touched the wharf. It swung and was held.
They got out. They didn't move toward the camp at first.
They looked back at the river first and the other side,
Without saying words. They stood there thus for a space
Like a row of tattered cranes at the edge of a stream,
Blinking at something.

"All right, you men," said an officer. "Come along."
Jack Ellyat's heart made a sudden lump in his chest.
It was a blue officer. They were back in their lines,
Back out of prison.
                        Bailey whirled out his arm
In a great wheel gesture. "Hell," he said in a low,
Moved voice, thumbed his nose across at the Stars and Bars
And burst into horrible tears. Jack Ellyat held him.
"Captain, when do we eat?" said the Jew in a wail.

BOOK SIX

Cudjo breathed on the silver urn
And rubbed till his hand began to burn,
With his hoarded scrap of chamois-skin.
The metal glittered like bright new tin
And yet, as he labored, his mouth was sad—
"Times is gettin' almighty bad.
Christmas a-comin', sure and swif',
But no use hollerin' 'Christmas Gif'!'
No use keepin' the silver fittin',
No use doin' nothin' but sittin'.

Old Marse Billy stayin' away,
Yankees shootin' at Young Marse Clay,
Grey hairs in Miss Mary's brush,
And a-whooin' wind in de berry-bush,
Dat young red setter done eat her pups,
We was washin' de tea set an' bust two cups,
Just come apart in Liza's han'—
Christmas, where has you gwine to, man?
Won't you never come back again?
I feels like a cat in de outdoors rain."
Christmas used to come without fail,
A big old man with a raccoon tail,
So fine and bushy it brushed the ground
And made folks sneeze when he waltzed around.
He was rolling river and lucky sun
And a laugh like a double-barrelled gun,
And the chip-straw hat on his round, bald head
Was full of money and gingerbread.
"Come in, Christmas, and have a cheer!
But, if he's comin', he won't stop here,
He likes folks cheerful and dinners smokin'
And famblies shootin' off caps and jokin',
But he won't find nothin' on dis plantation,
But a lot of grievin' conversation.

Dey's tooken de carpets and window-weights
To go and shoot at de Yankee States,
Dey's tooken Nelly, de cross-eye mule,
And whoever took her was one big fool;
Dey's tooken dis an' dey's tooken dat,
Till I kain't make out what dey's drivin' at.
But if Ole Marse Billy could see dis place
He'd cuss all Georgia blue in de face.
To see me wuhkin with dis ole shammy
Like a field-hand-nigger fum Alabammy,
And Ole Miss wearin' a corn-husk hat,
Dippin' ole close in de dyein' vat,
Scrapin' her petticoats up for lint
An' bilin' her tea out of julep-mint.

Young Marse Clay he'd feel mighty sad
If he'd seed de weddin' his sisters had.

De grooms was tall and de brides was fine,
But dey drunk de health in blackberry wine,
And supper was thu at half-past-nine.

Weddin's ust to last for a week,
But now we's rowin' up Hard Times Creek.
Somethin's conjured dis white-folks' South.
Somethin' big with a hongry mouth,
Eatin' an' eatin'—I done my bes',
Scattered de fedders and burnt de nes',
Filled de bottle an' made de hand
An' buried de trick in Baptis' land,
An' dat trick's so strong, I was skeered all night,
But, somehow or udder, it don' wuhk right.
Ef I got me a piece of squinch-owl's tail
An' some dead-folks' yearth fum de county jail,
It mout wuhk better—but I ain't sho',
And de wind keeps scrabblin' under de do',
Scratchin' and scratchin' his buzzard-claws,
Won't nuthin' feed you, hongry jaws?

Field hands keeps on hoein' de corn,
Stupidest niggers ever born,
All dey's good for is gravy-lickin',
Ram-buttin' and cotton-pickin';
Dey don't hear de wind in de slew,
But dat wind's blowin' over 'em too,
An' dat wind's res'less an' dat wind's wile,
An' dat wind aches like a motherless chile,
Won't nuthin' feed you, achin' wind?"

The hand stopped rubbing. The spoons were shined.
He put them back in the flannel bag
And stared at his scrap of chamois-rag.
War was a throat that swallowed things
And you couldn't cure it with conjurings.

————————

Sally Dupré watched over her dyeing-pots,
Evening was setting in with a light slow rain
That marched like a fairy army—there being nothing

From the white fog on the hill to the soaked door-stone
But a moving grey and silver hurry of lances,
Distinct yet crowded, thin as the edge of the moon,
Carried in no fleshed hand.
                              She thought to herself,
"I have stained my arms with new colors, doing this work,
The red is pokeberry-juice, the grey is green myrtle,
The deep black is queen's delight.
                                    If he saw me now
With my hands so parti-colored he would not know them.
He likes girls' hands that nothing has stained but lotions,
This is too fast a dye.
                         I will dye my heart
In a pot of queen's delight, in the pokeberry sap,
I will dye it red and black in the fool's old colors
And send it to him, wrapped in a calico rag,
To keep him warm through the rain.
                                    It will keep him warm.
And women in love do better without a heart.
What fools we are to wait the wheel of the year,
The year will not help our trouble.
                                     What fools we are
To give our parti-colored hearts to the rain.

I am tired of the slogans now and tired of the saving,
I want to dance all night in a brand-new dress
And forget about wars and love and the South and courage.

The South is an old high house full of charming ladies,
The war is a righteous war full of gallant actions,
And love is a white camellia worn in the hair.

But I am tired of talking to charming ladies
And the smell of the white camellia, I will dye
My hands twice as black as ink in the working waters
And wait like a fool for bitter love to come home.

He was wounded this year. They hurt him. They hurt you,
    darling.
I have no doubt she came with a bunch of flowers
And talked to your wound and you like a charming lady.
I have no doubt that she came.

Her heart is not parti-colored. She'll not go steeping
Her gentle hands in the pulp and the dead black waters
Till the crooked blot lies there like a devil's shadow,
And the heart is stained with the stain.

If I came to the bed where you lay sick and in fever,
I would not come with little tight-fisted flowers
But with the white heron's plume that lay in the forest
Till it was cooler than sleep.

The living balm would touch on your wound less gently,
The Georgia sun less fierce than my arms to hold you,
The steel bow less stubborn than my curved body
Strung against august death.

They hurt you, darling, they hurt you and I not with you,
I nowhere there to slit the cloth from your burning,
To find the head of the man who fired the bullet
And give his eyes to the crows.

House, house, house, it is not that my friend was wounded,
But that you kept him from me while he had freedom,
You and the girl whose heart is a snuffed white candle—
Now I will curse you both.

Comely house, high-courteous house of the gentle,
You must win your war for my friend is mixed in your quarrel,
But then you must fall, you must fall, for your walls divide us,
Your worn stones keep us apart.

I am sick of the bland camellias in your old gardens,
Your pride and passion are not my pride and my passion,
I am strangling to death in your cables of honeysuckle,
Your delicate lady-words.

I would rather dig in the earth than learn your patience,
I have need of a sky that never was cut for dresses
And a rough ground to tear my hands on like lion's clothing,
And a hard wheel to move.

The low roof by the marches of rainy weather,
The sharp love that carries the fool's old colors,

The bare bed that is not a saint's or a lady's,
The strong death at the end.

They hurt you, darling, they hurt you, and I not with you,
I nowhere by to see you, to touch my darling,
To take your fever upon me if I could take it
And burn my hands at your wound.

If I had been there—oh, how surely I would have found you,
How surely killed your foe—and sat by your bedside
All night long, like a mouse, like a stone unstirring,
Only to hear your slow breath moving the darkness,
Only to hear, more precious than childish beauty,
The slow tired beat of your heart."

———————

Wingate sat by a smoky fire
Mending a stirrup with rusty wire.
His brows were clenched in the workman's frown,
In a day or a week they'd be back in town,
He thought of it with a brittle smile
That mocked at guile for its lack of guile
And mocked at ease for its lack of ease.
It was better riding through rainy trees
And playing tag with the Union spies
Than telling ladies the pleasant lies,
And yet, what else could you do, on leave?

He touched a rent in his dirty sleeve,
That was the place that the bullet tore
From the blue-chinned picket whose belt he wore,
The man who hadn't been quick enough,
And the powder-burn on the other cuff
Belonged to the fight with the Yankee scout
Who died in Irish when he went out.
He thought of these things as a man might think
Of certain trees by a river-brink,
Seen in a flash from a passing train,
And, before you could look at them, gone again.
It was more important to eat and drink
Than give the pain or suffer the pain
And life was too rapid for memory.

"There are certain things that will cling to me,
But not the things that I thought would cling,
And the wound in my body cannot sting
Like the tame black crow with the bandaged wing,
The nervous eye and the hungry craw
That picked at the dressing-station straw
Till I was afraid it would pick my eyes
And couldn't lift hand to beat it off.
I can tell the ladies the usual lies
Of the wild night-duels when two scouts clash
And your only light is his pistol-flash;
But I remember a watering-trough
Lost in a little brushwood town
And the feel of Black Whistle slumping down
Under my knees in the yellow air,
Hit by a bullet from God knows where . . .
Not the long, mad ride round the Union lines
But the smell of the swamp at Seven Pines,
The smell of the swamp by Gaines's Mill,
And Lee in the dusk before Malvern Hill,
Riding along with his shoulders straight
Like a sending out of the Scæan Gate,
The cold intaglio of war.
'This is Virginia's *Iliad*,'
But Troy was taken nevertheless—
I remember the eyes my father had
When we saw our dead in the Wilderness—
I cannot remember any more—

Lucy will wear her English gown
When the Black Horse Troop comes back to town,
Pin her dress with a silver star
And tell our shadows how brave we are.
Lucy I like your white-and-gold—"

He blew on his hands for the day was cold,
And the damp, green wood gave little heat:
There was something in him that matched the sleet
And washed its hands in a rainy dream,
Till the stirrup-strap and the horses' steam
And Shepley and Bristol behind his back,
Playing piquet with a dog-eared pack

And the hiss of the sap in the smoky wood
Mixed for a moment in something good,
Something outside of peace or war
Or a fair girl wearing a silver star,
Something hardly as vain as pride
And gaunt as the men he rode beside.
It made no comments but it was there,
Real as the color of Lucy's hair
Or the taste of Henry Weatherby's wine.
He thought "These people are friends of mine.
And we certainly fooled the Yanks last week,
When we caught those wagons at Boiling Creek,
I guess we're not such a bad patrol
If we never get straight with the muster-roll,
I guess, next Spring, we can do it again—"

Bristol threw down a flyspecked ten,
"Theah," he said, in the soft, sweet drawl
That could turn as hard as a Minie-ball,
"This heah day is my lucky day,
And Shepley nevah could play piquet."
He stretched his arms in a giant yawn,
"Gentlemen, when are we movin' on?
I have no desire for a soldier's end,
While I still have winnin's that I can spend
And they's certain appointments with certain ladies
Which I'd miss right smart if I went to Hades,
Especially one little black-eyed charmer
Whose virtue, one hopes, is her only armor,
So if Sergeant Wingate's mended his saddle
I suggest that we all of us now skedaddle,
To employ a term that the Yankees favor—"
He tasted his words, for he liked the flavor.
"And yet, one dreads to be back," said he,
"One knows how tippled one well may be
If one meets with the oppor-tun-ity.
And even the charmers can likewise raise
Unpleasant doubts that may last for days—
And as one," he sighed, "of our martial lads,
I'd rather be chargin' Columbiads,
Than actin' sweet to some old smooth-bore
When he tells me how he could win the War

By burnin' the next Yank crossroads-store.
The Yanks aren't always too blame polite,
But they fight like sin when they've got to fight,
And after they've almost nailed your hide
To your stinkin' saddle in some ole ride,
It makes you mad when some nice home-guard
Tells you they nevah could combat hard.
I have no desire to complain or trouble
But I'd find this conflict as comfortable
As a big green pond for a duck to swim in,
If it wasn't for leave, and the lovin' women."

———————

The snow lay hard on the hills. You could burn your eyes
By too-long-looking into the cold ice-lens
Of infinite, pure, glittering, winter air.
It was as cold as that, as sparkling as that,
Where the crystal trees stood up like strange, brittle toys
After the sleet storm passed, till the setting sun
Hung the glass boughs with rainbows frozen to gems
And the long blue shadows pooled in the still hill-hollows.

The white and the purple lilacs of New England
Are frozen long, they will not bloom till the rains,
But when you look from the window, you see them there,
A great field of white lilacs.
                    A gathered sheaf
Of palest blossoms of lilac, stained with the purple evening.

Jack Ellyat turned away from the window now,
The frosty sleighbell of winter was in his ears,
He saw the new year, a child in a buffalo-robe,
Dragged in a sleigh whose runners were polished steel
Up the long hill of February, into chill light.
The child slept in the robe like a reindeer-colt,
Nuzzled under the winter. The bright bells rang.

He warmed his hands at the stove and shivered a little
Hearing that ice-sweet chime.
                    He was better now,
But his blood felt thin when he thought of skating along

222

Over black agate floors in the bonfire light
Or beating a girl's red mittens free of the snow,
And he slept badly at times, when his flesh recalled
Certain smells and sights that were prison.

He stared at the clock where Phaëton's horses lunged
With a queer nod of recognition. The rest had altered,
People and winter and nightmares and Ellen Baker,
Or stayed in a good dimension that he had lost,
But Phaëton was the same. He said to himself,
"I have met you twice, old, drunken charioteer,
Once in the woods, and once in a dirty shack
Where Death was a coin of spittle left on the floor.
I suppose we will meet again before there's an end,
Well, let it happen.
                    It must have been cold last year
At Fredericksburg. I'm glad I wasn't in that.
Melora, what's happened to you?"
                                  He saw Melora
Walking down from the woods in the low spring light.
His body hurt for a minute, but then it stopped.
He was getting well. He'd have to go back pretty soon.
He grinned, a little dryly, thinking of chance,
Father had seen the congressman after all,
Just before Shiloh. So now, nearly ten months later,
The curious wheels that are moved by such congressmen
Were sending him back to the Army of the Potomac,
Back with the old company, back with the Eastern voices,
Henry Fairfield limping along with his sticks,
Shot through both hips at Antietam.
                                    He didn't care,
Except for losing Bailey, which made it tough.
He tried to puzzle out the change in his world
But gave it up. Things and people looked just the same,
You could love or like or detest them just the same way,
But whenever you tried to talk of your new dimension
It didn't sound right, except to creatures like Bailey.
"I have met you twice, old, drunken charioteer,
The third time you may teach me how to be cool."

Ned, asleep by the stove, woke up and yawned,
"Hello Ned," said his master, with a half-smile,

"I told a girl about you, back in a wood,
You'd like that girl. She'd rub the back of your ears.
And Bailey'd like you too. I wish Bailey was here.
Want to go to war, Ned?" Ned yawned largely again.
Ellyat laughed. "You're right, old fella," he said,
"You get too mixed up in a war. You better stay here.
God, I'd like to sleep by a stove for a million years,
Turn into a dog and remember how to stand cold."
The clock struck five. Jack Ellyat jumped at the sound
Then he sank back. "No, fooled you that time," he said,
As if the strokes had been bullets.
                                        Then he turned
To see his mother, coming in with a lamp,
And taste the strange tastes of supper and quietness.

John Vilas heard the beating of another
Sleet at another and a rougher wall
While his hands knotted together and then unknotted.
Each time she had to moan, his hands shut down,
And now the moans were coming close together,
Close as bright streaks of hail.
                                        The younger children
Slept the uneasy sleep of innocent dogs
Who know there's something strange about the house,
Stranger than storms, and yet they have to sleep,
And someone has to watch them sleeping now.

"Harriet's right and Harriet's upstairs,
And Harriet cried like this when she gave birth,
Eighteen years back, in that chintz-curtained room,
And her long cry ran like an icicle
Into my veins. I can remember yet
The terrible old woman with the shawl
Who sat beside me, like deserted Fate,
Cursing me with those eyes each time she cried,
Although she must, one time, have cried like that
And been the object of as wild a cry,
And so far back,—and on—and always that,
The linked, the agonizing chain of cries
Brighter than steel, because earth will be earth

224

And the sun strike it, and the seed have force.
And yet no cry has touched me like this cry.

Harriet's right and Harriet's upstairs
And Harriet would have kept her from today,
And now today has come, I look at it,
Under the icicle, and wish it gone,
Because it hurts me to be sitting here,
Biting my fingers at my daughter's cry
And knowing Harriet has the harder task
As she has had for nearly twenty years.
And yet, what I have sought that I have sought
And cannot disavouch for my own pang,
Or be another father to the girl
Than he who let her run the woods alone
Looking for stones that have no business there.
For Harriet sees a dozen kinds of pain.
And some are blessed, being legitimate,
And some are cursed, being outside a law:
But she and I see only pain itself
And are hard-hearted with our epitaphs,
And yet I wish I could not hear that cry.
I know that it will pass because all things
Pass but the search that only ends with breath,
And, even after that, my daughter and I
May still get up from bondage, being such
Smoke as no chain of steel-bright cries can chain
To walk like Indian Summer through the woods
And be the solitaries of the wind
Till we are sleepy as old clouds at last.

She has a lover and will have a child
And I'm alone. I had forgotten that,
Though you'd not think it easy to forget.
No, we'll not go together.
                              The cries beat
Like hail upon the cold panes of my heart
Faster and faster, till they crack the glass
And I can know at last how old I am.

That is my punishment and my defence,
My ecstasy and my deep-seated bane.

I prayed to life for life once, in my youth,
Between the rain and a long stroke of cloud
'Till my soaked limbs felt common with the sky
And the black stone of heaven swung aside,
With a last clap of water, to reveal
Lonely and timid, after all that wrath,
The small, cold, perfect flower of the new moon
And now, perhaps, I'll pray again tonight,
Still to the life that used me as a man
Uses and wears a strong and riotous horse,
Still to the vagrants of no fortunate word.

Men who go looking for the wilderness-stone,
Eaters of life who run away from bread
And are not satisfied with lucky days!
Robbers of airy gold, skin-changing men
Who find odd brothers when the moon is full,
Stray alchemics who entertain an imp
And feed it plums within a hollow tree
Until its little belly is sufficed,
Men who have seen the bronze male-partridge beat
His drum of feathers not ten feet away,
Men who have listened to wild geese at night
Until your hearts were hollowed with that sound,
Moth-light and owl-light and first-dayspring men,
Seekers and seldom-finders of the woods,
But always seekers till your eyes are shut;
I have an elder daughter that I love
And, having loved from childhood, would not tame
Because I once was tamed.
                              If you're my friends,
Then she's your friend.
                         I do not ask for her
Refusal or compunction or the safe
Road between little houses and old gates
Where Death lies sleepy as a dog in the sun
And the slow cows come home with evening bells
Into the tired peace that's good for pain.
Those who are never tired of eating life
Must immolate themselves against a star
Sooner or late, as she turns crucified
Now, on that flagellating wheel of light

Which will not miss one revolution's turn
For any anguish we can bring to it,
Because it is our master and our stone,
Body of pain, body of sharpened fire,
Body of quenchless life, itself, itself,
That safety cannot buy or peddlers sell
Or the rich cowards leave their silly sons.
But, oh,
She's tired out, she's broken, she's athirst.
Wrap her in twilights now, she is so torn,
And mask again the cold, sweat-runnelled mask
With the deep silence of a leafy wood
So cool and dim its birds are all asleep
And will not fret her. Wipe her straining hands
With the soft, gleaming cobwebs April spins
Out of bright silver tears and spider silk
Till they are finer than the handkerchiefs
Of a young, wild, spear-bearing fairy-queen.
Soothe her and comfort her and let her hear
No harshness but the mumbling peaceful sound
The fed bee grumbles to his honey-bags
In the red foxglove's throat.
                              Oh, if you are
Anything but lost shadows, go to her!"

Melora did not make such words for herself,
Being unable, and too much in pain.
If wood-things were beside her, she did not see them,
But only a lamp, and hands.
                              The pains came hard now,
A fist that hardly opened before it shut,
A red stair mounting into an ultimate
Flurry of misty conflict, when it seemed
As if she fought against the earth itself
For mere breath and something other than mere breath.
She heard the roar of the tunnel, drowned in earth.
Earth and its expulsive waters, tearing her, being born.
Then it was yellow silence and a weak crying.

After the child was washed, they showed her the child,
Breakable, crumpled, breathing, swathed and indignant,
With all its nails and hands that moved of themselves—

A queer thing to come out of that, but then it was there.
"Looks healthy enough," said her mother in a tired voice.
Melora stared. "He's got blue eyes," she said finally.
Her mother sniffed. "A lot of 'em start out blue."
She looked at the child as if she wanted to tell it,
"You aren't respectable. What are you doing here?"
But the child began wailing. She rocked it mechanically.
The rain kept on through the night but nobody listened.
The parents talked for a while, then they fell asleep.
Even the new child slept with its fists tight shut.
Melora heard the rain for a single moment
And then deep, beautiful nothing. "Over," she thought.
She slept, handfasted to the wilderness-stone.

———————

Now the earth begins to roll its wheel toward the sun,
The deep mud-gullies are drying.
                          The sluggish armies
That have slept the bear-months through in their winter-camps,
Begin to stir and be restless.
                        They're tired enough
Of leaky huts and the rain and punishment-drill.
They haven't forgotten what it was like last time,
But next time we'll lick 'em, next time it won't be so bad,
Somehow we won't get killed, we won't march so hard.
"These huts looked pretty good when we first hit camp
But they look sort of lousy now—we might as well git—
Fight the Rebs—and the Yanks—and finish it up."
So they think in the bored, skin-itching months
While the roads are drying. "We're sick of this crummy place,
We might as well git, it doesn't much matter where."
But when they git, they are cross at leaving the huts,
"We fixed up ours first rate. We had regular lamps.
We knew the girls at the Depot. It wasn't so bad.
Why the hell do we have to git when we just got fixed?
Oh, well, we might as well travel."
                          So they go on,
The huts drop behind, the dry road opens ahead . . . .

Fighting Joe Hooker feels good when he looks at his men.
A blue-eyed, uncomplex man with a gift for phrase.
"The finest army on the planet," he says.

The phrase is to turn against him with other phrases
When he is beaten—but now he is confident.
Tall, sandy, active, sentimental and tart,
His horseman's shoulder is not yet bowed by the weight
Of knowing the dice are his and the cast of them,
The weight of command, the weight of Lee's ghostly name.
He rides, preparing his fate.
     In the other camps,
Lee writes letters, is glad to get buttermilk,
Wrings food and shoes and clothes from his commissariat,
Trusts in God and whets a knife on a stone.
Jackson plays with his new-born daughter, waiting for Spring,
His rare laugh clangs as he talks to his wife and child.
He is looking well. War always agrees with him,
And this, perhaps, is the happiest time of his life.
He has three months of it left.
     By the swollen flood
Of the Mississippi, stumpy Grant is a mole
Gnawing at Vicksburg. He has been blocked four times
But he will carry that beaver-dam at last.
There is no brilliant lamp in that dogged mind
And no conceit of brilliance to shake the hand,
But hand and mind can use the tools that they get
This long way out of Galena.
     Sherman is there
And Sherman loves him and finds him hard to make out,
In Sherman's impatient fashion—the quick, sharp man
Seeing ten thousand things where the slow sees one
And yet with a sort of younger brother awe
At the infinite persistence of that slow will
—They make a good pair of hunting dogs, Grant and Sherman,
The nervous, explosive, passionate, slashing hound
And the quiet, equable, deadly holder-on,
Faded-brown as a cinnamon-bear in Spring—
See them like that, the brown dog and the white dog,
Calling them back and forth through the scrubby woods
After the little white scut of Victory,
Or see them as elder brother and younger brother,
But remember this. In their time they were famous men
And yet they were not jealous, one of the other.
When the gold has peeled from the man on the gilded horse,
Riding Fifth Avenue, and the palm-girl's blind;

When the big round tomb gapes empty under the sky,
Vacant with summer air, when it's all forgotten,
When nobody reads the books, when the flags are moth-dust,
Write up that. You won't have to write it so often.
It will do as well as the railway-station tombs.

So with the troops and the leaders of the bear-armies,
The front-page-newspaper-things.
                                    Tall Lincoln reviews
Endless columns crunching across new snow.
They pass uncheering at the marching-salute.
Lincoln sits on his horse with his farmer's seat,
Watching the eyes go by and the eyes come on.
The gaunt, long body is dressed in its Sunday black,
The gaunt face, strange as an omen, sad and foreboding.
The eyes look at him, he looks back at the eyes;
They pass and pass. They go back to their camps at last.
"So that was him," they say. "So that's the old man.
I'm glad we saw him. He isn't so much on looks
But he looks like people you know. He looks sad all right,
I never saw nobody look quite as sad as that
Without it made you feel foolish. He don't do that.
He makes you feel—I dunno—I'm glad we could see him.
He was glad to see us but you could tell all the same
This war's plumb killin' him. You can tell by his face.
I never saw such a look on any man's face.
I guess it's tough for him. Well, we saw him, for once."

That day in Richmond, a mob of angry women
Swarm in the streets and riot for bread or peace.
They loot some shops, a few for the bread they need,
A few for thieving, most because they are moved
By discontent and hunger to do as the rest.
The troops are called out. The troops are about to fire,
But Davis gets on a wagon and calms the crowd
Before the tumbled bodies clutter the street.
He never did a better thing with his voice
And it should be told. Next day they riot again,
But this time the fire is weaker. They are dispersed,
A few arrested. Bread grows dearer than ever.
The housewives still go out with their market-baskets,
But coffee's four dollars a pound and tea eleven.

They come back with a scraping of this and a scrap of that
And try to remember old lazy, lagnappe days,
The slew-foot negro chanting his devilled crabs
Along the street, and the market-women piling
The wicker baskets with everything good and fresh;
Topping it off with a great green fist of parsley
That you used to pretty the sides of the serving-dish
And never bothered to eat.
                              They improvise dishes,
"Blockade pudding" . . . "Confederate fricassee,"
Serve hominy grits on the Royal Derby china
And laugh or weep in their cups of willow-bark tea.

Davis goes back from the riot, his shoulders stooped,
The glow of speech has left him and he feels cold.
He eats a scant meal quickly and turns to the endless
Papers piled on his desk, the squabbles and plans.
A haggard dictator, fretting the men he rules
And being fretted by them.
                              He dreams, perhaps,
Of old days, riding wild horses beside his wife
Back in his youth, on a Mississippi road.
That was a good time. It is past. He drowns in his papers.

The curtain is going up on that battlesmoked,
Crowded third act which is to decide this war
And yet not end it for years.
                              Turn your eyes away
From these chiefs and captains, put them back in their books.
Let the armies sleep like bears in a hollow cave.
War is an iron screen in front of a time,
With pictures smoked upon it in red and black,
Some gallant enough, some deadly, but all intense.
We look at the pictures, thinking we know the time,
We only know the screen.
                              Look behind it now
At the great parti-colored quilt of these patchwork States.
This part and that is vexed by a battle-worm,
But the ploughs go ahead, the factory chimneys smoke,
A new age curdles and boils in a hot steel caldron
And pours into rails and wheels and fingers of steel,
Steel is being born like a white-hot rose

In the dark smoke-cradle of Pittsburg—
                                        a man with a crude
Eye of metal and crystal looks at a smear
On a thin glass plate and wonders—
                                        a shawled old woman
Sits on a curbstone calling the evening news.
War, to her, is a good day when papers sell
Or a bad day when papers don't. War is fat black type.
Anything's realer than war.
                            By Omaha
The valleys and gorges are white with the covered wagons
Moving out toward the West and the new, free land.
All through the war they go on.
                                Five thousand teams
Pass Laramie in a month in the last war-year,
Draft-evaders, homesteaders, pioneers,
Old soldiers, Southern emigrants, sunburnt children. . . .
Men are founding colleges, finding gold,
Selling bad beef to the army and making fortunes,
Ploughing the stone-cropped field that their fathers ploughed.
(Anything's realer than war.)
                                A moth of a woman,
Shut in a garden, lives on scraps of Eternity
With a dog, a procession of sunsets and certain poems
She scribbles on bits of paper. Such poems may be
Ice-crystals, rubies cracked with refracted light,
Or all vast death like a wide field in ten short lines.
She writes to the tough, swart-minded Higginson
Minding his negro troops in a lost bayou,
"War feels to me like an oblique place."
                                        A man
Dreams of a sky machine that will match the birds
And another, dusting the shelves of a country store,
Saves his pennies until they turn into dimes.
(Anything's realer than war.)
                                A dozen men
Charter a railroad to go all across the Plains
And link two seas with a whistling iron horse.
A whiskered doctor stubbornly tries to find
The causes of childbed-fever—and, doing so,
Will save more lives than all these war-months have spent,
And never inhabit a railway-station tomb.

232

All this through the war, all this behind the flat screen. . . .

I heard the song of breath
Go up from city and country,
The even breath of the sleeper,
The tired breath of the sick,
The dry cough in the throat
Of the man with the death-sweat on him,
And the quiet monotone
We breathe but do not hear.

The harsh gasp of the runner,
The long sigh of power
Heaving the weight aloft,
The grey breath of the old.
Men at the end of strength
With their lungs turned lead and fire,
Panting like thirsty dogs;
A child's breath, blowing a flame.

The breath that is the voice,
The silver, the woodwinds speaking,
The dear voice of your lover,
The hard voice of your foe,
And the vast breath of wind,
Mysterious over mountains,
Caught in pines like a bird
Or filling all hammered heaven.

I heard the song of breath.
Like a great strand of music,
Blown between void and void,
Uncorporal as the light.
The breath of nations asleep,
And the piled hills they sleep in,
The word that never was flesh
And yet is nothing but life.

What are you, bodiless sibyl,
Unseen except as the frost-cloud
Puffed from a silver mouth
When the hard winter's cold?

We cannot live without breath,
And yet we breathe without knowledge,
And the vast strand of sound
Goes on, eternally sighing,
Without dimension or space,
Without beginning or end.

I heard the song of breath
And lost it in all sharp voices,
Even my own voice lost
Like a thread in that huge strand,
Lost like a skein of air,
And with it, continents lost
In the great throat of Death.
I trembled, asking in vain,
Whence come you, whither art gone?
The continents flow and melt
Like wax in the naked candle,
Burnt by the wick of time—
Where is the breath of the Chaldees,
The dark, Minoan breath?
I said to myself in hate,
Hearing that mighty rushing,
Though you raise a new Adam up
And blow fresh fire in his visage,
He has only a loan of air,
And gets but a breathing-space.
But then I was quieted.

I heard the song of breath,
The gulf hollow with voices,
Fused into one slow voice
That never paused or was faint.
Man, breathing his life,
And with him all life breathing,
The young horse and the snake,
Beetle, lion and dove,
Solemn harps of the fir,
Trumpets of sea and whirlwind
And the vast, tiny grass
Blown by a breath and speaking.
I heard these things. I heard

The multitudinous river.
When I came back to my life,
My voice was numb in my ears,
I wondered that I still breathed.

———————

Sophy, scared chambermaid in Pollet's Hotel,
Turned the cornhusk mattress and plumped the pillow
With slipshod hands.
                    Then she picked the pillow up
And sniffed it greedily.
                        Something in it smelt sweet.
The bright, gold lady had slept there the night before—
Oh, her lovely, lovely clothes! and the little green bottle
That breathed out flowers when you crept into the room
And pulled out the silver stopper just far enough
To get the sweetness, not far enough to be caught
If anyone came.
                    It made her thin elbows ache
To think how fine and golden the lady was
And how sweet she smelled, how sweet she looked at the men,
How they looked at her.
                        "I'd like to smell sweet," she thought,
"Smell like a lady."
                        She put the hard pillow back.
The lady and the green bottle had gone away.
—If only you had clever hands—after the next sleeper—
—You could steal green bottles—the room would smell stale again—
Hide it somewhere under your dress—as it always did—
Stale cigars and tired bodies—or even say
When they reached to give you the tip, "Don't give me a tip,
Just give me"—unwashed men with their six-weeks' beards,
Trying to hold you back when—"that little green bottle,
I want it so."—but the lady would never do it.
Ladies named Lucy. Lucy was a good name,
Flower-smelling. Sophy was just a name.

She took up her broom and swept ineffectively,
Thinking dim thoughts.
                        The ladies named Lucy came,
Sometimes in the winter, and then all the men got shaved

235

And you could look through the door at the people dancing.
But when battles drew near, the ladies went home to stay.
It was right they should. War wasn't a thing for ladies.

War was an endless procession of dirty boots.
Filling pitchers and emptying out the slops,
And making the cornhusk beds for the unshaved men
Who came in tired—but never too tired to wonder—
Look in the eyes—and hands—and suppose you didn't,
They didn't like it—and if you did, it was nothing—
But they always—and rough sometimes—and drunk now and
  then—
And a couple of nice ones—well, it didn't mean nothing.
It was merely hard to carry the heavy pails
When you didn't get fed enough and got up so soon.
But, now the army was moving, there wouldn't be
So many men or beds or slops for a while
And that meant something.
                    She sighed and dabbed with her broom.

Shippy, the little man with the sharp rat-eyes,
Came behind her and put his hands on her waist.
She let him turn her around. He held her awhile
While his eyes tried to look at her and over his shoulder
At once and couldn't.
                    She felt his poor body shake
But she didn't think much about it.
                              He murmured something.
She shook her head with the air of a frightened doll
And he let her go.
                    "Well, I got to go anyway,"
He said, in a gloomy voice. "I'm late as it is,
But I thought that maybe—" He let the sentence trail off.

"What do you want, next time I come back?" he said.
Her face was sharper. "You bring me a bottle, Charley,
The kind that lady had, with the Richmond scent.
Hers has got a big silver stopper."
                              He pursed his mouth.
"I don't know," he said. "I'll try. I'd like to all right.
You be a good girl now, Soph. Do you love me, Sophy?"

"Uh-huh," she said, in a tired voice, thinking of pitchers.

"Well, I—you're a good girl, Soph." He held her again.
"I'm late," he muttered. She looked at him and felt mean.
He was skimpy like her. They ought to be nice to each other.
She didn't like him much but she sort of loved him.
"You be a good girl till Charley comes back," he mumbled
Kissing her nervously. "I'll bring you the scent."

"It's got a name called French Lilies," she said. "Oh, Charley!"
They clung together a moment like mournful shadows.
He was crying a little, the wet tears fell on her chin,
She cried herself when he'd gone, she didn't know why,
But when she thought of the scent with the silver stopper
She felt more happy. She went to make the next bed.

———————

Luke Breckinridge, washing his shirt in a muddy pool,
Chewed on a sour thought.
                          Only yesterday
He had seen the team creak by toward Pollet's Hotel
With that damn little rat-eyed peddler driving his mules
As if he was God Almighty.
                          He conjured up
A shadow-Shippy before him to hate and bruise
As he beat his shirt with a stone.
                          "If we-uns was home,
I could just lay for him and shoot him out of the bresh,
Goin' to see my girl with his lousy mules.
Tryin' to steal my girl with his peddler's talk!"

But here, in the war, you could only shoot at the Yanks,
If you shot other folks, they found out about it and shot you,
Just like you was a spyer or something mean
Instead of a soldier. There wasn't no sense to it.
"Teach him to steal my girl—if I had him home,
Back in the mountains—I told her straight the last time,
You be a good girl, Soph, and I'll buy you a dress—
We can fix the cabin up fine—and if we have kids
We'll get ourselves married. Couldn't talk fairer than that,
And she's a good girl—but women's easy to change—
God-damn peddler, givin' her Richmond trash,

And we-uns movin' away to scrimmage the Yanks
Before I git a chance to see her agin
And find out if she's been good—He'll come back this way,
Drivin' his mules—plumb easy to lay for him,
But they'd catch me, shore."
                                        His mouth had a bitter twist,
His slow mind grubbed for a plan to settle his doubts.
At last he dropped his stone with a joyous whoop.
"Hey, Billy," he called to his neighbor. "Got your shirt dry?
Well, lend it here for a piece until mine's wrung out,
I got to go see the Captain."
                                        Billy demurred.
"I got friends enough in this shirt," he said with a drawl.
"I ain't hankerin' after no visitors out of yours.
I'm a modest man and my crawlies is sort of shy,
They don't mix well with strangers. They's Piedmont crawlies.
Besides, this shirt, she's still got more shirt than hole,
Yours ain't a shirt—it's a doughnut."
                                        They swore for a while
But finally Luke went off with the precious shirt,
Whistling the tuneless snatch of a mountain jig,
"Gawd help you, peddler," he thought, as he looked for the
   Captain.

Shippy drove his rattletrap cart along
Through the dusty evening, worried and ill at ease.
He ought to have taken the other road by the creek
But he'd wasted too much time at Pollet's Hotel
Looking for Sophy—and hardly seen her at that—
And now she wanted a bottle of scent.
                                        His soul
Shivered with fear like a thin dog in the cold,
Raging in vain at the terrible thing called Life.
—There must be a corner somewhere where you could creep,
Curl up soft and be warm—but he'd never found it.
The big boys always stole his lunch at the school
And rubbed his nose in the dirt—and when he grew up
It was just the same.
                                        There was something under his face,
Something that said, "Come, bully me—I won't bite."
He couldn't see it himself, but it must be there.
He was always going places and thinking, "This time,

They won't find out." But they always did find out
After a while.
           It had been that way at the store,
That way in the army, that way now as a spy.
Behind his eyes he built up a super-Shippy
Who ordered people around, loved glittering girls,
Threw out his chest and died for a bloody flag
And then revived to be thanked by gilt generals,
A schoolboy Shippy, eating the big boys' lunch.
It was his totem. He visioned that Shippy now,
Reckless Shippy with papers sewed in his boots,
Slyly carrying fate through the Rebel lines
To some bright place where—

                    The off mule stumbled and brayed.
He cursed it whimperingly and jerked at the reins,
While his heart jerked, too. The super-Shippy was gone.
He was alone and scared and late on the road.
My God, but he was scared of being a spy
And the mute-faced woman in Richmond and war and life!
He had some papers sewn in his boots all right
And they'd look at the papers while he stood sweating before
     them,
Crumple them up and bully him with cross speech,
"Couldn't you even find out where Heth's men are?
Can't you draw a map? You don't know about Stonewall Jackson?
Why don't you know it? What's this ford by the church?
My God, man, what do you think you are out there for?
You'll have to do better next time, I can tell you that.
We'll send you over Route 7. We had a man there,
But he's been reported killed—"
                    He shuddered in vain,
Seeing a rope and a tree and a dangling weight
And the mute-faced woman sending a paper off
In somebody's else's boots, and somebody saying
In an ice-cream voice to another scared little man.
"Next time, you'll try Route 7. We had a man there,
But he's been reported killed—"
                    Oh, there is a hole
Somewhere deep in the ground where the rabbits hide,
But I've never found it—
                    They stuck up signs and a flag

239

And it was war and you went and got scared to death
By the roar and the yells and the people trying to kill you
Till anything else seemed better—and there you were,
Driving mules with papers sewn in your boots,
But people still wanting to kill you—and no way out.
If you deserted, the mute-faced woman would know
And that would be the worst—and if you went back,
It would be Bull Run and yelling and all that blood
When it made you sick to your stomach. Even at school
You always had to fight. There was no way out.

Sophy was sweet and Sophy was a good girl
And Sophy was the warm earth where the rabbits hide
Away from danger, letting their hearts go slow,
But you couldn't stay with Sophy, you couldn't stay,
And she'd say she'd be a good girl—
                              but, in spite of himself,
He saw a big boy tearing a cardboard box
Apart, with greedy hands, in a bare school-yard,
Where a Shippy whimpered—
                         "Oh, Soph, I'll get you the scent,
Honest I will! Oh God, just let me get through,
Just this one time—and I'll pray—I'll be good—oh God,
Make these papers something they want!"

                                   He clucked to his mules.
Another mile and he'd be out on the pike
And pretty safe for a while.
                         His spirit returned
To building the super-Shippy from dust again.
His head began to nod with the sway of the cart. . . .
Half a dozen men rode out from a little clearing
And casually blocked the road. He pulled up his mules,
Staring around. He saw a face that he knew,
Now queer with triumph—Sophy filling a pail
And that gangling fellow lounging against the pump,
Hungry-eyed—
             It happened too fast to be scary.
You got stopped such a lot. It was only some new patrol.
"All the boys know me," he said. "Yes, I got my pass."
They took the pass but they did not give it back.
There was a waver shaking the dusty air,

The feel of a cord grown tauter. How dry his throat was!
He'd be driving on in a minute. "Well boys?" he said,
"Well, fellers?"
                    They didn't answer or look at him.
"I tell you that's the man," said the mountaineer.

The sergeant-feller looked dubiously at the rest,
Gentlemanly he looked like, a nice young feller
With his little black moustache and his thin, brown face,
He wouldn't do anything mean. It would be all right.
Another man was paring his nails with a knife,
His face was merry and reckless—nice feller, too,
Feller to stand you a drink and talk gay with the girls,
Not anybody to hurt you or twist your wrist.
They were all nice fellers except for the mountaineer.

They were searching him now, but they didn't do it mean.
He babbled to them all through it.
                    "Now boys, now boys,
You're making a big mistake, boys. They all know me,
They all know Charley the peddler."
                    The sergeant looked
Disgusted now—wonder why. Go ahead and look,
You'll never find it—Sophy—bottle of scent—

A horrible voice was saying, "Pull off his boots,"
He fought like a frightened rat then, weeping and biting,
But they got him down and found the papers all right.
Luke Breckinridge observed them with startled eyes,
"Christ," he thought, "so the skunk's a spy after all.
Well, I told 'em so—but I didn't reckon he was.
Little feist of a peddler, chasin' my girl,
Wanted to scare him off so he wouldn't come back—
Hell, they ought to make me a corporal now."
He was pleased.
                    Clay Wingate looked at the writhing man,
"Get up!" he said, in a hard voice, feeling sick.
But they had to drag it up before it would stand
And even then it still babbled.
                    His throat was dry
But that was all right—it was going to be all right—
He was alive—he was Shippy—he knew a girl—

241

He was going to buy her a bottle of first-class scent.
It couldn't all stop. He wasn't ready to die.
He was willing enough to be friends and call it a joke.
Let them take the mules and the cart and hurt him a lot
Only not that—it was other spies who were hung,
Not himself, not Shippy, not the body he knew
With the live blood running through it, making it warm.
He was real. He wore clothes. He could make all this go away
If he shut his eyes. They'd turn him loose in a minute.
They were all nice fellers. They wouldn't treat a man mean.
They couldn't be going to hang him.
                                        But they were.

                    ————————

Lucy Weatherby spread out gowns on a bed
And wondered which she could wear to the next levee.
The blue was faded, the rose brocade had a tear,
She'd worn the flowered satin a dozen times,
The apricot had never gone with her hair,
And somebody had to look nice at the evening parties.
But it was hard. The blockade runners of course—
But so few of them had space for gowns any more
And, really, they charged such prices!
                                        Of course it is
The war, and, of course, when one thinks of our dear, brave
    boys—
But, nevertheless, they like a girl to look fresh
When they come back from their fighting.
                                        When one goes up
To the winter-camps, it doesn't matter so much,
Any old rag will do for that sort of thing.
But here, in Richmond . . .
                            She pondered, mentally stitching,
Cutting and shaping, lost in a pleasant dream.

Fighting at Chancellorsville and Hooker beaten
And nobody killed that you knew so terribly well
Except Jo Frear's second brother—though it was sad
Our splendid general Jackson's lost his arm,
Such an odd man but so religious.
                                She hummed a moment

"That's Stonewall Jackson's way" in her clear cool voice.
"I really should have trained for nursing," she thought.
She heard a voice say. "Yes, the General's very ill,
But that lovely new nurse will save him if anyone can.
She came out from Richmond on purpose."
                                    The voice stopped speaking.
She thought of last month and the boys and the Black Horse
    Troop,
And the haggard little room in Pollet's Hotel
Whose slipshod chambermaid had such scared, round eyes.
She was just as glad they were fighting now, after all,
Huger had been so jealous and Clay so wild,
It was quite a strain to be engaged to them both
Especially when Jim Merrihew kept on writing
And that nice Alabama major—
                            She heard the bells
Ring for a wedding—but who was the man beside her?
He had a face made up of too many faces.
And yet, a young girl must marry—
                                You may dance,
Play in the sun and wear bright gowns to levees,
But soon or late, the hands unlike to your hands
But rough and seeking, will catch your lightness at last
And with strange passion force you. What is this passion,
This injury that women must bear for gowns?
It does not move me or stir me. I will not bear it.
There are women enough to bear it. If I have sweetness,
It is for another service. It is my own.
I will not share it. I'll play in the heat of the sun.
And yet, young girls must marry—what am I thinking?

She stepped from her hoops to try on the rose brocade,
But let it lie for a moment, while she stood up
To look at the bright ghost-girl in the long dark mirror,
Adoringly.
            "Oh, you honey," she thought. "You honey!
You look so pretty—and nobody knows but me.
Nobody knows."
            She kissed her little white shoulders,
With fierce and pitying love for their shining whiteness,
So soft, so smooth, so untarnished, so honey-sweet.
Her eyes were veiled. She swayed in front of the mirror.

"Honey, I love you," she whispered, "I love you, honey.
Nobody loves you like I do, do they, sugar?
Nobody knows but Lucy how sweet you are.
You mustn't get married, honey. You mustn't leave me.
We'll be pretty and sweet to all of them, won't we, honey?
We'll always have beaus to dance with and tunes to dance to,
But you mustn't leave me, honey. I couldn't bear it.
You mustn't ever leave me for any man."

In the dense heart of the thicketed Wilderness,
Stonewall Jackson lies dying for four long days.
They have cut off his arm, they have tried such arts as they know,
But no arts now can save him.
                        When he was hit
By the blind chance bullet-spatter from his own lines,
In the night, in the darkness, they stole him off from the field
To keep the men from knowing, but the men knew.
The dogs in the house will know when there's something wrong.
You do not have to tell them.
                        He marched his men
That grim first day across the whole Union front
To strike a sleepy right wing with a sudden stone
And roll it up—it was his old trick of war
That Lee and he could play like finger and thumb!
It was the last time they played so.
                        When the blue-coated
Unprepared ranks of Howard saw that storm,
Heralded by wild rabbits and frightened deer,
Burst on them yelling, out of the whispering woods,
They could not face it. Some men died where they stood,
The storm passed over the rest. It was Jackson's storm,
It was his old trick of war, for the last time played.
He must have known it. He loosed it and drove it on,
Hearing the long yell shake like an Indian cry
Through the dense black oaks, the clumps of second-growth pine,
And the red flags reel ahead through the underbrush.
It was the hour he did not stop to taste,
Being himself. He saw it and found it good,
But night was falling, the Union centre still held,
Another attack would end it. He pressed ahead

Through the dusk, pushing Little Sorrel, as if the horse
Were iron, and he were iron, and all his men
Not men but iron, the stalks of an iron broom
Sweeping a dire floor clean—and yet, as he rode,
A canny captain, planning a ruthless chess
Skilfully as night fell. The night fell too soon.
It is hard to tell your friend from your enemy
In such a night. So he rode too far in advance
And, turning back toward his lines, unrecognized,
Was fired upon in the night, in the stumbling darkness,
By his own men. He had ridden such rides before
Often enough and taken the chance of them,
But this chance was his bane.
                                    He lay on the bed
After the arm had been lopped from him, grim and silent,
Refusing importunate Death with terrible eyes.
Death was a servant and Death was a sulky dog
And Death crouched down by the Lord in the Lord's own time,
But he still had work to finish that Death would spoil.
He would live in spite of that servant.
                                    Now and then
He spoke, with the old curt justice that never once
Denied himself or his foe or any other
The rigid due they deserved, as he saw that due.
He spoke of himself and his storm. "A successful movement.
I think the most successful I ever made."
—He had heard that long yell shake like an Indian cry
Through the ragged woods and seen his flags go ahead.
Later on, they brought him a stately letter from Lee
That said in Lee's gracious way, "You have only lost
Your left arm, I my right."
                                    The dour mouth opened.
"Better ten Jacksons should fall than one Lee," it said
And closed again, while the heart went on with its task
Of beating off foolish, unnecessary Death.

The slow time wore. They had to tell him at last
That he must die. The doctors were brave enough,
No doubt, but they looked awhile at the man on the bed
And summoned his wife to do it. So she told him.
He would not believe at first. Then he lay awhile
Silent, while some slow, vast reversal of skies

Went on in the dying brain. At last he spoke.
"All right," he said.
                    She opened the Bible and read.
It was Spring outside the window, the air was warm,
The rough, plank house was full enough of the Spring.
They had had a good life together, those two middle-aged
Calm people, one reading aloud now, the other silent.
They had passed hard schools. They were in love with each other
And had been for many years. Now that tale was told.
They had been poor and odd, found each other trusty,
Begotten children, prayed, disliked to be parted,
Had family-jokes, known weather and other matters,
Planned for an age: they were famous now, he was dying.

The clock moved on, the delirium began.
The watchers listened, trying to catch the words;
Some awed, one broken-hearted, a few, no doubt,
Not glad to be there precisely, but in a way
Glad that, if it must happen, they could be there.
It is a human emotion.
                    The dying man
Went back at first to his battles, as soldiers do.
He was pushing a new advance
With the old impatience and skill, over tangled ground,
A cloudy drive that did not move as he willed
Though he had it clear in his mind. They were slow today.
"Tell A. P. Hill to push them—push the attack—
Get up the guns!"
                    The cloudy assault dispersed.
There were no more cannon. The ground was plain enough now.

He lay silent, seeing it so, while the watchers listened.
He had been dying once, but that was a dream.
The ground was plain enough now.
He roused himself and spoke in a different voice.
"Let us cross the river," he said, "and rest under the shade of
    the trees."

BOOK SEVEN

They came on to fish-hook Gettysburg in this way, after this
fashion.
Over hot pikes heavy with pollen, past fields where the wheat
was high.
Peaches grew in the orchards; it was a fertile country,
Full of red barns and fresh springs and dun, deep-uddered kine.

A farmer lived with a clear stream that ran through his very
house-room,
They cooled the butter in it and the milk, in their wide, stone
jars;
A dusty Georgian came there, to eat and go on to battle;
They dipped the milk from the jars, it was cold and sweet in
his mouth.

He heard the clear stream's music as the German housewife
served him,
Remembering the Shenandoah and a stream poured from a rock;
He ate and drank and went on to the gunwheels crushing the
harvest.
It was a thing he remembered as long as any guns.

Country of broad-backed horses, stone houses and long, green
meadows,
Where Getty came with his ox-team to found a steady town
And the little trains of my boyhood puffed solemnly up the
Valley
Past the market-squares and the lindens and the Quaker meeting-
house.

Penn stood under his oak with a painted sachem beside him,
The market-women sold scrapple when the first red maples
turned;
When the buckeyes slipped from their sheaths, you could gather
a pile of buckeyes,
Red-brown as old polished boots, good to touch and hold in the
hand.

The ice-cream parlor was papered with scenes from *Paul and
Virginia,*

The pigs were fat all year, you could stand a spoon in the cream.
—Penn stood under his oak with a feathered pipe in his fingers,
His eyes were quiet with God, but his wits and his bargain sharp.

So I remember it all, and the light sound of buckeyes falling
On the worn rose-bricks of the pavement, herring-boned, trodden
    for years;
The great yellow shocks of wheat and the dust-white road
    through Summer,
And, in Fall, the green walnut shells, and the stain they left for
    a while.

So I remember you, ripe country of broad-backed horses,
Valley of cold, sweet springs and dairies with limestone-floors;
And so they found you that year, when they scared your cows
    with their cannon,
And the strange South moved against you, lean marchers lost
    in the corn.

Two months have passed since Jackson died in the woods
And they brought his body back to the Richmond State House
To lie there, heaped with flowers, while the bells tolled,
Two months of feints and waiting.
                                            And now, at length,
The South goes north again in the second raid,
In the last cast for fortune.
                                    A two-edged chance
And yet a chance that may burnish a failing star;
For now, on the wide expanse of the Western board,
Strong pieces that fought for the South have been swept away
Or penned up in hollow Vicksburg.
                                            One cool Spring night
Porter's ironclads run the shore-batteries
Through a velvet stabbed with hot flashes.
                                            Grant lands his men.
Drives the relieving force of Johnston away
And sits at last in front of the hollow town
Like a huge brown bear on its haunches, terribly waiting.
His guns begin to peck at the pillared porches,
The sleepy, sun-spattered streets. His siege has begun.

Forty-eight days that siege and those guns go on
Like a slow hand closing around a hungry throat,
Ever more hungry.
                    The hunger of hollow towns,
The hunger of sieges, the hunger of lost hope.
As day goes by after day and the shells still whine
Till the town is a great mole-burrow of pits and caves
Where the thin women hide their children, where the tired men
Burrow away from the death that falls from the air
And the common sky turned hostile—and still no hope,
Still no sight in the sky when the morning breaks
But the brown bear there on his haunches, steadfastly waiting,
Waiting like Time for the honey-tree to fall.

The news creeps back to the watchers oversea.
They ponder on it, aloof and irresolute.
The balance they watch is dipping against the South.
It will take great strokes to redress that balance again.
There will be one more moment of shaken scales
When the Laird rams almost alter the scheme of things,
But it is distant.
                    The watchers stare at the board
Waiting a surer omen than Chancellorsville
Or any battle won on a Southern ground.

Lee sees that dip of the balance and so prepares
His cast for the surer omen and his last stroke
At the steel-bossed Northern shield. Once before he tried
That spear-rush North and was halted. It was a chance.
This is a chance. He weighs the chance in his hand
Like a stone, reflecting.
                          Four years from Harper's Ferry—
Two years since the First Manassas—and this last year
Stroke after stroke successful—but still no end.

He is a man with a knotty club in his hand
Beating off bulls from the breaks in a pasture fence
And he has beaten them back at each fresh assault,
McClellan—Burnside—Hooker at Chancellorsville—
Pope at the Second Manassas—Banks in the Valley—
But the pasture is trampled; his army needs new pasture.
An army moves like a locust, eating the grain,

And this grain is well-nigh eaten. He cannot mend
The breaks in his fence with famine or starving hands,
And if he waits the wheel of another year
The bulls will come back full-fed, shaking sharper horns
While he faces them empty, armed with a hunger-cracked
Unmagic stick.
            There is only this thing to do,
To strike at the shield with the strength that he still can use
Hoping to burst it asunder with one stiff blow
And carry the war up North, to the untouched fields
Where his tattered men can feed on the bulls' own grain,
Get shoes and clothes, take Washington if they can,
Hold the fighting-gauge in any event.
                      He weighs
The chance in his hand. I think that he weighed it well
And felt a high tide risen up in his heart
And in his men a high tide.
                They were veterans,
They had never been beaten wholly and blocked but once,
He had driven four Union armies within a year
And broken three blue commanders from their command.
Even now they were fresh from triumph.
                      He cast his stone
Clanging at fortune, and set his fate on the odds.

Lincoln hears the rumor in Washington.
They are moving North.
              The Pennsylvania cities
Hear it and shake, they are loose, they are moving North.
Call up your shotgun-militia, bury your silver,
Shoulder a gun or run away from the State,
They are loose, they are moving.
              Fighting Joe Hooker has heard it.
He swings his army back across the Potomac,
Rapidly planning, while Lee still visions him South.
Stuart's horse should have brought the news of that move
But Stuart is off on a last and luckless raid
Far to the East, and the grey host moves without eyes
Through crucial days.
              They are in the Cumberland now,

Taking minor towns, feeding fat for a little while,
Pressing horses and shoes, paying out Confederate bills
To slow Dutch storekeepers who groan at the money.
They are loose, they are in the North, they are here and there.
Halleck rubs his elbows and wonders where,
Lincoln is sleepless, the telegraph-sounders click
In the War Office day and night.
                                     There are lies and rumors,
They are only a mile from Philadelphia now,
They are burning York—they are marching on Baltimore—

Meanwhile, Lee rides through the heart of the Cumberland.
A great hot sunset colors the marching men,
Colors the horse and the sword and the bearded face
But cannot change that face from its strong repose.
And—miles away—Joe Hooker, by telegraph
Calls for the garrison left at Harper's Ferry
To join him. Elbow-rubbing Halleck refuses.
Hooker resigns command—and fades from the East
To travel West, fight keenly at Lookout Mountain,
Follow Sherman's march as far as Atlanta,
Be ranked by Howard, and tartly resign once more
Before the end and the fame and the Grand Review,
To die a slow death, in bed, with his fire gone out,
A campfire quenched and forgotten.
                                     He deserved
A better and brusquer end that marched with his nickname,
This disappointed, hot-tempered, most human man
Who had such faith in himself except for once,
And the once, being Chancellorsville, wiped out the rest.
He was often touchy and life was touchy with him,
But the last revenge was a trifle out of proportion.
Such things will happen—Jackson went in his strength,
Stuart was riding his horse when the bullet took him,
And Custer died to the trumpet—Dutch Longstreet lived
To quarrel and fight dead battles. Lee passed in silence.
McClellan talked on forever in word and print.
Grant lived to be President. Thomas died sick at heart.

So Hooker goes from our picture—and a spent aide
Reaches Meade's hut at three o'clock in the morning
To wake him with unexpected news of command.

251

The thin Pennsylvanian puts on his spectacles
To read the order. Tall, sad-faced and austere,
He has the sharp, long nose of a fighting-bird,
A prudent mouth and a cool, considering mind.
An iron-grey man with none of Hooker's panache,
But resolute and able, well skilled in war;
They call him "the damned old goggle-eyed snapping-turtle"
At times, and he does not call out the idol-shout
When he rides his lines, but his prudence is a hard prudence,
And can last out storms that break the men with panache,
Though it summons no counter-storm when the storm is done.

His sombre schoolmaster-eyes read the order well.
It is three days before the battle.
                          He thinks at first
Of a grand review, gives it up, and begins to act.

That morning a spy brings news to Lee in his tent
That the Union army has moved and is on the march.
Lee calls back Ewell and Early from their forays
And summons his host together by the cross-roads
Where Getty came with his ox-cart.
                          So now we see
These two crab-armies fumbling for each other,
As if through a fog of rumor and false report,
These last two days of sleepy, hay-harvest June.
Hot June lying asleep on a shock of wheat
Where the pollen-wind blows over the burnt-gold stubble
And the thirsty men march past, stirring thick grey dust
From the trodden pikes—till at last, the crab-claws touch
At Getty's town, and clutch, and the peaches fall
Cut by the bullets, splashing under the trees.

That meeting was not willed by a human mind,
When we come to sift it.
                          You say a fate rode a horse
Ahead of those lumbering hosts, and in either hand
He carried a skein of omen. And when, at last,
He came to a certain umbrella-copse of trees
That never had heard a cannon or seen dead men,
He knotted the skeins together and flung them down
With a sound like metal.

252

Perhaps. It may have been so.
All that we know is—Meade intended to fight
Some fifteen miles away on the Pipe Creek Line
And where Lee meant to fight him, if forced to fight,
We do not know, but it was not there where they fought.
Yet the riding fate,
Blind and deaf and a doom on a lunging horse,
Threw down his skeins and gathered the battle there.

The buttercup-meadows
Are very yellow.
A child comes there
To fill her hands.
The gold she gathers
Is soft and precious
As sweet new butter
Fresh from the churn.

She fills her frock
With the yellow flowers,
The butter she gathers
Is smooth as gold,
Little bright cups
Of new-churned sunshine
For a well-behaved
Hoop-skirted doll.

Her frock's full
And her hands are mothy
With yellow pollen
But she keeps on.
Down by the fence
They are even thicker.
She runs, bowed down with
Buttercup-gold.

She sees a road
And she sees a rider.
His face is grey
With a different dust.
He talks loud.

He rattles like tinware.
He has a long sword
To kill little girls.

He shouts at her now,
But she does not answer.
"Where is the town?"
But she will not hear.
There are other riders
Jangling behind him.
"We won't hurt you, youngster!"
But they have swords.

The buttercups fall
Like spilt butter.
She runs away.
She runs to her house.
She hides her face
In her mother's apron
And tries to tell her
How dreadful it was.

———————

Buford came to Gettysburg late that night
Riding West with his brigades of blue horse,
While Pettigrew and his North Carolinians
Were moving East toward the town with a wagon-train,
Hoping to capture shoes.
                    The two came in touch.
Pettigrew halted and waited for men and orders.
Buford threw out his pickets beyond the town.

The next morning was July first. It was hot and calm.
On the grey side, Heth's division was ready to march
And drive the blue pickets in. There was still no thought
Of a planned and decisive battle on either side
Though Buford had seen the strength of those two hill-ridges
Soon enough to be famous, and marked one down
As a place to rally if he should be driven back.

He talks with his staff in front of a tavern now.
An officer rides up from the near First Corps.

"What are you doing here, sir?"
                                        The officer
Explains. He, too, has come there to look for shoes.
—Fabulous shoes of Gettysburg, dead men's shoes,
Did anyone ever wear you, when it was done,
When the men were gone, when the farms were spoiled with the
    bones,
What became of your nails and leather? The swords went home,
The swords went into museums and neat glass cases,
The swords look well there. They are clean from the war.
You wouldn't put old shoes in a neat glass case,
Still stuck with the mud of marching.
                                        And yet, a man
With a taste for such straws and fables, blown by the wind,
Might hide a pair in a labelled case sometime
Just to see how the leather looked, set down by the swords.

The officer is hardly through with his tale
When Buford orders him back to his command.
"Why, what is the matter, general?"
                                        As he speaks
The far-off hollow slam of a single gun
Breaks the warm stillness. The horses prick up their ears.
"That's the matter," says Buford and gallops away.

———————

Jake Diefer, the barrel-chested Pennsylvanian,
Marched toward Getty's town past orderly fences,
Thinking of harvest.
                        The boy was growing up strong
And the corn-haired woman was smart at managing things
But it was a shame what you had to pay hired men now
Though they'd had good crops last year and good prices too.
The crops looked pretty this summer.
                                        He stared at the long
Gold of the wheat reflectively, weighing it all,
Turning it into money and cows and taxes,
A new horse-reaper, some first-class paint for the barn,
Maybe a dress for the woman.
                                His thoughts were few,
But this one tasted rough and good in his mouth

Like a spear of rough, raw grain. He crunched at it now.
—And yet, that wasn't all, the paint and the cash,
They were the wheat but the wheat was—he didn't know—
But it made you feel good to see some good wheat again
And see it grown up proper.
                              He wasn't a man
To cut a slice of poetry from a farm.
He liked the kind of manure that he knew about
And seldom burst into tears when his horses died
Or found a beautiful thought in a bumble-bee,
But now, as he tramped along like a laden steer,
The tall wheat, rustling, filled his heart with its sound.

Look at that column well, as it passes by,
Remembering Bull Run and the cocksfeather hats,
The congressmen, the raw militia brigades
Who went to war with a flag and a haircloth trunk
In bright red pants and ideals and ignorance,
Ready to fight like picture-postcard boys
While fighting still had banners and a sword
And just as ready to run in blind mob-panic. . . .
These men were once those men. These men are the soldiers,
Good thieves, good fighters, excellent foragers,
The grumbling men who dislike to be killed in war
And yet will hold when the raw militia break
And live where the raw militia needlessly die,
Having been schooled to that end.
                                   The school is not
A pretty school. They wear no cocksfeather hats.
Some men march in their drawers and their stocking feet.
They have handkerchiefs round their heads, they are footsore
    and chafed,
Their faces are sweaty leather.
                                And when they pass
The little towns where the people wish them godspeed,
A few are touched by the cheers and the crying women
But most have seen a number of crying women,
And heard a number of cheers.
                               The ruder yell back
To the sincere citizens cool in their own front yards,
"Aw, get a gun and fight for your home yourself!"
They grin and fall silent. Nevertheless they go on.

256

Jake Diefer, the barrel-chested Pennsylvanian,
The steer-thewed, fist-plank-splitter from Cumberland,
Came through the heat and the dust and the mounting roar
That could not drown the rustle of the tall wheat
Making its growing sound, its windrustled sound,
In his heart that sound, that brief and abiding sound,
To a fork and a road he knew.
                              And then he heard
That mixed, indocile noise of combat indeed
And as if it were strange to him when it was not strange.
—He never took much account of the roads they went,
They were always going somewhere and roads were roads.
But he knew this road.
                       He knew its turns and its hills,
And what ploughlands lay beyond it, beyond the town,
On the way to Chambersburg.
                            He saw with wild eyes
Not the road before him or anything real at all
But grey men in an unreal wheatfield, tramping it down,
Filling their tattered hats with the ripe, rough grain
While a shell burst over a barn.
                                 "Grasshoppers!" he said
Through stiff dry lips to himself as he tried to gauge
That mounting roar and its distance.
                                     "The Johnnies is there!
The Johnnies and us is fighting in Gettysburg,
There must be Johnnies back by the farm already,
By Jesus, those damn Johnnies is on my farm!"

That battle of the first day was a minor battle
As such are counted.
                     That is, it killed many men.
Killed more than died at Bull Run, left thousands stricken
With wounds that time might heal for a little while
Or never heal till the breath was out of the flesh.
The First Corps lost half its number in killed and wounded.
The pale-faced women, huddled behind drawn blinds
Back in the town, or in apple-cellars, hiding,
Thought it the end of the world, no doubt.
                                           And yet,

257

As the books remark, it was only a minor battle.
There were only two corps engaged on the Union side,
Longstreet had not yet come up, nor Ewell's whole force,
Hill's corps lacked a division till evening fell.
It was only a minor battle.
                              When the first shot
Clanged out, it was fired from a clump of Union vedettes
Holding a farm in the woods beyond the town.
The farmer was there to hear it—and then to see
The troopers scramble back on their restless horses
And go off, firing, as a grey mass came on.

He must have been a peaceable man, that farmer.
It is said that he died of what he had heard and seen
In that one brief moment, although no bullet came near him
And the storm passed by and did not burst on his farm.
No doubt he was easily frightened. He should have reflected
That even minor battles are hardly the place
For peaceable men—but he died instead, it is said.
There were other deaths that day, as of Smiths and Clancys,
Otises, Boyds, Virginia and Pennsylvania,
New York, Carolina, Wisconsin, the gathered West,
The tattered Southern marchers dead on the wheat-shocks.
Among these deaths a few famous.
                              Reynolds is dead,
The model soldier, gallant and courteous,
Shot from his saddle in the first of the fight.
He was Doubleday's friend, but Doubleday has no time
To grieve him, the Union right being driven in
And Heth's Confederates pressing on toward the town.
He holds the onrush back till Howard comes up
And takes command for a while.
                              The fighting is grim.
Meade has heard the news. He sends Hancock up to the field.
Hancock takes command in mid-combat. The grey comes on.
Five color-bearers are killed at one Union color,
The last man, dying, still holds up the sagging flag.
The pale-faced women creeping out of their houses,
Plead with retreating bluecoats, "Don't leave us boys,
Stay with us—hold the town." Their faces are thin,
Their words come tumbling out of a frightened mouth.
In a field, far off, a peaceable farmer puts

His hands to his ears, still hearing that one sharp shot
That he will hear and hear till he dies of it.
It is Hill and Ewell now against Hancock and Howard
And a confused, wild clamor—and the high keen
Of the Rebel yell—and the shrill-edged bullet song
Beating down men and grain, while the sweaty fighters
Grunt as they ram their charges with blackened hands.

Till Hancock and Howard are beaten away at last,
Outnumbered and outflanked, clean out of the town,
Retreating as best they can to a fish-hook ridge,
And the clamor dies and the sun is going down
And the tired men think about food.
                                  The dust-bitten staff
Of Ewell, riding along through the captured streets,
Hear the thud of a bullet striking their general.
Flesh or bone? Death-wound or rub of the game?
"The general's hurt!" They gasp and volley their questions.
Ewell turns his head like a bird, "No, I'm not hurt, sir,
But, supposing the ball had struck you, General Gordon,
We'd have the trouble of carrying you from the field.
You can see how much better fixed for a fight I am.
It don't hurt a mite to be shot in your wooden leg."

So it ends. Lee comes on the field in time to see
The village taken, the Union wave in retreat.
Meade will not reach the ground till one the next morning.

———————

So it ends, this lesser battle of the first day,
Starkly disputed and piecemeal won and lost
By corps-commanders who carried no magic plans
Stowed in their sleeves, but fought and held as they could.
It is past. The board is staked for the greater game
Which is to follow—The beaten Union brigades
Recoil from the cross-roads town that they tried to hold.
And so recoiling, rest on a destined ground.
Who chose that ground?
                        There are claimants enough in the books.
Howard thanked by Congress for choosing it
As doubtless, they would have thanked him as well had he

Chosen another, once the battle was won,
And there are a dozen ifs on the Southern side,
How, in that first day's evening, if one had known,
If Lee had been there in time, if Jackson had lived,
The heights that cost so much blood in the vain attempt
To take days later, could have been taken then.
And the ifs and the thanks and the rest are all true enough
But we can only say, when we look at the board,
"There it happened There is the way of the land.
There was the fate, and there the blind swords were crossed."

———

You took a carriage to that battlefield.
Now, I suppose, you take a motor-bus,
But then, it was a carriage—and you ate
Fried chicken out of wrappings of waxed paper,
While the slow guide buzzed on about the war
And the enormous, curdled summer clouds
Piled up like giant cream puffs in the blue.
The carriage smelt of axle-grease and leather
And the old horse nodded a sleepy head
Adorned with a straw hat. His ears stuck through it.
It was the middle of hay-fever summer
And it was hot. And you could stand and look
All the way down from Cemetery Ridge,
Much as it was, except for monuments
And startling groups of monumental men
Bursting in bronze and marble from the ground,
And all the curious names upon the gravestones. . . .

So peaceable it was, so calm and hot,
So tidy and great-skied.
                         No men had fought
There but enormous, monumental men
Who bled neat streams of uncorrupting bronze,
Even at the Round Tops, even by Pickett's boulder,
Where the bronze, open book could still be read
By visitors and sparrows and the wind:
And the wind came, the wind moved in the grass,
Saying . . . while the long light . . . and all so calm . . .

"Pickett came
And the South came
And the end came,
And the grass comes
And the wind blows
On the bronze book
On the bronze men
On the grown grass,
And the wind says
'Long ago
Long
Ago.' "

Then it was time to buy a paperweight
With flags upon it in decalcomania
And hope you wouldn't break it, driving home.

———————

Draw a clumsy fish-hook now on a piece of paper,
To the left of the shank, by the bend of the curving hook,
Draw a Maltese cross with the top block cut away.
The cross is the town. Nine roads star out from it
East, West, South, North.
                          And now, still more to the left
Of the lopped-off cross, on the other side of the town,
Draw a long, slightly-wavy line of ridges and hills
Roughly parallel to the fish-hook shank.
(The hook of the fish-hook is turned away from the cross
And the wavy line.)
                     There your ground and your ridges lie.
The fish-hook is Cemetery Ridge and the North
Waiting to be assaulted—the wavy line
Seminary Ridge whence the Southern assault will come.

The valley between is more than a mile in breadth.
It is some three miles from the lowest jut of the cross
To the button at the far end of the fish-hook shank,
Big Round Top, with Little Round Top not far away.
Both ridges are strong and rocky, well made for war.
But the Northern one is the stronger shorter one.
Lee's army must spread out like an uncoiled snake

261

Lying along a fence-rail, while Meade's can coil
Or halfway coil, like a snake part clung to a stone.
Meade has the more men and the easier shifts to make,
Lee the old prestige of triumph and his tried skill.
His task is—to coil his snake round the other snake
Halfway clung to the stone, and shatter it so,
Or to break some point in the shank of the fish-hook line
And so cut the snake in two.
                              Meade's task is to hold.

That is the chess and the scheme of the wooden blocks
Set down on the contour map.
                              Having learned so much,
Forget it now, while the ripple-lines of the map
Arise into bouldered ridges, tree-grown, bird-visited,
Where the gnats buzz, and the wren builds a hollow nest
And the rocks are grey in the sun and black in the rain,
And the jacks-in-the-pulpit grow in the cool, damp hollows.
See no names of leaders painted upon the blocks
Such as "Hill," or "Hancock," or "Pender"—
                                           but see instead
Three miles of living men—three long double miles
Of men and guns and horses and fires and wagons,
Teamsters, surgeons, generals, orderlies,
A hundred and sixty thousand living men
Asleep or eating or thinking or writing brief
Notes in the thought of death, shooting dice or swearing,
Groaning in hospital wagons, standing guard
While the slow stars walk through heaven in silver mail,
Hearing a stream or a joke or a horse cropping grass
Or hearing nothing, being too tired to hear.
All night till the round sun comes and the morning breaks,
Three double miles of live men.
Listen to them, their breath goes up through the night
In a great chord of life, in the sighing murmur
Of wind-stirred wheat.
                       A hundred and sixty thousand
Breathing men, at night, on two hostile ridges set down.

Jack Ellyat slept that night on the rocky ground
Of Cemetery Hill while the cold stars marched,

And if his bed was harder than Jacob's stone
Yet he could sleep on it now and be glad for sleep.

He had been through Chancellorsville and the whistling wood,
He had been through this last day. It is well to sleep
After such days.
    He had seen, in the last four months,
Many roads, much weather and death, and two men fey
Before they died with the prescience of death to come,
John Haberdeen and the corporal from Millerstown.
Such things are often remembered even in sleep.
He thought to himself, before he lay on the ground,
"We got it hot today in that red-brick town
But we'll get it hotter tomorrow."
       And when he woke
And saw the round sun risen in the clear sky,
He could feel that thought steam up from the rocky ground
And touch each man.
    One man looked down from the hill,
"That must be their whole damn army," he said and whistled,
"It'll be a picnic today, boys. Yes, it'll be
A regular basket-picnic." He whistled again.

"Shut your trap about picnics, Ace," said another man,
"You make me too damn hungry!"
       He sighed out loud.
"We had enough of a picnic at Chancellorsville,"
He said. "I ain't felt right in my stummick since.
Can you make 'em out?"
      "Sure," said Ace, "but they're pretty far."

"Wonder who we'll get? That bunch we got yesterday
Was a mean-shootin' bunch."
       "Now don't you worry," said Ace,
"We'll get plenty."
    The other man sighed again.
"Did you see that darky woman selling hot pies,
Two days ago, on the road?" he said, licking his lips,
"Blackberry pies. The boys ahead got a lot
And Jake and me clubbed together for three. And then
Just as we were ready to make the sneak,
Who comes up with a roar but the provost-guard?"

Did we get any pies? I guess you know if we did.
I couldn't spit for an hour, I felt so mad.
Next war I'm goin' to be provost-guard or bust."

A thin voice said abruptly, "They're moving—lookit—
They're moving. I tell you—lookit—"
                              They all looked then.
A little crackling noise as of burning thornsticks
Began far away—ceased wholly—began again—
"We won't get it awhile," thought Ellyat. "They're trying the
    left.
We won't get it awhile, but we'll get it soon.
I feel funny today. I don't think I'm going to be killed
But I feel funny. That's their whole army all right.
I wonder if those other two felt like this,
John Haberdeen and the corporal from Millerstown?
What's it like to see your name on a bullet?
It must feel queer. This is going to be a big one.
The Johnnies know it. That house looks pretty down there.
Phaëton, charioteer in your drunken car,
What have you got for a man that carries my name?
We're a damn good company now, if we say it ourselves,
And the Old Man knows it—but this one's bound to be tough.
I wonder what they're feeling like over there.

Charioteer, you were driving yesterday,
No doubt, but I did not see you. I see you now.
What have you got today for a man with my name?"

———————

The firing began that morning at nine o'clock,
But it was three before the attacks were launched.
There were two attacks, one a drive on the Union left
To take the Round Tops, the other one on the right.
Lee had planned them to strike together and, striking so,
Cut the Union snake in three pieces.
                              It did not happen.
On the left, Dutch Longstreet, slow, pugnacious and stubborn,
Hard to beat and just as hard to convince,
Has his own ideas of the battle and does not move
For hours after the hour that Lee had planned,
Though, when he does, he moves with pugnacious strength.

Facing him, in the valley before the Round Tops,
Sickles thrusts out blue troops in a weak right angle,
Some distance from the Ridge, by the Emmettsburg pike.
There is a peach orchard there, a field of ripe wheat
And other peaceable things soon not to be peaceful.

They say the bluecoats, marching through the ripe wheat,
Made a blue-and-yellow picture that men remember
Even now in their age, in their crack-voiced age.
They say the noise was incessant as the sound
Of all wolves howling, when that attack came on.
They say, when the guns all spoke, that the solid ground
Of the rocky ridges trembled like a sick child.
We have made the sick earth tremble with other shakings
In our time, in our time, in our time, but it has not taught us
To leave the grain in the field.
                              So the storm came on
Yelling against the angle.
                    The men who fought there
Were the tried fighters, the hammered, the weather-beaten,
The very hard-dying men.
                    They came and died
And came again and died and stood there and died,
Till at last the angle was crumpled and broken in,
Sickles shot down, Willard, Barlow and Semmes shot down,
Wheatfield and orchard bloody and trampled and taken,
And Hood's tall Texans sweeping on toward the Round Tops
As Hood fell wounded.
                    On Little Round Top's height
Stands a lonely figure, seeing that rush come on—
Greek-mouthed Warren, Meade's chief of engineers.
—Sometimes, and in battle even, a moment comes
When a man with eyes can see a dip in the scales
And, so seeing, reverse a fortune. Warren has eyes
And such a moment comes to him now. He turns
—In a clear flash seeing the crests of the Round Tops taken,
The grey artillery there and the battle lost—
And rides off hell-for-leather to gather troops
And bring them up in the very nick of time,
While the grey rush still advances, keening its cry.
The crest is three times taken and then retaken
In fierce wolf-flurries of combat, in gasping Iliads

Too rapid to note or remember, too obscure to freeze in a song.
But at last, when the round sun drops, when the nun-footed night,
Dark-veiled walker, holding the first weak stars
Like children against her breast, spreads her pure cloths there,
The Union still holds the Round Tops and the two hard keys of
    war.

Night falls. The blood drips in the rocks of the Devil's Den.
The murmur begins to rise from the thirsty ground
Where the twenty thousand dead and wounded lie.
Such was Longstreet's war, and such the Union defence,
The deaths and the woundings, the victory and defeat
At the end of the fish-hook shank.
                      And so Longstreet failed
Ere Ewell and Early struck the fish-hook itself
At Culp's Hill and the Ridge and at Cemetery Hill,
With better fortune, though not with fortune enough
To plant hard triumph deep on the sharp-edged rocks
And break the scales of the snake.
                    When that last attack
Came, with its cry, Jack Ellyat saw it come on.

They had been waiting for hours on that hard hill,
Sometimes under fire, sometimes untroubled by shells.
A man chewed a stick of grass and hummed to himself.
Another played mumbledeypeg with a worn black knife.
Two men were talking girls till they got too mad
And the sergeant stopped them.
                Then they waited again.

Jack Ellyat waited, hearing that other roar
Rise and fall, be distant and then approach.
Now and then he turned on his side and looked at the sky
As if to build a house of peace from that blue,
But could find no house of peace there.
               Only the roar,
The slow sun sinking, the fey touch at his mind. . . .

He was lying behind a tree and a chunk of rock
On thick, coarse grass. Farther down the slope of the hill

There were houses, a rough stone wall, and blue loungy men.
Behind them lay the batteries on the crest.

He wondered if there were people still in the houses.
One house had a long, slant roof. He followed the slant
Of the roof with his finger, idly, pleased with the line.

The shelling burst out from the Southern guns again.
Their own batteries answered behind them. He looked at his
      house
While the shells came down. I'd like to live in that house.
Now the shelling lessened.
                              The man with the old black knife
Shut up the knife and began to baby his rifle.
They're coming, Jack thought. This is it.
                                        There was an abrupt
Slight stiffening in the bodies of other men,
A few chopped ends of words scattered back and forth,
Eyes looking, hands busy in swift, well-accustomed gestures.
This is it. He felt his own hands moving like theirs
Though he was not telling them to. This is it. He felt
The old familiar tightness around his chest.
The man with the grass chewed his stalk a little too hard
And then suddenly spat it out.
                              Jack Ellyat saw
Through the falling night, that slight, grey fringe that was war
Coming against them, not as it came in pictures
With a ruler-edge, but a crinkled and smudgy line
Like a child's vague scrawl in soft crayon, but moving on
But with its little red handkerchiefs of flags
Sagging up and down, here and there.
                                    It was still quite far,
It was still like a toy attack—it was swallowed now
By a wood and came out larger with larger flags.
Their own guns on the crest were trying to break it up
—Smoking sand thrown into an ant-legged line—
But it still kept on—one fringe and another fringe
And another and—
                  He lost them all for a moment
In a dip of ground.
                    This is it, he thought with a parched
Mind. It's a big one. They must be yelling all right

267

Though you can't hear them. They're going to do it this time.
Do it or bust—you can tell from the way they come—
I hope to Christ that the batteries do their job
When they get out of that dip.

 Hell, they've lost 'em now,
And they're still coming.

 He heard a thin gnat-shrieking
"Hold your fire till they're close enough, men!"

 The new lieutenant.
The new lieutenant looked thin. "Aw, go home," he muttered,
"We're no militia—What do you think we are?"

Then suddenly, down by his house, the low stone wall
Flashed and was instantly huge with a wall of smoke.
He was yelling now. He saw a red battleflag
Push through smoke like a prow and be blotted out
By smoke and flash.

 His heart knocked hard in his chest.
"Do it or bust," he mumbled, holding his fire
While the rags of smoke blew off.

 He heard a thick chunk
Beside him, turned his head for a flicker of time.
The man who had chewed on the grass was injuredly trying
To rise on his knees, his face annoyed by a smile.
Then the blood poured over the smile and he crumpled up.
Ellyat stretched out a hand to touch him and felt the hand
Rasped by a file.

 He jerked back the hand and sucked it.
"Bastards," he said in a minor and even voice.

All this had occurred, it seemed, in no time at all,
But when he turned back, the smoky slope of the hill
Was grey—and a staggering red advancing flag
And those same shouting strangers he knew so well,
No longer ants—but there—and stumblingly running—
And that high, shrill, hated keen piercing all the flat thunder.

His lips went back. He felt something swell in his chest
Like a huge, indocile bubble.

 "By God," he said,
Loading and firing, "You're not going to get this hill,
You're not going to get this hill. By God, but you're not!"

268

He saw one grey man spin like a crazy dancer
And another fall at his heels—but the hill kept growing them.
Something made him look toward his left.
                                        A yellow-fanged face
Was aiming a pistol over a chunk of rock.
He fired and the face went down like a broken pipe
While something hit him sharply and took his breath.
"Get back, you suckers," he croaked, "Get back there, you
    suckers!"
He wouldn't have time to load now—they were too near.
He was up and screaming. He swung his gun like a club
Through a twilight full of bright stabbings, and felt it crash
On a thing that broke. He had no breath any more.
He had no thoughts. Then the blunt fist hit him again.

He was down in the grass and the black sheep of night ran over
    him . . .

———————

That day, Melora Vilas sat by the spring
With her child in her arms and felt the warm wind blow
Ruffling the little pool that had shown two faces
Apart and then clung together for a brief while
As if the mouths had been silver and so fused there. . . .

The wind blew at the child's shut fists but it could not open
    them.
The child slept well. The child was a strong, young child.

"Wind, you have blown the green leaf and the brown leaf
And in and out of my restless heart you blow,
Wakening me again.
                    I had thought for a while
My heart was a child and could sleep like any child,
But now that the wind is warm, I remember my lover,
Must you blow all summer, warm wind?"

"Divide anew this once-divided flesh
Into twelve shares of mercy and on each
Bestow a fair and succourable child,
Yet, in full summer, when the ripened stalks
Bow in the wind like golden-headed men,

Under the sun, the shares will reunite
Into unmerciful and childless love."

She thought again, "No, it's not that, it's not that,
I love my child with an 'L' because he's little,
I love my child with an 'S' because he's strong.
With an 'M' because he's mine.
                                    But I'm restless now.
We cut the heart on the tree but the bark's grown back there.
I've got my half of the dime but I want his.
The winter-sleep is over."

The shadows were longer now. The child waked and cried.
She rocked and hushed it, feeling the warm wind blow.
"I've got to find him," she said.

About that time, the men rode up to the house
From the other way. Their horses were rough and wild.
There were a dozen of them and they came fast.
Bent should have been out in the woods but he had come down
To mend a split wagon-wheel. He was caught in the barn.
They couldn't warn him in time, though John Vilas tried,
But they held John Vilas and started to search the place
While the younger children scuttled around like mice
Squeaking "It's drafters, Mom—it's the drafters again!"
Even then, if Bent had hidden under the hay
They might not have found him, being much pressed for time,
But perhaps he was tired of hiding.
                                    At any rate
When Melora reached the edge of the little clearing,
She saw them there and Bent there, up on a horse,
Her mother rigid as wood and her father dumb
And the head man saying, gently enough on the whole,
"Don't you worry, ma'am—he'll make a good soldier yet
If he acts proper."
                    That was how they got Bent.

On the crest of the hill, the sweaty cannoneers,
The blackened Pennsylvanians, picked up their rammers
And fought the charge with handspikes and clubs and stones,

Biting and howling. It is said that they cried
Wildly, "Death on the soil of our native state
Rather than lose our guns." A general says so.
He was not there. I do not know what they cried
But that they fought, there was witness—and that the grey
Wave that came on them fought, there was witness too.
For an instant that wheel of combat—and for an instant
A brief, hard-breathing hush.
                    Then came the hard sound
Of a column tramping—blue reinforcements at last,
A doomsday sound to the grey.
                  The hard column came
Over the battered crest and went in with a yell.
The grey charge bent and gave ground, the grey charge was
  broken.
The sweaty gunners fell to their guns again
And began to scatter the shells in the ebbing wave.

Thus ended the second day of the locked bull-horns
And the wounding or slaying of the twenty thousand.
And thus night came to cover it.
               So the field
Was alive all night with whispers and words and sighs,
So the slow blood dripped in the rocks of the Devil's Den.
Lincoln, back in his White House, asks for news.
The War Department has little. There are reports
Of heavy firing near Gettysburg—that is all.
Davis, in Richmond, knows as little as he.
In hollow Vicksburg, the shells come down and come down
And the end is but two days off.
               On the field itself
Meade calls a council and considers retreat.
His left has held and the Round Tops still are his.
But his right has been shaken, his centre pierced for a time,
The enemy holds part of his works on Culp's Hill,
His losses have been most stark.
              He thinks of these things
And decides at last to fight it out where he stands.

————————

Ellyat lay upon Cemetery Hill.
His wounds had begun to burn.

He was rising up
Through cold and vacant darknesses into faint light,
The yellow, watery light of a misty moon.
He stirred a little and groaned.
There was something cool
On his face and hands. It was dew. He lay on his back
And stared at a blowing cloud and a moist, dark sky.
"Old charioteer," he thought.
He remembered dully
The charge. The charge had come. They had beaten the charge.
Now it was moist dark sky and the dew and his pain.

He tried to get his canteen but he couldn't reach it.
That made him afraid.
"I want some water," he said.
He turned his head through stiff ages.
Two feet away
A man was lying quietly, fast asleep,
A bearded man in an enemy uniform.
He had a canteen. Ellyat wet his lips with his tongue.
"Hey Johnnie, got some water?" he whispered weakly.
Then he saw that the Johnnie had only half a head,
And frowned because such men could not lend canteens.

He was half-delirious now, and it seemed to him
As if he had two bodies, one that was pain
And one that lay beyond pain, on a couch of dew,
And stared at the other with sober wondering eyes.
"Everyone's dead around here but me," he thought,
"And as long as I don't sing out, they'll think that I'm dead
And those stretcher-bearers won't find me—there goes their lan-
tern
No, it's the moon—Sing out and tell 'em you're here."
The hot body cried and groaned. The cool watched it idly.
The yellow moon burst open like a ripe fruit
And from it rolled on a dark, streaked shelf of sky
A car and horses, bearing the brazen ball
Of the unbearable sun, that halted above him
In full rush forward, yet frozen, a motion congealed,
Heavy with light.
Toy death above Gettysburg.

He saw it so and cried out in a weak, thin voice
While something jagged fitted into his heart
And the cool body watched idly.
                                    And then it was
A lantern, bobbing along through the clumped dead men,
That halted now for an instant. He cried again.
A voice said, "Listen, Jerry, you're hearing things,
I've passed that feller twice and he's dead all right,
I'll bet you money."
                        Ellyat heard himself piping,
"I'm alive, God damn you! Can't you hear I'm alive?"

Something laughed, quite close now.
                                    "All right, Bub," said a cloud,
"We'll take your word for it. My, but the boy's got language!
Go ahead and cuss while we get you up on the stretcher—
It helps some—easy there, Joe."
                                    Jack Ellyat fell
Out of his bodies into a whispering blackness
Through which, now and then, he could hear certain talking
    clouds
Cough or remark.
                    One said. "That's two and a half
You owe me, Joe. You're pickin' 'em wrong tonight."
"Well, poor suckers," said Joseph. "But all the same,
If this one doesn't last till the dressing station
The bet's off—take it slower, Jerry—it hurts him."

————————

Another clear dawn breaks over Gettysburg,
Promising heat and fair weather—and with the dawn
The guns are crashing again.
                                    It is the third day.
The morning wears with a stubborn fight at Culp's Hill
That ends at last in Confederate repulse
And that barb-end of the fish-hook cleared of the grey.

Lee has tried his strokes on the right and left of the line.
The centre remains—that centre yesterday pierced
For a brief, wild moment in Wilcox's attack,
But since then trenched, reinforced and alive with guns.

273

It is a chance. All war is a chance like that.
Lee considers the chance and the force he has left to spend
And states his will.
                    Dutch Longstreet, the independent,
Demurs, as he has demurred since the fight began.
He had disapproved of this battle from the first
And that disapproval has added and is to add
Another weight in the balance against the grey.
It is not our task to try him for sense or folly,
Such men are the men they are—but an hour comes
Sometimes, to fix such men in most fateful parts,
As now with Longstreet who, if he had his orders
As they were given, neither obeyed them quite
Nor quite refused them, but acted as he thought best,
So did the half-thing, failed as he thought he would,
Felt justified and wrote all of his reasons down
Later in controversy.
                    We do not need
Such controversies to see that pugnacious man
Talking to Lee, a stubborn line in his brow
And that unseen fate between them.
                              Lee hears him out
Unmoved, unchanging.
                    "The enemy is there
And I am going to strike him," says Lee, inflexibly.

Wingate cursed with an equal stress
The guns in the sky and his weariness,
The nightmare riding of yesterday
When they slept in the saddle by whole platoons
And the Pennsylvania farmer's grey
With hocks as puffy as toy balloons,
A graceless horse, without gaits or speed,
But all he had for his time of need.
"I'd as soon be riding a Jersey cow."
But the Black Horse Troop was piebald now
And the Black Horse Troop was worn to the blade
With the dull fatigue of this last, long raid.
Huger Shepley rode in a tense
Gloom of the spirit that found offence

274

In all things under the summer skies
And the recklessness in Bristol's eyes
Had lost its color of merriment.
Horses and men, they were well-nigh spent.
Wingate grinned as he heard the "Mount,"
"Reckon we look sort of no-account,
But we're here at last for somebody's fight."
They rode toward the curve of the Union right.

———

At one o'clock the first signal-gun was fired
And the solid ground began to be sick anew.
For two hours then that sickness, the unhushed roar
Of two hundred and fifty cannon firing like one.

By Philadelphia, eighty-odd miles away,
An old man stooped and put his ear to the ground
And heard that roar, it is said, like the vague sea-clash
In a hollow conch-shell, there, in his flowerbeds.
He had planted trumpet-flowers for fifteen years
But now the flowers were blowing an iron noise
Through earth itself. He wiped his face on his sleeve
And tottered back to his house with fear in his eyes.

The caissons began to blow up in the Union batteries. . . .

———

The cannonade fell still. All along the fish-hook line,
The tired men stared at the smoke and waited for it to clear;
The men in the centre waited, their rifles gripped in their hands,
By the trees of the riding fate, and the low stone wall, and the
      guns.

These were Hancock's men, the men of the Second Corps,
Eleven States were mixed there, where Minnesota stood
In battle-order with Maine, and Rhode Island beside New York,
The metals of all the North, cooled into an axe of war.

The strong sticks of the North, bound into a fasces-shape,
The hard winters of snow, the wind with the cutting edge,

And against them came that summer that does not die with the
    year,
Magnolia and honeysuckle and the blue Virginia flag.

Tall Pickett went up to Longstreet—his handsome face was
    drawn.
George Pickett, old friend of Lincoln's in days gone by with the
    blast,
When he was a courteous youth and Lincoln the strange shawled
    man
Who would talk in a Springfield street with a boy who dreamt of
    a sword.

Dreamt of a martial sword, as swords are martial in dreams,
And the courtesy to use it, in the old bright way of the tales.
Those days are gone with the blast. He has his sword in his hand.
And he will use it today, and remember that using long.

He came to Longstreet for orders, but Longstreet would not
    speak.
He saw Old Peter's mouth and the thought in Old Peter's mind.
He knew the task that was set and the men that he had to lead
And a pride came into his face while Longstreet stood there
    dumb.

"I shall go forward, sir," he said and turned to his men.
The commands went down the line. The grey ranks started to
    move.
Slowly at first, then faster, in order, stepping like deer,
The Virginians, the fifteen thousand, the seventh wave of the
    tide.

There was a death-torn mile of broken ground to cross,
And a low stone wall at the end, and behind it the Second Corps,
And behind that force another, fresh men who had not yet
    fought.
They started to cross that ground. The guns began to tear them.

From the hill they say that it seemed more like a sea than a wave,
A sea continually torn by stones flung out of the sky,
And yet, as it came, still closing, closing and rolling on,
As the moving sea closes over the flaws and rips of the tide.

You could mark the path that they took by the dead that they
 left behind,
Spilled from that deadly march as a cart spills meal on a road,
And yet they came on unceasing, the fifteen thousand no more,
And the blue Virginia flag did not fall, did not fall, did not fall.

They halted but once to fire as they came. Then the smoke closed
 down
And you could not see them, and then, as it cleared again for a
 breath,
They were coming still but divided, gnawed at by blue attacks,
One flank half-severed and halted, but the centre still like a tide.

Cushing ran down the last of his guns to the battle-line.
The rest had been smashed to scrap by Lee's artillery fire.
He held his guts in his hand as the charge came up the wall
And his gun spoke out for him once before he fell to the ground.

Armistead leapt the wall and laid his hand on the gun,
The last of the three brigadiers who ordered Pickett's brigades,
He waved his hat on his sword and "Give 'em the steel!" he cried,
A few men followed him over. The rest were beaten or dead.

A few men followed him over. There had been fifteen thousand
When that sea began its march toward the fish-hook ridge and
 the wall.
So they came on in strength, light-footed, stepping like deer,
So they died or were taken. So the iron entered their flesh.

Lee, a mile away, in the shade of a little wood,
Stared, with his mouth shut down, and saw them go and be slain,
And then saw for a single moment, the blue Virginia flag
Planted beyond the wall, by that other flag that he knew.

The two flags planted together, one instant, like hostile flowers.
Then the smoke wrapped both in a mantle—and when it had
 blown away,
Armistead lay in his blood, and the rest were dead or down,
And the valley grey with the fallen and the wreck of the broken
 wave.

Pickett gazed around him, the boy who had dreamt of a sword
And talked with a man named Lincoln. The sword was still in
 his hand.

He had gone out with fifteen thousand. He came back to his lines
with five.
He fought well till the war was over, but a thing was cracked in
his heart.

———————

Wingate, waiting the sultry sound
That would pour the troop over hostile ground,
Petted his grey like a loving son
And wondered whether the brute would run
When it came to fighting, or merely shy
There was a look in the rolling eye
That he knew too well to criticize
Having seen it sometimes in other eyes.
"Poor old Fatty," he said, "Don't fret,
It's tough, but it hasn't happened yet
And we may get through it if you behave,
Though it looks just now like a right close shave.
There's something funny about this fight—"

He thought of Lucy in candlelight,
White and gold as the evening star,
Giving bright ribbons to men at war.
But the face grew dimmer and ever dimmer,
The gold was there but the gold was fainter,
And a slow brush streaked it with something grimmer
Than the proper tint of a lady's painter
Till the shadow she cast was a ruddy shadow.
He rubbed his eyes and stared at the meadow. . . .

"There was a girl I used to go with,
   Long ago, when the skies were cooler,
There was a tree we used to grow with
   Marking our heights with a stolen ruler.

There was a cave where we hid and fought once.
   There was a pool where the wind kept writing.
There was a possum-child we caught once.
   Caged it awhile, for all its biting.

There was a gap in a fence to see there,
   Down where the sparrows were always wrangling.

There was a girl who used to be there,
  Dark and thin, with her long braids dangling.

Dark and thin in her scuffed brown slippers
  With a boy's sling stuck in her apron-pocket,
With a sting in her tongue like a gallinipper's
  And the eyes of a ghost in a silver locket.

White and gold, white and gold,
You cannot be cold as she was cold,
Cold of the air and the running stream
And cold of the ice-tempered dream.

Gold and white, gold and white,
You burn with the heat of candlelight.
But what if I set you down alone
Beside the burning meteor-stone?

Blow North, blow South, blow hot, blow cold,
My body is pledged to white and gold,
My honor given to kith and kin,
And my doom-clothes ready to wrap me in
For the shut heart and the open hand
As long as Wingate Hall shall stand
And the fire burn and the water cool
And a fool beget another fool—

But now, in the hour before this fight,
I have forgotten gold and white.
I will remember lost delight.
She has the Appleton mouth, it seems,
And the Appleton way of riding,
But if she quarrels or when she gleams,
Something comes out from hiding.

She can sew all day on an Appleton hem
And look like a saint in plaster,
But when the fiddles begin to play,
And her feet beat fast but her heart beats faster,
An alien grace is alive in them
And she looks like her father, the dancing-master,
The scapegrace elegant, 'French Dupré.' "

Then the word came and the bugle sang
And he was part of the running clang,
The rush and the shock and the sabres licking
And the fallen horses screaming and kicking.
His grey was tired and his arm unsteady
And he whirled like a leaf in a shrieking eddy
Where every man was fighting his neighbor
And there was no room for the tricks of sabre
But only a wild and nightmare sickling.
His head felt burnt—there was something trickling
Into his eyes—then the new charge broke
The eddy apart like scattered smoke;
The cut on his head half made him blind.
If he had a mind, he had lost that mind.

He came to himself in a battered place,
Staring at Wainscott Bristol's face,
The dried blood made it a ferret's mask.

"What happened?" he croaked.

                              "Well, you can ask,"
Said Bristol, drawling, "But don't ask me,
For any facts of the jamboree.
I reckon we've been to an Irish wake
Or maybe cuttin' a johnny-cake
With most of the Union cavalry-corps.
I don't know yet, but it was a war.
Are you crazy still? You were for a piece.
You yelled you were Destiny's long-lost niece
And wanted to charge the whole Yank line
Because they'd stolen your valentine.
You fought like a fool but you talked right wild.
You got a bad bump, too."

                              Wingate smiled
"I reckon I did, but I don't know when.
Did we win or what?"

                              "And I say again,"
Said Bristol, heavily, "don't ask me.
Inquire of General Robert Lee.
I know we're in for a long night ride
And they say we got whipped on the other side.
What's left of the Troop are down by the road.

We lost John Leicester and Harry Spode
And the Lawley boys and Ballantyne.
The Major's all right—but there's Jim Divine
And Francis Carroll and Judson White—
I wish I had some liquor tonight."

Wingate touched the cut on his head.
It burned, but it no longer bled.
"I wish I could sleep ten years," he said.

———————

The night of the third day falls. The battle is done.
Lee entrenches that night upon Seminary Ridge.
All next day the battered armies still face each other
Like enchanted beasts.
                    Lee thinks he may be attacked,
Hopes for it, perhaps, is not, and prepares his retreat.

Vicksburg has fallen, hollow Vicksburg has fallen,
The cavedwellers creep from their caves and blink at the sun.
The pan of the Southern balance goes down and down.
The cotton is withering.

Army of Northern Virginia, haggard and tattered,
Tramping back on the pikes, through the dust-white summer,
With your wounds still fresh, your burden of prisoners,
Your burden of sick and wounded,
"One long groan of human anguish six miles long."
You reach the swollen Potomac at long last,
A foe behind, a risen river in front,
And fording that swollen river, in the dim starlight,
In the yellow and early dawn,
Still have heart enough for the tall, long-striding soldiers
To mock the short, half swept away by the stream.
"Better change our name to Lee's Waders, boys!"
"Come on you shorty—get a ride on my back."
"Aw, it's just we ain't had a bath in seven years
And General Lee, he knows we need a good bath."

So you splash and slip through the water and come at last
Safe, to the Southern side, while Meade does not strike;

Safe to take other roads, safe to march upon roads you know
For two long years. And yet—each road that you take,
Each dusty road leads to Appomattox now.

BOOK EIGHT

It is over now, but they will not let it be over.

It was over with John Brown when the sun rose up
To show him the town in arms and he did not flee,
Yet men were killed after that, before it was over,
And he did not die until November was cool
—Yellow leaves falling through a blue-grey dusk,
The first winds of November whirl and scatter them—
So now, the Confederacy,
Sick with its mortal sickness, yet lives on
For twenty-one falling months of pride and despair,
Half-hopes blown out in the lighting, heroic strokes
That come to nothing, and death piled hard upon death.

Follow that agony if you must and can
By the brushwood names, by the bloody prints in the woods,
Cold Harbor and Spottsylvania and Yellow Tavern
And all the lost court-houses and country stores
In the Wilderness, where the bitter fighting passed,
(No fighting bitterer)—follow the rabbit-runs
Through the tangled wilds where the hair of the wounded men
Caught fire from the burning trees, where they lay in the swamps
Like half-charred logs—find the place they called "Hell's Half
    Acre."
Follow the Indian names in the Indian West,
Chickamauga and Chattanooga and all the words
That are sewn on flags or cut in an armory wall.
My cyclorama is not the shape of the world
Nor even the shape of this war from first to last,
But like a totem carved, like a totem stained
With certain beasts and skies and faces of men
That would not let me be too quiet at night
Till they were figured.
                    Therefore now, through the storm,

The war, the rumor, the grinding of the machine,
Let certain sounds, let certain voices be heard.

A Richmond lady sits in a Richmond square
Beside a working-girl. They talk of the war,
They talk of the food and the prices in low-pitched voices
With hunger fretting them both. Then they go their ways.
But, before she departs, the lady has asked a question—
The working-girl pulls up the sleeve of her dress
And shows the lady the sorry bone of her arm.

Grant has come East to take up his last command
And the grand command of the armies.
                                        It is five years
Since he sat, with a glass, by the stove in a country store,
A stumpy, mute man in a faded Army overcoat,
The eldest-born of the Grants but the family-failure,
Now, for a week, he shines in the full array
Of gold cord and black-feathered hat and superb blue coat,
As he talks with the trim, well-tailored Eastern men.
It is his only moment of such parade.
When the fighting starts, he is chewing a dead cigar
With only the battered stars to show the rank
On the shoulderstraps of the private's uniform.

It is sullen Cold Harbor. The Union attack has failed,
Repulsed with a ghastly slaughter. The twilight falls.
The word goes round the attack will be made again
Though all know now that it cannot be made and win.
An anxious officer walks through his lines that night.
There has been no mutiny yet, throughout all these years,
But he wonders now. What are the men doing now?
He sees them there. They are silently writing their names
On bits of rag and sewing the scraps of cloth
To their jackets while they can, before the attack.
When they die, next morning, somebody may read the names.

Pickett's son is born on a night of mid-July
While the two armies face each other, and Pickett's men
Light bonfires of celebration along his lines.
The fire is seen from the tents of the other camp.
The news goes back to Grant and his chief of staff.

"Haven't we any wood for the little Pickett?" says Grant,
And the Union bonfires are lighted for Pickett's son.
—All night those two lines of brush-fire, facing each other—
Next day they send the baby a silver service.
Next week or so they move upon Pickett's works.

On a muddy river, little toy boats go out.
The soldiers are swapping coffee for rank tobacco,
A Northern badge for a Southern souvenir,
A piece of white-flour bread for a hunk of corn-pone.
A Northern lieutenant swims the river at night
To go to a Southern dance at a backwoods store,
Joke with the girls, swim back, and fight the next day
With his hosts of the night before.
                                        On disputed ground,
A grey-clad private worms his way like a snake,
The Union sentries see him and start to fire.
"Aw, shut up, Yank," he calls in a weary voice,
"I just skun out to salvage the chaplain's hat,
It's the only one he's got and it just blew off."
The firing stops.
                        "All right, Johnny," the sentries call,
"Get your hat, but be quick about it. We won't hurt you
But you better be back by the time our relief gets here."

A Southern sharpshooter crouched in a blue-gum tree
Drills a tiny blue-coated figure between the eyes
With a pea-ball fired from a smooth-bore squirrel-rifle.
The dead man's brother waits three days for his shot,
Then the sharpshooter crashes down through the breaking boughs
Like a lumpy bird, spread-eagled out of his nest.

The desolate siege of Petersburg begins.
The grain goes first, then the cats and the squeaking mice,
The thin cats stagger starving about the streets,
Die or are eaten. There are no more cats
In Petersburg—and in Charleston the creeping grass
Grows over the wharves where the ships of the world came in.
The grass and the moss grow over the stones of the wharves.
A Georgia belle eats sherbet near Andersonville
Where the Union prisoners rot. Another is weeping
The death of her brother, killed in a Union raid.

In the North, the factory chimneys smoke and fume;
The minstrels have raised their prices, but every night
Bones and Tambo play to a crowded house.
The hotels are full. The German Opera is here.
The ladies at Newport drive in their four-in-hands.
The old woman sells her papers about the war
The country widows stitch on a rusty black.

In the Shenandoah Valley, the millwheels rot.
(Sheridan has been there.) Where the houses stood,
Strong houses, built for weather, lasting it out,
The chimneys stand alone. The chimneys are blackened.
(Sheridan has been there.) This Valley has been
The granary of Lee's army for years and years.
Sheridan makes his report on his finished work.
"If a crow intends to fly over the Valley now
He'll have to carry his own provisions," says Sheridan.

The lonely man with the chin like John Calhoun's
Knows it is over, will not know it is over.
Many hands are turning against him in these last years.
He makes mistakes. He is stubborn and sick at heart.
He is inflexible with fate and men.
It is over. It cannot be. He fights to the end,
Clinging to one last dream—of somehow, somewhere,
A last, miraculous battle where he can lead
One wing of the Southern army and Lee the other
And so wrench victory out of the failing odds.
Why is it a dream? He has studied grand strategy,
He was thought a competent soldier in Mexico,
He was Secretary of War once—
                                He is the rigid
Scholar we know and have seen in another place,
Lacking that scholar's largeness, but with the same
Tight mouth, the same intentness on one concept,
The same ideal that must bend all life to its will
Or break to pieces—and that is the best of him.
The pettiness is the pettiness of a girl
More than a man's—a brilliant and shrewish girl,
Never too well in body yet living long.
He has that unforgiveness of women in him
And women will always know him better than men

285

Except for a few, in spite of Mexican wars,
In spite of this last, most desolate, warlike dream.
Give him the tasks that other scholar assumed,
He would not have borne them as greatly or with such skill
And yet—one can find a likeness.
                                  So now he dreams
Hopelessly of a fight he will never fight
And if worst comes to worst, perhaps, of a last
Plutarch-death on a shield.
                              It is not to be.
He will snatch up a cloak of his wife's by accident
In the moment before his capture, and so be seen,
The proud man turned into farce, into sorry farce
Before the ignorant gapers.
                              He shades his eyes
To rest them a moment, turns to his work again.

The gaunt man, Abraham Lincoln, lives his days.
For a while the sky above him is very dark.
There are fifty thousand dead in these last, bleak months
And Richmond is still untaken.
                                The papers rail,
Grant is a butcher, the war will never be done.
The gaunt man's term of office draws to an end,
His best friends muse and are doubtful. He thinks himself
For a while that when the time of election comes
He will not be re-elected. He does not flinch.
He draws up a paper and seals it with his own hand.
His cabinet signs it, unread.
                                Such writing might be
A long historic excuse for defeated strength.
This is very short and strict with its commonsense.
"It seems we may not rule this nation again.
If so, we must do our best, while we still have time,
To plan with the new rulers who are to come
How best to save the Union before they come,
For they will have been elected upon such grounds
That they cannot possibly save it, once in our place."

The cloud lifts, after all. They bring him the news.
He is sure of being President four years more.
He thinks about it. He says, "Well, I guess they thought

They'd better not swap horses, crossing a stream."
The deserters begin to leave the Confederate armies. . . .

Luke Breckinridge woke up one sunshiny morning
Alone, in a roadside ditch, to be hungry again,
Though he was used to being hungry by now.
He looked at his rifle and thought, "Well, I ought to clean it."
He looked at his feet and he thought, "Well, I ought to get
Another bunch of rags if we-uns is goin'
To march much more—these rags is down to my hide."
He looked at his ribs through the tears in his dirty shirt
And he thought, "Well, I sure am thin as a razorback.
Well, that's the way it is. Well, I ought to do somethin'.
I ought to catch up with the boys. I wish I remembered
When I had to quit marchin' last night. Well, if I start now,
I reckon I'm bound to catch 'em."
                                    But when he rose
He looked at the road and saw where the march had passed
—Feet going on through the dust and the sallow mud,
Feet going on forever—
                        He saw that track.
He was suddenly very tired.
He had been tired after fighting often enough
But this was another weariness.

He rubbed his head in his hands for a minute or so,
As if to rub some slow thought out of his mind
But it would not be rubbed away.
                                  "I'm near it," he thought,
"The hotel ain't a mile from here if Sophy's still there.
Well, they wouldn't give me a furlough when I ast.
Well, it's been a long time."
                              On the way to the plank hotel
He still kept mumbling, "I can catch up to the boys."
But another thought too vague to be called a thought
Washed over the mumble, drowning it, forcing it down.

The grey front door was open. No one was there.
He stood for a moment silent, watching the sun
Fall through the open door and pool in the dust.

287

"Sophy!" he called. He waited. Then he went in.
The flies were buzzing over the dirty plates
In the dining room and nobody there at all.
It made him feel tired. He started to climb the stairs.
"Hey, Sophy!" he called and listened. There was a creak
From somewhere, a little noise like a dusty rat
Running across a dusty, sun-splattered board.
His hands felt stronger.

                                He was on the second floor
Slamming the doors of empty room after room
And calling "Sophy!" At last he found the locked door.
He broke it down with his shoulder in a loud noise.
She was lying in bed with the covers up to her chin
And her thin hands clutching the covers.
                                "Well, Soph," he said.
"Well, it's you," she said.
                                They stared at each other awhile.

"The rest of 'em's gone," she said. "They went off last night.
We haven't had no business. The nigger said
The Yanks were coming. They didn't have room in the cart.
They said I could stay for a while and take care of things
Or walk if I wanted. I guess Mr. Pollet's crazy.
He was talking things to himself all the time they went.
I never slept in a bed like this before.
I didn't know you could sleep so soft in a bed."

"Did they leave any shoes?" said Luke.
                                She shook her head.
"I reckon you could maybe tear up a quilt.
I reckon they wouldn't mind."
                                Luke grinned like a wolf.
"I reckon they hadn't better," he said. "Not much.
Got anything to eat? I'm hungry as hell."

They ate what food she could find and she washed his feet
And bound them up in fresh rags.
                                He looked at the rags.
"Do for a while," he said. "Well, come along, Soph.
We got a long way to go."
                                Her eyes were big at him.
"The Yanks were comin'," she said. "You mean the war's over?"

288

He said, "I ain't had shoes for God knows how long."
He said, "If it was all Kelceys, you wouldn't mind.
Now I'm goin' to get me some shoes and raise me a crop,
And when we get back home, we'll butcher a hog.
There's allus hogs in the mountains."
                                    "Well," she said.
"Well, you get your duds," he said.
                              She didn't have much.
They went along two days without being stopped.
She walked pretty well for a thin sort of girl like that.
He told her she'd get fatter when they were home.

The third day, they were tramping along toward dusk,
On a lonely stretch of road, when she heard the horse-hoofs.
Luke had heard them before and shifted his rifle then.

The officer came in sight. He was young and drawn.
His eyes were old in their sockets. He reined his horse.
"You're goin' the wrong way, soldier. What's your regiment?"

Luke's eyes grew little. "–th Virginia," he drawled,
"But I'm on furlough."
                      "H'm," said the officer,
"Where are your furlough-papers?"
                                 Luke's hand slid down
By his trigger guard. "This here's my furlough," he said,
Resting the piece in the palm of the other hand.
The officer seemed to debate a thing in his mind
For a long instant. Then he rode on, in silence.
Luke watched him out of sight. When he was quite gone,
The hand slid back, the rifle was shouldered again.

———————

The night had fallen on the narrow tent.
–Deep night of Virginia summer when the stars
Are burning wax in the near, languid sky
And the soft flowers hardly close all night
But bathe in darkness, as a woman bathes
In a warm, fragrant water and distill
Their perfume still, without the fire of the sun.

The army was asleep as armies sleep.
War lying on a casual sheaf of peace
For a brief moment, and yet with armor on,
And yet in the child's deep sleep, and yet so still.
Even the sentries seemed to walk their posts
With a ghost-footfall that could match that night.

The aide-de-camp knew certain lines of Greek
And other such unnecessary things
As birds and music, that are good for peace
But are not deemed so serviceable for war.
He was a youth with an inquisitive mind
And doubtless had a failing for romance,
But then he was not twenty, and such faults
May sometimes be excused in younger men
Even when such creatures die, as they have done
At one time or another, for some cause
Which we are careful to point out to them
Much later, was no cause worth dying for,
But cannot reach them with our arguments
Because they are uneconomic dust.

So, when the aide-de-camp came toward the tent,
He knew that he was sleepy as a dog,
And yet the starlight and the gathered scents
Moved in his heart—like the unnecessary
Themes of a music fallen from a cloud
In light, upon a dark water.
                              And though he had
Some bitterness of mind to chew upon,
As well as messages that he must give
Before he slept, he halted in his tracks.

He saw, imprinted on the yellow light
That made the tent a hollow jack-o'-lantern,
The sharp, black shadow of a seated man,
The profile like the profile on a bust.
Lee in his tent, alone.
He had some shadow-papers in his hand,
But you could see he was not reading them,
And, if he thought, you could not read his thoughts,
Even as shadows, by any light that shines.

"You'd know that face among a million faces,"
Thought the still watcher, "and yet, his hair and beard
Have quite turned white, white as the dogwood-bloom
That blossomed on the way to Chancellorsville
When Jackson was alive and we were young
And we were winning and the end was near.
And now, I guess, the end is near enough
In spite of everything that we can do,
And he's alone tonight and Jackson's dead.

I saw him in the Wilderness that day
When he began to lead the charge himself
And the men wouldn't let him.
                              Gordon spoke
And then the men themselves began to yell
"Lee to the rear—General Lee to the rear!"
I'll hear that all my life. I'll see those paws
Grabbing at Traveller and the bridle-rein
And forcing the calm image back from death.

Reckon that's what we think of you, Marse Robert,
Reckon that's what we think, what's left of us,
The poor old devils that are left of us.
I wonder what he thinks about it all.
He isn't staring, he's just sitting there.
I never knew a man could look so still
And yet look so alive in his repose.

It doesn't seem as if a cause could lose
When it's believed in by a man like that.
And yet we're losing.
                       And he knows it all.
No, he won't ever say it. But he knows.

I'd feel more comfortable if he'd move.

We had a chance at Spottsylvania,
We had some chances in the Wilderness.
We always hurt them more than we were hurt
And yet we're here—and they keep coming on.

What keeps us going on? I wish I knew.
Perhaps you see a man like that go on

And then you have to follow.
                              There can't be
So many men that men have followed so.

And yet, what is it for? What is it for?
What does he think?
                    His hands are lying there
Quiet as stones or shadows in his lap.
His beard is whiter than the dogwood bloom,
But there is nothing ruined in his face,
And nothing beaten in those steady eyes.
If he's grown old, it isn't like a man,
It's more the way a river might grow old.

My mother knew him at old dances once.
She said he liked to joke and he was dark then,
Dark and as straight as he can stand today.
If he would only move, I could go forward.

You see the faces of spear-handling kings
In the old books they taught us from at school;
Big Agamemnon with his curly beard,
Achilles in the cruelty of his youth,
And Œdipus before he tore his eyes.

I'd like to see him in that chariot-rank,
With Traveller pulling at the leader-pole.
I don't think when the winged claws come down
They'll get a groan from him.
                              So we go on.
Under the claws. And he goes on ahead.

The sharp-cut profile moved a fraction now,
The aide-de-camp went forward on his errand.

The years ride out from the world like couriers gone to a throne
That is too far for treaty, or, as it may be, too proud;
The years marked with a star, the years that are skin and bone.
The years ride into the night like envoys sent to a cloud.

Perhaps they dismount at last, by some iron ring in the skies,
Dismount and tie their stallions and walk with an armored tread
Where an outlaw queen of the air receives strange embassies
Under a tree of wisdom, between the quick and the dead.

Perhaps they are merely gone, as the white foam flies from the bit,
But the sparkling noise of their riding is ever in our ears.—
The men who came to the maze without foreknowledge of it,
The losers and the finders, under the riding years.

They pass, and the finders lose, the losers find for a space.
There are love and hate and delusion and all the tricks of the
      maze.
There are always losers and finders. There is no abiding-place
And the years are unreturning. But, here and there, there were
      days.

Days when the sun so shone that the statue gave its cry
And a bird shook wings or a woman walked with a certain mirth,
When the staff struck out a spring from the stones that had long
      been dry,
And the plough moved on from the hilltop, but its share had
      opened the earth.

So the bird is caught for an instant, and so the bird escapes.
The years are not halted by it. The losers and finders wait.
The years move on toward the sunset, the tall, far-trafficking
      shapes,
Each with a bag of news to lay at a ghostly gate.

Riders shaking the heart with the hoofs that will not cease,
Will you never lie stretched in marble, the hands crossed over the
      breast,
Some with hounds at your feet to show that you passed in peace,
And some with your feet on lions?
                                        It is time that you were at rest.

John Vilas clucked to the scurvy rack of bones
Between the shafts. The rickety cart moved on
Like a tired insect, creaking through the dust.

There was another day behind them now
And any number of such days ahead
Unrolling like a long block-printed cloth
Pattered with field and stream and snake-rail fence,
And now and then, a flash of cavalry
Fording a backwoods creek; a big, slow star
Mounting in silver over lonely woods
While the fire smelled of pine and a cougar cried;
A warm barn, full of the sweet milky breath
Of cows; a lank-haired preacher on a mule;
A red-cheeked woman who rushed after them
Armed with a hot and smoking apple-pie
And would not take a penny from the old man
Who held the mended reins as if they were
The vast, slow-sweeping scythe of Time himself
—Old Time and the last children of his age,
Drawn in a rattling cart, too poor to thieve,
By a gaunt horse, too ancient to die,
Over a rutted road, day after day,
Returning to the East from whence he came.

It was a portent in the little towns.
The time had bred odd voyagers enough;
Disbanded soldiers, tramping toward the West
In faded army blouses, singing strange songs,
Heroes and chickenthieves, true men and liars,
Some with old wounds that galled them in the rains
And some who sold the wounds they never had
Seven times over in each new saloon;
Queer, rootless families, plucked up by war
To blow along the roads like tumbleweed,
Who fed their wild-haired children God knows how
But always kept a fierce and cringing cur,
Famished for scraps, to run below the cart;
Horsedealers, draft-evaders, gipsymen;
Crooked creatures of a thousand dubious trades
That breed like gnats from the débris of war;
Half-cracked herb-doctor, patent-medicine man
With his accordeon and his inked silk hat;
Sellers of snake-oil balm and lucky rings
And the old, crazy hatless wanderer
Who painted "God is Love" upon the barns

And on the rocks, "Prepare to Meet Thy God"
Lost tribes and maverick nations of the road—
The shiftless people, who are never still
But blow before the wind unquietly
And will so blow, until the last starved cur
Yaps at the last fat farmer, and lies down
With buckshot tearing at his ravening heart,
For the slow years to pick his carcass clean
And turn the little chapel of his bones
Into a dust so sifted by the wind
No winds that blow can sift it any more.

There were unquiet people on the road,
There were outlandish strays and travellers,
Drifting the little towns from day to day,
Stopping to mend a wheel or patch a shoe,
Beg, steal or sleep or write God's judgments out
And then pass on.   And yet, when these three came,
John Vilas and his daughter and her child,
Like snail-drawn Time, along the dusty track,
The story had gone on ahead of them.
And there was something in the rickety cart
Or the gaunt horse or in his driver's eyes
That made a fable of their journeying,
Until you heard John Vilas was that same
Lost Jew that wanders after every war
But cannot die in any, being curst.
He was the skipper, who first brought the slaves.
He was John Brown, arisen from his stone.
He was the drummer who had lost his way
At Valley Forge and frozen in the snow,
To rove forevermore, a dread old man
Beating a phantom drum across the wind.
He was a dozen such uncanny fetches,
And, while one must not talk with him too long,
There was no luck at all in crossing him,
Because, and in the end, the man was Time;
White-headed Time, stoop-shouldered on his scythe,
Driving a daughter and a daughter's son
Beyond the war, to some wrought-iron gate
Where they would drop their heavy load at last

—Load of all war and all misfortune's load—
On the green grass of a New England grave
Set on the sea-cliffs, looking toward the sea.

While, for the other tale, the woman's tale,
The heart-faced girl with the enormous eyes,
Roving from little town to little town
Still looking for her soldier—it became
Mixed with each story of such fortune told
Behind drawn blinds, by women, in the dusk,
Until she too grew fabulous as a song
Sung to a beechwood fiddle, and all the old
Barely-recorded chants that are the land
And no one poet's or musician's
—"Old Dan Tucker," "The Belle of Albany,"
The girl who died for love in the high woods
And cruel Barbara Allen in her pride.

So she became a concertina tune
Played in plank taverns by a blind, old man,
A jew's-harp strain, a comb-and-banjo song,
The music of a soapbox violin
Shrilled out against the tree-toads and the crickets
Through the hot nights of June. So, though she passed
Unknowing, yet she left the legend-touch
Bright as a splash of sumach still behind
Wherever the gaunt horse pulled on his load.
Till, later, those who knew no more of her
Living, than they might know of such removed
And singable creations as "Lord Randall,"
"Colombo," "Little Musgrave," or "Jay Gould's Daughter"
Yet knew enough of her to sing about
And fit her name, Melora, to the same
Slow-dropping minor of the water and earth—
The minor of the country barber-shops
That keens above the grave of Jesse James
And the lone prairie where the cowboy died,
The desolate minor of the jail-bird's song,
Luscious with sorrow, and the minor notes
That tell about the tragic end of such
As loved too well to have such cruel fathers
But were so loving, even in the dust,

A red-rose brier grew out of their dead hearts
And twined together in a lover's knot
For all the county people to admire,
And every lost, waif ballad we have made
And, making, scorned because it smelt of the earth,
And now would seek, but cannot make again—
So she became a legend and a name.

John Vilas, moving always toward the East,
Upon his last adventure, felt the sun
Strike at his bones and warm them like the last
Heat of the wood so long within the fire
That long ago the brightness ate its heart
And yet it lies and burns upon the iron
Unready still to crumble and be cool
The white, transmuted log of purest ash
Still glowing with a late and borrowed flame.

"This is the sun of age," he thought, "and so
We enter our last journeys with that sun
Which we have watched sink down ten thousand times
Knowing he would arise like Dedalus
On the first wings of morning, and exult
Like our own youth, fresh-risen from its bed
And inexhaustible of space and light.
But now the vessel which could not be filled
By violence or desire or the great storm,
Runs over with its weight of little days
And when this sun sinks now, we'll sink with him
And not get up again.   I find it fit
That I, who spent the years of my desire
In the lost forest, seeking the lost stone,
With little care for Harriet or the rest,
With little trust in safety or the world,
Should now retrace at last, and in my age,
The exact highway of my youth's escape
From everything that galled it and take on,
Like an old snake resuming his cast skins,
The East I fled, the little towns I mocked,
The dust I thought was shaken from my shoes,
The sleepiness from which I ran away.

Harriet's right and Harriet is just
And Harriet's back in that chintz-curtained room
From which I took her, twenty years ago,
With all the children who were always hers
Because I gave them nothing but my seed
And hardly heard their laughter or their tears
And hardly knew their faces or their names,
Because I listened for the wind in the bough,
Because my daughters were the shooting-stars,
Because my sons were the forgotten streams
And the wild silvers of the wilderness.

Men who go looking for the wilderness-stone
And find it, should not marry or beget,
For, if they do so, they may work a wrong
Deeper than any mere intent of pain.
And yet, what I have sought that I have sought
And cannot disavouch, although it is
The double knife that cuts the giver's hand
And the unwilling taker's.
                    So I took
My wife, long since, from that chintz-curtained room
And so she has gone back to it again
After these years, with children of those years,
And, being kind, she will not teach them there
To curse me, as I think, though if she did
She could find reason in her neighbor's eyes,
And, being Harriet, she will bring them up
As all such children should and must be reared
In all such houses, till the end of time,
As if she had not been away at all.
And so, at last, she'll get the peace she should.
And yet, some time, a child may run away.

We have had sons and daughters, she and I,
And, of them all, one daughter and one son
In whom our strange bloods married with the true
Marriage that is not merely sheath and sword.
The rest are hers. Those two were partly mine.

I taught my son to wander in the woods
Till he could step the hidden paths with me

Light as a whisper, indolent as Spring.
I would not tame his sister when I might,
I let her follow patterans of leaves,
Looking for stones rejected by the wise.
I kept them by me jealously and long.

And yet, the day they took him, when he sat
There on his horse, before they all rode off,
It was his mother who looked out of him
And it was to his mother that he looked.

That is my punishment and my offence
And that is how it was. And he is dead.
Dead of a fever, buried in the South,
Dead in this war I thought a whirligig
For iron fools to play with and to kill
Other men's sons, not mine. He's buried deep.
I kept him by me jealously and long.
Well, he walked well, alive. He was my son.
I'll not make tags of him.
                              We got the news.
She could not stay beside me after that.
I see so clearly why she could not stay.

So I retrace the hard steps of my youth
Now with this daughter, in a rattling cart
Drawn by a horse as lean as famine's self,
And am an omen in the little towns—
Because this daughter has too much of me
To be content with bread made out of wheat.
To be in love and give it up for rest,
To live serene without a knife at heart.

Such is the manner and the bound escape
Of those a disproportion drives unfed
From the world's table, without meat or grace,
Though both are wholesome, but who seek instead
Their solitary victual like the fox.
And who at last return as I return
In the ironic wagon of the years,
Back to the pasture that they found too green,
Broken of every knowledge but the last

Knowledge of how escape is not a door
But a slow-winding road whose hundred coils
Return upon each other, soon or late
—And how and when and under what cold stars
The old wound bleeds beneath the armored mind.

And yet, this journey is not desolate
Nor am I desolate in it, as we crawl
Slowly from little town to little town
Always against the sun, and the horse nods,
And there's my daughter talking, and her child
Sleeping or waking, and we stop awhile
And then go on awhile, and I can feel
The slow sun creeping through me summerlong.
Until, at times, I fall into a doze
Awake, a daydream without apparitions
And, falling so, inhabit for a space
A second childhood, calmer than the first,
But wise in the same fashion, and so touch
For a long, drowsy hour of afternoon,
The ripened thing, the autumn at the heart,
The one full star of evening that is age.

Yes, I must be a second child sometimes,
For as we pass and as they watch us pass,
It seems to me their eyes make stories of us
And I can hear those stories murmuring
Like pigeons in a loft when I'm asleep,
Till sometimes I must wonder for a while
If I've not changed myself for someone else
Or grown a story without knowing it,
And, with no intermediary death,
Stepped out of flesh and taken on a ghost.

For at such times, it almost seems to me
As if I were no longer what I am
But the deluded shade of Peter Rugg
Still looking for his Boston through the storm,
Or the strange spook of Johnny Appleseed,
Crept out of heaven on a windless night
To see if his wild orchards prosper still
And leave a heap of Baldwins and sweet russets

—Moonglittered, scrubbed with rags of silver cloud
And Indian magic—by the lucky doors
Of such good people as take care of them—
While for my daughter, though I know she's real,
She and her story, yet, in the waking dream
She mixes with that song I used to know
About the Spanish lady of old days
Who loved the Englishman and sought for him
All through green England in her scarlet shoes,
Knowing no word of English but his name.

I hear her voice, where the guitar is mixed
With the sweet, jangling mule-bells of Castile,
I see her face under its high shell-comb
—And then it is my daughter's—and I wake—
And yet know, even in waking, that we are
Somewhere between a story and a dream.
And so, you see, I find a kind of peace
In this last foray, will not rail at the sun,
Eat, drink and sleep, in spite of what is past,
Talk with my daughter, watch the turning skies.
The Spanish lady found her Englishman.
Well, we may find this boy I've half-forgot,
Although our story is another story.

So life works in us for a little while
And then the ferment's quiet.
                              So we do
Wrongs much beyond intent, and suffer them.
So we go looking for the wilderness-stone.

I shall smell lilac in Connecticut
No doubt, before I die, and see the clean
White, reticent, small churches of my youth,
The gardens full of phlox and mignonette,
The pasture-bars I broke to run away.

It was my thought to lie in an uncropped
And savage field no plough had ever scored,
Between a bee-tree and a cast deer-horn.
It was my thought to lie beside a stream
Too secret for the very deer to find,

Too solitary for remembrance.
It was a dream. It does not matter now.

Bury me where the soldiers of retreat
Are buried, underneath the faded star,
Bury me where the courtiers of escape
Fall down, confronted with their earth again.
Bury me where the fences hold the land
And the sun sinks beyond the pasture-bars
Never to fall upon the wilderness-stone.

And yet I have escaped, in spite of all."

———

Lucy Weatherby smoothed out clothes in a trunk
With a stab at her heart.
                        The trunk was packed to the lid.
There wasn't an empty corner anywhere,
Pack as she would—but the blue dress wouldn't go in.

Of course she'd be getting a lot of new dresses soon
And the blue was old—but she couldn't leave it behind.
If only Henry wasn't so selfish, at times!
But Henry was like all brothers and like all men,
Expecting a lady to travel to Canada
With just one trunk and the boxes!
                        It was too bad.
He had a trunk of his own for razors and shirts,
And yet she couldn't take two—and there were the hoops;
He kept on fussing because she wouldn't leave them
When she knew he was hoping to take all those silly books
As if you couldn't buy books wherever you went!

She pinched her cheek and stared at the trunk again.
The green could come out, of course, and the blue go in,
But she couldn't bear the idea of leaving the green.

The war, of course, and one thinks so much of the war,
And those terrible Yankees actually at our gates,
In spite of our fine, brave boys and poor Mr. Davis,
In spite of wearing old dresses for two whole years
And sending the servants out to work at the forts,

In spite of the cheers and the songs and the cause and the right.
Only, one must not be selfish. One must be brave.
One must think about Henry's health and be sensible,
And Henry actually thinks we can get away. . . .

The blue or the green? She couldn't decide it yet,
And there were all those letters to write tonight.
She'd simply have to write to Clay and Huger
About Henry's health—and how it just breaks my heart,
But one cannot leave one's sick brother—and afterwards,
One can always send one's address—and I'm sure if they do
We'll give them a real, old-fashioned Richmond welcome,
Though they say that the British leftenants are simply sweet
And every Southern girl is an absolute belle.
They play the "Bonnie Blue Flag" at the dances there,
And Sara Kenefick is engaged to an earl.
She saw herself, for an instant, walking the safe
Street of a calm and British-looking town.
She had on a new dress. Her shoes and her hat were new.
A white-haired, dim-faced man in a British coat
Walked beside her and looked and was listening,
While she told him all about it, and hearing the guns,
And how they'd actually lived without butcher's meat
For weeks and weeks—and the wounded—and General Lee—
And only Henry's health had forced them at last
To leave the dear South. She choked. He patted her hand.
He hoped they would stay in Canada for a while.

The blue or the green? It was dreadfully hard to choose,
And with all the letters to write—and Jim Merrihew
And that nice Alabama Major—
                              She heard the bells
Ring for a wedding, but this was a different groom,
This was a white-haired man with stars on his coat,
This was an Order wrapped in an English voice.

Honey, sugar-lump honey I love so dearly,
You have eluded the long pursuit that sought you,
You have eluded the hands that would so enclose you
And with strange passion force you.
                              What was this passion?
We do not know, you and I, but we would not bear it

And are gone free.
                    So at last, if fair girls must marry,
As young girls should, it is after another fashion
And not with youth but wisely.
                    So we are ransomed,
And I am yours forever and you are mine,
Honey, sugar-lump honey.
                    So we attain,
The white-haired bridegrooms with the stars on their coats
And yet have the beaus to dance with, for we like dancing,
So all the world finds our wifely devotion charming,
So we play all day in the heat of the sun.

She held the blue dress under her chin once more
And smoothed it with one white hand. Then she put it down
Smiling a little. No, it couldn't go in,
But she would see if she couldn't help Henry pack,
And if she did, the blue could go with his shirts.
It hardly mattered, leaving some shirts behind.

————————

        Sherman's buzzin' along to de sea,
        Jubili, Jubilo!
        Sherman's buzzin' along to de sea,
        Like Moses ridin' on a bumblebee,
        Settin' de prisoned and de humble free!
        Hit's de year of Jubilo!

        Massa was de whale wid de big inside,
        Jubili, Jubilo!
        Massa was de lion and de lion's hide.
        But de Lord God smacked him in his hardheart pride,
        And de whale unswallered, and de lion died!
        Hit's de year of Jubilo!

        Oh, hit don't matter if you's black or tan,
        Jubili, Jubilo!
        Hit don't matter if you's black or tan,
        When you hear de noise of de freedom-ban'
        You's snatched baldheaded to de Promise Lan',
        Hit's de year of Jubilo!

Oh, hit don't matter if you pine or ail,
Jubili, Jubilo!
Hit don't matter if you pine or ail,
Hit don't matter if you's been in jail,
De Lord's got mercy for your mumblin' tale!
Hit's de year of Jubilo!

Every nigger's gwine to own a mule,
Jubili, Jubilo!
Every nigger's gwine to own a mule,
An' live like Adam in de Golden Rule,
An' send his chillun to de white-folks' school!
In de year of Jubilo!

Fall down on your knees and bless de Lord,
Jubili, Jubilo!
Fall down on your knees and bless de Lord,
Dat chased old Pharaoh wid a lightnin'-sword,
And rose up Izzul fum de withered gourd,
Hit's de year of Jubilo!

Shout thanksgivin' and shout it loud!
Jubili, Jubilo!
Shout thanksgivin' and shout it loud,
We was dead and buried in de Lazrus-shroud,
But de Lord came down in a glory-cloud,
An' He gave us Jubilo!

So Sherman goes from Atlanta to the sea
Through the red-earth heart of the land, through the pine-smoke
    haze
Of the warm, last months of the year.
                        In the evenings
The skies are green as the thin, clear ice on the pools
That melts to water again in the heat of noon.
A few black trees are solemn against those skies.
The soldiers feel the winter touching the air
With a little ice.
                    But when the sun has come up,
When they halt at noonday, mopping their sweaty brows,
The skies are blue and soft and without a cloud.

Strange march, half-war, half trooping picnic-parade,
Cutting a ruinous swathe through the red-earth land;
March of the hardy bummers and coffee-coolers
Who, having been told to forage, loot as they can
And leave a wound that rankles for sixty years.
March of the honest, who did not loot when they could
And so are not remembered in Southern legend.
Rough-bearded Sherman riding the red-earth roads,
Writing home that his rascals are fat and happy,
Saying or else not saying that war is hell,
Saying he almost trembles himself to think
Of what will happen when Charleston falls in the hands
Of those same rascals—and yet, when we read that march
Hardly the smoking dragon he has been called,
But the mere rough-handed man who rode with a hard
Bit through the land, unanxious to spare his foe
Nor grimly anxious to torture for torture's sake,
Smashing this and that,—and yet, in the end,
Giving such terms to the foe struck down at last
That the men in Washington disavow them and him
For over-kindness.
                    So now, through the pine-smoke Fall,
The long worm of his army creeps toward Savannah
Leaving its swathe behind.
                    In the ruined gardens
The buried silver lies well hid in the ground.
A looter pocks bullet-marks in an old oil-portrait.
A woman wails and rages against the thieves
Who carry her dead child's clothes on their drunken bayonets.
A looter swings from a pine tree for thefts too crude.
A fresh-faced boy gets scars he will carry long
Hauling a crippled girl from a burning house,
But gets no thanks but hate from the thing he saved,
And everywhere,
A black earth stirs, a wind blows over black earth,
A wind blows into black faces, into old hands
Knotted with long rheumatics, cramped on the hoe,
Into old backs bent double over the cotton,
The wind of freedom, the wind of the jubilo.

They stray from the lost plantations like children strayed,
Grinning and singing, following the blue soldiers,

They steal from the lonesome cabins like runaways
Laden with sticks and bundles and conjur-charms;
A huge black mother carries her sucking child
Wrapped in a quilt, a slim brown girl and her lover
Wander November woods like Adam and Eve,
Living on roots and rabbits and liberty,
An old grey field hand dimly plods through the mud,
Looking for some vague place he has heard about
Where Linkum sits at a desk in his gold silk hat
With a bag of silver dollars in either hand
For every old grey field hand that comes to him,
All God's chillun got shoes there and fine new clothes,
All God's chillun got peace there and roastin'-ears,
Hills of barbecue, rivers of pot-licker,
Nobody's got to work there, never no more.

His feet are sore with the road but he stumbles on,
A hundred, a thousand others stumble as he,
Chanting, dizzied, drunken with a strange fever,
A child's delight, a brightness too huge to grasp,
The hidden nation, untaught, unrecognized,
Free at last, but not yet free with the free,
Ignorant, joyful, wronged, child-minded and searching,
Searching the army's road for this new wild thing
That means so much but can't be held in the hand,
That must be there, that yet is so hard to find,
This dream, this pentecost changing, this liberty.

Some wander away to strange death or stranger life,
Some wander awhile and starve and come back at last,
Some stay by the old plantation but will not work
To the great disgust of masters and mistresses,
Sing idly, gamble, sleep through the lazy hours,
Waiting for friendly heaven to rain them down
The mule and the forty acres of their desire.
Some, faithful beyond the bond that they never signed,
Hold to that bond in ruin as in the sun,
Steal food for a hungry mistress, keep her alive,
Keep the house alive, try to pick the weeds from the path,
Gather the wood and chop it and make the fire,
With pitying scorn for the runaway sheep of freedom,
Freedom's a ghost and freedom's a foolish talk,

What counts is making the fire as it should be made. . . .
Oh, blackskinned epic, epic with the black spear,
I cannot sing you, having too white a heart,
And yet, some day, a poet will rise to sing you
And sing you with such truth and mellowness,
—Deep mellow of the husky, golden voice
Crying dark heaven through the spirituals,
Soft mellow of the levee roustabouts,
Singing at night against the banjo-moon—
That you will be a match for any song
Sung by old, populous nations in the past,
And stand like hills against the American sky,
And lay your black spear down by Roland's horn.

Meanwhile, in Georgia, the scythe of the march mows on,
The Southern papers discount it as best they can.
Lincoln is anxious, Davis more anxious still.
The war is in its last winter of strife and pain.

———————

Cudjo buried the silverware
On a graveyard night of sultry air
While the turned sods smelled of the winter damp
And Mary Lou Wingate held the lamp.
They worked with a will. They did not speak.
The light was yellow. The light was weak.
A tomb-light casting a last, brief flame
Over the grave of Wingate fame.
The silver bowl of the Wingate toasts,
The spoons worn hollow by Wingate ghosts,
Sconce and ladle and bead-rimmed plate
With the English mark and the English weight,
The round old porringer, dented so
By the first milk-teeth of the long ago,
And the candlesticks of Elspeth Mackay
That she brought with her youth on her wedding-day
To light the living of Wingate Hall
While the mornings break and the twilights fall
And the night and the river have memories. . . .

There was a spook in Cudjo's eyes
As he lowered the chests where they must lie

308

And patted the earth back cunningly.
He knew each chest and its diverse freight
As a blind man knows his own front gate
And, decade by decade and piece by piece,
With paste and shammy and elbow-grease,
He had made them his, by the pursed-up lips
And the tireless, polishing fingertips,
Till now as he buried them, each and all,
What he buried was Wingate Hall,
Himself and the moon and the toddy-sippers,
The river mist and the dancing-slippers,
Old Marse Billy and Mary Lou
And every bit of the world he knew,
Master and lady and house and slave,
All smoothed down in a single grave.
He was finished at length. He shook his head.
"Mistis, reckon we's done," he said.
They looked at each other, black and white,
For a slow-paced moment across the light.

Then he took the lamp and she smoothed her shawl
And he lit her back to the plundered Hall,
To pray, with her old serene observance
For the mercy of God upon faithful servants
And a justice striking all Yankees dead
On her cold, worn knees by the great carved bed,
Where she had lain by a gentleman's side,
Wife and mother and new-come bride,
Sick with the carrying, torn with the borning,
Waked by the laughter on Christmas morning,
Through love and temper and joy and grief,
And the years gone by like the blowing leaf.

She finished her prayer with Louisa's child,
And, when she had risen, she almost smiled.
She struck her hand on the bedstead head,
"They won't drive me from my house," she said,
As the wood rang under her wedding-ring.
Then she stood for a moment, listening,
As if for a step, or a gentleman's name,
But only the gnats and the echoes came.

Cudjo, being less fortified,
Covered his ears with his hands and tried
To shut the noise of the risen wind
Out of the trouble of his mind.
He thought, "Ain't right for dat wind to blow.
She wasn't blowing awhile ago.
Jus' riz up fum de earth somewhere
When we buried dat orphan silver dere.
Got to hide it, and so we tried,
But silver like dat don't like to hide,
Silver's ust to be passed aroun'
Don't like lyin' in lonesome groun',
Wants to come back to de Hall, all right.
Silver, I always shone you bright,
You could see yo'self in de shine—
Silver, it wasn't no fix of mine!
Don't you come projeckin' after me!"

His eyes were shut but he still could see
The slow chests rising out of the ground
With an ominous clatter of silver sound,
The locks undoing, the bags unfastening,
And every knife and platter and spoon
Clinking out of the grave and hastening
Back to the Hall, in the witches' moon;
And the wind in the chimney played such tricks
That it was no wind, be it soft or loud,
But Elspeth seeking her candlesticks
All night long in her ruffled shroud,
The deep voice haunting the ocean-shell
To give her judgment and weave her spell,
"Thrift and love for the house and the chief
And a scone on the hob for the son of grief,
But a knife in the ribs for the pleasant thief."

Cudjo heard it, and Cudjo shook,
And Cudjo felt for the Holy Book,
And the wind blew on without peace or rest,
Blowing the straws from the dried-up nest.

———

Bailey, tramping along with Sherman's bummers,
Grumbled and found life pleasant and hummed his tune.

He was well, the blood ran in him, he ate for ten,
He and the gang had salvaged a wall-eyed nig
To fix their victuals—and if the captain was on,
The captain had a blind eye.
                            Last night it was turkey,
The night before it was duck—well, you couldn't expect
Such things to keep on forever, but while they did
It was pretty soft—it was war like it ought to be.
The Old Man marched 'em hard, but that was all right,
The Old Man knew his job and the nig was a buster
And the gang was as good a gang as you'd hope to find,
None of your coffee-coolers and straggle-tails
But a regular gang that ran like an eight-day clock.
Oh it was gravy, it was the real duck soup,
Marchin' into Atlanta after the fight
And then this marchin'—well, they were due for it,
And he was a sergeant now.
                            And up in his pack
Were souvenirs for the red-haired widow in Cairo,
Some of 'em bought and some just sort of picked up
But not a damn one stolen, to call it stealin'.
He wasn't a coffee-cooler or a slick Susio.
Poor little kid—she'd had a pretty tough time—
Cry like a fool when she gets a squint at that brooch—
They said you couldn't tell about widows much,
But what the hell—he wasn't a barnyard virgin—
He liked a woman who'd been over the bumps
And kept her get-up-and-git and her sassiness.
Spitfire-sweetie, you're my valentine now,
Bet the kids have red hair—well you can't help that—
But they'll all look like Poppa or he'll know why.

He mused a moment, thinking of Ellyat now.
There was another kid and a crazy kid,
Sort of missed him, hope he's gettin' it soft,
Must have got a banger at Gettysburg,
Wrote me a letter a couple of months ago,
Maybe six, I dunno, I sort of forget.
Ought to give him his old spread-eagle now,
Darn good kid, but done enough for his pay.
Hope he finds that girl he was talkin' about,
Sounds like a pretty good piece for a storm-and-strife,

Skinny, though—we like 'em more of a weight,
Don't we, Carrots?
                    Well, it's all in a life.
Ought to write him sometime if we get a chance,
Wish we was West—we'd have him out to the weddin',
Me and Bessie, show him the Cairo girls,
Hand him the fireman's grip and give him a time.

His heart was overflowing with charity,
But his throat was dry as the bottom of his canteen.
There was a big, white house, some way from the road. . . .

He found his captain, saluted and put his question.
The captain's eyes were satiric but not displeased.
"All right, Sergeant, take your detail and forage,
We're running low on bacon, it seems to me,
And if you happen to find a pigeon or two
Remember the Colonel's penchant for pigeon-pie.
But don't waste time and don't put your hopes too high,
The Nth Corps must have gone by there hours ago
And they're the biggest thieves in this whole, wide army.
You'll be back, in ranks, all sober, in just two hours
Or you won't have stripes. And if I find one more man
Trying to take a pet with him on this march,
I don't care if it's only a treetoad, I'll skin him alive."

So Bailey came to the door of Wingate Hall,
With the high wind blowing against him and gave his orders
"Make it quick now, boys—don't cut any monkeyshines,
But be sure and get the pigeons if they're around.
Clark, you and Ellis stay with me by the door,
I'm going to talk to the house if there's anyone left."

He knocked and called. There was a long, heavy silence.
"Hey you, the house!" The silence made him feel queer.
He cursed impatiently and pushed at the door.
It swung wide open. He turned to Ellis and Clark.
"I'm goin' in," he said. "If you hear me yell
Come in bilin'."
                    They watched him with mocking eyes.
"Wish to hell they'd make me a sergeant, Clark,"
"A three-stripe souvenir sergeant."

312

                              "Aw, hell," said Clark,
"Bailey's all right. He'll let us in on the juice
If there's any lawful juice that a man could get."
"Sure he's all right. Who says that he ain't all right!"
"But all the same, he's a sergeant."
                              Bailey, meanwhile
Was roving like a lost soul through great, empty rooms
And staring at various objects that caught his eye.
Funny old boy with a wig, hung up on the wall,
Queer sort of chairs, made your hands feel dirty to touch 'em
Though they were faded.
                      Everything faded and old
And quiet—and the wind blowin'—he moved as on tiptoe
Though he couldn't say why he did.
                              Old workbasket there.
He opened it idly—most of the things were gone
But there was a pair of little, gold-mounted scissors
Made like a bird, with the blades the beak of the bird.
He picked it up and opened and shut the blades.
Hadn't rusted—sort of handsome and queer—
Bessie would certainly like it—
                      He held it a minute.
Wouldn't take up any room. Then he frowned at the thing.
"Aw hell," he said, "I got enough souvenirs.
I ain't no damn coffee-cooler."

He started to put the scissors back in the case
And turned to face a slight grey-headed old woman
Dressed in black, with eyes that burned through his skin
And a voice that cut at his mind like a rawhide whip,
Calling him fifty different kinds of a thief
And Yankee devil and liar and God knows what,
Tearing the throat of her dress with her thin old hands
And telling him he could shoot her down like a dog
But he'd steal her children's things over her dead body.
My God, as if you went around shootin' old women
For fun, my God!
                      He couldn't even explain.
She was like all of 'em, made him sick in his lunch.
"Oh hell," he yelled. "Shut up about your damn scissors,
This is a war, old lady!"
                      "That's right," she said,

313

"Curse a helpless female, you big, brave soldier."
Well, what was a man to do?
                          He got out of the house,
Sore and angry, mean as a man could feel,
But her voice still followed, reviling, making him burn.
Now, where in hell was that detail?
                          He saw them now,
All except Clark and Ellis, gathered around
A white-polled nigger wringing his hands and weeping.
One man had a neck-wrung pigeon stuffed in his blouse.
Well, that was something.
                          He laid his hand on the nigger.
"Hey, Uncle, where's the well? You folks got a well?"
But the nigger just kept on crying like an old fool.
"He thinks we're goin' to scalp him," said one of the men,
"I told him twict that he's free but the shine won't listen.
I give him some money, too, but he let it drop.
The rest of 'em run away when the army came."

"Well, tell him he's safe and make him rustle some water,
I'm dry as a preacher's tongue. Where's Ellis and Clark?"

He found Clark solemnly prodding the hard dirt floor
Of a negro cabin, while Ellis lighted the task
With a splinter of burning pine.
                          His rage exploded
In boiling lava. They listened respectfully.
"And next time, I give you an order," he ended up,
"Why you——— ——— ———"
                          Clark wiped his face with his sleeve.
"Sorry, Sergeant," he said in an awed, low voice.
"Well you better be! What the hell do you think you're at,
Playin' tit-tat-toe or buryin' somebody's dog?"
"Well, Sergeant," said Ellis, humbly, "I allus heard
They buried stuff, sometimes, under these here cabins.
Well, I thought we could take a look—well—"
                          "Huh?" said Bailey.
He seized the torch and looked at the trodden floor
For an instant. Then his pride and his rage returned.
"Hell's fire!" he said, and threw the splinter aside,
"That's just about what you would think, you and Clark!
Come out of there on the double! Yes, I said you!"

314

They were halfway down the driveway when Ellis spoke.
"Sergeant," he said. "There's somethin' on fire back there."
Bailey stopped—looked back—a smoke-puff climbed in the sky
And the wind was high.
              He hesitated a moment.
The cabin must have caught from the burning splinter.
Then he set his jaw. Well, suppose the cabin had caught?
—Damned old woman in black who called him a thief.
Serve her right if all her cabins burnt up.
The house wouldn't catch—and here they were, losing time—

"Oh well," he said. "That nigger'll put it out.
It ain't our detail—mosey along with it there—
The Cap won't mind if we run it on him a little,
Now we got the Colonel's squab, but we better step."

They hurried along. The smoke rose higher behind them.
The wind blew the burning flakes on Wingate Hall.

Sally Dupré stared out of her bedroom window
As she had stared many times at that clump of trees.
And saw the smoke rise out of it, thick and dark.

They hadn't had much trouble at Appleton.
It was too far off the main road—and, as for the slaves,
Those who straggled after the troops were better away.
The aunts complained, of course—well, the aunts complained.
They were old, and, at least, they had a man in the house,
Even if the man were but crippled old Uncle Paul.
It was the end of the world for him and the aunts.
It wasn't for her.
            The years had worn on her youth,
Much had worn, but not the crook from her smile
Nor the hidden lightness out of her narrow feet.

She looked at the smoke again, and her eyes were grey
And then they were black as that smoke. She felt the fire
Run on her flesh. "It's Wingate Hall and it's burning?
House that married my lover before he saw me,
You are burning, burning away in a little smoke,
Burning the wall between us with your fierce burning,

315

Burning the strife between us in your black flame,
Burning down."
                    She trod for an instant there
A light glass floor of omen, brighter than sleet
Over a hurtless fire.
                    Then she caught her breath.
The flesh was cool, the blackness died from her eyes.
"We'll have to get the slaves if the slaves will go.
I know Ned will. I'm not sure about Bob or Jim.
Uncle Paul must give me his pistol. I'll have to start them.
They won't go without me. The aunts won't be any use.
Why wouldn't she come over here when we all first heard?
I know why she wouldn't. I never liked her so much.
Hurry, Sally!"
                    She ran downstairs like the wind.

They worked at the Hall that night till the dawn came up,
Two smoke-stained women, Cudjo and Bob and Ned,
But when the dawn had risen, the Hall was gone
And Elspeth's candles would not light it again.

———————

Wingate wearily tried to goad
A bag of bones on a muddy road
Under the grey and April sky
While Bristol hummed in his irony
"If you want a good time, jine the cavalry!
Well, we jined it, and here we go,
The last event in the circus-show,
The bareback boys in the burnin' hoop
Mounted on cases of chicken-croup,
The rovin' remains of the Black Horse Troop!
Though the only horse you could call real black
Is the horsefly sittin' on Shepley's back,
But, women and children, do not fear,
They'll feed the lions and us, next year.
And, women and children, dry your eyes,
The Southern gentleman never dies.
He just lives on by his strength of will
Like a damn ole rooster too tough to kill
Or a brand-new government dollar-bill
That you can use for a trousers-patch

Or lightin' a fire, if you've got a match,
Or makin' a bunny a paper collar,
Or anythin' else—except a dollar.

Old folks, young folks, never you care,
The Yanks are here and the Yanks are there,
But no Southern gentleman knows despair.
He just goes on in his usual way,
Eatin' a meal every fifteenth day
And showin' such skill in his change of base
That he never gets time to wash his face
While he fights with a fury you'd seldom find
Except in a Home for the Crippled Blind,
And can whip five Yanks with a palmleaf hat,
Only the Yanks won't fight like that.

Ladies and gentlemen, here we go!
The last event in the minstrel show!
Georgia's genuine gamboliers,
(Ladies and gentlemen, dry those tears!)
See the sergeant, eatin' the hay
Of his faithful horse, in a lifelike way!
See the general, out for blood,
And try to tell the man from the mud!
See the platoon in its savage lair,
A half-grown boy on a wheezy mare.
Ladies and gentlemen, pass the hat!
We've got one trick that you won't forget,
'The Vanishin' Commissariat'
And nobody's found the answer yet!
Here we go, here we go,
The last parade of the circus-show,
Longstreet's orphans, Lee's everlastin's
Half cast-iron and half corn-pone,
And if gettin' to heaven means prayer and fastin's
We ought to get there on the fasts alone.

Here we go with our weddin' bells,
Mr. Davis's immortelles,
Mr. Lincoln's Thanksgivin' turkey,
Run right ragged but actin' perky,
Chased right handsome, but still not carved,

—We had fleas, but the fleas all starved.
We had rations and new recruits,
Uniforms and cavalry-boots,
Must have mislaid, for we can't find 'em.
They all went home with their tails behind 'em.
Here we are, like the old man's mutton,
Pretty well sheared, but not past buttin',
Lee's last invalids, heart and hand,
All wropped up in a woolen band,
Oh, Dixie land. . . . oh, Dixie land! . . ."
He tossed his hat and caught it again
And Wingate recalled, without grief or pain
Or any quietus but memory
Lucy, under another sky,
White and gold as a lily bed,
Giving toy ribbons to all her dead.
She had been pretty and she was gone,
But the dead were here—and the dead rode on,
Over a road of mud and stones,
Each one horsed on a bag of bones.

Lucy, you carried a golden head,
But I am free of you, being dead.
Father's back in that cluttered hall
Where the beds are solid from wall to wall
And the scrubbed old floor has a rusty stain.
He'll never ride with the dogs again,
Call Bathsheba or Planter's Child
In the old, high quaver that drives them wild
—Rocketing hounds on a red-hot scent—
After such wounds, men do not ride.
I think that his heart was innocent.
I know he rode by the riverside,
Calling Blue Ruin or Georgia Lad
With the huntsman's crotchet that sets them mad.
His face was ruddy—his face is white—
I wonder if Father died last night?
That cloud in the sky is a thunderhead.
The world I knew is a long time dead.

Shepley looks like a knife on guard,
Reckon he's taking it mighty hard,

Reckon he loved her and no mistake,
Glad it isn't my wedding cake,
Wainscott oughtn't to plague him so,
Means all right but he doesn't know.
"Here we go, here we go,
The last events of the minstrel-show!"

Shepley suddenly turned his head.
"Mr. Bristol's funny," he said.
The voice was flat with an injury.
Bristol stared at him, puzzledly.
"What's the matter with you, Huger?
Lost your dog or your rosy cheeks?
Haven't been human for weeks and weeks.
I'll sing you a hymn, if you're so inclined,
But the rest of the boys don't seem to mind.
Are you feelin' poorly or just unkind?"

Shepley looked at him with the blind
Eyes of a man too long at war
And too long nursing a secret sore.
"Mr. Bristol's funny," said he,
In a level voice of enmity.
Bristol laughed, but his face grew red.
"Well, if you take it like that—" he said.

"Here we go, here we go,
The old Confederate minstrel-show!"
His mouth was merry, he tossed his hat,
"Belles skedaddled and left us flat—"

Shepley leaned from his swaying hips
And flicked him over the singing lips.
"Will you take it?" he said, "or let it go?
You never could sing for shucks, you know."
The color drained out of Bristol's face.
He bowed with an odd, old-fashioned grace.
"Name your people and choose your land,
I don't take a slap from God's own hand.
Mr. Shepley, your servant, sir."

They stared at each other across a blur.
The troop stared with them, halted and still.

A rider lunged from the top of the hill,
Dusty man with a bandaged hand
Spilling his orders.
                    "Who's in command?
Well, it doesn't signify, more or less.
You can hold the Yanks for a while, I guess.
Make 'em think you're the whole rear guard
If you can do it—they're pressin' hard
And somebody's got to lose some hair.
Keep 'em away from that bend down there
As long as a horse or a man can stand.
You might give 'em a charge, if you think you can,
And we'll meet sometime in the Promised Land,
For I can't spare you another man."

Bristol whistled, a shrill, sweet slur.
"Beg to acknowledge the orders, sir.
Boys, we're booked for the shivaree.
Give our regards to the infantry
And tell Marse Robert, with fortitude,
We stacked up pretty as hickory-wood.
While might I ask, while bein' polite,
How many Yank armies we aim to fight?"

"Well," said the other, "about a corps.
Roughly speakin'—there may be more."

"Thank you," said Bristol, "that's mighty sweet,
You will not remain at the mourner's seat?
No sir? Well, I imagined not,
For from this time hence it will be right hot."
He turned to Shepley with his punctilious
Air of the devil turned supercilious
When the damned display a vulgar nettlement.
"Sir, I regret that our little settlement
Must be postponed for a fitter season,
But war and necessity know no reason,
And should we survive in this comin' fracas
I'll do you the honors—you damned old jackass!"

Shepley grinned at his sometime friend.
They took the cover they must defend.

320

Wingate, fighting from tree to tree,
Felt a red-hot skewer surgeon his knee
And felt his shoulder hitting the ground.
He rolled on his side and made a sound,
Dimly seeing through failing sight
The last brief passion of his last fight.
One Cotter dying, the other dead
With the brains run out of his shattered head.
Stuart Cazenove trying to squirm
His way to the road like a scythe-cut worm,
Weakly humming "Cadet Rousselle",
Shot through the belly and half in hell,
While Shepley croaked through a bloody spray,
"Come on, you bastards, and get your pay.
We've fought you mounted and fought you standin'
And I got a hole I could put my hand in—
And they're comin', Wayne—and it hurts my head—"
Bristol looked at him, lying dead.
"Got the start of me, Shep," he said.
"Dirty welchers, killin' Huger
Before we could settle up properly."
He stooped to the body and took its pistol
And Wingate saw, through a rising mist,
The last, cold madness of Wainscott Bristol,
Walking out like a duellist
With his torn coat buttoned up at the throat
As if it were still the broadcloth coat
Duellists button to show no fleck
Of telltale white at the wrists or neck.
He stepped from his cover and dropped his hat.
"Yanks, come get it!" he said and spat
While his pistols cracked with a single crack,
"Here we go on the red dog's back!
High, low, jack and the goddam game."
And then the answering volley came.

Wingate waked from a bloodshot dream.
They were touching his leg and he heard his scream.
A blue-chinned man said a word or two.
"Well now, Johnny, you ought to do
Till the sawbones comes with his movin'-van,
And you're lucky you're livin', little man.

321

But why the hell did you act so strict,
Fightin' like that when you know you're licked,
And where's the rest of your damn brigade?"
The voice died out as the ripples fade
Into the flow of the running stream,
And Wingate sank to the bloodshot dream.

Richmond is fallen—Lincoln walks in its streets,
Alone, unguarded, stops at George Pickett's house,
Knocks at George Pickett's door. George Pickett has gone
But the strange, gaunt figure talks to George Pickett's wife
A moment—she thinks she is dreaming, seeing him there—
"Just one of George Pickett's old friends, m'am."
                                        He turns away.
She watches him down the street with wondering eyes.
The red light falls upon him from the red sky.
Houses are burning, strange shadows flee through the streets.
A gang of loafers is broaching a liquor-barrel
In a red-lit square. The liquor spills on the cobbles.
They try to scoop it up in their dirty hands.

A long, blue column tramps by, shouting "John Brown's Body."
The loafers scatter like wasps from a half-sucked pear,
Come back when the column is gone.
                                A half-crazy slave
Mounts on a stoop and starts to preach to the sky.
A white-haired woman shoos him away with a broom.
He mumbles and reels to the shadows.
                                A general passes,
His escort armed with drawn sabres. The sabres shine
In the red, low light.
                        Two doors away, down the street,
A woman is sobbing the same long sob all night
Beside a corpse with crossed hands.
                                Lincoln passes on.

On the way to Appomattox, the ghost of an army
Staggers a muddy road for a week or so
Through fights and weather, dwindling away each day.
For a brief while Davis is with them and then he goes

322

To be tracked by his private furies into the last
Sad farce of his capture, and, later, to wear his chains.
Benjamin is with them for some few days,
Still sleek, still lively, still impeccably dressed,
Taking adversity as he took success
With the silk-ribbed fan of his slight, unchangeable smile.
Behind that fan, his mind weighs war and defeat
In an old balance.
                    One day he is there and smiling.
The next he is gone as if he had taken fernseed
And walked invisible so through the Union lines.
You will not find that smile in a Northern prison
Though you seek from now till Doomsday. It is too wise.
You will find the chief with the chin like John Calhoun's,
Gadfly-stung, tormented by hostile fate,
You will find many gallant blockheads and tragic nobles
But not the black-eyed man with life in his eyes.

So this week, this death-march, these final, desperate strokes,
These last blood-spots on the harvest—until, at length,
The battered grey advance guard, hoping to break
A last, miraculous hole through the closing net,
Sees Ord's whole corps as if risen out of the ground
Before them, blocking all hope.
                              The letters are written,
The orders given, while stray fighting goes on
And grey men and blue men die in odd clumps of ground
Before the orders can reach them.
                              An aide-de-camp
Seeks a suitable house for the council from a chance farmer.
The first one found is too dirty to please his mind,
He picks another.
                  The chiefs and the captains meet,
Lee erect in his best dress uniform,
His dress-sword hung at his side and his eyes unaltered.
Chunky Grant in his mudsplashed private's gear
With the battered stars on his shoulders.
                                        They talk a while
Of Mexico and old days.
                        Then the terms are stated.
Lee finds them generous, says so, makes a request.
His men will need their horses for the spring-ploughing.

Grant assents at once.
     There is no parade of bright swords
Given or taken. Grant saw that there should not be.
It is over, then. . . .
     Lee walks from the little room.
His face is unchanged. It will not change when he dies.
But as he steps on the porch and looks toward his lines
He strikes his hands together once with a sound. . . .

In the room he has left, the blue men stare at each other
For a space of heartbeats, silent. The grey ride off.
They are gone—it is over. . . .

The room explodes like a bomb, they are laughing and shouting,
Yelling strange words, dragging chairs and tables outdoors,
Bearded generals waltzing with one another
For a brief, wild moment, punching each others' ribs,
Everyone talking at once and nobody listening,
"It's over—it's done—it's finished!"
     Then, order again.
The grey ghost-army falls in for the last time,
Marching to stack its arms.
     As the ranks move forward
The blue guns go to "Present." Gordon sees the gesture.
He sweeps his sabre down in the full salute.
There are no cheers or words from blue lines or grey.
Only the sound of feet. . . .
It is over, now. . . .
     The arms are stacked from the war.
A few bronzed, tattered grey men, weeping or silent,
Tear some riddled bits of cloth from the color-staffs
And try to hide them under their uniforms.

———————

Jake Diefer, ploughing, a day of the early Spring,
Smelt April steam from the ground as he turned it up
And wondered how the new forty would do this year.

The stump of his left arm ached in the living wind.
It was not a new pain.

When he got back to the house
The woman would ease it some with her liniments
But there wasn't much you could do.
                                        The boy had been smart.
The boy had fixed the jigger so he could plough.
It wasn't an arm you could show to company
With a regular-looking hand, but it did the work.
The woman still hankered after the varnished one
They'd seen that day in the Philadelphia store
—Well, he'd tried it on, and it was a handsome arm,
And, if the new forty did well—
                                        Meanwhile, the huge
Muscles of his right shoulder bulged with the strain
As the plough sheared on.
                                        Sometimes, the blade of the plough
Still turned up such odd harvest as bullets leave,
A spoilt canteen, the brass of a cartridge-pouch,
An eyeless skull, too white for the grin it wore.
But these were rarer now.
                                        They had cleaned the well.
They could drink from the well again.
                                        The earth was in plough.

He turned his team and started the backward furrow.
He was clumsy still, in some matters, but he could manage.
This year he'd see his own wheat.
                                        He thought to himself:
"You ain't the feller you was but the ground looks good.
It smells like good plantin' weather. We cleaned the well.
Maybe some time we'll get you that varnished arm,
For Sundays, maybe. It'd look good on Sundays."
He gazed ahead.
                                        By the end of the farther fence
A ragamuffin-something leaned on the rail,
Regarding him and his team.
                                        "Tramp feller," he thought,
"Colored man, too—well, he can't hang around this farm,
Him or no other tramps. I wish I could get
An honest to God cheap hired man."
                                        The team drew near.
The negro did not move.
                                        Jake halted the team.

325

They stared at each other. One saw a crippled ox,
The other a scar-faced spectre with haunted eyes
Still dressed in the rags of a shoddy uniform.
"Well, feller?" said Jake.
                    The negro said " 'Scuse me, Sarjun."
He scratched his head with the wreck of a forage-cap.
His eyes remembered a darkness.
                                "Huh!" said Jake,
Sharply, "Where did you get it?"
                            The negro shrank.
"I was in de Crater, boss," he said with a dull
Stain in his voice. "You mebbe heard about us.
You mebbe heard of de Crater at Petersburg.
I doan' like thinkin' about it. You need a fiel'-han'?"

Jake thought for a moment. "Crater," he said at last.
"Yuh, I heard about that Crater."
                            The wind blew on,
Hurting his arm. "I wasn't to there," he said.
"I knew some boys that was there."
                        The negro said,
"I'd work for my keep, boss, honest. I knows a team.
I knows how to work. I got hurt bad in de Crater
But I knows how to work a farm."
                        He coughed and was dumb.
Jake looked at him as he might have looked at a horse,
Measuringly.
            "I ain't runnin' a hospital,"
He said, in an aggrieved voice. "You was to the Crater.
I seen the way you colored folks farm down South.
It ain't no way to farm. You ought to be et.
We'll eat you up to the house when it's mealin'-time.
I don't know where we'll sleep you. How do I know
You can work your keep?"
                        The negro said nothing at all.
His eyes had resumed their darkness.
                                "Huddup!" said Jake,
As the team swung round.
                    "Dat's ploughin'!" the negro said.

Jake spat. "The woman'll fix you a snack to eat
If you holler the house."

The negro shook his head.
"I'll wait till you's done furrowin', boss," he said.
"Mebbe I kin help you unhitch when it's time for dat."

"Well," said Jake, "I ain't payin' a hired man much."

"Dey call me Spade," said the negro.
                                    The plough went on.
The negro watched it, cutting the furrow clean.

———————

Jack Ellyat, an old cudgel in his fist,
Walked from the town, one day of melting ice,
Past fields still patched with old snow but warm in the sun,
His heart and mind being something like those fields. . . .
Behind him, in the town, the spangled flags
Still fluttered or hung limp for fallen Richmond,
And here or there, in corners, you could see
The burst firecracker-cases, rotten with rain,
The guttered stumps of torches flung away
And other odds and ends of celebration
Not yet swept up.
                    The old cannon in the Square
Still had a blackened mouth from its salutes,
The little boys would not be good all week
And everything wore airs of Monday morning. . . .

Jack Ellyat, remembering it all,
Was glad enough when he got past the houses
And could see nothing but the road ahead
Going up hills and down.
                          "It's over now.
Finished for good. Well, I was part of it.
Well, it is over."
                    When he reached the crest
Of the Long Hill, he paused and felt the wind
Blow on his face, and leaned upon his stick,
Gazing at troubled Spring.
                            He carried still
Wounds of a sort, some healed into the scars
And some that hardly would be healed awhile,

327

Being in stuff few surgeries can reach,
But he was well enough, although the wind
Felt colder than it had in other Springs.

"Oh, yes," he thought, "I guess that I'm all right.
I guess I'm lucky. I remember once
Coming along this road with poor old Ned
Before they fired on Sumter. Well, it's over.
I was a part of it."
                    He flipped a stone
Down toward the hill and watched it strike and strike
And then lie quiet, while his mind recalled
The long, white, bloodless months of getting well
And the strange feel of first civilian clothes.
Well, that was over, too, and he was back,
And everybody knew he'd settled down,
Only he couldn't stand it any more.

He had a picture of Melora's face,
Dim with long looking-at, a carried image,
He tried to see it now, but it was faint.
He'd tried to find her but he couldn't find her.
Couldn't get any news while he was sick,
And then, at last, the news that they were gone—
That and no more—and nobody knew where.

He saw the clock upon the mantelpiece
Back in the house, ticking its fettered time
To fettered Phaëton.
                    "I'll settle down.
I will forget. I'll wear my riddled coat
Fourth of Julys and have boys gape at me.
I'll drink and eat and sleep, marry a girl;
Be a good lawyer, wear the hunger out.
I hardly knew her. It was years ago.
Why should the hunger stay? A dozen men
Might find a dozen girls and lose them so
And never once think of it, but perhaps
As a dim fragrance, lost with their first youth,
A seashell in a box of cedarwood,
A silver mist that vanished with the day.

It was such years ago. She must have changed.
I know that I have changed.
                    We find such things
And lose them, and must live in spite of it.
Only a fool goes looking for the wind
That blew across his heartstrings yesterday,
Or breaks his hands in the obscure attempt
To dig the knotted roots of Time apart,
Hoping to resurrect the golden mask
Of the lost year inviolate from the ground.
Only a fool drives horses in the sky."

And here he was, out walking on this road
For no more reason than a crazy yarn
Just heard, about some gipsy travellers
Going through towns and looking for a soldier.
And even and supposing it were she . . .

He saw Melora walking down from the wood
With the sun behind her, low in the western cloud.
He saw the long shadow that her slight body made.

The fetters fell like straws from the clock of time.
The horses moved from the gate.
                  This life, this burning,
This fictive war that is over, this toy death,
These were the pictures of Phaëton.
                      This is Phaëton.
He cast a final look down at the town,
Another at the fields still patched with snow.
The wind blew on his face. He moved away
Out toward the crossroads, where the wagons pass,
And when he got there, waited patiently
Under a windbreak of three twisted elms
Half-hidden from the road.
                "Find her," he said.
"I guess we'll go back West then. Well, that's that."
The wind burned at his flesh. He let it burn,
Staring at a lost year.
              So he perceived
A slow cart creaking up a slope of hill,

Drawn by a horse as gaunt as poverty
And driven by a woman with great eyes.

———

Edmund Ruffin, old Secessionist,
Firer of the first gun that rang against Sumter,
Walks in his garden now, in the evening-cool,
With a red, barred flag slung stiffly over one arm
And a silver-butted pistol in his right hand.
He has just heard of Lee's surrender and Richmond's fall
And his face is marble over his high black stock.
For a moment he walks there, smelling the scents of Spring,
A gentleman taking his ease, while the sun sinks down.
Now it is well-nigh sunken. He smiles with the close,
Dry smile of age. It is time. He unfolds the flag,
Cloaks it around his shoulders with neat, swift hands,
Cocks the pistol and points it straight at his heart.
The hammer falls, the dead man slumps to the ground.
The blood spurts out in the last light of the sun
Staining the red of the flag with more transient red.

———

The gaunt man, Abraham Lincoln, woke one morning
From a new dream that yet was an old dream
For he had known it many times before
And, usually, its coming prophesied
Important news of some sort, good or bad,
Though mostly good as he remembered it.

He had been standing on the shadowy deck
Of a black formless boat that moved away
From a dim bank, into wide, gushing waters—
River or sea, but huge—and as he stood,
The boat rushed into darkness like an arrow,
Gathering speed—and as it rushed, he woke.

He found it odd enough to tell about
That day to various people, half in jest
And half in earnest—well, it passed the time
And nearly everyone had some pet quirk,
Knocking on wood or never spilling salt,

330

Ladders or broken mirrors or a Friday,
And so he thought he might be left his boat,
Especially now, when he could breathe awhile
With Lee surrendered and the war stamped out
And the long work of binding up the wounds
Not yet begun—although he had his plans
For that long healing, and would work them out
In spite of all the bitter-hearted fools
Who only thought of punishing the South
Now she was beaten.
                        But this boat of his.
He thought he had it.
                        "Johnston has surrendered.
It must be that, I guess—for that's about
The only news we're waiting still to hear."
He smiled a little, spoke of other things.
That afternoon he drove beside his wife
And talked with her about the days to come
With curious simplicity and peace.
Well, they were getting on, and when the end
Came to his term, he would not be distressed.
They would go back to Springfield, find a house,
Live peaceably and simply, see old friends,
Take a few cases every now and then.
Old Billy Herndon's kept the practice up,
I guess he'll sort of like to have me back.
We won't be skimped, we'll have enough to spend,
Enough to do—we'll have a quiet time,
A sort of Indian summer of our age.

He looked beyond the carriage, seeing it so,
Peace at the last, and rest.

They drove back to the White House, dressed and ate,
Went to the theatre in their flag-draped box.
The play was a good play, he liked the play,
Laughed at the jokes, laughed at the funny man
With the long, weeping whiskers.
                        The time passed.
The shot rang out. The crazy murderer
Leaped from the box, mouthed out his Latin phrase,
Brandished his foolish pistol and was gone.

Lincoln lay stricken in the flag-draped box.
Living but speechless. Now they lifted him
And bore him off. He lay some hours so.
Then the heart failed. The breath beat in the throat.
The black, formless vessel carried him away.

———————

Sally, waiting at Appleton
On an autumn day of clear, bright sun,
Felt her heart and body begin to burn
As she hummed the lesson she had to learn.
"Yellow cornmeal and a jackass colt
And a door that swings on a broken bolt.
Comfort the old and pity the wise
And see your lover with open eyes.
Mend the broken and patch the frayed
And carry the sorrow undismayed
When your lover limps in the falling rain,
Never quite to be whole again.
Clear the nettle and plant the corn
And keep your body a hunting-horn.
Succor your love at fire and frost
When your lover remembers the blood he lost,
And break your hands on the hard-moved wheel
Till they are tougher than hands of steel,
Till the new grass grows on the barren plain
And the house is built from the dust again,
With thrift and love for the house and the chief,
A scone on the hob for the son of grief,
A knife in the ribs for the pleasant thief,
While the night and the river have memories . . ."
She stared at the future with equal eyes.
And yet, in her glance, there was something still
Not to be ground by Wingate will
Or under the honor of Elspeth's name,
A dancing flicker that went and came
But did not falter for joy or grief
Or the years gone by with the blowing leaf.
—French Dupré with his alien grace
Always turning the buried ace.
French Dupré in his dancer's pride,
Leading a reel with his stolen bride—

332

She smiled a little and turned to see
A weed-grown path and a scarlet tree
And Wingate coming there, painfully.

John Brown's body lies a-mouldering in the grave.
Spread over it the bloodstained flag of his song,
For the sun to bleach, the wind and the birds to tear,
The snow to cover over with a pure fleece
And the New England cloud to work upon
With the grey absolution of its slow, most lilac-smelling rain,
Until there is nothing there
That ever knew a master or a slave
Or, brooding on the symbol of a wrong,
Threw down the irons in the field of peace.
John Brown is dead, he will not come again,
A stray ghost-walker with a ghostly gun.
Let the strong metal rust
In the enclosing dust
And the consuming coal
That was the furious soul
And still like iron groans,
Anointed with the earth,
Grow colder than the stones
While the white roots of grass and little weeds
Suck the last hollow wildfire from the singing bones.

Bury the South together with this man,
Bury the bygone South.
Bury the minstrel with the honey-mouth,
Bury the broadsword virtues of the clan,
Bury the unmachined, the planters' pride,
The courtesy and the bitter arrogance,
The pistol-hearted horsemen who could ride
Like jolly centaurs under the hot stars.
Bury the whip, bury the branding-bars,
Bury the unjust thing
That some tamed into mercy, being wise,
But could not starve the tiger from its eyes
Or make it feed where beasts of mercy feed.
Bury the fiddle-music and the dance,

The sick magnolias of the false romance
And all the chivalry that went to seed
Before its ripening.

And with these things, bury the purple dream
Of the America we have not been,
The tropic empire, seeking the warm sea,
The last foray of aristocracy
Based not on dollars or initiative
Or any blood for what that blood was worth
But on a certain code, a manner of birth,
A certain manner of knowing how to live,
The pastoral rebellion of the earth
Against machines, against the Age of Steam,
The Hamiltonian extremes against the Franklin mean,
The genius of the land
Against the metal hand,
The great, slave-driven bark,
Full-oared upon the dark,
With gilded figurehead,
With fetters for the crew
And spices for the few,
The passion that is dead,
The pomp we never knew,
Bury this, too.

Bury this destiny unmanifest,
This system broken underneath the test,
Beside John Brown and though he knows his enemy is there
He is too full of sleep at last to care.

He was a stone, this man who lies so still,
A stone flung from a sling against a wall,
A sacrificial instrument of kill,
A cold prayer hardened to a musket-ball:
And yet, he knew the uses of a hill,
And he must have his justice, after all.

He was a lover of certain pastoral things,
He had the shepherd's gift.
When he walked at peace, when he drank from the watersprings,
His eyes would lift

To see God, robed in a glory, but sometimes, too,
Merely the sky,
Untroubled by wrath or angels, vacant and blue,
Vacant and high.

He knew not only doom but the shape of the land,
Reaping and sowing.
He could take a lump of any earth in his hand
And feel the growing.

He was a farmer, he didn't think much of towns,
The wheels, the vastness.
He liked the wide fields, the yellows, the lonely browns,
The black ewe's fastness.

Out of his body grows revolving steel,
Out of his body grows the spinning wheel
Made up of wheels, the new, mechanic birth,
No longer bound by toil
To the unsparing soil
Or the old furrow-line,
The great, metallic beast
Expanding West and East,
His heart a spinning coil,
His juices burning oil,
His body serpentine.
Out of John Brown's strong sinews the tall skyscrapers grow,
Out of his heart the chanting buildings rise,
Rivet and girder, motor and dynamo,
Pillar of smoke by day and fire by night,
The steel-faced cities reaching at the skies,
The whole enormous and rotating cage
Hung with hard jewels of electric light,
Smoky with sorrow, black with splendor, dyed
Whiter than damask for a crystal bride
With metal suns, the engine-handed Age,
The genie we have raised to rule the earth,
Obsequious to our will
But servant-master still,
The tireless serf already half a god—

Touch the familiar sod
Once, then gaze at the air

335

And see the portent there,
With eyes for once washed clear
Of worship and of fear:
There is its hunger, there its living thirst,
There is the beating of the tremendous heart
You cannot read for omens.
                              Stand apart
From the loud crowd and look upon the flame
Alone and steadfast, without praise or blame.
This is the monster and the sleeping queen
And both have roots struck deep in your own mind,
This is reality that you have seen,
This is reality that made you blind.

So, when the crowd gives tongue
And prophets, old or young,
Bawl out their strange despair
Or fall in worship there,
Let them applaud the image or condemn
But keep your distance and your soul from them.
And, if the heart within your breast must burst
Like a cracked crucible and pour its steel
White-hot before the white heat of the wheel,
Strive to recast once more
That attar of the ore
In the strong mold of pain
Till it is whole again,
And while the prophets shudder or adore
Before the flame, hoping it will give ear,
If you at last must have a word to say,
Say neither, in their way,
"It is a deadly magic and accursed,"
Nor "It is blest," but only "It is here."

YOUNG ADVENTURE

Young Adventure

PORTRAIT OF A BOY

AFTER the whipping he crawled into bed,
    Accepting the harsh fact with no great weeping.
How funny uncle's hat had looked striped red!
He chuckled silently. The moon came, sweeping
A black, frayed rag of tattered cloud before
In scorning; very pure and pale she seemed,
Flooding his bed with radiance. On the floor
Fat motes danced. He sobbed, closed his eyes and dreamed.

Warm sand flowed round him. Blurts of crimson light
Splashed the white grains like blood. Past the cave's mouth
Shone with a large, fierce splendor, wildly bright,
The crooked constellations of the South;
Here the Cross swung; and there, affronting Mars,
The Centaur stormed aside a froth of stars.
Within, great casks, like wattled aldermen,
Sighed of enormous feasts, and cloth of gold
Glowed on the walls like hot desire. Again,
Beside webbed purples from some galleon's hold,
A black chest bore the skull and bones in white
Above a scrawled "Gunpowder!" By the flames,
Decked out in crimson, gemmed with syenite,
Hailing their fellows with outrageous names,
The pirates sat and diced. Their eyes were moons.
"Doubloons!" they said. The words crashed gold. "Doubloons!"

339

PORTRAIT OF A BABY

He lay within a warm, soft world
Of motion. Colors bloomed and fled,
Maroon and turquoise, saffron, red,
Wave upon wave that broke and whirled
To vanish in the grey-green gloom,
Perspectiveless and shadowy.
A bulging world that had no walls,
A flowing world, most like the sea,
Compassing all infinity
Within a shapeless, ebbing room,
An endless tide that swells and falls . . .
He slept and woke and slept again.
As a veil drops, Time dropped away;
Space grew a toy for children's play,
Sleep bolted fast the gates of Sense—
He lay in naked impotence;
Like a drenched moth that creeps and crawls
Heavily up brown, light-baked walls,
To fall in wreck, her task undone,
Yet somehow striving toward the sun.
So, as he slept, his hands clenched tighter,
Shut in the old way of the fighter,
His feet curled up to grip the ground,
His muscles tautened for a bound;
And though he felt, and felt alone,
Strange brightness stirred him to the bone,
Cravings to rise—till deeper sleep
Buried the hope, the call, the leap;
A wind puffed out his mind's faint spark.
He was absorbed into the dark.
He woke again and felt a surge
Within him, a mysterious urge
That grew one hungry flame of passion;
The whole world altered shape and fashion.
Deceived, befooled, bereft and torn,
He scourged the heavens with his scorn,
Lifting a bitter voice to cry
Against the eternal treachery—
Till, suddenly, he found the breast,

And ceased, and all things were at rest,
The earth grew one warm languid sea
And he a wave. Joy, tingling, crept
Throughout him. He was quenched and slept.

So, while the moon made broad her ring,
He slept and cried and was a king.
So, worthily, he acted o'er
The endless miracle once more.
Facing immense adventures daily,
He strove still onward, weeping, gayly,
Conquered or fled from them, but grew
As soil-starved, rough pine-saplings do.
Till, one day, crawling seemed suspect.
He gripped the air and stood erect
And splendid. With immortal rage
He entered on man's heritage!

PORTRAIT OF YOUNG LOVE

If you were with me—as you're not, of course,
I'd taste the elegant tortures of Despair
With a slow, languid, long-refining tongue;
Puzzle for days on one particular stare,
Or if you knew a word's peculiar force,
Or what you looked like when you were quite young.

You'd lift me heaven-high—till a word grated.
Dash me hell-deep—oh that luxurious Pit,
Fatly and well encushioned with self-pity,
Where Love's an epicure not quickly sated!
What mournful musics wander over it,
Faint-blown from some long-lost celestial city!

Such bitter joyousness I'd have, and action,
Were you here—be no more the fool who broods
On true Adventure till he wakes her scorning—
But we're too petty for such noble warning.
And I find just as perfect satisfaction
In analyzing these, and other moods!

THE GENERAL PUBLIC

"Ah, did you once see Shelley plain?"—BROWNING.

"SHELLEY? Oh, yes, I saw him often then,"
The old man said. A dry smile creased his face
With many wrinkles. "That's a great poem, now!
That one of Browning's! Shelley? Shelley plain?
The time that I remember best is this—

"A thin mire crept along the rutted ways,
And all the trees were harried by cold rain
That drove a moment fiercely and then ceased,
Falling so slow it hung like a grey mist
Over the school. The walks were like blurred glass.
The buildings reeked with vapor, black and harsh
Against the deepening darkness of the sky;
And each lamp was a hazy yellow moon,
Filling the space about with golden motes,
And making all things larger than they were.
One yellow halo hung above a door,
That gave on a black passage. Round about
Struggled a howling crowd of boys, pell-mell,
Pushing and jostling like a stormy sea,
With shouting faces, turned a pasty white
By the strange light, for foam. They all had clods,
Or slimy balls of mud. A few gripped stones.
And there, his back against the battered door,
His pile of books scattered about his feet,
Stood Shelley while two others held him fast,
And the clods beat upon him. 'Shelley! Shelley!'
The high shouts rang through all the corridors,
'Shelley! Mad Shelley! Come along and help!'
And all the crowd dug madly at the earth,
Scratching and clawing at the streaming mud,
And fouled each other and themselves. And still
Shelley stood up. His eyes were like a flame
Set in some white, still room; for all his face
Was white, a whiteness like no human color,
But white and dreadful as consuming fire.
His hands shook now and then, like slender cords

Which bear too heavy weights. He did not speak.
So I saw Shelley plain."
                        "And you?" I said.

"I? I threw straighter than the most of them,
And had firm clods. I hit him—well, at least
Thrice in the face. He made good sport that night."

YOUNG BLOOD

*"But, sir," I said, "they tell me the man is like
to die!" The Canon shook his head, indulgently.
"Young blood, Cousin," he boomed. "Young
blood! Youth will be served!"*
                        —D'HERMONVILLE'S FABLIAUX.

HE WOKE up with a sick taste in his mouth
And lay there heavily, while dancing motes
Whirled through his brain in endless, rippling streams,
And a grey mist weighed down upon his eyes
So that they could not open fully. Yet
After some time his blurred mind stumbled back
To its last ragged memory—a room;
Air foul with wine; a shouting, reeling crowd
Of friends who dragged him, dazed and blind with drink
Out to the street; a crazy rout of cabs;
The steady mutter of his neighbor's voice,
Mumbling out dull obscenity by rote;
And then . . . well, they had brought him home it seemed,
Since he awoke in bed—oh, damn the business!
He had not wanted it—the silly jokes,
"One last, great night of freedom ere you're married!"
"You'll get no fun then!" "H-ssh, don't tell that story,
He'll have a wife soon!"—God! the sitting down
To drink till you were sodden! . . .
                        Like great light
She came into his thoughts. That was the worst.
To wallow in the mud like this because
His friends were fools. He was not fit to touch,

343

To see, oh far, far off, that silver place
Where God stood manifest to man in her. . . .
Fouling himself. . . . One thing he brought to her,
At least. He had been clean; had taken it
A kind of point of honor from the first.
Others might wallow but he didn't care
For those things. . . .
                Suddenly his vision cleared.
And something seemed to grow within his mind.
Something was wrong—the color of the wall—
The queer shape of the bedposts—everything
Was changed, somehow . . . his room. Was this his room?

. . . He turned his head—and saw beside him there
The sagging body's slope, the paint-smeared face,
And the loose, open mouth, lax and awry,
The breasts, the bleached and brittle hair . . . these things.
. . . As if all Hell were crushed to one bright line
Of lightning for a moment. Then he sank,
Prone beneath an intolerable weight.
And bitter loathing crept up all his limbs.

THE BREAKING POINT

IT WAS not when temptation came,
Swiftly and blastingly as flame,
And seared me white with burning scars;
When I stood up for age-long wars
And held the very Fiend at grips;
When all my mutinous body rose
To range itself beside my foes,
And, like a greyhound in the slips,
The beast that dwells within me roared,
Lunging and straining at his cord. . . .
For all the blusterings of Hell,
It was not then I slipped and fell;
For all the storm, for all the hate,
I kept my soul inviolate.

But when the fight was fought and won,
And there was Peace as still as Death

On everything beneath the sun.
Just as I started to draw breath,
And yawn, and stretch, and pat myself,
—The grass began to whisper things—
And every tree became an elf,
That grinned and chuckled counselings:
Birds, beasts, one thing alone they said,
Beating and dinning at my head.
I could not fly. I could not shun it.
Slimily twisting, slow and blind,
It crept and crept into my mind.
Whispered and shouted, sneered and laughed,
Screamed out until my brain was daft,
One snaky word, "*What if you'd done it?*"
And I began to think . . .
                                    Ah, well,
What matter how I slipped and fell?
Or you, you gutter-searcher, say!
Tell where you found me yesterday!

POOR DEVIL!

WELL, I was tired of life; the silly folk,
The tiresome noises, all the common things
I loved once, crushed me with an iron yoke.
I longed for the cool quiet and the dark,
Under the common sod where louts and kings
Lie down, serene, unheeding, careless, stark,
Never to rise or move or feel again,
Filled with the ecstasy of being dead. . . .

I put the shining pistol to my head
And pulled the trigger hard—I felt no pain,
No pain at all; the pistol had missed fire
I thought; then, looking at the floor, I saw
My huddled body lying there—and awe
Swept over me. I trembled—and looked up.
About me was—not that, my heart's desire,
That small and dark abode of death and peace—
But all from which I sought a vain release!

The sky, the people and the staring sun
Glared at me as before. I was undone.
My last state ten times worse than was my first.
Helpless, I stood, befooled, betrayed, accursed,
Fettered to Life forever, horribly;
Caught in the meshes of Eternity,
No further doors to break or bars to burst.

THE GOLDEN CORPSE

(Eight Sonnets for Donald Malcolm Campbell)

STRIPPED country, shrunken as a beggar's heart,
Inviolate landscape, hardened into steel,
Where the cold soil shatters under heel
Day after day like armor cracked apart.

Winter Connecticut, whose air is clean
As a new icicle to cut the throat,
Whose black and rigid trees will not demean
Themselves to swagger in a crystal coat.

I hate you as a bastard hates his name
When your cramped hills are hostile with the white,
But, every year, when March comes in the same,
A frozen river rolling in the night,

I must go back and hunt among your snow
Something I lost there, much too long ago.

2

It was not innocence, it was not scorn,
And yet it had these names and many more.
It was a champion blowing on a horn,
It was the running of a golden boar.

It was a stallion, trampling the skies
To rags of lightning with his glittering shoes,
It was a childish god with lazy eyes,
It was an indolent and reckless Muse-

346

More than all these, it was a spirit apart,
Purely of fire and air and the mind.
No fear could eat the temper from its heart
Nor any fleshly bandage make it blind.

It was a silver dagger in the blast.
It was the first of youth, and it has passed.

3

I left it in a bare and windy street
Between two sets of bells whose casual chimes
Answer each other, janglingly and sweet,
Like the concord of long-repeated rhymes.

I left it in a since-demolished bar,
And underneath a rain-streaked paving-stone.
And, men and things being what they are,
The hidden ghost had better couch alone.

I shall not rattle with an iron fist
The relics, scattered into sticks of chalk,
Of what was once the carcass of a hawk
That sat like Wrath on an archangel's wrist.

Nor disinter, to make my house look smart,
That thunder-broken and ferocious heart.

4

Men that dig up a mandrake know dis-ease.
This body is committed to its bones
Down where the taproots of New England trees
Suck bare existence from the broken stones.

All summer cannot quicken it with heat,
Nor Spring perturb it with a budding bough,
Nor all the glittering devils of the sleet
In snowing Winter rack its quiet now.

But, in October, when the apples fall,
And leaves begin to rust before the cold,

There may occur, by some unnoticed wall,
A sigh, a whisper in the rotten gold.

A breath that hardly can be called a breath
From Death that will not yet acknowledge Death.

5

Unnoticed—for the years have hardier tasks
Than listening to a whisper or a sigh.
They creep among us with a bag of masks
And fit them to our brows obsequiously.

Some are of iron, to affront the gay,
And some of bronze, to satirize the brave,
But most are merely a compost of clay
Cut in the sleepy features of a slave.

With such astuteness do they counterfeit,
We do not realize the masks are on
Till, gaudy in our folly, bit by bit
We notice that a neighbor's face seems drawn.

And then, with fingers turned to lumps of stone,
Touch the inhuman cast that was our own.

6

There is no doubt such workmanship is sage.
The bound and ordered skies could not abide
A creature formed of elemental rage
For longer than a moment of its pride.

The hand that stooped to Adam from the cloud
And touched his members with a fiery spine
Designed as well the pattern of the shroud
That should convince him he was not divine.

And there are sorceries more excellent
Than the first conflagration of the dust,
But none are quite so single in intent
Or unsophisticated with distrust.

The ripened fruit is golden to the core
But an enchantment fosters it no more.

7

Therefore, in neither anguish nor relief,
I offer to the shadow in the air
No image of a monumental grief
To mock its transience from a stony chair,

Nor any tablets edged in rusty black.
Only a branch of maple, gathered high
When the crisp air first tastes of applejack,
And the blue smokes of Autumn stain the sky.

A branch whose leaves cling to the withering staff
Like precious toys of gilt and scarlet paint,
An emblem Life and Death share half-and-half,
A brittle sceptre for a dying saint.

Unburning fire, an insubstantial Host,
A violence dreamt, a beauty of the ghost.

8

So much in memory. For the future, this.
The checkerboarded house of Day and Night
Is but a cavern where a swallow flies
To beat its wings an instant at the light

And then depart, where the incessant storm
Shepherds the planets like a drunken nurse.
It does not need an everlasting form
To dignify an ecstasy so terse.

But while the swallow fluttered and was quick
I have marked down its passage in the dark
And charred its image on a broken stick
With the brief flame of an uncertain spark.

The fire can have it now, the rain can rain on it,
And the ice harden like a god's disdain on it.

349

MY FAIR LADY

My Fair Lady

TO ROSEMARY

*I*F *you were gone afar,*
And lost the pattern
Of all your delightful ways,
And the web undone,
How would one make you anew,
From what dew and flowers,
What burning and mingled atoms,
Under the sun?

Not from too-satin roses,
Or those rare blossoms,
Orchids, scentless and precious
As precious stone.
But out of lemon-verbena,
Rose-geranium,
These alone.

Not with running horses,
Or Spanish cannon,
Organs, voiced like a lion,
Clamor and speed.
But perhaps with old music-boxes,
Young, tawny kittens,
Wild-strawberry-seed.

Even so, it were more
Than a god could compass
To fashion the body merely,
The lovely shroud.
But then—ah, how to recapture

That evanescence,
The fire that cried in pure crystal
Out of its cloud!

CHEMICAL ANALYSIS

SHE's slender hands and pretty lips,
And seafoam and rosemary.
Her ears are pointed at the tips,
She stayed so long in Fairy.

NOMENCLATURE

SOME people have names like pitchforks, some people have names
    like cakes,
Names full of sizzling esses like a family quarrel of snakes,
Names black as a cat, vermilion as the cockscomb-hat of a fool—
But your name is a green, small garden, a rush asleep in a pool.

When God looked at the diffident cherubs and dropped them out
    of the sky,
He named them like Adam's animals, while Mary and Eve stood
    by,
The poor things huddled before him in scared little naked flocks
--And he gave you a name like sunlight, and clover, and holly-
    hocks.

For your mouth with its puzzled jesting, for your hair like a dark
    soft bird,
Shy humor and dainty walking, sweet laughter and subtle word,
As a fairy walks with a mushroom to keep the rain from its things
You carry your name forever, like a scepter alive with wings.

Neither change nor despair shall touch it nor the seasons make it
    uncouth,
It will burn like an Autumn maple when your proud age talks to
    your youth,
Wise child, clean friend, adoration, light arrow of God, white
    flame,
I would break my body to pieces to call you once by your name!

DIFFERENCE

My MIND's a map. A mad sea-captain drew it
Under a flowing moon until he knew it;
Winds with brass trumpets, puffy-cheeked as jugs,
And states bright-patterned like Arabian rugs.
"Here there be tygers." "Here we buried Jim."
Here is the strait where eyeless fishes swim
About their buried idol, drowned so cold
He weeps away his eyes in salt and gold.
A country like the dark side of the moon,
A cider-apple country, harsh and boon,
A country savage as a chestnut-rind,
A land of hungry sorcerers.
                                    Your mind?

—Your mind is water through an April night,
A cherry-branch, plume-feathery with its white,
A lavender as fragrant as your words,
A room where Peace and Honor talk like birds,
Sewing bright coins upon the tragic cloth
Of heavy Fate, and Mockery, like a moth,
Flutters and beats about those lovely things.
You are the soul, enchanted with its wings,
The single voice that raises up the dead
To shake the pride of angels.
                                    I have said.

A SAD SONG

ROSEMARY, *Rosemary,*
There's a Pig in your garden,
With silk bristles frizzy
And tushes of snow!
But Rosemary was cautious,
She said, "Beg your pardon!
I'm really too busy
To look down below."

Rosemary, Rosemary,
There's a Bird in your kitchen!
His voice is gold water,
He says, "Pretty Poll!"
But Rosemary heard nothing,
Putting stitch after stitch in
The dress of a daughter,
Her thirty-sixth doll.

Rosemary, Rosemary,
A silver-winged Rabbit!
He bridles and gentles
And wants you astride!
"I prefer," said Rosemary,
"To ride a Good Habit."
She went buying black lentils—
She did till she died.

A NONSENSE SONG

ROSEMARY, Rosemary, let down your hair!
The cow's in the hammock, the crow's in the chair!
I was making you songs out of sawdust and silk,
But they came in to call and they spilt them like milk.

The cat's in the coffee, the wind's in the east,
He screams like a peacock and whines like a priest
And the saw of his voice makes my blood turn to mice—
So let down your long hair and shut off his advice!

Pluck out the thin hairpins and let the waves stream,
Brown-gold as brook-waters that dance through a dream,
Gentle-curled as young cloudlings, sweet-fragrant as bay,
Till it takes all the fierceness of living away.

Oh, when you are with me, my heart is white steel.
But the bat's in the belfry, the mold's in the meal,
And I think I hear skeletons climbing the stair!
—Rosemary, Rosemary, let down your bright hair!

TO ROSEMARY, ON THE METHODS BY WHICH SHE MIGHT BECOME AN ANGEL

Not where the sober sisters, grave as willows,
Walk like old twilights by the jasper sea,
Nor where the plump hunt of cherubs holly-hilloes
Chasing their ruddy fox, the sun, you'll be!

Not with the stained-glass prophets, bearded grimly,
Not with the fledgling saved, meek Wisdom's lot,
Kissing a silver book that glimmers dimly,
For acolytes are mild and you are not.

They'll give you a curled tuba, tall as Rumor,
They'll sit you on a puff of Autumn cloud,
Gilded-fantastic as your scorn and humor
And let you blow that tuba much too loud.

Against the unceasing chant to sinless Zion,
Three impudent seraph notes, three starry coals,
Sweet as wild grass and happy as a lion
—And all the saints will throw you aureoles.

EVENING AND MORNING

Over the roof, like burnished men,
The stars tramp high.
You blink—the fire blinks back again
With a cock's red eye.
Lay your book away to doze,
Say your silly prayers,
See that nothing grabs your toes
And run upstairs!

Sandman eyes and heavy head,
Sleep comes soon,
Pouring on your quiet bed
The great, cool moon.

357

Nod's green wheel of moss turns round,
Dripping dreams and peace,
Gentle as a pigeon's sound,
Soft as fleece.

Think of warm sheep shuffling home,
Stones sunk deep,
Bees inside a honeycomb—
Sleep—Sleep.
Smile as when young Una smiled,
Hard and sweet and gay,
Bitter saint, fantastic child,
Fold your wings away.

Dawn, the owl, is fluttering
At Day's bright bars.
Night, the lame man, puttering,
Puffs out the stars.
Wake! and hear an airy shout
Crack the egg of cloud,
And see the golden bird creep out,
Ruffling and proud.

IN A GLASS OF WATER BEFORE RETIRING

Now the day
Burns away.
Most austere
Night is here
—Time for sleep.

And, to sleep,
If you please,
For release
Into peace,
Think of these.

Snails that creep,
Silver-slow;

Streams that flow,
Murmuring,
Murmuring;
Bells that chime,
Sweet—clear—c-o-o-l;
Of a pool
Hushed so still
Stars drowse there,
Sleepy-fair;
Of a hill
Drenched with night,
Drowned with moon's
Lovely light;
Of soft tunes,
Played so slow,
Kind and low,
You sink down,
Into down,
Into rest,
Into the perfect whiteness,
The drowsy, drowsy lightness,
The warm, clean, sleepy feathers of a
    slumbering bird's white breast.

LEGEND

THE trees were sugared like wedding-cake
With a bright hoar frost, with a very cold snow,
When we went begging for Jesus' sake,
Penniless children, years ago.

Diamond weather—but nothing to eat
In that fine, bleak bubble of earth and skies.
Nothing alive in the windy street
But two young children with hungry eyes.

"We must go begging or we will die.
I would sell my soul for an apple-core!"
So we went mendicant, you and I,
Knock-knock-knock at each snow-choked door.

Knock-knock-knock till our fingers froze.
Nobody even replied, "Good day!",
Only the magistrate, toasting his toes,
Howled at us sleepily, "Go away!"

"Rosemary dear, what shall we do?"
"Stephen, I know not. Beseech some saint!
My nose has turned to an icicle blue,
And my belly within me is very faint."

"If there be saints, they are fast asleep,
Lounging in Heaven, in wraps of feather."
"Talk not so, or my eyes will weep
Till the ice-tears rattle and clink together."

"Saints are many—on which shall I call?
He must be kindly, without constraint."
"I think you had better pray to Saint Paul.
I have heard people call him a neighborly saint."

Down he flopped on his cold, bare knees
—Breath that smoked in the bitter air—
Crossing his body with hands afreeze,
He sought Saint Paul in a vehement prayer.

Scarce had these shiverers piped, "Amen,"
Cheeping like fledglings, crying for bread,
When good Saint Paul appeared to them then,
With a wide gold halo around his head.

He waved his episcopal hand, and smiled,
And the ground was spread like a banquet-table!
"Here is much good food for each hungry child,
And I hope you will eat as long as you're able.

"Here are good, thick cloaks for your ragged backs,
And strong, warm boots for your feet," said he,
"And for Stephen, gloves and a little axe,
And a little fur muff for Rosemary."

They thanked him humbly, saying a Pater,
Before they had touched a morsel even,

But he said, "Your thanks are for One far greater"
And pointed his right arm up at Heaven.

"For you are the sparrows around God's door,
He will lift you up like His own great banner.
But the folk who made you suffer so sore—
He shall deal with them in another manner.

"It is His own will to transport those folk
To a region of infinite ice and snow."
And his breath was a taper of incense-smoke,
And he lifted a finger—and it was so.

And the folk were gone—and the saint was fled—
And we stared and stared at the wintry land.
And in front of us there was a banquet spread.
And a little fur muff on Rosemary's hand.

DULCE RIDENTEM

THE bee, he has white honey,
The Sunday child her muff,
The rich man lots of money
Though never quite enough,
The apple has a Springtime smell,
The star-fields silver grain,
But I have youth, the cockleshell,
And the sweet laugh of Jane.

The lark's tune goes so clearly
But Jane's is clear wells.
The cuckoo's voice currs cheerly,
But Jane's is new bells.
Whether she chuckles like a dove,
Or laughs like April rain,
It is her heart and hands and love,
The moth-wing soul of Jane.

ALL NIGHT LONG

WE WERE in bed by nine, but she did not hear the clock,
She lay in her quiet first sleep, soft-breathing, head by her arm,
And the rising, radiant moon spilled silver out of its crock
On her hair and forehead and eyes as we rested, gentle and warm.

All night long it remained, that calm, compassionate sheet,
All the long night it wrapped us in whiteness like ermine-fur,
I did not sleep all the night, but lay, with wings on my feet,
Still, the cool at my lips, seeing her, worshipping her.

Oh, the bright sparks of dawn when day broke, burning and
    wild!
Oh, the first waking glance from her sleepy, beautiful eyes!
With a heart and a mind newborn as a naked, young, golden
    child,
I took her into my arms. We saw the morning arise!

DAYS PASS: MEN PASS

WHEN, like all liberal girls and boys,
We too get rid of sight
—The juggler with his painted toys
The elf and her delight—

In the cool place where jests are few
And there's no time to weep
For all the untamed hearts we knew
Creeping like moths to sleep.

This eagerness that burns us yet
Will rot like summer snow,
And we'll forget as winds forget
When they have ceased to blow.

Oh, we'll grow sleepy, lacking mirth!
But there will still endure
Somewhere, like innocence and earth,
The things your wish made pure.

Wide moonlight on a harvest dew,
White silk, too dear to touch,
These will be you and always you
When I am nothing much.

The flowers with the hardy eyes,
The bread that feeds the gods,
These will be you till Last Assize
When I'm improper sods.

Oh dear immortal, while you can,
Commit one mortal sin.
And let me love you like a man
Till Judgment Day comes in!

ILLA

THIS is only the shadow of what she was once;
The rest is Honor's.
Nevertheless, O Death, be humble in claiming
Even that shadow.

HANDS

MY WIFE's hands are long and thin,
Fit to catch a spirit in,
Fit to set a subtle snare
For something lighter than the air.

My brother's hands are long and fine,
Good at verse and pouring wine,
Good to spend and bad to hoard
And good to hold a singing sword.

My own hands are short and blunt
Being children of affront,
Base mechanics at the most
That have sometimes touched a ghost.

363

I ask between the running sands,
A blessing upon four hands,
And for mine an iron stake
They can do their best to break.

Now God the Son and God the Sire
And God the triple-handed fire,
Make these blessings come to be
Out of your civility
For four hands of courtesy.

                        Amen.

MEMORY

They can have the names and the dates,
It will do them little service.
They can open the locked chest
And steal the wine and the gold.
There is nothing to be said
But this—the clasp of her body
Was better than milk to the child
Or wisdom to the old.

We die with our first breath.
And, if we die, what matter?
There was a ghost in the flesh,
A ghost that went and came.
Though the moon burn like a lamp
It will not be that brightness—
I said her name in my sleep,
Waking, I said her name.

BALLADS AND TALES

Ballads and Tales

AMERICAN NAMES

I HAVE fallen in love with American names,
The sharp names that never get fat,
The snakeskin-titles of mining-claims,
The plumed war-bonnet of Medicine Hat,
Tucson and Deadwood and Lost Mule Flat.

Seine and Piave are silver spoons,
But the spoonbowl-metal is thin and worn,
There are English counties like hunting-tunes
Played on the keys of a postboy's horn,
But I will remember where I was born.

I will remember Carquinez Straits,
Little French Lick and Lundy's Lane,
The Yankee ships and the Yankee dates
And the bullet-towns of Calamity Jane.
I will remember Skunktown Plain.

I will fall in love with a Salem tree
And a rawhide quirt from Santa Cruz,
I will get me a bottle of Boston sea
And a blue-gum nigger to sing me blues.
I am tired of loving a foreign muse.

Rue des Martyrs and Bleeding-Heart-Yard,
Senlis, Pisa, and Blindman's Oast,
It is a magic ghost you guard
But I am sick for a newer ghost,
Harrisburg, Spartanburg, Painted Post.

Henry and John were never so
And Henry and John were always right?
Granted, but when it was time to go
And the tea and the laurels had stood all night,
Did they never watch for Nantucket Light?

I shall not rest quiet in Montparnasse.
I shall not lie easy at Winchelsea.
You may bury my body in Sussex grass,
You may bury my tongue at Champmédy.
I shall not be there. I shall rise and pass.
Bury my heart at Wounded Knee.

THE BALLAD OF WILLIAM SYCAMORE

(1790-1871)

MY FATHER, he was a mountaineer,
His fist was a knotty hammer;
He was quick on his feet as a running deer,
And he spoke with a Yankee stammer.

My mother, she was merry and brave,
And so she came to her labor,
With a tall green fir for her doctor grave
And a stream for her comforting neighbor.

And some are wrapped in the linen fine,
And some like a godling's scion;
But I was cradled on twigs of pine
In the skin of a mountain lion.

And some remember a white, starched lap
And a ewer with silver handles;
But I remember a coonskin cap
And the smell of bayberry candles.

The cabin logs, with the bark still rough,
And my mother who laughed at trifles,
And the tall, lank visitors, brown as snuff,
With their long, straight squirrel-rifles.

I can hear them dance, like a foggy song,
Through the deepest one of my slumbers,
The fiddle squeaking the boots along
And my father calling the numbers.

The quick feet shaking the puncheon-floor,
And the fiddle squealing and squealing,
Till the dried herbs rattled above the door
And the dust went up to the ceiling.

There are children lucky from dawn till dusk,
But never a child so lucky!
For I cut my teeth on "Money Musk"
In the Bloody Ground of Kentucky!

When I grew tall as the Indian corn,
My father had little to lend me,
But he gave me his great, old powder-horn
And his woodsman's skill to befriend me.

With a leather shirt to cover my back,
And a redskin nose to unravel
Each forest sign, I carried my pack
As far as a scout could travel.

Till I lost my boyhood and found my wife,
A girl like a Salem clipper!
A woman straight as a hunting-knife
With eyes as bright as the Dipper!

We cleared our camp where the buffalo feed,
Unheard-of streams were our flagons;
And I sowed my sons like the apple-seed
On the trail of the Western wagons.

They were right, tight boys, never sulky or slow,
A fruitful, a goodly muster.
The eldest died at the Alamo.
The youngest fell with Custer.

The letter that told it burned my hand.
Yet we smiled and said, "So be it!"

But I could not live when they fenced the land,
For it broke my heart to see it.

I saddled a red, unbroken colt
And rode him into the day there;
And he threw me down like a thunderbolt
And rolled on me as I lay there.

The hunter's whistle hummed in my ear
As the city-men tried to move me,
And I died in my boots like a pioneer
With the whole wide sky above me.

Now I lie in the heart of the fat, black soil,
Like the seed of a prairie-thistle;
It has washed my bones with honey and oil
And picked them clean as a whistle.

And my youth returns, like the rains of Spring,
And my sons, like the wild-geese flying;
And I lie and hear the meadow-lark sing
And have much content in my dying.

Go play with the towns you have built of blocks,
The towns where you would have bound me!
I sleep in my earth like a tired fox,
And my buffalo have found me.

THE HEMP

I. The Planting of the Hemp

CAPTAIN HAWK *scourged clean the seas*
(Black is the gap below the plank)
From the Great North Bank to the Caribbees.
(Down by the marsh the hemp grows rank.)

His fear was on the seaport towns,
The weight of his hand held hard the downs.
And the merchants cursed him, bitter and black,
For a red flame in the sea-fog's wrack
Was all of their ships that might come back.

For all he had one word alone,
One clod of dirt in their faces thrown,
"The hemp that shall hang me is not grown!"

His name bestrode the seas like Death,
The waters trembled at his breath.

This is the tale of how he fell,
Of the long sweep and the heavy swell,
And the rope that dragged him down to hell.

The fight was done, and the gutted ship,
Stripped like a shark the sea-gulls strip,

Lurched blindly, eaten out with flame,
Back to the land from whence she came,
A skimming horror, an eyeless shame.

And Hawk stood up on his quarter-deck,
And saw the sky and saw the wreck.

Below, a butt for sailors' jeers,
White as the sky when a white squall nears,
Huddled the crowd of the prisoners.

Over the bridge of the tottering plank,
Where the sea shook and the gulf yawned blank,
They shrieked and struggled and dropped and sank.

371

Pinioned arms and hands bound fast.
One girl alone was left at last.

Sir Henry Gaunt was a mighty lord.
He sat in state at the Council board.

The governors were as naught to him.
From one rim to the other rim
Of his great plantations, flung out wide
Like a purple cloak, was a full month's ride.

Life and death in his white hands lay,
And his only daughter stood at bay,
Trapped like a hare in the toils that day.

He sat at wine in his gold and his lace,
And far away, in a bloody place,
Hawk came near, and she covered her face.

He rode in the fields, and the hunt was brave,
And far away, his daughter gave
A shriek that the seas cried out to hear,
And he could not see and he could not save.

Her white soul withered in the mire
As paper shrivels up in fire,
And Hawk laughed, and he kissed her mouth,
And her body he took for his desire.

II. The Growing of the Hemp

Sir Henry stood in the manor room,
And his eyes were hard gems in the gloom.

And he said, "Go, dig me furrows five
Where the green marsh creeps like a thing alive—
There at its edge where the rushes thrive."

And where the furrows rent the ground
He sowed the seed of hemp around.

And the blacks shrink back and are sore afraid
At the furrows five that rib the glade,
And the voodoo work of the master's spade.

For a cold wind blows from the marshland near,
And white things move, and the night grows drear,
And they chatter and crouch and are sick with fear.

But down by the marsh, where the grey slaves glean,
The hemp sprouts up, and the earth is seen
Veiled with a tenuous mist of green.

And Hawk still scourges the Caribbees,
And many men kneel at his knees.

Sir Henry sits in his house alone,
And his eyes are hard and dull like stone.

And the waves beat, and the winds roar,
And all things are as they were before.

And the days pass, and the weeks pass,
And nothing changes but the grass.

But down where the fireflies are like eyes,
And the damps shudder, and the mists rise,
The hemp-stalks stand up toward the skies.

And down from the poop of the pirate ship
A body falls, and the great sharks grip.

Innocent, lovely, go in grace!
At last there is peace upon your face.

And Hawk laughs loud as the corpse is thrown,
"The hemp that shall hang me is not grown!"

Sir Henry's face is iron to mark,
And he gazes ever in the dark.

And the days pass, and the weeks pass,
And the world is as it always was.

But down by the marsh the sickles beam,
Glitter on glitter, gleam on gleam,
And the hemp falls down by the stagnant stream.

And Hawk beats up from the Caribbees,
Swooping to pounce in the Northern seas.

Sir Henry sits sunk deep in his chair,
And white as his hand is grown his hair.

And the days pass, and the weeks pass,
And the sands roll from the hourglass.

But down by the marsh, in the blazing sun,
The hemp is smoothed and twisted and spun.
The rope made, and the work done.

III. The Using of the Hemp

Captain Hawk scourged clean the seas,
(Black is the gap below the plank)
From the Great North Bank to the Caribbees.
(Down by the marsh the hemp grows rank.)

He sailed in the broad Atlantic track
And the ships that saw him came not back.

Till once again, where the wide tides ran,
He stopped to harry a merchantman.

He bade her stop. Ten guns spoke true
From her hidden ports, and a hidden crew,
Lacking his great ship through and through.

Dazed and dumb with the sudden death,
He scarce had time to draw a breath

Before the grappling-irons bit deep
And the boarders slew his crew like sheep.

Hawk stood up straight, his breast to the steel;
His cutlass made a bloody wheel.

His cutlass made a wheel of flame.
They shrank before him as he came.

And the bodies fell in a choking crowd,
And still he thundered out aloud,

"The hemp that shall hang me is not grown!"
They fled at last. He was left alone.

Before his foe Sir Henry stood.
"The hemp is grown and my word made good!"

And the cutlass clanged with a hissing whir
On the lashing blade of the rapier.

Hawk roared and charged like a maddened buck.
As the cobra strikes, Sir Henry struck,

Pouring his life in a single thrust,
And the cutlass shivered to sparks and dust.

Sir Henry stood on the blood-stained deck,
And set his foot on his foe's neck.

Then, from the hatch, where the torn decks slope,
Where the dead roll and the wounded grope,
He dragged the serpent of the rope.

The sky was blue and the sea was still,
The waves lapped softly, hill on hill,
And between one wave and another wave
The doomed man's cries were little and shrill.

The sea was blue and the sky was calm,
The air dripped with a golden balm.
Like a wind-blown fruit between sea and sun,
A black thing writhed at a yard-arm.

Slowly then, and awesomely,
The ship sank, and the gallows-tree,
And there was nought between sea and sun—
Nought but the sun and the sky and the sea.

But down by the marsh, where the fever breeds,
Only the water chuckles and pleads;
For the hemp clings fast to a dead man's throat,
And blind Fate gathers back her seeds.

THE MOUNTAIN WHIPPOORWILL

OR, HOW HILL-BILLY JIM WON THE GREAT FIDDLERS' PRIZE

(*A Georgia Romance*)

UP IN the mountains, it's lonesome all the time,
(Sof' win' slewin' thu' the sweet-potato vine).

Up in the mountains, it's lonesome for a child,
(Whippoorwills a-callin' when the sap runs wild).

Up in the mountains, mountains in the fog,
Everythin's as lazy as an old houn' dog.

Born in the mountains, never raised a pet,
Don't want nuthin' an' never got it yet.

Born in the mountains, lonesome-born,
Raised runnin' ragged thu' the cockleburrs and corn.

Never knew my pappy, mebbe never should.
Think he was a fiddle made of mountain laurel-wood.

Never had a mammy to teach me pretty-please.
Think she was a whippoorwill, a-skitin' thu' the trees.

Never had a brother ner a whole pair of pants,
But when I start to fiddle, why, yuh got to start to dance!

Listen to my fiddle—Kingdom Come—Kingdom Come!
Hear the frogs a-chunkin' "Jug o' rum, Jug o' rum!"
Hear that mountain-whippoorwill be lonesome in the air,
An' I'll tell yuh how I traveled to the Essex County Fair.

Essex County has a mighty pretty fair,
All the smarty fiddlers from the South come there.

Elbows flyin' as they rosin up the bow
For the First Prize Contest in the Georgia Fiddlers' Show.

376

Old Dan Wheeling, with his whiskers in his ears,
King-pin fiddler for nearly twenty years.

Big Tom Sargent, with his blue wall-eye,
An' Little Jimmy Weezer that can make a fiddle cry.

All sittin' roun', spittin' high an' struttin' proud,
(Listen, little whippoorwill, yuh better bug yore eyes!)
Tun-a-tun-a-tunin' while the jedges told the crowd
Them that got the mostest claps'd win the bestest prize.

Everybody waitin' for the first twecdle-dee,
When in comes a-stumblin'—hill-billy me!

Bowed right pretty to the jedges an' the rest,
Took a silver dollar from a hole inside my vest,

Plunked it on the table an' said, "There's my callin' card!
An' anyone that licks me—well, he's got to fiddle hard!"

Old Dan Wheeling, he was laughin' fit to holler,
Little Jimmy Weezer said, "There's one dead dollar!"

Big Tom Sargent had a yaller-toothy grin,
But I tucked my little whippoorwill spang underneath my chin,
An' petted it an' tuned it till the jedges said, "Begin!"

Big Tom Sargent was the first in line;
He could fiddle all the bugs off a sweet-potato vine.

He could fiddle down a possum from a mile-high tree.
He could fiddle up a whale from the bottom of the sea.

Yuh could hear hands spankin' till they spanked each other raw,
When he finished variations on "Turkey in the Straw."

Little Jimmy Weezer was the next to play;
He could fiddle all night, he could fiddle all day.

He could fiddle chills, he could fiddle fever,
He could make a fiddle rustle like a lowland river.

377

He could make a fiddle croon like a lovin' woman.
An' they clapped like thunder when he'd finished strummin'.

Then came the ruck of the bob-tailed fiddlers,
The let's go-easies, the fair-to-middlers.

They got their claps an' they lost their bicker,
An' settled back for some more corn-licker.

An' the crowd was tired of their no-count squealing,
When out in the center steps Old Dan Wheeling.

He fiddled high and he fiddled low,
(Listen, little whippoorwill; yuh got to spread yore wings!)
He fiddled with a cherrywood bow.
(Old Dan Wheeling's got bee-honey in his strings.)

He fiddled the wind by the lonesome moon,
He fiddled a most almighty tune.

He started fiddling like a ghost,
He ended fiddling like a host.

He fiddled north an' he fiddled south,
He fiddled the heart right out of yore mouth.

He fiddled here an' he fiddled there.
He fiddled salvation everywhere.

When he was finished, the crowd cut loose,
(Whippoorwill, they's rain on yore breast.)
An' I sat there wonderin', "What's the use?"
(Whippoorwill, fly home to yore nest.)

But I stood up pert an' I took my bow,
An' my fiddle went to my shoulder, so.

An'—they wasn't no crowd to get me fazed—
But I was alone where I was raised.

Up in the mountains, so still it makes yuh skeered.
Where God lies sleepin' in his big white beard.

An' I heard the sound of the squirrel in the pine,
An' I heard the earth a-breathin' thu' the long night-time.

They've fiddled the rose, an' they've fiddled the thorn,
But they haven't fiddled the mountain-corn.

They've fiddled sinful an' fiddled moral,
But they haven't fiddled the breshwood-laurel.

They've fiddled loud, an' they've fiddled still,
But they haven't fiddled the whippoorwill.

I started off with a *dump-diddle-dump*,
(*Oh, hell's broke loose in Georgia!*)
Skunk-cabbage growin' by the bee-gum stump,
(*Whippoorwill, yo're singin' now!*)

Oh, Georgia booze is mighty fine booze,
The best yuh ever poured yuh,
But it eats the soles right offen yore shoes,
For Hell's broke loose in Georgia.

My mother was a whippoorwill pert,
My father, he was lazy,
But I'm Hell broke loose in a new store shirt
To fiddle all Georgia crazy.

Swing yore partners—up an' down the middle!
Sashay now—oh, listen to that fiddle!
Flapjacks flippin' on a red-hot griddle,
An' hell broke loose,
Hell broke loose,
Fire on the mountains—snakes in the grass.
Satan's here a-bilin'—oh, Lordy, let him pass!
Go down Moses, set my people free,
Pop goes the weasel thu' the old Red Sea!
Jonah sittin' on a hickory-bough,
Up jumps a whale—an' where's yore prophet now?
Rabbit in the pea-patch, possum in the pot,
Try an' stop my fiddle, now my fiddle's gettin' hot!
Whippoorwill, singin' thu' the mountain hush,
Whippoorwill, shoutin' from the burnin' bush,

Whippoorwill, cryin' in the stable-door,
Sing to-night as yuh never sang before!
Hell's broke loose like a stompin' mountain-shoat,
Sing till yuh bust the gold in yore throat!
Hell's broke loose for forty miles aroun'
Bound to stop yore music if yuh don't sing it down.
Sing on the mountains, little whippoorwill,
Sing to the valleys, an' slap 'em with a hill,
For I'm struttin' high as an eagle's quill,
An' Hell's broke loose,
Hell's broke loose,
Hell's broke loose in Georgia!

They wasn't a sound when I stopped bowin',
(*Whippoorwill, yuh can sing no more.*)
But, somewhere or other, the dawn was growin',
(*Oh, mountain whippoorwill!*)

An' I thought, "I've fiddled all night an' lost.
Yo're a good hill-billy, but yuh've been bossed."

So I went to congratulate old man Dan,
—But he put his fiddle into my han'—
An' then the noise of the crowd began.

KING DAVID

DAVID sang to his hook-nosed harp:
"The Lord God is a jealous God!
His violent vengeance is swift and sharp!
And the Lord is King above all gods!

"Blest be the Lord, through years untold,
The Lord Who has blessed me a thousand fold!

"Cattle and concubines, corn and hives
Enough to last me a dozen lives.

"Plump, good women with noses flat,
Marrowful blessings, weighty and fat.

"I wax in His peace like a pious gourd,
The Lord God is a pleasant God,
Break mine enemy's jaw, O Lord!
For the Lord is King above all gods!"

His hand dropped slack from the tunable strings,
A sorrow came on him—a sorrow of kings.

A sorrow sat on the arm of his throne,
An eagle sorrow with claws of stone.

"I am merry, yes, when I am not thinking,
But life is nothing but eating and drinking.

"I can shape my psalms like daggers of jade,
But they do not shine like the first I made.

"I can harry the heathen from North to South,
But no hot taste comes into my mouth.

"My wives are comely as long-haired goats,
But I would not care if they cut their throats!

"Where are the maids of the desert tents
With lips like flagons of frankincense?

"Where is Jonathan? Where is Saul?
The captain-towers of Zion wall?

"The trees of cedar, the hills of Nod,
The kings, the running lions of God?

"Their words were a writing in golden dust,
Their names are myrrh in the mouths of the just.

"The sword of the slayer could never divide them—
Would God I had died in battle beside them!"

The Lord looked down from a thunder-clap.
(The Lord God is a crafty God.)
He heard the strings of the shrewd harp snap.
(The Lord Who is King above all gods.)

He pricked the king with an airy thorn,
It burnt in his body like grapes of scorn.

The eyelids roused that had drooped like lead.
David lifted his heavy head.

The thorn stung at him, a fiery bee,
"The world is wide. I will go and see
From the roof of my haughty palace," said he.

2

Bathsheba bathed on her vine-decked roof.
(The Lord God is a mighty God.)
Her body glittered like mail of proof.
(And the Lord is King above all gods.)

Her body shimmered, tender and white
As the flesh of aloes in candlelight.

King David forgot to be old or wise.
He spied on her bathing with sultry eyes.

A breath of spice came into his nose.
He said, "Her breasts are like two young roes."

His eyes were bright with a crafty gleam.
He thought, "Her body is soft as cream."

He straightened himself like an unbent bow
And called a servant and bade him go.

3

Uriah the Hittite came to his lord,
Dusty with war as a well-used sword.

A close, trim man like a belt, well-buckled;
A jealous gentleman, hard to cuckold.

David entreated him, soft and bland,
Offered him comfits from his own hand.

Drank with him deep till his eyes grew red,
And laughed in his beard as he went to bed.

The days slipped by without hurry or strife,
Like apple-parings under a knife,
And still Uriah kept from his wife.

Lean fear tittered through David's psalm,
"This merry husband is far too calm."

David sent for Uriah then,
They greeted each other like pious men.

"Thou hast borne the battle, the dust and the heat.
Go down to thy house and wash thy feet!"

Uriah frowned at the words of the king.
His brisk, hard voice had a leaden ring.

"While the hosts of God still camp in the field
My house to me is a garden sealed.

"How shall I rest while the arrow yet flies?
The dust of the war is still in my eyes."

David spoke with his lion's roar:
"If Peace be a bridle that rubs you sore,
You shall fill your belly with blood and war!"

Uriah departed, calling him kind.
His eyes were serpents in David's mind.

He summoned a captain, a pliable man,
"Uriah the Hittite shall lead the van.

"In the next assault, when the fight roars high,
And the Lord God is a hostile God,
Retire from Uriah that he may die.
For the Lord is King above all gods."

4

The messenger came while King David played
The friskiest ditty ever made.

"News, O King, from our dubious war!
The Lord of Hosts hath prevailed once more!

"His foes are scattered like chirping sparrows,
Their kings lie breathless, feathered with arrows.

"Many are dead of your captains tall.
Uriah the Hittite was first to fall."

David turned from the frolicsome strings
And rent his clothes for the death of kings.

Yet, as he rent them, he smiled for joy.
The sly, wide smile of a wicked boy.

"The powerful grace of the Lord prevails!
He has cracked Uriah between His nails!

"His blessings are mighty, they shall not cease.
And my days henceforth shall be days of peace!"

His mind grew tranquil, smoother than fleece.
He rubbed his body with scented grease.
And his days thenceforward were days of peace.

His days were fair as the flowering lime
—For a little time, for a little time.

And Bathsheba lay in his breast like a dove,
A vessel of amber, made for love.

5

When Bathsheba was great with child,
(The Lord God is a jealous God!)
Portly and meek as a moon grown mild,
(The Lord is King above all gods!)

Nathan, the prophet, wry and dying,
Preached to the king like a locust crying:

"Hearken awhile to a doleful thing!
There were two men in thy land, O King!

"One was rich as a gilded ram.
One had one treasure, a poor ewe-lamb.

"Rich man wasted his wealth like spittle.
Poor man shared with his lamb spare victual.

"A traveler came to the rich man's door.
'Give me to eat, for I hunger sore!'

"Rich man feasted him fatly, true,
But the meat that he gave him was fiend's meat, too,
Stolen and roasted, the poor man's ewe!

"Hearken, my lord, to a deadly thing!
What shall be done with these men, O King?"

David hearkened, seeing it plain,
His heart grew heavy with angry pain:
"Show me the rich man that he be slain!"

Nathan barked as a jackal can.
"Just, O King! And thou art the man!"

David rose as the thunders rise
When someone in Heaven is telling lies.
But his eyes were weaker than Nathan's eyes.

His huge bulk shivered like quaking sod,
Shoulders bowing to Nathan's rod,
Nathan, the bitter apple of God.

His great voice shook like a runner's, spent,
"My sin has found me! Oh, I repent!"

Answered Nathan, that talkative Jew:
"For many great services, comely and true,
The Lord of Mercy will pardon you.

"But the child in Bathsheba, come of your seed,
Shall sicken and die like a blasted weed."

David groaned when he heard him speak.
The painful tears ran hot on his cheek.

Ashes he cast on his kingly locks.
All night long he lay on the rocks.

Beseeching his Lord with a howling cry:
"O Lord God, O my jealous God,
Be kind to the child that it may not die,
For Thou art King above all gods!"

6

Seven long nights he lay there, howling,
A lion wounded, moaning and growling.

Seven long midnights, sorrowing greatly,
While Sin, like a dead man, embraced him straitly.

Till he was abased from his lust and pride
And the child was born and sickened and died.

He arose at last. It was ruddy Day.
And his sin like water had washed away.

He cleansed and anointed, took fresh apparel,
And worshiped the Lord in a tuneful carol.

His servants, bearing the child to bury,
Marveled greatly to see him so merry.

He spoke to them mildly as mid-May weather:
"The child and my sin are perished together.

"He is dead, my son. Though his whole soul yearn to me,
I must go to him, he may not return to me.

"Why should I sorrow for what was pain?
A cherished grief is an iron chain."

He took up his harp, the sage old chief.
His heart felt clean as a new green leaf.

His soul smelt pleasant as rain-wet clover.
"I have sinned and repented and that's all over.

"In his dealings with heathen, the Lord is hard.
But the humble soul is his spikenard."

His wise thoughts fluttered like doves in the air.
"I wonder is Bathsheba still so fair?

"Does she weep for the child that our sin made perish?
I must comfort my ewe-lamb, comfort and cherish.

"The justice of God is honey and balm.
I will soothe her heart with a little psalm."

He went to her chamber, no longer sad,
Walking as light as a shepherd lad.

He found her weeping, her garments rent,
Trodden like straw by God's punishment.
He solaced her out of his great content.

Being but woman, a while she grieved,
But at last she was comforted, and conceived.

Nine months later she bore him a son.
(The Lord God is a mighty God!)
The name of that child was SOLOMON.
He was God's tough staff till his days were run!
(And the Lord is King above all gods!)

THE RETORT DISCOURTEOUS

(Italy—16th Century)

But what, by the fur on your satin sleeves,
The rain that drags at my feather
And the great Mercurius, god of thieves,
Are we thieves doing together?

Last night your blades bit deep for their hire,
And we were the sickled barley.
To-night, atoast by the common fire,
You ask me to join your parley.

Your spears are shining like Iceland spar,
The blood-grapes drip for your drinking;
For you folk follow the rising star,
I follow the star that's sinking!

My queen is old as the frosted whins,
Nay, how could her wrinkles charm me?
And the starving bones are bursting the skins
In the ranks of her ancient army.

You marshal a steel-and-silken troop,
Your cressets are fed with spices,
And you batter the world like a rolling hoop
To the goal of your proud devices.

I have rocked your thrones—but your fight is won.
To-night, as the highest bidder,
You offer a share of your brigand-sun,
Consider, old bull, consider!

Ahead, red Death and the Fear of Death,
Your vultures, stoop to the slaughter.
But I shall fight you, body and breath,
Till my life runs out like water!

My queen is wan as the Polar snows.
Her host is a rout of specters.
But I gave her Youth like a burning rose,
And her age shall not lack protectors!

I would not turn for the thunderclap
Or the face of the woman who bore me,
With her battered badge still scarring my cap,
And the drums of defeat before me.

Roll your hands in the honey of life,
Kneel to your white-necked strumpets!
You came to your crowns with a squealing fife
But I shall go out with trumpets!

Poison the steel of the plunging dart,
Holloa your hounds to their station!
I march to my ruin with such a heart
As a king to his coronation.

Your poets roar of your golden feats—
I have herded the stars like cattle.
And you may die in the perfumed sheets,
But I shall die in battle.

THREE DAYS' RIDE

"From *Belton Castle to Solway side,*
Hard by the bridge, is three days' ride."

We had fled full fast from her father's keep,
And the time was come that we must sleep.

The first day was an ecstasy,
A golden mist, a burgeoning tree;
We rode like gods through a world new-made,
The hawthorn scented hill and glade,
A faint, still sweetness in the air—
And, oh, her face and the wind in her hair!
And the steady beat of our good steeds' hooves,
Bearing us northward, strong and fast,
To my high black tower, stark to the blast,
Like a swimmer stripped where the Solway moves.

And ever, riding, we chanted a song,
Challenging Fortune, loud and long,
"*From Belton Castle to Solway side,*
Strive as you may, is three days' ride!"

She slept for an hour, wrapped in my cloak,
And I watched her till the morning broke;
The second day—and a harsher land,
And grey bare hills on either hand;
A surly land and a sullen folk,
And a fog that came like bitter smoke.

The road wound on like a twisted snake,
And our horses sobbed as they topped the brake.
Till we sprang to earth at Wyvern Fen,
Where fresh steeds stamped, and were off again.

Weary and sleepless, bruised and worn,
We still had strength for laughter and scorn;
Love held us up through the mire and mist,
Love fed us, while we clasped and kissed,
And still we sang as the night closed in,
Stealthy and slow as a hidden sin,
"From Belton Castle to Solway side,
Ride how you will, is three days' ride."

My love drooped low on the black mare's back,
Drowned in her hair . . . the reins went slack . . .
Yet she could not sleep, save to dream bad dreams
And wake all trembling, till at last
Her golden head lay on my breast.

At last we saw the first faint gleams
Of day. Dawn broke. A sickly light
Came from the withered sun—a blight
Was on the land, and poisonous mist
Shrouded the rotting trees, unkissed
By any wind, and black crags glared
Like sightless, awful faces, spared
From death to live accursed for aye.

Dragging slow chains the hours went by.
We rode on, drunk and drugged with sleep,
Too deadly weary now to say
Whether our horses kept the way
Or no—like slaves stretched on a heap
Of poisoned arrows. Every limb
Shot with sharp pain; pain seemed to swim
Like a red cloud before our eyes. . . .

The mist broke, and a moment showed,
Sharp as the Devil's oxen-goad,
The spear-points where the hot chase rode.

Idly I watched them dance and rise
Till white wreaths wiped them out again . . .
My love jerked at the bridle rein;
The black mare, dying, broke her heart
In one swift gallop; for my part

I dozed; and ever in my brain,
Four hoofs of fire beat out refrain,
A dirge to light us down to death,
A silly rhyme that saith and saith,
"From Belton Castle to Solway side,
Though great hearts break, is three days' ride!"
The black mare staggered, reeled and fell,
Bearing my love down . . . a great bell
Began to toll . . . and sudden fire
Flared at me from the road, a pyre
It seemed, to burn our bodies in . . .
And I fell down, far down, within
The pit's mouth . . . and my brain went blind. . . .

I woke—a cold sun rose behind
Black evil hills—my love knelt near
Beside a stream, her golden hair
Streaming across the grass—below
The Solway eddied to and fro,
White with fierce whirlpools . . . my love turned. . . .
Thank God, some hours of joy are burned
Into the mind, and will remain,
Fierce-blazing still, in spite of pain!

They came behind us as we kissed,
Stealthily from the dripping mist,
Her brothers and their evil band.
They bound me fast and made me stand.
They forced her down upon her knees.
She did not strive or cry or call,
But knelt there dumb before them all—
I could not turn away my eyes—
There was no fear upon her face,
Although they slew her in that place.
The daggers rent and tore her breast
Like dogs that snarl above a kill,
Her proud face gazed above them still,
Seeking rest—Oh, seeking rest!
The blood swept like a crimson dress
Over her bosom's nakedness,
A curtain for her weary eyes,
A muffling-cloth to stop her sighs . . .

And she was gone—and a red thing lay
Silent, on the trampled clay.

Beneath my horse my feet are bound,
My hands are bound behind my back,
I feel the sinews start and crack—
And ever to the hoof-beats' sound,
As we draw near the gallows-tree,
Where I shall hang right speedily,
A crazy tune rings in my brain,
Four hoofs of fire tramp the refrain,
Crashing clear o'er the roaring crowd,
Steadily galloping, strong and loud,
"From Belton Castle to Solway side,
Hard by the bridge, is three days' ride!"

ALEXANDER THE SIXTH DINES WITH
THE CARDINAL OF CAPUA

Next, then, the peacock, gilt
With all its feathers. Look, what gorgeous dyes
Flow in the eyes!
And how deep, lustrous greens are splashed and spilt
Along the black, that like a sea-wave's crest
Scatters soft beauty o'er th' emblazoned breast!

A strange fowl! But most fit
For feasts like this, whereby I honor one
Pure as the sun!
Yet glowing with the fiery zeal of it!
Some wine? Your goblet's empty? Let it foam!
It is not often that you come to Rome.

You like the Venice glass?
Rippled with lines that float like women's curls,
Neck like a girl's,
Fierce-glowing as a chalice in the Mass?
You start—'twas artist then, not Pope who spoke!
Ave Maria stella!—ah, it broke!

'Tis said they break alone
When poison writhes within. A foolish tale!
What, you look pale?
Caraffa, fetch a silver cup! . . . You own
A Birth of Venus, now—or so I've heard,
Lovely as the breast-plumage of a bird.

Also a Dancing Faun,
Hewn with the lithe grace of Praxiteles;
Globed pearls to please
A sultan; golden veils that drop like lawn—
How happy I could be with but a tithe
Of your possessions, fortunate one! Don't writhe

But take these cushions here!
Now for the fruit! Great peaches, satin-skinned,
Rough tamarind,
Pomegranates red as lips—oh they come dear!
But men like you we feast at any price—
A plum perhaps? They're looking rather nice.

I'll cut the thing in half.
There's yours! Now, with a one-side-poisoned knife
One might snuff life
And leave one's friend with—"fool" for epitaph.
An old trick? Truth! But when one has the itch
For pretty things and isn't very rich. . . .

There, eat it all or I'll
Be angry! You feel giddy? Well, it's hot!
This bergamot
Take home and smell—it purges blood of bile;
And when you kiss Bianca's dimpled knee,
Think of the poor Pope in his misery!

Now you may kiss my ring.
Ho there, the Cardinal's litter!—You must dine
When the new wine
Is in, again with me—hear Bice sing,
Even admire my frescoes—though they're nought
Beside the calm Greek glories you have bought.

Godspeed, Sir Cardinal,
And take a weak man's blessing! Help him there
To the cool air! . . .
Lucrezia here? You're ready for the ball?
—He'll die within ten hours, I suppose—
MhM! Kiss your poor old father, little rose!

The remaining poems in this section are from
A Book of Americans
by
Rosemary and Stephen Vincent Benét.

SOUTHERN SHIPS AND SETTLERS

1606-1732

O, where are you going, "Goodspeed" and "Discovery"?
With meek "Susan Constant" to make up the three?
We're going to settle the wilds of Virginia,
For gold and adventure we're crossing the sea.

And what will you find there? Starvation and fever.
We'll eat of the adder and quarrel and rail.
All but sixty shall die of the first seven hundred,
But a nation begins with the voyage we sail.

O, what are you doing, my handsome Lord Baltimore?
Where are you sending your "Ark" and your "Dove"?
I'm sending them over the ocean to Maryland
To build up a refuge for people I love.

Both Catholic and Protestant there may find harbor,
Though I am a Catholic by creed and by prayer.
The South is Virginia, the North is New England.
I'll go in the middle and plant my folk there.

O, what do you seek, "Carolina" and "Albemarle",
Now the Stuarts are up and the Roundheads are down?
We'll seek and we'll find, to the South of Virginia,
A site by two rivers and name it Charles Town.

And, in South Carolina, the cockfighting planters
Will dance with their belles by a tropical star.
And, in North Carolina, the sturdy Scotch-Irish
Will prove at King's Mountain the metal they are.

O, what are you dreaming, cock-hatted James Oglethorpe?
And who are the people you take in the "Anne"?
They're poor English debtors whom hard laws imprison,
And poor, distressed Protestants, fleeing a ban.

I'll settle them pleasantly on the Savannah,
With Germans and Highlanders, thrifty and strong.
They shall eat Georgia peaches in huts of palmetto,
And their land shall be fertile, their days shall be long.

All
We're the barques and the sailors, the bread on the waters,
The seed that was planted and grew to be tall,
And the South was first won by our toils and our dangers,
So remember our journeys. Remember us all.

COTTON MATHER

1663-1728

Grim Cotton Mather
Was always seeing witches,
Daylight, moonlight,
They buzzed about his head,
Pinching him and plaguing him
With aches and pains and stitches,
Witches in his pulpit,
Witches by his bed.

Nowadays, nowadays,
We'd say that he was crazy,
But everyone believed him
In old Salem town
And nineteen people
Were hanged for Salem witches
Because of Cotton Mather
And his long, black gown.

Old Cotton Mather
Didn't die happy.
He could preach and thunder,

396

He could fast and pray,
But men began to wonder
If there *had* been witches—
When he walked in the streets
Men looked the other way.

CAPTAIN KIDD

1650?-1701

This person in the gaudy clothes
Is worthy Captain Kidd.
They say he never buried gold.
I think, perhaps, he did.

They say it's all a story that
His favorite little song
Was "Make these lubbers walk the plank!"
I think, perhaps, they're wrong.

They say he never pirated
Beneath the Skull-and-Bones.
He merely traveled for his health
And spoke in soothing tones.
In fact, you'll read in nearly all
The newer history books
That he was mild as cottage cheese
—*But I don't like his looks!*

FRENCH PIONEERS

1534-1759

New France, New Spain, New England,
Which will it be?
Who will win the new land?
The land across the sea?

They came here, they toiled here,
They broke their hearts afar,

397

Normandy and Brittany,
Paris and Navarre.

They lost here, at last here,
It wasn't so to be.
Let us still remember them,
Men from oversea.

Marquette and Joliet,
Cartier, La Salle,
Priest, corsair, gentleman,
Gallants one and all.

France was in their quick words,
France was in their veins.
They came here, they toiled here.
They suffered many pains.

Lake and river, stream and wood,
Seigneurs and dames—
They lived here, they died here,
They left singing names.

THOMAS JEFFERSON

1743-1826

Thomas Jefferson,
What do you say
Under the gravestone
Hidden away?

"I was a giver,
I was a molder,
I was a builder
With a strong shoulder."

Six feet and over,
Large-boned and ruddy,
The eyes grey-hazel
But bright with study.

The big hands clever
With pen and fiddle
And ready, ever,
For any riddle.

From buying empires
To planting 'taters,
From Declarations
To trick dumb-waiters.

"I liked the people,
The sweat and crowd of them,
Trusted them always
And spoke aloud of them.

"I liked all learning
And wished to share it
Abroad like pollen
For all who merit.

"I liked fine houses
With Greek pilasters,
And built them surely,
My touch a master's.

"I liked queer gadgets
And secret shelves,
And helping nations
To rule themselves.

"Jealous of others?
Not always candid?
But huge of vision
And open-handed.

"A wild-goose-chaser?
Now and again,
Build Monticello,
You little men!

"Design my plow, sirs,
They use it still,

Or found my college
At Charlottesville.

"And still go questing
New things and thinkers,
And keep as busy
As twenty tinkers.

"While always guarding
The people's freedom—
You need more hands, sir?
I didn't need 'em.

"They call you rascal?
They called me worse.
You'd do grand things, sir,
But lack the purse?

"I got no riches.
I died a debtor.
I died free-hearted
And that was better.

"For life was freakish
But life was fervent,
And I was always
Life's willing servant.

"Life, life's too weighty?
Too long a haul, sir?
I lived past eighty.
I liked it all, sir."

JOHN JAMES AUDUBON

1780-1851

Some men live for warlike deeds,
Some for women's words.
John James Audubon
Lived to look at birds.

Pretty birds and funny birds,
All our native fowl
From the little cedar waxwing
To the Great Horned Owl.

Let the wind blow hot or cold,
Let it rain or snow,
Everywhere the birds went
Audubon would go.

Scrambling through a wilderness,
Floating down a stream,
All around America
In a feathered dream.

Thirty years of traveling,
Pockets often bare,
(Lucy Bakewell Audubon
Patched them up with care).

Followed grebe and meadowlark,
Saw them sing and splash.
(Lucy Bakewell Audubon
Somehow raised the cash).

Drew them all the way they lived
In their habitats.
(Lucy Bakewell Audubon
Sometimes wondered "Cats?")

Colored them and printed them
In a giant book,
"Birds of North America"—
All the world said, "Look!"

Gave him medals and degrees,
Called him noble names,
—Lucy Bakewell Audubon
Kissed her queer John James.

DANIEL BOONE

1735-1820

When Daniel Boone goes by, at night,
The phantom deer arise
And all lost, wild America
Is burning in their eyes.

WESTERN WAGONS

They went with axe and rifle, when the trail was still to blaze,
They went with wife and children, in the prairie-schooner days,
With banjo and with frying pan—Susanna, don't you cry!
For I'm off to California to get rich out there or die!

We've broken land and cleared it, but we're tired of where we
    are.
They say that wild Nebraska is a better place by far.
There's gold in far Wyoming, there's black earth in Ioway,
So pack up the kids and blankets, for we're moving out today!

The cowards never started and the weak died on the road,
And all across the continent the endless campfires glowed.
We'd taken land and settled—but a traveler passed by—
And we're going West tomorrow—Lordy, never ask us why!

We're going West tomorrow, where the promises can't fail.
O'er the hills in legions, boys, and crowd the dusty trail!
We shall starve and freeze and suffer. We shall die, and tame
    the lands.
But we're going West tomorrow, with our fortune in our hands.

CREATURES OF EARTH

Creatures of Earth

THE INNOVATOR

(A Pharaoh Speaks)

I SAID, "Why should a pyramid
Stand always dully on its base?
I'll change it! Let the top be hid,
The bottom take the apex-place!"
And as I bade they did.

The people flocked in, scores on scores,
To see it balance on its tip.
They praised me with the praise that bores,
My godlike mind on every lip.
—Until it fell, of course.

And then they took my body out
From my crushed palace, mad with rage,
—Well, half the town *was* wrecked, no doubt—
Their crazy anger to assuage
By dragging it about.

The end? Foul birds defile my skull.
The new king's praises fill the land.
He clings to precept, simple, dull;
His pyramids on bases stand.
But—Lord, how usual!

SNOWFALL

HEAVEN is hell, if it be as they say,
An endless day.
A pen of terrible radiance, on whose walls
No shadow falls,
No sunset ever comes because no sun has ever risen,
Where, like bewildered flies,
Poor immortalities
Interminably crawl, caught in a crystal prison.

Yet, if there is but night to recompense
Impertinence,
How can we bear to live so long and know
The end is so?
Creatures that hate the dark, to utmost dark descending?
The worm's dull enmity,
To feel it—but not see!
To be afraid at night and know that night unending!

There is a time when, though the sun be weak,
It is not bleak
With perfect and intolerable light,
Nor has the night
Yet put those eyes to sleep that do not wish for slumber;
When, on the city we know,
The pale, transmuting snow
Falls softly, in sighing flakes, immaculate, without number.

Whisperingly it drifts, and whisperingly
Fills earth and sky
With fragile petals, tranquil as a swan's
Blanch pinions.
And where it falls is silence, subtle and mild.
That silence is not cruel
But calm as a frozen jewel,
And clasped to its cold frail breast Earth sucks in rest like a child.

If there can be a heaven, let it wear
Even such an air.
Not shamed with sun nor black without a ray,

But gently day.
A tired street, whereon the snow falls, whitely,
An infant, cradled in fleece,
An ancient, drowsy with peace,
Unutterable peace, too pure to shine too brightly.

BAD DREAM

OUT of the stroke, the change,
The body locked in its death
Like a stream locked in the ice,
The whiteness under the cheek,
The lips forever set
In the look that is always strange
Because we remember yet
How they spoke, how the mere breath
Was enough to make them speak.

I saw the soul arise,
Naked, shaped like a blade,
Free, inhuman and bright,
And where the body was laid
I saw it hover.
It had no need of eyes.
It had forgotten the grief,
The long pain and the brief,
The daybreak, the burning night,
The touch of water and light.
These were over.

It was free. It would not return.
I saw its brightness spurn
Like the heel of a fugitive
The body it hung above,
The body which gave it birth—
It is this I cannot forgive.
It is thus they answer our love
When they are gone from the earth.

FOR ALL BLASPHEMERS

ADAM was my grandfather,
A tall, spoiled child,
A red, clay tower
In Eden, green and mild.
He ripped the Sinful Pippin
From its sanctimonious limb.
Adam was my grandfather—
And I take after him.

Noah was my uncle
And he got dead drunk.
There were planets in his liquor-can
And lizards in his bunk.
He fell into the Bottomless
Past Hell's most shrinking star.
Old Aunt Fate has often said
How much alike we are.

Lilith, she's my sweetheart
Till my heartstrings break,
Most of her is honey-pale
And all of her is snake.
Sweet as secret thievery,
I kiss her all I can,
While Somebody Above remarks
"That's not a nice young man!"

Bacchus was my brother,
Nimrod is my friend.
All of them have talked to me
On how such courses end.
But when His Worship takes me up
How can I fare but well?
For who in gaudy Hell will care?
—And I shall be in Hell.

ARCHITECTS

My son has built a fortified house
To keep his pride from the thunder,
And his steadfast heart from the gnawing mouse
That nibbles the roots of wonder.

My daughter's wit has hammered and filed
Her slight and glittering armor.
She hides in its rings like a dragon-child,
And nothing on earth can harm her.

My wife has molded a coffin of lead
From the counterfeit tears of mourners.
She rests in it, calm as a saint long dead,
And the Four Winds kneel at its corners.

I have scooped my den with a crafty thumb
In the guts of an arid acre.
And it may not last till Kingdom Come
—But it will not cripple its maker.

It is six feet long by three feet deep
And some may call it narrow.
But, when I get into it, I can keep
The nakedness of an arrow.

DINNER IN A QUICK LUNCH ROOM

Soup should be heralded with a mellow horn,
Blowing clear notes of gold against the stars;
Strange *entrées* with a jangle of glass bars
Fantastically alive with subtle scorn;
Fish, by a plopping, gurgling rush of waters,
Clear, vibrant waters, beautifully austere;
Roast, with a thunder of drums to stun the ear,
A screaming fife, a voice from ancient slaughters!

Over the salad let the woodwinds moan;
Then the green silence of many watercresses;
Dessert, a balalaika, strummed alone;

Coffee, a slow, low singing no passion stresses;
Such are my thoughts as—clang! crash! bang!—I brood
And gorge the sticky mess these fools call food!

OPERATION

(For J. F. C., Jr.)

BOUND to the polished table, arm and leg,
I lay and watched, with loud, disgusting fear,
The army of the instruments draw near,
Hook, saw, sleek scissor and distorted peg;
My eyes were like a spaniel's when they beg,
The nurses' purpose was so very clear
. . . And though I tried to bite one in the ear
She stayed as white and silent as an egg.

Time, the superb physician, drew his breath,
"I'll just remove Youth, Health and Love," he said,
"The rest is for Consulting-Surgeon Death."
God, how I hated that peremptory head!
As through the ether came his sickening drawl
"Now this won't hurt. . . . Oh, it won't hurt at all."

THE TRAPEZE PERFORMER

(For C. M.)

FIERCE little bombs of gleam snap from his spangles,
Sleek flames glow softly on his silken tights,
The waiting crowd blurs to crude darks and whites
Beneath the lamps that stare like savage bangles;
Safe in a smooth and sweeping arc he dangles
And sees the tanbark tower like old heights
Before careening eyes. At last he sights
The waiting hands and sinuously untangles.

Over the sheer abyss so deadly-near,
He falls, like wine to its appointed cup,

Turns like a wheel of fireworks, and is mine.
Battering hands acclaim our triumph clear.
—And steadfast muscles draw my sonnet up
To the firm iron of the fourteenth line.

JUDGMENT

"HE'LL let us off with fifty years!" one said.
And one, "I always knew that Bible lied!"
One who was philanthropic stood aside,
Patting his sniveling virtues on the head.
"Yes, there may be some—pain," another wheezed.
"One rending touch to fit the soul for bliss."
"A bare formality!" one seemed to hiss.
And everyone was pink and fed and pleased.

Then thunder came, and with an earthquake sound
Shook those fat corpses from their flabby languor.
The sky was furious with immortal anger,
We miserable sinners hugged the ground:
Seeing through all the torment, saying, "Yes,"
God's quiet face, serenely merciless.

GHOSTS OF A LUNATIC ASYLUM

HERE, where men's eyes were empty and as bright
As the blank windows set in glaring brick,
When the wind strengthens from the sea—and night
Drops like a fog and makes the breath come thick;

By the deserted paths, the vacant halls,
One may see figures, twisted shades and lean,
Like the mad shapes that crawl an Indian screen,
Or paunchy smears you find on prison walls.

Turn the knob gently! There's the Thumbless Man,
Still weaving glass and silk into a dream,
Although the wall shows through him—and the Khan
Journeys Cathay beside a paper stream.

A Rabbit Woman chitters by the door—
—Chilly the grave-smell comes from the turned sod—
Come—lift the curtain—and be cold before
The silence of the eight men who were God!

FOR THOSE WHO ARE AS RIGHT
AS ANY

"Spirit, they charge you that the time is ill.
The great wall sinks in the slime!"
*"I am a spirit, still.
I do not walk with the time."*

"The sky shivers, the king is a beast run wild,
The lords are sullen and base!"
*"When the sun rose up in the East like a great child,
I saw the gold and the face."*

"Come, draw your steel for the right, for the time wears on!
It is only a little way to Jerusalem!"
*"I have seen the floating swan
And the lion, bloody with dawn,
I will make pictures of them."*

"What, lift no sword in the battle?"

                     "I am swordless."

"No cause, no cry?"

                     "I am lordless."
*"I am shadow, shadow that passes across the meadow
And goes its way."*

"By God, against God, in our name, we will slay you, then!"
"Slay."

"And, when we have slain them all, we will build for men
The city called Marvelous, the glittering town,
And none shall be exalted or cast down
But all at ease, all hatreds reconciled."

*"I am air and I live. I live again and again.
I am wind and fire. But I am not reconciled."*

GIRL CHILD

Like a flower, like a tulip,
So fresh, so hardy,
So slim, so hasting,
The nose tip-tilted,
The mouth her mother's,
The eyes brighter
Than rabbit's or squirrel's
Suddenly peering
From bough or burrow;
All this in motion,
Motion and swaying,
As if all life
Were a wave of ocean,
As if all life
Were the clean stalk springing
Brightly, greenly,
From earth unworn,
To sway with sunlight,
To drink clear freshets,
Swiftly, oh, swiftly
To swell its bubble,
The staunch red flower
Hardy and mortal,
The bright flag
On the new hill,
Mortal, gallant,
As a cockerel's cry.

To this child,
To all swift children,
My great thanks
For their clear honor,
The hound running,
The flying fire.

OLD MAN HOPPERGRASS

Flesh, if you were stone or tree,
I'd be happier with ye.

When I was young, I slept like stone,
When I was young, I grew like tree.
Now I lie, abed, alone,
And I wonder if 'tis me.

Wake at night and ease me
But it does not please me,
Stick I am, sick I am,
Apple pared to quick I am,
Woman-nursed and queer.
Once I had a sweet tooth,
A sharp tooth, a neat tooth,
Cocked my hat and winked my eye
As the pretty girls went by,
Pretty girls and punkin-pie—
Dear! oh, dear!

Old man's a hoppergrass
Kicking in the wheat.

Can't eat his fill,
Can't drink his will,
Can't climb his hill,
Can't have his Jill.

And, when he talks sense,
Relations say,
"Better let Father
Have his way."

A stone's a stone
And a tree's a tree,
But what was the sense
Of aging me?

It's no improvement
That *I* can see.

And the night's long
And the night-sleep brief
And I hear the rustle
Of the fallen leaf,
"Old man Hoppergrass,
Come and see!"

Well, I won't for a little,
Not while I'm me.

But the sun's not as hot
As it used to be.

THE LOST WIFE

In the daytime, maybe, your heart's not breaking,
For there's the sun and the sky and working
And the neighbors to give you a word or hear you,
But, ah, the long nights when the wind comes shaking
The cold, black curtain, pulling and jerking,
And no one there in the bed to be near you.

And worse than the clods on the coffin falling
Are the clothes in the closet that no one wears now
And the things like hairpins you're always finding.
And you wouldn't mind the ghost of her calling
As much as knowing that no one cares now
If the carpet fades when the sun gets blinding.

I look in the houses, when twilight narrows,
And in each a man comes back to a woman.
The thought of that coming has spurs to ride me.
—Death, you have taken the great like sparrows,
But she was so slight, so small, so human.
You might have left her to lie beside me.

SPARROW

Lord, may I be
A sparrow in a tree.

No ominous and splendid bird of prey
But something that is fearful every day
Yet keeps its small flesh full of heat and lightness.
Pigeons are better dressed and robins stouter,
The white owl has all winter in his whiteness
And the blue heron is a kingly dream
At evening, by the pale stream,
But, even in the lion's cage, in Zoos,
You'll find a sparrow, picking up the crumbs
And taking life precisely as it comes
With the black, wary eye that marks the doubter;
Squabbling in crowds, dust-bathing in the sun,
Small, joyous, impudent, a gutter-child
In Lesbia's bosom or December's chill,
Full of impertinence and hard to kill
As Queen Anne's lace and poppies in the wheat—
I won't pretend the fellow has a Muse
But that he has advice, and good advice,
All lovers know who've walked the city's street
And wished the stones were bread.
Peacocks are handsomer and owls more wise.
(At least, by all repute.)
And parrots live on flattery and fruit,
Live to great age. The sparrow's none of these.
The sparrow is a humorist, and dies.
There are so many things that he is not.
He will not tear the stag nor sweep the seas
Nor fall, majestical, to a king's arrow.
Yet how he lives, and how he loves in living
Up to the dusty tip of every feather!
How he endures oppression and the weather
And asks for neither justice nor forgiving!
Lord, in your mercy, let me be a sparrow!
His rapid heart's so hot.
And some can sing—song-sparrows, so they say—
And, one thing, Lord—the times are iron, now.
Perhaps you have forgot.
They shoot the wise and brave on every bough.
But sparrows are the last things that get shot.

THANKS

For these my thanks, not that I eat or sleep,
Sweat or survive, but that at seventeen
I could so blind myself in writing verse
That the wall shuddered and the cry came forth
And the numb hand that wrote was not my hand
But a wise animal's.
Then the exhaustion and the utter sleep.

O flagrant and unnecessary body,
So hard beset, so clumsy in your skill!
For these my thanks, not that I breathe and ache,
Talk with my kind, swim in the naked sea,
But that the tired monster keeps the road
And even now, even at thirty-eight,
The metal heats, the flesh grows numb again
And I can still go muttering down the street
Not seeing the interminable world
Nor the ape-faces, only the live coal.

COMPLAINT OF BODY, THE ASS,
AGAINST HIS RIDER, THE SOUL

BODY

Well, here we go!
I told you that the weather looked like snow.
Why couldn't we have stayed there at the inn?
There was good straw and barley in the bin
And a grey jenny with a melting eye,
Neat-hoofed and sly—I rather like them sly—
Master a trader and a man of sense.
He likes his life and dinner. So do I.
Sleeps warm and doesn't try to cross a pass
A mountain-goat would balk at in his prime,
Where the hail falls as big as Peter's Pence
And every stone you slip on rolls a mile!
But that's not you, of course—that's not our style—
We're far too dandipratted and sublime!
Which of us is the ass?

Good ground, beyond the snow?
I've heard that little song before, you know.
Past cliff and ragged mount
And the wind's skinning-knife,
Far and forever far,
The water of the fount,
The water that is life
And the bright star?
Give me my water from a decent trough,
Not dabs of ice licked out of freezing stone
And, as for stars, why, let the stars alone,
You'll have us both in glory soon enough!

Alas, alack!
I'm carrying an idiot on my back.
I'm carrying Mr. Who to God Knows Where.
Oh, do not fix me with that burning stare
Of beauteous disdain!
I'm not a colt. I know my ass's rights.
A stall and fodder and sound sleep of nights.

One can't expect to live on sugarcane
But what's the sense, when one grows old and stiff,
Of scrambling up this devil-haunted cliff
To play hot cockles with the Northern Lights?
I'll balk, that's what I'll do!
And all the worse for you!
Oh, lash me if you like—I know your way—
Rake my poor sides and leave the bloody weal
Beneath your spurring steel.
My lungs are fire and my limbs are lead.

Go on ahead? I can't go on ahead.
Desert you in your need? Nay, master, nay.

Nay, master, nay; I grumble as I must
And yet, as you perceive, I do go on,
Grudging, impenitent and full of fear
And knowing my own death.
You have no fear because you have no breath.
Your silver essence knows nor cold nor heat.
Your world's beyond. My only world is here.
(Oh, the sweet rollings in the summer dust,
The smell of hay and thistles and the street,
The quick life, done so soon!)
You'll have your guerdon when the journey's done,
You'll play the hero where the wine is poured,
You and the moon— but I
Who served you well and shall become a bone,
Why do I live when it must be to die?
Why should I serve—and still have no reward?

SOUL

Your plaint is sound, yet I must rule you still
With bridle, bit and will.
For, without me, you are the child unborn
And the infertile corn.
I am not cruelty but I am he,
Drowning in sea, who yet disdains the sea,
And you that sea, that shore

And the brave, laboring oar,
Little upon the main,
That drives on reefs I know not of but does not drive in vain.
For I'm your master but your scholar, too,
And learn great things of you.
And, though I shall forsake you, nothing loth,
To grumble with the clods,
To sleep into the stone,
I'll answer for us both
When I stand up alone.
For it is part as your ambassador
I go before
To tell the gods who sit above the show,
How, in this world they never stoop to know,
Under what skies, against what mortal odds,
The dust grows noble with desire and pain,
And that not once but every day anew.

NIGHTMARES AND VISITANTS

Nightmares and Visitants

NOTES TO BE LEFT IN
A CORNERSTONE

THIS is for you who are to come, with Time,
And gaze upon our ruins with strange eyes.

So, always, there were the streets and the high, clear light
And it was a crowded island and a great city;
They built high up in the air.

I have gone to the museum and seen the pictures.

And yet shall not know this body. It was other;
Though the first sight from the water was even so,
The huge blocks piled, the giants standing together,
Noble with plane and mass and the squareness of stone,
The buildings that had skeletons like a man
And nerves of wire in their bodies, the skyscrapers,
Standing their island, looking toward the sea.
But the maps and the models will not be the same.
They cannot restore that beauty, rapid and harsh,
That loneliness, that passion or that name.

Yet the films were taken?
                    Most carefully and well,
But the skin is not the life but over the life.
The live thing was a different beast, in its time,
And sometimes, in the fall, very fair, like a knife sharpened
On stone and sun and blue shadow. That was the time
When girls in red hats rode down the Avenue
On the tops of busses, their faces bright with the wind,

And the year began again with the first cool days.
All places in that country are fair in the fall.

You speak as if the year began with the fall.

It was so. It began then, not with the calendar.
It was an odd city. The fall brought us new life,
Though there was no festival set and we did not talk of it.

That seems to me strange.
                              It was not strange, in that city.
We had four seasons: the fall of the quick, brief steps
Ringing on stone and the thick crowds walking fast,
The clear sky, the rag of sunset beyond great buildings,
The bronze flower, the resurrection of the year.
The squirrels ran in the dry Park, burying nuts.
The boys came from far places with cardboard suitcases.
It is hard to describe, but the lights looked gay at night then
And everything old and used had been put away.
There were cheap new clothes for the clerks and the clerks'
    women.
There was frost in the blood and anything could begin.
The shops were slices of honeycomb full of honey,
Full of the new, glassed honey of the year.
It seemed a pity to die then, a great pity.
The great beast glittered like sea-water in the sun,
His heart beating, his lungs full of air and pride,
And the strong shadow cutting the golden towers.

Then the cold fell, and the winter, with grimy snow,
With the overcoatless men with the purple hands
Walking between two signboards in the street
And the sign on their backs said "Winter" and the soiled papers
Blew fretfully up and down and froze in the ice
As the lukewarm air blew up from the grated holes.
This lasted a long time, till the skin was dry
And the cheeks hot with the fever and the cough sharp.
On the cold days, the cops had faces like blue meat,
And then there was snow and pure snow and tons of snow
And the whole noise stopping, marvellously and slowly,
Till you could hear the shovels scraping the stone,
Scritch-scratch, scritch-scratch, like the digging of iron mice.

424

Nothing else but that sound, and the air most pure,
Most pure, most fragrant and most innocent,
And, next day, the boys made dirty balls of the snow.

This season lasted so long we were weary of it.
We were very weary indeed when the spring came to us.
And it came.
I do not know how even yet, but there was a turning,
A change, a melting, a difference, a new smell
Though not that of any flower.
                              It came from both
Rivers, I think, or across them. It sneaked in
On a market truck, a girl in a yellow hat
With a pinched, live face and a bunch of ten-cent narcissus
And the sky was soft and it was easy to dream.
You could count the spring on your fingers, but it came.
Ah, brief it was in that city, but good for love!
The boys got their stick-bats out then, the youths and girls
Talked hoarsely under street lamps, late in the night.

And then it was tiger-summer and the first heat,
The first thunder, the first black pile of aching cloud,
The big warm drops of rain that spatter the dust
And the ripping cloth of lightning.
                              Those were the hot
Nights when the poor lay out on the fire-escapes
And the child cried thinly and endlessly. Many streets
Woke very late in the night, then.
And barbarously the negro night bestrode
The city with great gold rings in his ears
And his strong body glistening with heat.
He had, I think, a phial in one hand
And from it took a syringe, dry as dust,
To dope tired bodies with uneasy sleep.
The backs of my hands are sweating with that sleep
And I have lain awake in the hot bed
And heard the fierce, brief storm bring the relief,
The little coolness, the water on the tongue,
The new wind from the river, dear as rain.

I have not studied the weather-reports intensively.
Should I do so?
                              You will not get it from weather-reports.

There was the drunkard's city and the milkman's,
The city of the starving and the fed,
The city of the night-nurse and the scrubbed wall.
All these locked into each other like sliding rings
And a man, in his time, might inhabit one of them
Or many, as his fate took him, but always, always,
There were the blocks of stone and the windows gazing
And the breath that did not stop. It was never quite still.
You could always hear some sound, though you forgot it,
And the sound entered the flesh and was part of it.

It was high but no one planned it to be so high.
They did not think, when they built so. They did not say,
"This will make life better, this is due to the god,
This will be good to live in." They said "Build!"
And dug steel into the rocks.
                              They were a race
Most nervous, energetic, swift and wasteful,
And maddened by the dry and beautiful light
Although not knowing their madness.
                              So they built
Not as men before but as demons under a whip
And the light was a whip and a sword and a spurning heel
And the light wore out their hearts and they died praising it.

And for money and the lack of it many died,
Leaping from windows or crushed by the big truck.
They shot themselves in washrooms because of money.
They were starved and died on the benches of subway-stations,
The old men, with the caved cheeks, yellow as lard,
The men with the terrible shoes and the open hands,
The eyeing and timid crowd about them gathered.
Yet it is not just to say money was all their god
Nor just to say that machine was all their god.
It is not just to say any one thing about them.
They built the thing very high, far over their heads.
Because of it, they gave up air, earth and stars.

Will you tell me about the people, if you please?

They are all gone, the workers on the high steel,
The best of their kind, cat-footed, walking on space,

The arcs of the red-hot rivet in the air;
They are gone with the empty, arrogant women of price,
The evening women, curried till their flesh shone;
With the big, pale baker, the flour in his creases,
Coming up to breathe from his hell on a summer night;
They are gone as if they were not.
The blue-chinned men of the hotel-lobbies are gone,
Though they sat like gods in their chairs;
Night-watchmen and cleaning-women and millionaires;
The maimed boy, clean and legless and always sitting
On his small, wheeled platform, by the feet of the crowd;
The sharp, sad newsmen, the hackers spinning their wheels;
The ardent, the shy, the brave;
The women who looked from mean windows, every day,
A pillow under their elbows, heavily staring;
They are gone, gone with the long cars and the short ones,
They have dropped as smoothly as coins through the slot of
     Time,
Mrs. Rausmeyer is gone and Mrs. Costello
And the girl at Goldstein & Brady's who had the hair.
Their lipsticks have made no mark on the evening sky.
It is long ago this all was. It is all forgotten.

And yet, you lie uneasy in the grave.

I cannot well lie easy in the grave.
All cities are the loneliness of man
And this was very lonely, in its time
(Sea-haunted, river-emblemed, O the grey
Water at ends of streets and the boats hooting!
The unbelievable, new, bright, girl moon!),
Most cruel also, but I walked it young,
Loved in it and knew night and day in it.
There was the height and the light. It was like no other.
When the gods come, tell them we built this out of steel,
Though men use steel no more.
And tell the man who tries to dig this dust,
He will forget his joy before his loneliness.

SHORT ODE

It is time to speak of these
Who took the long, strange journey overseas,
Who fell through the air in flames.
Their names are many. I will not name their names
Though some were people I knew;
After some years the ghost itself dies, too,
And that is my son's picture on the wall
But his girl has been long married and that is all.
They died in mud, they died in camps of the flu.
They are dead. Let us leave it so.
The ones I speak of were not forced, I know.
They were men of my age and country, they were young men
At Belleau, at the seaports, by the Aisne.
They went where their passion took them and are not.
They do not answer mockery or praise.

You may restore the days
They lived beneath and you may well restore
The painted image of that fabled war,
But not those faces, not the living ones
Drowned in the water, blown before the guns
In France or Belgium or the bitter sea
(And the foreign grave is far, and men use the name,
But they did not go for votes or the pay they got
Or the brave memorial speech by the D.A.R.)
It is far, the foreign grave. It is very far
And the time is not the same.
But certain things are true
Despite the time, and these were men that I knew,
Sat beside, walked beside,
In the first running of June, in the careless pride.
It is hard to think back, to find them, to see their eyes
And none born since shall see those, and the books are lies,
Being either praise or blame.
But they were in their first youth. It is not the same.
You, who are young, remember that youth dies.
Go, stranger, and to Lacedemon tell,
They were shot and rotted, they fell

Burning, on flimsy wings.
And yet it was their thought that they did well.
And yet there are still the tyrants and the kings.

LITANY FOR DICTATORSHIPS

For all those beaten, for the broken heads,
The fosterless, the simple, the oppressed,
The ghosts in the burning city of our time . . .

For those taken in rapid cars to the house and beaten
By the skilful boys, the boys with the rubber fists,
—Held down and beaten, the table cutting their loins,
Or kicked in the groin and left, with the muscles jerking
Like a headless hen's on the floor of the slaughter-house
While they brought the next man in with his white eyes staring.
For those who still said "Red Front!" or "God Save the Crown!"
And for those who were not courageous
But were beaten nevertheless.
For those who spit out the bloody stumps of their teeth
Quietly in the hall,
Sleep well on stone or iron, watch for the time
And kill the guard in the privy before they die,
Those with the deep-socketed eyes and the lamp burning.

For those who carry the scars, who walk lame—for those
Whose nameless graves are made in the prison-yard
And the earth smoothed back before morning and the lime scat-
    tered.

For those slain at once. For those living through months and
    years
Enduring, watching, hoping, going each day
To the work or the queue for meat or the secret club,
Living meanwhile, begetting children, smuggling guns,
And found and killed at the end like rats in a drain.

For those escaping
Incredibly into exile and wandering there.
For those who live in the small rooms of foreign cities

And who yet think of the country, the long green grass,
The childhood voices, the language, the way wind smelt then,
The shape of rooms, the coffee drunk at the table,
The talk with friends, the loved city, the waiter's face,
The gravestones, with the name, where they will not lie
Nor in any of that earth. Their children are strangers.

For those who planned and were leaders and were beaten
And for those, humble and stupid, who had no plan
But were denounced, but grew angry, but told a joke,
But could not explain, but were sent away to the camp,
But had their bodies shipped back in the sealed coffins,
"Died of pneumonia." "Died trying to escape."

For those growers of wheat who were shot by their own wheat-
    stacks,
For those growers of bread who were sent to the ice-locked
    wastes,
And their flesh remembers their fields.

For those denounced by their smug, horrible children
For a peppermint-star and the praise of the Perfect State,
For all those strangled or gelded or merely starved
To make perfect states; for the priest hanged in his cassock,
The Jew with his chest crushed in and his eyes dying,
The revolutionist lynched by the private guards
To make perfect states, in the names of the perfect states.

For those betrayed by the neighbors they shook hands with
And for the traitors, sitting in the hard chair
With the loose sweat crawling their hair and their fingers rest-
    less
As they tell the street and the house and the man's name.

And for those sitting at table in the house
With the lamp lit and the plates and the smell of food,
Talking so quietly; when they hear the cars
And the knock at the door, and they look at each other quickly
And the woman goes to the door with a stiff face,
Smoothing her dress.   "We are all good citizens here.
We believe in the Perfect State."
                              And that was the last

Time Tony or Karl or Shorty came to the house
And the family was liquidated later.
It was the last time.
                           We heard the shots in the night
But nobody knew next day what the trouble was
And a man must go to his work. So I didn't see him
For three days, then, and me near out of my mind
And all the patrols on the streets with their dirty guns
And when he came back, he looked drunk, and the blood was
   on him.

For the women who mourn their dead in the secret night,
For the children taught to keep quiet, the old children,
The children spat-on at school.
                           For the wrecked laboratory,
The gutted house, the dunged picture, the pissed-in well,
The naked corpse of Knowledge flung in the square
And no man lifting a hand and no man speaking.

For the cold of the pistol-butt and the bullet's heat,
For the rope that chokes, the manacles that bind,
The huge voice, metal, that lies from a thousand tubes
And the stuttering machine-gun that answers all.

For the man crucified on the crossed machine-guns
Without name, without resurrection, without stars,
His dark head heavy with death and his flesh long sour
With the smell of his many prisons—John Smith, John Doe,
John Nobody—oh, crack your mind for his name!
Faceless as water, naked as the dust,
Dishonored as the earth the gas-shells poison
And barbarous with portent.
                           This is he.
This is the man they ate at the green table
Putting their gloves on ere they touched the meat.
This is the fruit of war, the fruit of peace,
The ripeness of invention, the new lamb,
The answer to the wisdom of the wise.
And still he hangs, and still he will not die,
And still, on the steel city of our years
The light fails and the terrible blood streams down.

We thought we were done with these things but we were
 wrong.
We thought, because we had power, we had wisdom.
We thought the long train would run to the end of Time.
We thought the light would increase.
Now the long train stands derailed and the bandits loot it.
Now the boar and the asp have power in our time.
Now the night rolls back on the West and the night is solid.
Our fathers and ourselves sowed dragon's teeth.
Our children know and suffer the armed men.

ODE TO THE AUSTRIAN SOCIALISTS

(FEBRUARY 12—FEBRUARY 15, 1934)

They shot the Socialists at half-past five
In the name of victorious Austria.
                                        The sky
Was blue with February those four cold days
And the little snow lay lightly on the hard ground.
(Vienna's the laughing city of tunes and wine,
Of *Schlagobers* and starved children . . . and a great ghost . . .)
They had called the general strike but the plans went wrong
Though the lights failed, that first night.
                                        It is odd to turn
The switch by your bed and have no lamp go on
And then look out of the windows at the black street
Empty, except for a man with a pistol, running.
We have built our cities for lights and the harsh glare
And, when the siren screams at the winter stars,
It is only a fire, an ambulance, nothing wrong,
Just part of the day. You can walk to the corner store
And never duck at a bullet. The lights are there
And, if you see a man with a pistol, running,
You phone the police or wait for tomorrow's papers.
It is different, with the lights out and the shots beginning. . . .

These were ordinary people.
The kind that go to the movies and watch parades,
Have children, take them to parks, ride in trolley cars,

The workmen at the next bench, the old, skilful foreman;
You have seen the backs of their necks a million times
In any crowd and forgotten—seen their faces,
Anonymous, tired, good-humored, faces of skill.
(The quick hands moving deftly among machines,
Hands of the baker and the baker's wife,
Hands gloved with rubber, mending the spitting wire,
Hands on controls and levers, big, square-palmed hands
With the dint of the tool upon them,
Dull, clumsy fingers laboring a dull task
And others, writing and thoughtful, or sensitive
As a setter's mouth.) You have seen their hats and their shoes
Everywhere, in every city. They wear no costumes.
Their pockets have lint in them, and tobacco-dust.
Their faces are the faces of any crowd.

It was Monday when this began.
                                    They were slow to start it
But they had been pushed to the wall. They believed in peace,
Good houses, meetings, elections and resolutions,
Not the sudden killing in corners, the armored cars
Sweeping the square, the bombs and the bloody heads,
But they'd seen what happened next door, in another country,
To people who believed in peace and elections
And the same tide was rising here. They could hear the storm.
They took to their guns at last, in the workmen's quarters,
Where they'd built the houses for peace and the sure future.

The houses were tall and fine,
Great blocks of manstone, built by people for people,
Not to make one man rich. When you do not build
To make one man rich, you can give people light and air,
You can have room to turn round—room after the day—
You can have books and clean water and healthy sleep,
A place for children to grow in.
All over the world men knew about those houses.

Let us remember Karl Marx Hof, Goethe Hof,
The one called Matteoti and all the rest.
They were little cities built by people for people.
They were shelled by six-inch guns.
                                    It is strange to go

433

Up the known stairs to the familiar room
And point the lean machine-gun out of the window,
Strange to see the black of that powder upon your hands. . . .

They had hidden arms against need but they could not find them
In many cases, being ordinary people.
The other side was much readier—Fey and Dollfuss
And all the shirts were quite ready.
                 When you believe
In parks and elections and meetings and not in death,
Not in Caesar,
It is hard to realize that the day may come
When you send your wife and children down to the cellar
To be out of the way of shells, and mount the known
Countable stairs to the familiar room,
The unfamiliar pistol cold in your fist
And your mouth dry with despair.
                It is hard to think
In spite of all oppression, all enmity,
That that is going to happen.
And so, when it does happen, your plans go wrong.
(White flags on the Karl Marx Hof and the Goethe Hof
And the executions, later.)
             A correspondent
Of the British press remarked, when the thing was done
And they let him in to see it, that on the whole
The buildings were less damaged than you'd expect
From four days' bullets. True, he had seen, before,
A truckload of undertakers and cheap, pine coffins
Go to the disputed district.
But the buildings stood, on the whole. They had built them
   well.

These were ordinary people and they are dead.
Dead where they lived, by violence, in their own homes,
Between the desk and the door and the kitchen chair,
Dead in the courtyards where the children played
(The child's jaw smashed by a bullet, the bloody crib,
The woman sprawled like a rag on the clean stairs)
Uncaesarlike, unwarlike, merely dead.

Dead, or in exile many, or afraid
(And those who live there still and wake in the night,

Remembering the free city)
Silent or hunted and their leaders slimed.
The communists said they would not fight but they fought
Four days of bitter February,
Ill-led, outnumbered, the radio blaring lies
And the six-inch guns against them and all hope gone,
Four days in the Karl Marx Hof and the Goethe Hof
And nobody knows yet how many dead
And sensible men give in and accept the flag,
The badge, the arm-band, the gag, the slave-tyranny,
The shining, tin peace of Caesar.
                              They were not sensible,
Four days of February, two years ago.

Bring no flowers here,
Neither of mountain nor valley,
Nor even the common flowers of the waste field
That still are free to the poor;
No wreaths upon these graves, these houseless graves;
But bring alone the powder-blackened brass
Of the shell-case, the slag of bullets, the ripped steel
And the bone-spattering lead,
Infertile, smelling acridly of death,
And heap them here, till the rusting of guns, for remembrance.
                                                    1936.

DO YOU REMEMBER, SPRINGFIELD?

(VACHEL LINDSAY, NOVEMBER 10, 1879–DECEMBER 5, 1931)

The Illinois earth is black
(Do you remember, Springfield?)
The State is shaped like a heart,
Shaped like an arrowhead.

The black earth goes deep down.
(Do you remember, Springfield?)
Three feet under the plow
You can find the black earth still.

435

The towns settled, the woods
Fine in the spring and autumn,
The waters large and rolling,
The black earth ready to hand.

Surely this earth, this air
Should bear the prophet-singers,
Minstrels like colts unbroken,
Minstrels of leaves and corn.

Baltimore gave a stone,
A stone to another singer
(Do you remember, Springfield?)
But that was in years gone by.

A cat to tear at his breast
And a glass to work him madness,
That was the gift to Poe:
But things are different here.

There are votes here to be bought
And rich men here to buy them;
What more could a poet ask
Of the streets where Lincoln strode?

The Board of Health is superb.
The ladies watchful and cultured.
What more could a poet need
Or the heart of man desire?

Gather the leaves with rakes,
The burning autumn, Springfield,
Gather them in with rakes
Lest one of them turn to gold.

A leaf is only a leaf,
It is worth nothing, in Springfield.
It is worth as little as song,
Little as light and air.

Trap the lark in the corn,
Let it tell of your bounty, Springfield.

If you burn its eyes with a wire
It still will sing for a space.

A man is another affair.
We understand that, in Springfield.
If he sings, why, let him sing
As long as we need not hear.

He came with singing leaves;
It was really most unfortunate.
The Lindsays and the Frazees
Are sturdy pioneer stock.

He came with broncos and clouds
And the cornsilk of the moonlight.
It is not a usual thing
In Springfield, Illinois.

We will show his room and his book
For that brings trade to the city.
We try to use everything.
If you like, you can see his grave.

His mouth is stopped with earth,
The deep, black earth of Springfield.
He will not sing any more.
It is fine earth for the mute.

Let us give the Arts their due
And Lincoln a marble courthouse.
Both are respectably dead.
They need not trouble us, now.

Break the colts to the plow
And make them pull their hearts out.
Break the broncos of dancing
And sell them for bones and hide.

ODE TO WALT WHITMAN

(MAY 31, 1819–MARCH 26, 1892)

Now comes Fourth Month and the early buds on the trees.
By the roads of Long Island, the forsythia has flowered,
In the North, the cold will be breaking; even in Maine
The cold will be breaking soon; the young, bull-voiced freshets
Roar from green mountains, gorging the chilly brooks
With the brown, trout-feeding waters, the unlocked springs;
Now Mississippi stretches with the Spring rains. . . .

It is forty years and more,
The time of the ripeness and withering of a man,
Since you lay in the house in Camden and heard, at last,
The great, slow footstep, splashing the Third Month snow
In the little, commonplace street
—Town snow, already trampled and growing old,
Soot-flecked and dingy, patterned with passing feet,
The bullet-pocks of rain, the strong urine of horses,
The slashing, bright steel runners of small boys' sleds
Hitching on behind the fast cutters.
They dragged their sleds to the tops of the hills and yelled
The Indian yell of all boyhood, for pure joy
Of the cold and the last gold light and the swift rush down
Belly-flopping into darkness, into bedtime.
You saw them come home, late, hungry and burning-cheeked,
The boys and girls, the strong children,
Dusty with snow, their mittens wet with the silver drops of
  thawed snow.

All winter long, you had heard their sharp footsteps passing,
The skating crunch of their runners,
An old man, tied to a house, after many years,
An old man with his rivery, clean white hair,
His bright eyes, his majestic poverty,
His fresh pink skin like the first strawberry-bloom,
His innocent, large, easy old man's clothes
—Brown splotches on the hands of clean old men
At County Farms or sitting on warm park-benches
Like patient flies, talking of their good sons,
"Yes, my son's good to me"—

438

An old man, poor, without sons, waiting achingly
For spring to warm his lameness,
For spring to flourish,
And yet, when the eyes glowed, neither old nor tied.

All winter long there had been footsteps passing,
Steps of postmen and neighbors, quick steps of friends,
All winter long you had waited that great, snow-treading step,
The enemy, the vast comrade,
The step behind, in the wards, when the low lamp flickered
And the sick boy gasped for breath,
"*Lean on me! Lean upon my shoulder! By God, you shall not
die!*"
The step ahead, on the long, wave-thundering beaches of Pau-
manok,
Invisible, printless, weighty,
The shape half-seen through the wet, sweet sea-fog of youth,
Night's angel and the dark Sea's,
The grand, remorseless treader,
Magnificent Death.

"Let me taste all, my flesh and my fat are sweet,
My body hardy as lilac, the strong flower.
I have tasted the calamus; I can taste the nightbane."

Always the water about you since you were born,
The endless lapping of water, the strong motion,
The gulls by the ferries knew you, and the wild sea-birds,
The sandpiper, printing the beach with delicate prints.
At last, old, wheeled to the wharf, you still watched the water,
The tanned boys, flat-bodied, diving, the passage of ships,
The proud port, distant, the people, the work of harbors. . . .

"I have picked out a bit of hill with a southern exposure.
I like to be near the trees. I like to be near
The water-sound of the trees."

Now, all was the same in the cluttered, three-windowed room,
Low-ceiled, getting the sun like a schooner's cabin,
The crowding photos hiding the ugly wall-paper,
The floor-litter, the strong chair, timbered like a ship,
The hairy black-and-silver of the old wolfskin;

In the back-yard, neither lilac nor pear yet bloomed
But the branch of the lilac swelling with first sap;
And there, in the house, the figures, the nurse, the woman,
The passing doctor, the friends, the little clan,
The disciple with the notebook who's always there.

All these and the pain and the water-bed to ease you
And you said it rustled of oceans and were glad
And the pain shut and relaxed and shut once more.

"Old body, counsellor, why do you thus torment me?
Have we not been friends from our youth?"

But now it came,
Slow, perceived by no others,
The splashing step through the grey, soft, Saturday rain,
Inexorable footstep of the huge friend.
"Are you there at last, fine enemy?
Ah, haste, friend, hasten, come closer!
Breathe upon me with your grave, your releasing lips!
I have heard and spoken; watched the bodies of boys
Flash in the copper sun and dive to green waters,
Seen the fine ships and the strong matrons and the tall axemen,
The young girls, free, athletic; the drunkard, retching
In his poor dream; the thief taken by officers;
The President, calm, grave, advising the nation;
The infant, with milk-wet lips in his bee-like slumber.
They are mine; all, all are mine; must I leave them, truly?
I have cherished them in my veins like milk and fruit.
I have warmed them at my bare breast like the eggs of pigeons.
The great plains of the buffalo are mine, the towns, the hills, the
    ship-bearing waters.
These States are my wandering sons.
I had them in my youth; I cannot desert them.
The green leaf of America is printed on my heart forever."

Now it entered the house, it marched upon the stair.
By the bedside the faces dimmed, the huge shoulder blotting
    them,
—It is so they die on the plains, the great, old buffalo,
The herd-leaders, the beasts with the kingly eyes,
Innocent, curly-browed,

They sink to the earth like mountains, hairy and silent,
And their tongues are cut by the hunter.
                              Oh, singing tongue!
Great tongue of bronze and salt and the free grasses,
Tongue of America, speaking for the first time,
Must the hunter have you at last?

Now, face to face, you saw him
And lifted the right arm once, as a pilot lifts it,
Signalling with the bell,
In the passage at night, on the river known yet unknown,
—Perhaps to touch his shoulder, perhaps in pain—
Then the rain fell on the roof and the twilight darkened
And they said that in death you looked like a marvelous old, wise
    child.

2

It is Fourth Month now and spring in another century,
Let us go to the hillside and ask; he will like to hear us;
"Is it good, the sleep?"

                    "It is good, the sleep and the waking.
I have picked out a bit of hill where the south sun warms me.
I like to be near the trees."

Nay, let him ask, rather.
"Is it well with you, comrades?
The cities great, portentous, humming with action?
The bridges mightily spanning wide-breasted rivers?
The great plains growing the wheat, the old lilac hardy, well-
    budded?
Is it well with these States?"

"The cities are great, portentous, a world-marvel,
The bridges arched like the necks of beautiful horses.
We have made the dry land bloom and the dead land blossom."

"Is it well with these States?"

"The old wound of your war is healed and we are one nation.
We have linked the whole land with the steel and the hard high-
    ways.

We have fought new wars and won them. In the French field
There are bones of Texarkana and Little Falls,
Aliens, our own; in the low-lying Belgian ground;
In the cold sea of the English; in dark-faced islands.
Men speak of them well or ill; they themselves are silent."

"Is it well with these States?"

"We have made many, fine new toys.
We—
There is a rust on the land.
A rust and a creeping blight and a scaled evil,
For six years eating, yet deeper than those six years,
Men labor to master it but it is not mastered.
There is the soft, grey, foul tent of the hatching worm
Shrouding the elm, the chestnut, the Southern cypress.
There is shadow in the bright sun, there is shadow upon the
    streets.
They burn the grain in the furnace while men go hungry.
They pile the cloth of the looms while men go ragged.
We walk naked in our plenty."

                                    "My tan-faced children?"

"These are your tan-faced children.
These skilled men, idle, with the holes in their shoes.
These drifters from State to State, these wolvish, bewildered boys
Who ride the blinds and the box-cars from jail to jail,
Burnt in their youth like cinders of hot smokestacks,
Learning the thief's crouch and the cadger's whine,
Dishonored, abandoned, disinherited.
These, dying in the bright sunlight they cannot eat,
Or the strong men, sitting at home, their hands clasping nothing,
Looking at their lost hands.
These are your tan-faced children, the parched young,
The old man rooting in waste-heaps, the family rotting
In the flat, before eviction,
With the toys of plenty about them,
The shiny toys making ice and music and light,
But no price for the shiny toys and the last can empty.
The sleepers in blind corners of the night.
The women with dry breasts and phantom eyes.

442

The walkers upon nothing, the four million.
These are your tan-faced children."

                "But the land?"

"Over the great plains of the buffalo-land,
The dust-storm blows, the choking, sifting, small dust.
The skin of that land is ploughed by the dry, fierce wind
And blown away, like a torrent;
It drifts foot-high above the young sprouts of grain
And the water fouls, the horses stumble and sicken,
The wash-board cattle stagger and die of drought.
We tore the buffalo's pasture with the steel blade.
We made the waste land blossom and it has blossomed.
That was our fate; now that land takes its own revenge,
And the giant dust-flower blooms above five States."

"But the gains of the years, who got them?"

                         "Many, great gains.
Many, yet few; they robbed us in the broad daylight,
Saying, 'Give us this and that; we are kings and titans;
We know the ropes; we are solid; we are hard-headed;
We will build you cities and railroads.'—as if *they* built them!
They, the preying men, the men whose hearts were like engines,
Gouging the hills for gold, laying waste the timber,
The men like band-saws, moving over the land.
And, after them, the others,
Soft-bodied, lacking even the pirate's candor,
Men of paper, robbing by paper, with paper faces,
Rustling like frightened paper when the storm broke.
The men with the jaws of moth and aphis and beetle,
Boring the dusty, secret hole in the corn,
Fixed, sucking the land, with neither wish nor pride
But the wish to suck and continue.
They have been sprayed, a little.
But they say they will have the land back again, these men."

"There were many such in my time.
I have seen the rich arrogant and the poor oppressed.
I have seen democracy, also. I have seen
The good man slain, the knave and the fool in power,

The democratic vista botched by the people,
Yet not despaired, loving the giant land,
Though I prophesied to these States."

"Now they say we must have one tyranny or another
And a dark bell rings in our hearts."

"Was the blood spilt for nothing, then?"

3

Under dry winter
Arbutus grows.
It is careless of man.
It is careless of man.

Man can tear it,
Crush it, destroy it;
Uproot the trailers,
The thumb-shaped leafings.

A man in grey clothes
May come there also,
Lie all day there
In weak spring sunlight.

White, firm-muscled,
The flesh of his body;
Wind, sun, earth
In him, possessing him.

In his heart
A flock of birds crying.
In his belly
The new grass growing.

In his skull
Sunlight and silence,
Like a vast room
Full of sunlight and silence.

In the lines of his palms
The roads of America,

In the knots of his hands
The anger of America.

In the sweat of his flesh
The sorrows of America,
In the seed of his loins
The glory of America.

The sap of the birch-tree
Is in his pelt,
The maple, the red-bud
Are his nails and parings.

He grows through the earth and is part of it like the roots of
 new grass.

Little arbutus
Delicate, tinted,
Tiny, tender,
Fragile, immortal.

If you can grow,
A man can grow
Not like others
But like a man.

Man is a bull
But he has not slain you
And this man lies
Like a lover beside you.

Beside the arbutus,
The green-leaved Spring,
He lies like a lover
By his young bride,
In the white hour,
The white, first waking.

4

They say, they say, they say and let them say.
Call you a revolutionist—you were one—
A nationalist—you were one—a man of peace,

445

A man describing battles, an old fraud,
A Charlus, an adept self-advertiser,
A "good, grey poet"—oh, God save us all!
God save us from the memoirs and the memories!
And yet, they count. They have to. If they didn't
There'd be no Ph.Ds. And each disciple
Jealously guards his own particular store
Of acorns fallen from the oak's abundance
And spits and scratches at the other gatherers.
"I was there when he died!"

                 "He was not there when he died!"
"It was me he trusted, me! X got on his nerves!
He couldn't stand X in the room!"

                 "Y's well-intentioned
But a notorious liar—and, as for Z . . ."

So all disciples, always and forever.
—And the dire court at Longwood, those last years,
The skull of Sterne, grinning at the anatomists,
Poe's hospital-bed, the madness of the Dean,
The bright, coughing blood Keats wrote in to the girl,
The terrible corpse of France, shrunk, naked and solitary—
Oh, yes, you were spared some things.
Though why did Mrs. Davis sue the estate
And what did you mean when you said——

                 And who cares?
You're still the giant lode we quarry
For gold, fools' gold and all the earthy metals,
The matchless mine.
Still the trail-breaker, still the rolling river.

You and your land, your turbulent, seeking land
Where anything can grow.

And they have wasted the pasture and the fresh valley,
Stunk the river, shot the ten thousand sky-darkening pigeons
To build sham castles for imitation Medici
And the rugged sons of the rugged sons of death.
The slum, the sharecropper's cabin, the senseless tower,
The factory town with the dirty stoops of twilight,
The yelling cheapness, the bitter want among plenty,
But never Monticello, never again.

And there are many years in the dust of America
And they are not ended yet.

Far north, far north are the sources of the great river,
The headwaters, the cold lakes,
By the little sweet-tasting brooks of the blond country,
The country of snow and wheat,
Or west among the black mountains, the glacial springs.
Far north and west they lie and few come to them, few taste
    them,
But, day and night, they flow south,
By the French grave and the Indian, steadily flowing,
By the forgotten camps of the broken heart,
By the countries of black earth, fertile, and yellow earth and red
    earth,
A growing, a swelling torrent:
Rivers meet it, and tiny rivulets,
Meet it, stain it,
Great rivers, rivers of pride, come bowing their watery heads
Like muddy gift-bearers, bringing their secret burdens,
Rivers from the high horse-plains and the deep, green Eastern
    pastures
Sink into it and are lost and rejoice and shout with it, shout
    within it,
They and their secret gifts,
A fleck of gold from Montana, a sliver of steel from Pittsburgh,
A wheat-grain from Minnesota, an apple-blossom from Ten-
    nessee,
Roiled, mixed with the mud and earth of the changing bottoms
In the vast, rending floods,
But rolling, rolling from Arkansas, Kansas, Iowa,
Rolling from Ohio, Wisconsin, Illinois,
Rolling and shouting:
Till, at last, it is Mississippi,
The Father of Waters; the matchless; the great flood
Dyed with the earth of States; with the dust and the sun and
    the seed of half the States;
The huge heart-vein, pulsing and pulsing; gigantic; ever broader,
    ever mightier;
It rolls past broken landings and camellia-smelling woods; strange
    birds fly over it;

447

It rolls through the tropic magic, the almost-jungle, the warm
    darkness breeding the warm, enormous stars;
It rolls to the blue Gulf; ocean; and the painted birds fly.
The grey moss mixes with it, the hawk's feather has fallen in it,
The cardinal feather, the feather of the small thrush
Singing spring to New England,
The apple-pip and the pepper-seed and the checkerberry,
And always the water flowing, earthy, majestic,
Fed with snow and heat, dew and moonlight.
Always the wide, sure water,
Over the rotted deer-horn
The gold, Spanish money,
The long-rusted iron of many undertakings,
Over De Soto's bones and Joliet's wonder,
And the long forest-years before them, the brief years after,
The broad flood, the eternal motion, the restless-hearted
Always, forever, Mississippi, the god.

                                        April, 1935.

METROPOLITAN NIGHTMARE

It rained quite a lot, that spring. You woke in the morning
And saw the sky still clouded, the streets still wet,
But nobody noticed so much, except the taxis
And the people who parade. You don't, in a city.
The parks got very green. All the trees were green
Far into July and August, heavy with leaf,
Heavy with leaf and the long roots boring and spreading,
But nobody noticed that but the city gardeners
And they don't talk.
                        Oh, on Sundays, perhaps, you'd notice:
Walking through certain blocks, by the shut, proud houses
With the windows boarded, the people gone away,
You'd suddenly see the queerest small shoots of green
Poking through cracks and crevices in the stone
And a bird-sown flower, red on a balcony,
But then you made jokes about grass growing in the streets
And politics and grass-roots—and there were songs
And gags and a musical show called "Hot and Wet."
It all made a good box for the papers. When the flamingo

Flew into a meeting of the Board of Estimate,
The new Mayor acted at once and called the photographers.
When the first green creeper crawled upon Brooklyn Bridge,
They thought it was ornamental. They let it stay.

That was the year the termites came to New York
And they don't do well in cold climates—but listen, Joe,
They're only ants and ants are nothing but insects.
It was funny and yet rather wistful, in a way
(As Heywood Broun pointed out in the *World-Telegram*)
To think of them looking for wood in a steel city.
It made you feel about life. It was too divine.
There were funny pictures by all the smart, funny artists
And Macy's ran a terribly clever ad:
"The Widow's Termite" or something.
                                    There was no
Disturbance. Even the Communists didn't protest
And say they were Morgan hirelings. It was too hot,
Too hot to protest, too hot to get excited,
An even, African heat, lush, fertile and steamy,
That soaked into bone and mind and never once broke.
The warm rain fell in fierce showers and ceased and fell.
Pretty soon you got used to its always being that way.

You got used to the changed rhythm, the altered beat,
To people walking slower, to the whole bright
Fierce pulse of the city slowing, to men in shorts,
To the new sun-helmets from Best's and the cops' white uni-
    forms,
And the long noon-rest in the offices, everywhere.
It wasn't a plan or anything. It just happened.
The fingers tapped the keys slower, the office-boys
Dozed on their benches, the bookkeeper yawned at his desk.
The A. T. & T. was the first to change the shifts
And establish an official siesta-room,
But they were always efficient. Mostly it just
Happened like sleep itself, like a tropic sleep,
Till even the Thirties were deserted at noon
Except for a few tourists and one damp cop.
They ran boats to see the big lilies on the North River
But it was only the tourists who really noticed
The flocks of rose-and-green parrots and parrakeets

Nesting in the stone crannies of the Cathedral.
The rest of us had forgotten when they first came.

There wasn't any real change, it was just a heat spell,
A rain spell, a funny summer, a weather-man's joke,
In spite of the geraniums three feet high
In the tin-can gardens of Hester and Desbrosses.
New York was New York. It couldn't turn inside out.
When they got the news from Woods Hole about the Gulf
    Stream,
The *Times* ran an adequate story.
But nobody reads those stories but science-cranks.

Until, one day, a somnolent city-editor
Gave a new cub the termite yarn to break his teeth on.
The cub was just down from Vermont, so he took the time.
He was serious about it. He went around.
He read all about termites in the Public Library
And it made him sore when they fired him.
                                    So, one evening,
Talking with an old watchman, beside the first
Raw girders of the new Planetopolis Building
(Ten thousand brine-cooled offices, each with shower)
He saw a dark line creeping across the rubble
And turned a flashlight on it.
                            "Say, buddy," he said,
"You better look out for those ants. They eat wood, you know,
They'll have your shack down in no time."
                                The watchman spat.
"Oh, they've quit eating wood," he said, in a casual voice,
"I thought everybody knew that."
                        —and, reaching down,
He pried from the insect jaws the bright crumb of steel.

NIGHTMARE, WITH ANGELS

An angel came to me and stood by my bedside,
Remarking in a professorial-historical-economic and irritated
    voice,
"If the Romans had only invented a decent explosion-engine!
Not even the best, not even a Ford V-8

But, say, a Model T or even an early Napier,
They'd have built good enough roads for it (they knew how to
build roads)
From Cape Wrath to Cape St. Vincent, Susa, Babylon and Mos-
cow,
And the motorized legions never would have fallen,
And peace, in the shape of a giant eagle, would brood over the
entire Western World!"
He changed his expression, looking now like a combination of
Gilbert Murray, Hilaire Belloc and a dozen other scientists,
writers, and prophets,
And continued, in angelic tones,
"If the Greeks had known how to coöperate, if there'd never
been a Reformation,
If Sparta had not been Sparta, and the Church had been the
Church of the saints,
The Argive peace like a free-blooming olive-tree, the peace of
Christ (who loved peace) like a great, beautiful vine enwrap-
ping the spinning earth!
Take it nearer home," he said.
"Take these Mayans and their star-clocks, their carvings and
their great cities.
Who sacked them out of their cities, drowned the cities with a
green jungle?
A plague? A change of climate? A queer migration?
Certainly they were skilful, certainly they created.
And, in Tenochtitlan, the dark obsidian knife and the smoking
heart on the stone but a fair city,
And the Incas had it worked out beautifully till Pizarro smashed
them.
The collectivist state was there, and the ladies very agreeable.
They lacked steel, alphabet and gunpowder and they had to get
married when the government said so.
They also lacked unemployment and overproduction.
For that matter," he said, "take the Cro-Magnons,
The fellows with the big skulls, the handsome folk, the excellent
scribers of mammoths,
Physical gods and yet with the sensitive brain (they drew the
fine, running reindeer).
What stopped them? What kept us all from being Apollos and
Aphrodites
Only with a new taste to the nectar,

451

The laughing gods, not the cruel, the gods of song, not of war?
Supposing Aurelius, Confucius, Napoleon, Plato, Gautama, Alex-
    ander—
Just to take half a dozen—
Had ever realized and stabilized the full dream?
How long, O Lord God in the highest? How long, what now,
    perturbed spirit?"

He turned blue at the wingtips and disappeared as another angel
    approached me.
This one was quietly but appropriately dressed in cellophane,
    synthetic rubber and stainless steel,
But his mask was the blind mask of Ares, snouted for gas-masks.
He was neither soldier, sailor, farmer, dictator nor munitions-
    manufacturer.
Nor did he have much conversation, except to say,
"You will not be saved by General Motors or the pre-fabricated
    house.
You will not be saved by dialectic materialism or the Lambeth
    Conference.
You will not be saved by Vitamin D or the expanding universe.
In fact, you will not be saved."
Then he showed his hand:
In his hand was a woven, wire basket, full of seeds, small metallic
    and shining like the seeds of portulaca;
Where he sowed them, the green vine withered, and the smoke
    and the armies sprang up.

NIGHTMARE NUMBER THREE

We had expected everything but revolt
And I kind of wonder myself when they started thinking—
But there's no dice in that now.
                    I've heard fellows say
They must have planned it for years and maybe they did.
Looking back, you can find little incidents here and there,
Like the concrete-mixer in Jersey eating the wop
Or the roto press that printed "Fiddle-dee-dee!"
In a three-color process all over Senator Sloop,
Just as he was making a speech. The thing about that

Was, how could it walk upstairs? But it was upstairs,
Clicking and mumbling in the Senate Chamber.
They had to knock out the wall to take it away
And the wrecking-crew said it grinned.
                                        It was only the best
Machines, of course, the superhuman machines,
The ones we'd built to be better than flesh and bone,
But the cars were in it, of course . . .
                        and they hunted us
Like rabbits through the cramped streets on that Bloody Mon-
    day,
The Madison Avenue busses leading the charge.
The busses were pretty bad—but I'll not forget
The smash of glass when the Duesenberg left the show-room
And pinned three brokers to the Racquet Club steps
Or the long howl of the horns when they saw men run,
When they saw them looking for holes in the solid ground . . .

I guess they were tired of being ridden in
And stopped and started by pygmies for silly ends,
Of wrapping cheap cigarettes and bad chocolate bars
Collecting nickels and waving platinum hair
And letting six million people live in a town.
I guess it was that. I guess they got tired of us
And the whole smell of human hands.
                                        But it was a shock
To climb sixteen flights of stairs to Art Zuckow's office
(Nobody took the elevators twice)
And find him strangled to death in a nest of telephones,
The octopus-tendrils waving over his head,
And a sort of quiet humming filling the air. . . .
Do they eat? . . . There was red . . . But I did not stop to look.
I don't know yet how I got to the roof in time
And it's lonely, here on the roof.
                                For a while, I thought
That window-cleaner would make it, and keep me company.
But they got him with his own hoist at the sixteenth floor
And dragged him in, with a squeal.
You see, they coöperate. Well, we taught them that
And it's fair enough, I suppose. You see, we built them.
We taught them to think for themselves.
It was bound to come. You can see it was bound to come.

453

And it won't be so bad, in the country. I hate to think
Of the reapers, running wild in the Kansas fields,
And the transport planes like hawks on a chickenyard,
But the horses might help. We might make a deal with the
    horses.
At least, you've more chance, out there.
                                        And they need us, too.
They're bound to realize that when they once calm down.
They'll need oil and spare parts and adjustments and tuning up.
Slaves? Well, in a way, you know, we were slaves before.
There won't be so much real difference—honest, there won't.
(I wish I hadn't looked into that beauty-parlor
And seen what was happening there.
But those are female machines and a bit high-strung.)
Oh, we'll settle down. We'll arrange it. We'll compromise.
It wouldn't make sense to wipe out the whole human race.
Why, I bet if I went to my old Plymouth now
(Of course you'd have to do it the tactful way)
And said, "Look here! Who got you the swell French horn?"
He wouldn't turn me over to those police cars;
At least I don't think he would.
                                Oh, it's going to be jake.
There won't be so much real difference—honest, there won't—
And I'd go down in a minute and take my chance—
I'm a good American and I always liked them—
Except for one small detail that bothers me
And that's the food proposition. Because, you see,
The concrete-mixer may have made a mistake,
And it looks like just high spirits.
But, if it's got so they like the flavor . . . well . . .

1936

All night they marched, the infantrymen under pack,
But the hands gripping the rifles were naked bone
And the hollow pits of the eyes stared, vacant and black,
When the moonlight shone.

The gas mask lay like a blot on the empty chest,
The slanting helmets were spattered with rust and mold,

But they burrowed the hill for the machine-gun nest
As they had of old.

And the guns rolled, and the tanks, but there was no sound,
Never the gasp or rustle of living men
Where the skeletons strung their wire on disputed ground. . . .
I knew them, then.

"It is eighteen years," I cried. "You must come no more."
"We know your names. We know that you are the dead.
Must you march forever from France and the last, blind war?"
"*Fool! From the next!*" they said.

FOR CITY SPRING

Now grimy April comes again,
Maketh bloom the fire-escapes,
Maketh silvers in the rain,
Maketh winter coats and capes
Suddenly all worn and shabby
Like the fur of winter bears,
Maketh kittens, maketh baby,
Maketh kissing on the stairs.
Maketh bug crawl out of crack,
Maketh ticklings down the back
As if sunlight stroked the spine
To a hurdy-gurdy's whine
And the shower ran white wine.

April, April, sing cuckoo,
April, April, maketh new
Mouse and cockroach, man and wife,
Everything with blood and life;
Bloweth, groweth, flourisheth,
Danceth in a ragged skirt
On the very stoop of Death
And will take no mortal hurt.
Maketh dogs to whine and bound,
Maketh cats to caterwaul,
Maketh lovers, all around,
Whisper in the hall.

455

Oh, and when the night comes down
And the shrieking of the town
Settles to the steady roar
Of a long sea-beaten shore,
April hieth, April spieth
Everywhere a lover lieth,
Bringeth sweetness, bringeth fever,
Will not stop at "I would liever,"
Will not heed, "Now God a mercy!"
Turneth Moral topsy-versy,
Bringeth he and she to bed,
Bringeth ill to maidenhead,
Bringeth joyance in its stead.
By May, by May, she lieth sped,
Yet still we praise that crocus head,
April!

FOR CITY LOVERS

Do not desire to seek who once we were,
Or where we did, or what, or in whose name.
Those buildings have been torn down. When the first wreckers
Tore the house open like a pack of cards
And the sun came in all over, everywhere,
They found some old newspapers and a cork
And footprints on the very dusty floor
But neither mouse nor angel.
                                    Then even these
Went, even the little marks of shabby shoes,
The one sharp impress of the naked heel.

You cannot call us up there any more.
The number has been changed. There was a card
Downstairs, with names and such, under the bell.
But that's long gone. Yes, and we, they and you
And telegrams and flowers and the years
Went up and down these stairs, day after day,
And kept the stair-rail polished with our hands.
But we have moved to other neighborhoods.

Do not arraign that doorsill with your eyes
Nor try to make your hardened mind recall
How the old windows looked when they were lit
Or who the woman was on the third floor.
There are no ghosts to raise. There is the blank
Face of the stone, the hard line of the street,
The boys crying through twilight. That is all.

Go buy yourself a drink and talk about it.
Carry a humming head home through the rain.
But do not wear rosemary, touch cold iron,
Or leave out food before you go to bed.
For there's no fear of ghosts. That boy and girl
Are dust the sparrows bathe in, under the sun:
Under the virgin rock their bones lie sunken
Past pave and conduit and hidden waters
Stifled like unborn children in the darkness,
Past light and speech, cable and rooted steel,
Under the caissons, under the foundation.

Peace, peace, for there are people with those names
Somewhere or elsewhere, and you must not vex
Strangers with words about an old address.
But, for those others, do not be afraid.
They are beyond you. They are too deep down
For steel to pierce, for engines to uncover.
Not all the desperate splitters of the earth,
Nitro or air-drill or the chewing shovel
Shall ever mouth them up from where they lie.

NIGHTMARE FOR FUTURE REFERENCE

That was the second year of the Third World War,
The one between Us and Them.
                         Well we've gotten used.
We don't talk much about it, queerly enough.
There was all sorts of talk the first years after the Peace,
A million theories, a million wild suppositions,
A million hopeful explanations and plans,
But we don't talk about it, now. We don't even ask.

We might do the wrong thing. I don't guess you'd understand
  that.
But you're eighteen, now. You can take it. You'd better know.

You see, you were born just before the war broke out.
Who started it? Oh, they said it was Us or Them
And it looked like it at the time. You don't know what that's like.
But anyhow, it started and there it was,
Just a little worse, of course, than the one before,
But mankind was used to that. We didn't take notice.
They bombed our capital and we bombed theirs.
You've been to the Broken Towns? Yes, they take you there.
They show you the look of the tormented earth.
But they can't show the smell or the gas or the death
Or how it felt to be there, and a part of it.
But we didn't know. I swear that we didn't know.

I remember the first faint hint there was something wrong,
Something beyond all wars and bigger and strange,
Something you couldn't explain.
                                   I was back on leave—
Strange, as you felt on leave, as you always felt—
But I went to see the Chief at the hospital
And there he was, in the same old laboratory,
A little older, with some white in his hair
But the same eyes that went through you and the same tongue.
They hadn't been able to touch him—not the bombs
Nor the ruin of his life's work nor anything.
He blinked at me from behind his spectacles
And said, "Huh. It's you. They won't let me have guinea pigs
Except for the war work, but I steal a few.
And they've made me a colonel—expect me to salute.
Damn fools. A damn-fool business. I don't know how.
Have you heard what Erickson's done with the ductless glands?
The journals are four months late. Sit down and smoke."
And I did and it was like home.
                                   He was a great man.
You might remember that—and I'd worked with him.
Well, finally he said to me, "How's your boy?"
"Oh—healthy," I said. "We're lucky."
                                   "Yes," he said,
And a frown went over his face. "He might even grow up,

458

Though the intervals between wars are getting shorter.
I wonder if it wouldn't simplify things
To declare mankind in a permanent state of siege.
It might knock some sense in their heads."
                                "You're cheerful," I said.
"Oh, I'm always cheerful," he said. "Seen these, by the way?"
He tapped some charts on a table.
                        "Seen what?" I said.
"Oh," he said, with that devilish, sidelong grin of his,
"Just the normal city statistics—death and birth.
You're a soldier now. You wouldn't be interested.
But the birth rate's dropping—"
                        "Well, really, sir," I said,
"We know that it's always dropped, in every war."

"Not like this," he said. "I can show you the curve.
It looks like the side of a mountain, going down.
And faster, the last three months—yes, a good deal faster.
I showed it to Lobenheim and he was puzzled.
It makes a neat problem—yes?" He looked at me.

"They'd better make peace," he said. "They'd better make peace."

"Well, sir," I said, "if we break through, in the spring—"

"Break through?" he said. "What's that? They'd better make
    peace.
The stars may be tired of us. No, I'm not a mystic.
I leave that to the big scientists in bad novels.
But I never saw such a queer maternity curve.
I wish I could get to Ehrens, on their side.
He'd tell me the truth. But the fools won't let me do it."

His eyes looked tired as he stared at the careful charts.
"Suppose there are no more babies?" he said. "What then?
It's one way of solving the problem."
                                "But, sir—" I said.
"But, sir!" he said. "Will you tell me, please, what is life?
Why it's given, why it's taken away?
Oh, I know—we make a jelly inside a test tube,
We keep a cock's heart living inside a jar.
We know a great many things and what do we know?

We think we know what finished the dinosaurs,
But do we? Maybe they were given a chance
And then it was taken back. There are other beasts
That only kill for their food. No, I'm not a mystic,
But there's a certain pattern in nature, you know,
And we're upsetting it daily. Eat and mate
And go back to the earth after that, and that's all right.
But now we're blasting and sickening earth itself.
She's been very patient with us. I wonder how long."

Well, I thought the Chief had gone crazy, just at first,
And then I remembered the look of no man's land,
That bitter landscape, pockmarked like the moon,
Lifeless as the moon's face and horrible,
The thing we'd made with the guns.
                                                    If it were earth,
It looked as though it hated.
                                        "Well?" I said,
And my voice was a little thin. He looked hard at me.
"Oh—ask the women," he grunted. "Don't ask me.
Ask them what they think about it."
                                              I didn't ask them,
Not even your mother—she was strange, those days—
But, two weeks later, I was back in the lines
And somebody sent me a paper—
Encouragement for the troops and all of that—
All about the fall of Their birth rate on Their side.

I guess you know, now. There was still a day when we fought
And the next day, the women knew. I don't know how they
    knew,
But they smashed every government in the world
Like a heap of broken china, within two days,
And we'd stopped firing by then. And we looked at each other.

We didn't talk much, those first weeks. You couldn't talk.
We started in rebuilding and that was all,
And at first, nobody would even touch the guns,
Not even to melt them up. They just stood there, silent,
Pointing the way they had and nobody there.
And there was a kind of madness in the air,
A quiet, bewildered madness, strange and shy.

460

You'd pass a man who was muttering to himself
And you'd know what he was muttering, and why.
I remember coming home and your mother there.
She looked at me, at first didn't speak at all,
And then she said, "Burn those clothes. Take them off and burn
   them
Or I'll never touch you or speak to you again."
And then I knew I was still in my uniform.

Well, I've told you, now. They tell you now at eighteen.
There's no use telling before.
                              Do you understand?
That's why we have the Ritual of the Earth,
The Day of Sorrow, the other ceremonies.
Oh yes, at first people hated the animals
Because they still bred, but we've gotten over that.
Perhaps they can work it better, when it's their turn,
If it's their turn—I don't know. I don't know at all.
You can call it a virus, of course, if you like the word,
But we haven't been able to find it. Not yet. No.
It isn't as if it had happened all at once.
There were a few children born in the last six months
Before the end of the war, so there's still some hope.
But they're almost grown. That's the trouble. They're almost
   grown.
Well, we had a long run. That's something. At first they thought
There might be a nation somewhere—a savage tribe.
But we were all in it, even the Eskimos,
And we keep the toys in the stores, and the colored books,
And people marry and plan and the rest of it,
But, you see, there aren't any children. They aren't born.

MINOR LITANY

This being a time confused and with few clear stars,
Either private ones or public,
Out of its darkness I make a litany
For the lost, for the half-lost, for the desperate,
For all of those who suffer, not in the flesh.
I will say their name, but not yet.
                              This is for those

461

Who talk to the bearded man in the quiet office,
Sensibly, calmly, explaining just how it was,
And suddenly burst into noisy, quacking tears;
For those who live through the party, wishing for death;
For those who take the sensible country walks,
Wondering if people stare;
For those who try to hook rugs in the big, bright room
And do it badly and are pleased with the praise;
For the night and the fear and the demons of the night;
For the lying back on the couch and the wincing talk.

This is for those who work and those who may not,
For those who suddenly come to a locked door,
And the work falls out of their hands;
For those who step off the pavement into hell,
Having not observed the red light and the warning signals
Because they were busy or ignorant or proud.

This is for those who are bound in the paper chains
That are stronger than links of iron; this is for those
Who each day heave the papier-mache rock
Up the huge and burning hill,
And there is no rock and no hill, but they do not know it.

This is for those who wait till six for the drink,
Till eleven for the tablet;
And for those who cannot wait but go to the darkness;
And for those who long for the darkness but do not go,
Who walk to the window and see the body falling,
Hear the thud of air in the ears,
And then turn back to the room and sit down again,
None having observed the occurrence but themselves.

Christ, have mercy upon us.
Freud, have mercy upon us.
Life, have mercy upon us.

This is for those
Who painfully haul the dark fish out of the dark,
The child's old nightmare, embalmed in its own pain,
And, after that, get well or do not get well,
But do not forget the sulphur in the mouth

Or the time when the world was different, not for a while.
And for those also, the veterans
Of another kind of war,
Who say "No thanks" to the cocktails, who say "No thanks.
Well, yes, give me Coca-Cola" with the trained smile,
Those who hid the bottles so cleverly in the trunk,
Who bribed the attendant, who promised to be good,
Who woke in the dirty bed in the unknown town.
They are cured, now, very much cured.
They are tanned and fine. Their eyes are their only scars.

This is for those with the light white scars on the wrists,
Who remember the smell of gas and the vomiting,
And it meant little and it is a well-known symptom
And they were always careful to phone, before.
Nevertheless, they remember.
                                    This is for those
Who heard the music suddenly get too loud,
Who could not alter the fancy when it came.

Chloral, have mercy upon us.
Amytal, have mercy upon us.
Nembutal, have mercy upon us.

This occurs more or less than it did in the past times.
There are statistics. There are no real statistics.
There is also no heroism. There is merely
Fatigue, pain, great confusion, sometimes recovery.

The name, as you know, is Legion.
What's your name, friend? Where are you from and how did
      you get here?
The name is Legion. It's Legion in the case history.
Friends, Romans, countrymen,
Mr. and Mrs. Legion is the name.

NIGHTMARE AT NOON

THERE are no trenches dug in the park, not yet.
There are no soldiers falling out of the sky.
It's a fine, clear day, in the park. It is bright and hot.
The trees are in full, green, summer-heavy leaf.
An airplane drones overhead but no one's afraid.
There's no reason to be afraid, in a fine, big city
That was not built for a war. There is time and time.

There was time in Norway and time, and the thing fell.
When they woke, they saw the planes with the black crosses.
When they woke, they heard the guns rolling in the street.
They could not believe, at first. It was hard to believe.
They had been friendly and thriving and inventive.
They had had good arts, decent living, peace for years.
Those were not enough, it seems.
There were people there who wrote books and painted pictures,
Worked, came home tired, liked to be let alone.
They made fun of the strut and the stamp and the strained salute,
They made fun of the would-be Caesars who howl and foam.
That was not enough, it seems. It was not enough.
When they woke, they saw the planes with the black crosses.

There is grass in the park. There are children on the long meadow
Watched by some hot, peaceful nuns. Where the ducks are fed
There are black children and white and the anxious teachers
Who keep counting them like chickens. It's quite a job
To take so many school-kids out to the park,
But when they've eaten their picnic, they'll go home.
(And they could have better homes, in a rich city.)
But they won't be sent to Kansas or Michigan
At twenty-four hours' notice,
Dazed, bewildered, clutching their broken toys,
Hundreds on hundreds filling the blacked-out trains.
Just to keep them safe, just so they may live not die.
Just so there's one chance that they may not die but live.
That does not enter our thoughts. There is plenty of time.

In Holland, one hears, some children were less lucky.
It was hard to send them anywhere in Holland.
It is a small country, you see. The thing happened quickly.

464

The bombs from the sky are quite indifferent to children.
The machine-gunners do not distinguish. In Rotterdam
One quarter of the city was blown to bits.
That included, naturally, ordinary buildings
With the usual furnishings, such as cats and children.
It was an old, peaceful city, Rotterdam,
Clean, tidy, full of flowers.
But that was not enough, it seems.
It was not enough to keep all the children safe.
It was ended in a week, and the freedom ended.

There is no air-raid siren yet, in the park.
All the glass still stands, in the windows around the park.
The man on the bench is reading a Yiddish paper.
He will not be shot because of that, oddly enough.
He will not even be beaten or imprisoned.
Not yet, not yet.
You can be a Finn or a Dane and an American.
You can be German or French and an American,
Jew, Bohunk, Nigger, Mick—all the dirty names
We call each other—and yet American.
We've stuck to that quite a while.
Go into Joe's Diner and try to tell the truckers
You belong to a Master Race and you'll get a laugh.
What's that, brother? Double-talk?
I'm a stranger here myself but it's a free country.
It's a free country . . .
Oh yes, I know the faults and the other side,
The lyncher's rope, the bought justice, the wasted land,
The scale on the leaf, the borers in the corn,
The finks with their clubs, the grey sky of relief,
All the long shame of our hearts and the long disunion.
I am merely remarking—as a country, we try.
As a country, I think we try.

They tried in Spain but the tanks and the planes won out.
They fought very well and long.
They fought to be free but it seems that was not enough.
They did not have the equipment. So they lost.
They tried in Finland. The resistance was shrewd,
Skilful, intelligent, waged by a free folk.

They tried in Greece, and they threw them back for a while
By the soul and spirit and passion of common men.
Call the roll of fourteen nations. Call the roll
Of the blacked-out lands, the lands that used to be free.

But do not call it loud. There is plenty of time.
There is plenty of time, while the bombs on London fall
And turn the world to wind and water and fire.
There is time to sleep while the fire-bombs fall on London.
They are stubborn people in London.

We are slow to wake, good-natured as a country.
(It is our fault and our virtue.) We like to raise
A man to the highest power and then throw bricks at him.
We don't like war and we like to speak our minds.
We're used to speaking our minds.
                                There are certain words,
Our own and others', we're used to—words we've used,
Heard, had to recite, forgotten,
Rubbed shiny in the pocket, left home for keepsakes,
Inherited, stuck away in the back-drawer,
In the locked trunk, at the back of the quiet mind.

Liberty, equality, fraternity.
To none will we sell, refuse or deny, right or justice.
We hold these truths to be self-evident.

I am merely saying—what if these words pass?
What if they pass and are gone and are no more,
Eviscerated, blotted out of the world?
We're used to them, so used that we half-forget,
The way you forget the looks of your own house
And yet you can walk around it, in the darkness.
You can't put a price on sunlight or the air,
You can't put a price on these, so they must be easy.
They were bought with belief and passion, at great cost.
They were bought with the bitter and anonymous blood
Of farmers, teachers, shoemakers and fools
Who broke the old rule and the pride of kings.
And some never saw the end and many were weary,
Some doubtful, many confused.
They were bought by the ragged boys at Valmy mill,

The yokels at Lexington with the long light guns
And the dry, New England faces,
The iron barons, writing a charter out
For their own iron advantage, not the people,
And yet the people got it into their hands
And marked it with their own sweat.
It took long to buy these words.
It took a long time to buy them and much pain.

Thenceforward and forever free.
Thenceforward and forever free.
No man may be bound or fined or slain till he has been judged
     by his peers.
To form a more perfect Union.

The others have their words too, and strong words,
Strong as the tanks, explosive as the bombs.

The State is all, worship the State!
The Leader is all, worship the Leader!
Strength is all, worship strength!
Worship, bow down or die!

I shall go back through the park to my safe house,
This is not London or Paris.
This is the high, bright city, the lucky place,
The place that always had time.
The boys in their shirtsleeves here, the big, flowering girls,
The bicycle-riders, the kids with the model planes,
The lovers who lie on the grass, uncaring of eyes,
As if they lay on an island out of time,
The tough kids, squirting the water at the fountain,
Whistled at by the cop.
The dopes who write "Jimmy's a dope" on the tunnel walls.
These are all quite safe and nothing will happen to them.
Nothing will happen, of course.
Go tell Frank the Yanks aren't coming, in Union Square.
Go tell the new brokers' story about the President.
Whatever it is. That's going to help a lot.
There's time to drink your highball—plenty of time.
Go tell fire it only burns in another country,

Go tell the bombers this is the wrong address,
The hurricane to pass on the other side.
Go tell the earthquake it must not shake the ground.

The bell has rung in the night and the air quakes with it.

I shall not sleep tonight when I hear the plane.

1940.

LISTEN TO THE PEOPLE

Listen to the People:

Independence Day, 1941

NARRATOR:

This is Independence Day,
Fourth of July, the day we mean to keep,
Whatever happens and whatever falls
Out of a sky grown strange;
This is firecracker day for sunburnt kids,
The day of the parade,
Slambanging down the street.
Listen to the parade!
There's J. K. Burney's float,
Red-white-and-blue crepe-paper on the wheels,
The Fire Department and the local Grange,
There are the pretty girls with their hair curled
Who represent the Thirteen Colonies,
The Spirit of East Greenwich, Betsy Ross,
Democracy, or just some pretty girls.
There are the veterans and the Legion Post
(Their feet are going to hurt when they get home),
The band, the flag, the band, the usual crowd,
Good-humored, watching, hot,
Silent a second as the flag goes by,
Kidding the local cop and eating popsicles,
Jack Brown and Rosie Shapiro and Dan Shay,
Paul Bunchick and the Greek who runs the Greek's,
The black-eyed children out of Sicily,
The girls who giggle and the boys who push,
All of them there and all of them a nation.
And, afterwards,
There'll be ice-cream and fireworks and a speech
By Somebody the Honorable Who,
The lovers will pair off in the kind dark

And Tessie Jones, our honor-graduate,
Will read the Declaration.
That's how it is. It's always been that way.
That's our Fourth of July, through war and peace,
That's our Fourth of July.

And a lean farmer on a stony farm
Came home from mowing, buttoned up his shirt
And walked ten miles to town,
Musket in hand.
He didn't know the sky was falling down
And, it may be, he didn't know so much.
But people oughtn't to be pushed around
By kings or any such.
A workman in the city dropped his tools.
An ordinary, small-town kind of man
Found himself standing in the April sun,
One of a ragged line
Against the skilled professionals of war,
The matchless infantry who could not fail,
Not for the profit, not to conquer worlds,
Not for the pomp or the heroic tale
But first, and principally, since he was sore.
They could do things in quite a lot of places.
They shouldn't do them here, in Lexington.

He looked around and saw his neighbors' faces. . . .

AN ANGRY VOICE:

Disperse, ye villains! Damn you, why don't you disperse?

A CALM VOICE:

*Stand your ground, men. Don't fire unless fired upon. But, if
they mean to have a war, let it begin here!*

NARRATOR, RESUMING:

Well, that was that. And later, when he died
Of fever or a bullet in the guts,
Bad generalship, starvation, dirty wounds
Or any one of all the thousand things
That kill a man in wars,
He didn't die handsome but he did die free

472

And maybe that meant something. It could be.
Oh, it's not pretty! Say it all you like!
It isn't a bit pretty. Not one bit.
But that is how the liberty was won.
That paid for the firecrackers and the band.

A YOUNG VOICE, RADICAL:

Well, what do you mean, you dope?
Don't you know this is an imperialist, capitalist country, don't
    you?
Don't you know it's all done with mirrors and the bosses get the
    gravy, don't you?
Suppose some old guy with chin whiskers did get his pants shot
    off at a place called Lexington?
What does it mean to me?

AN OLDER VOICE, CONSERVATIVE:

My dear fellow, I myself am a son of a son of a son of the Ameri-
    can Revolution,
But I can only view the present situation with the gravest alarm,
Because we are rapidly drifting into a dictatorship
And it isn't my kind of dictatorship, what's more.
The Constitution is dead and labor doesn't know its place,
And then there's all that gold buried at Fort Knox
And the taxes—oh, oh, oh!
Why, what's the use of a defense-contract if you can't make
    money out of your country?
Things are bad—things are very bad.
Already my Aunt Emmeline has had to shoot her third footman.
(He broke his leg passing cocktails and it was really a kindness.)
And, if you let the working-classes buy coal, they'll only fill it
    with bathtubs.
Don't you realize the gravity of the situation, don't you?
Won't you hide your head in a bucket and telegraph your con-
    gressman, opposing everything possible, including peace and
    war?

A TOTALITARIAN VOICE, PERSUASIVE:

My worthy American listeners,
I am giving you one more chance.
Don't you know that we are completely invincible, don't you?

Won't you just admit that we are the wave of the future, won't you?

You are a very nice, mongrel, disgusting people—
But, naturally, you need new leadership.
We can supply it. We've sent the same brand to fourteen nations.
It comes in the shape of a bomb and it beats as it sweeps as it cleans.
For those of you who like order, we can supply order.
We give the order. You take it.
For those of you who like efficiency, we can supply efficiency.
Look what we did to Coventry and Rotterdam!
For those of you who like Benito Mussolini, we can supply Benito Mussolini.
(He's three doors down to the left, at the desk marked second Vice President.)
Now be sensible—give up this corrupt and stupid nonsense of democracy,
And you can have the crumbs from our table and a trusty's job in our world-jail.

RADICAL VOICE:

Forget everything but the class-struggle. Forget democracy.

CONSERVATIVE VOICE:

Hate and distrust your own government. Whisper, hate and never look forward.
Look back wistfully to the good old, grand old days—the days when the boys said "The public be damned!" and got away with it.
Democracy's a nasty word, invented by the Reds.

TOTALITARIAN VOICE:

Just a little collaboration and you too can be part of the New Order.
You too can have fine new concentration camps and shoes made out of wood pulp. You too can be as peaceful as Poland, as happy and gay as France. Just a little collaboration. We have so many things to give you.
We can give you your own Hess, your own Himmler, your own Goering—all home grown and wrapped in cellophane. We've done it elsewhere. If you'll help, we can do it here.

474

RADICAL VOICE:
Democracy's a fake—

CONSERVATIVE:
Democracy's a mistake—

TOTALITARIAN:
Democracy is finished. We are the future.

(MUSIC UP AND OMINOUS)

NARRATOR, RESUMING:
The sky is dark, now, over the parade,
The sky's an altered sky, a sky that might be.

There's J. K. Burney's float
With funny-colored paper on the wheels
Or no—excuse me—used to be J. K.'s.
But the store's under different management
Like quite a lot of stores.
You see, J. K. got up in church one day,
After it all had happened and walked out,
The day they instituted the new order.
They had a meeting. Held it in the church.
He just walked out. That's all.
That's all there is to say about J. K.,
Though I remember just the way he looked,
White-faced and chin stuck out.
I think they could have let the church alone.
It's kind of dreary, shutting up the church.
But don't you say I said so. Don't you say!
Listen to the parade!
There are the pretty girls with their hair curled,
Back from the labor camp.
They represent the League of Strength Through Joy.
At least, I guess it's that.
No, they don't go to high-school any more.
They get told where they go. We all get told.
And, now and then, it happens like Jack Brown,
Nice fellow, Jack. Ran the gas-station here.

475

But he was married to a You-Know-Who.
Fond of her, too.
I don't know why we never used to mind.
Why, she walked round like anybody else,
Kept her kids clean and joined the Ladies' Social.
Just shows you, doesn't it? But that's all done.
And you won't see her in the crowd today,
Her or the kids or Jack,
Unless you look six feet under the ground,
The lime-washed ground, the bitter prison ground
That hides the martyrs and the innocent,
And you won't see Dan Shay.
Dan was a Union man
And now we don't have Unions any more.
They wouldn't even let him take his specs,
The day the troopers came around for him.
And yet he needed specs. He had grey hair.
Funny—you keep remembering things like that.
Maybe he's still alive. It's hard to say.

(Half hysterically)

Listen to the parade!
The marching, marching, marching feet,
All with the same hard stamp!
The bands, the bands, the bands, the flags, the flags,
The sharp, mechanical, inhuman cheer
Dragged from the straining throats of the stiff crowd!
It's Independence—sorry, my mistake!
It's National Day—the Day of the New Order!
We let it happen—we forgot the old,
Bleak words of common sense, "Unite or Die,"
We fiddled and we squabbled and we scrapped,
We led a filibuster in the Senate,
We were quite ready for a sacrifice
Sometime, next Tuesday—but not yet, not now!
And the clock struck—and the bad dream was here.

A VOICE:

But you can't do this to me! I subscribed to the Party funds!

476

A VOICE:

You can't do this to me. We got laws. We got courts. We got unions.

A VOICE:

You can't do this to me. Why, I believe in Karl Marx!

A VOICE:

You can't do this to me. The Constitution forbids it.

A VOICE:

I was always glad to coöperate.

A VOICE:

It looked to me like good business.

A VOICE:

It looked to me like the class struggle.

A VOICE:

It looked to me like peace in our time.

TOTALITARIAN VOICE:

Thank you, ladies and gentlemen. Democracy is finished.
    You are finished. We are the present!

(MUSIC UP AND DOWN)

NARRATOR:

That is one voice. You've heard it. Don't forget it.
And don't forget it can be slick or harsh,
Violent or crooning, but it's still the same
And it means death.

Are there no other voices? None at all?
No voice at all out of the long parade
That marched so many years,
Out of the passion of the Puritans,

477

The creaking of the wagons going west,
The guns of Sharpsburg, the unnumbered dead,
Out of the baffled and bewildered hosts
Who came here for a freedom hardly known,
Rebel and exile, bondservant and outcast.
Out of the bowels of the immigrant ship,
The strange, sick voyage, the cheating and the scorn
And yet, at the end, Liberty.
Liberty with a torch in her right hand,
Whoever cheated and whoever lied,
Liberty for my children, Liberty
Slowly worked out, deceived a thousand times,
But never quite forgotten, always growing,
Growing like wheat and corn.
"I remember a man named Abe Lincoln.
I remember the words he used to say."
Oh, we can call on Lincoln and Tom Paine,
Adams and Jefferson.
Call on the great words spoken that remain
Like the great stars of evening, the fixed stars,
But that is not enough.
The dead are mighty and are part of us
And yet the dead are dead. This is our world,
Our time, our choice, our anguish, our decision.
This is our world. We have to make it now,
A hundred and thirty millions of us have to
And make it well, or suffer the bad dream.
What have we got to say?

A WOMAN'S VOICE:

I don't know. I'm a woman with a house.
I do my work. I take care of my man.
I've got a right to say how things should be.
I've got a right to have my kids grow up
The way they ought to grow. Don't stop me there.
Don't tread on me, don't hinder me, don't cross me.
I made my kids myself. I haven't got
Big words to tell about them.
But, if you ask about democracy,
Democracy's the growing and the bearing,
Mouth at the breast and child still to be born.
Democracy is kids and the green grass.

NARRATOR:

What have we got to say,
People, you people?

MAN'S VOICE:

I guess I haven't thought about it much.
I been too busy. Way I figure it
It's this way. We've got something. If it's crummy
The bunch of us can change what we don't like
In our own way and mean it.
I got a cousin back in the old country.
He says it's swell there but he couldn't change
A button on his pants without an order
From somebody's pet horse. Maybe he likes it.
I'm sticking here. That's all. Well, sign me off.

NARRATOR:

People, you people, living everywhere,
Sioux Falls and Saugatuck and Texarkana,
Memphis and Goshen, Harrodsburg and Troy,
People who live at postmarks with queer names,
Blue Eye and Rawhide, Santa Claus and Troublesome,
People by rivers, people of the plains,
People whose contour-plows bring back the grass
To a dust-bitten and dishonored earth,
And those who farm the hillside acres still
And raise up fortitude between the stones,
Millions in cities, millions in the towns,
People who spit a mile from their front doors
And gangling kids, ballplaying in the street,
All races and all stocks, all creeds and cries,
And yet one people, one, and always striving. . . .

A MAN:

I'm on relief.
I know what they say about us on relief,
Those who never were there.
All the same, we made the park.
We made the road and the check-dam and the culvert.
Our names are not on the tablets. Forget our names.
But, when you drive on the road, remember us, also.

Remember Johnny Lombardo and his pick,
Remember us, when you build democracy,
For we, too, were part and are part.

NARRATOR:

One nation, one.
And the voices of young and old, of all who have faith,
Jostling and mingling, speaking from the ground,
Speaking from the old houses and the pride,
Speaking from the deep hollows of the heart.

MAN'S VOICE:

I was born in '63.
There were many then who despaired of the Republic,
Many fine and solid citizens.
They had good and plausible reasons and were eloquent.
I grew up in the Age of Brass, the Age of Steel.
I have known and heard of three wars.
All through my life, whenever the skies were dark,
There came to me many fine and solid citizens,
Wringing their hands, despairing of the Republic,
Because of an income tax or a depression,
Because their party had lost the last election,
Because we couldn't do this and shouldn't do that.
And yet, each time, I saw the Republic grow
Like a great elm tree, through each fault and failure,
The stubborn rock, the parched soil,
And spread its branches over all the people.
Look at the morning sun. There is the Republic.
Not yesterday, but there, the breaking day.

TOTALITARIAN VOICE:

But, my worthy American listeners,
All this is degenerate talk.
The future rolls like a wave and you cannot fight it.

A VOICE:

Who says we can't?

A VOICE:

Who says so?

A VOICE:

What's his racket?

A VOICE:

How does he get that way?

A VOICE:

You mean to tell me
A little shrimp like that could run the world,
A guy with a trick moustache and a bum salute
Run us, run you and me?

TOTALITARIAN VOICE:

You mistake me.
Others have often made the same mistake
Often and often and in many countries.
I never play upon a people's strength.
I play upon their weaknesses and fears.
I make their doubts my allies and my spies.
I have a most convincing mask of peace
Painted by experts, for one kind of sucker,
And for another—I'm a business man,
Straight from the shoulder, talking trade and markets
And much misunderstood.
I touch this man upon his pocketbook,
That man upon his hatred for his boss,
That man upon his fear.
I offer everything, for offering's cheap.
I make no claims until I make the claims.
I'm always satisfied until I'm not
Which happens rather rapidly to those
Who think I could be satisfied with less
Than a dismembered and digested world.
My secret weapon is no secret weapon.
It is to turn all men against all men
For my own purposes. It is to use
Good men to do my work without their knowledge,
Not only the secret traitor and the spy.
It is to raise a question and a doubt
Where there was faith. It is to subjugate

481

Men's minds before their bodies feel the steel.
It is to use
All envy, all despair, all prejudice
For my own work.
If you've an envy or a prejudice
A nicely grown, well-rounded piece of hate,
I'll play on it and use it to your ruin.
My generals are General Distrust,
General Fear, General Half-A-Heart,
General It's-Too-Late,
General Greed and Major-General Hate,
And they go walking in civilian clothes
In your own streets and whisper in your ears.
I won't be beaten just by sitting tight.
They tried that out in France. I won't be beaten
By hiding in the dark and making faces,
And certainly I never will be beaten
By those who rather like my kind of world,
Or, if not like it, think that it must come,
Those who have wings and burrow in the ground.
For I'm not betting only on the tanks,
The guns, the planes, the bombers,
But on your own division and disunion.
On your own minds and hearts to let me in,
For, if that happens, all I wish for happens.
So what have you to say?
What have you got to bet against my bet?
Where's your one voice?

AMERICAN VOICE:

Our voice is not one voice but many voices.
Not one man's, not the greatest, but the people's.
The blue sky and the forty-eight States of the people.
Many in easy times but one in the pinch
And that's what some folks forget.
Our voice is all the objectors and dissenters
And they sink and are lost in the groundswell of the people,
Once the people rouse, once the people wake and listen.
People, you people, growing everywhere,
What have you got to say?
There's a smart boy here with a question and he wants answers.
What have you got to say?

A VOICE:

We are the people. Listen to us now.

A VOICE:

Says you we're puny? We built Boulder Dam,
We built Grand Coulee and the T. V. A.
We built them out of freedom and our sweat.

VOICE:

Says you we're faint of heart and little of mind?
We poured like wheat through the gaps of the Appalachians.
We made the seas of wheat, the seas of corn.
We made five States a sea of wheat and corn.

VOICE, LAUGHING:

We built the cities and the skyscrapers,
All the proud steel. We built them up so high
The eagles lost their way.

VOICE:

That's us. When did you do a job like that?

VOICE:

Wasn't enough.

VOICE:

No, and you bet it wasn't.
Not with the apple-sellers in the streets,
Not with the empty shops, the hungry men.

VOICE:

But we learned some things in that darkness and kept free.
We didn't fold up and yell for a dictator.
We built, even in the darkness. We learned our trade
By the licks we took and we're building different now.

VOICE:

We lost our way for a while but we've found our way.
We know it and we'll hold it and we'll keep it.
We'll tell it to the world. We're saying it.

VOICE:

Freedom to speak and pray.

VOICE:

Freedom from want and fear.

VOICE:

That's what we're building.

VOICE:

Now and here and now.

VOICE:

Forever and forever and forever.

NARRATOR:

People, you people, risen and awake. . . .

VOICE:

That's what we're building and we'll build it here.
That's what we're building and we'll build it now,
Build it and make it shine across the world,
A refuge and a fortress and a hope,
Breaking old chains and laughing in the sun.
This is the people's cause, the people's might.
We have set up a standard for the free
And it shall not go down.
That's why we drill the plate and turn the wheel,
Build the big planes.
That's why a million and a half of us
Learn here and now how free men stand in arms.
Don't tread on us, don't hinder us, don't cross us.
We won't have tyranny here.

VOICE:

We don't give one long low hoot for your master race.
We think your slick new order's a bowl of raspberries.
We'll pick the small and the free and the enduring,
Wherever we find them and wherever they are.
We won't have tyranny here.

484

VOICE:

We'll stick by Rosie Shapiro and Dan Shay,
Paul Bunchick and the Greek who runs the Greek's,
And all of 'em like that, wherever they are.
We'll stick by the worn old stones in Salem churchyard,
The Jamestown church and the bones of the Alamo.
We won't have tyranny here.

VOICE:

It's a long way out of the past and a long way forward.
It's a tough way, too, and there's plenty of trouble in it.
It's a black storm crowding the sky and a cold wind blowing,
Blowing upon us all.
See it and face it. That's the way it is.
That's the way it'll be for a time and a time.
Even the easy may have little ease.
Even the meek may suffer in their meekness.
But we've ridden out storms before and we'll ride out this one,
Ride it out and get through.
It won't be done by the greedy and the go-easies.
The stuffed shirts, the "yes but" men and the handsome phonies,
The men who want to live in their father's pockets,
The folks who barely believe and the bitter few.
It'll be done by the river of the people,
The mountain of the people, the great plain
Grown to the wheat of the people,
Plowed by their suffering, harrowed by their hope,
Tall with their endless future.
It'll be done by the proud walker, Democracy,
The walker in proud shoes.
Get on your feet, Americans, and say it!
Forget your grievances, wherever you are,
The little yesterday's hates and the last year's discord.
This is your land, this is your independence,
This is the people's cause, the people's might.
Say it and speak it loud, United, free. . .

MANY VOICES:

United, free.

485

VOICE:

Whatever happens and whatever falls.
We pledge ourselves to liberty and faith.

MANY VOICES:

To liberty and faith.

VOICE:

We pledge ourselves to justice, law and hope
And a free government by our own men
For us, our children and our children's children.

MANY VOICES:

For us, our children and our children's children.

VOICE:

Not for an old dead world but a new world rising.

VOICE:

For the toil, the struggle, the hope and the great goal.

(MUSIC UP AND DOWN)

NARRATOR:

You've heard the long parade
And all the voices that cry out against it,
Some of our own, and one that's not our own
And never will be while we're still the people.

(Quietly)

What do the people say?
Well, you've just heard some questions and some answers,
Not all, of course. No man can say that's all.
A man's a humbug if he says that's all.
But look in your own minds and memories
And find out what you find and what you'd keep.
It's time we did that and it won't be earlier.
I don't know what each one of you will find,
What memory, what token, what tradition,
It may be only half a dozen words

486

Carved on a stone, carved deeper in the heart,
It might be all a life, but look and find it—
Sun on Key West, snow on New Hampshire hills,
Warm rain on Georgia and the Texas wind
Blowing across an empire and all part,
All one, all indivisible and one—
Find it and keep it and hold on to it,
For there's a buried thing in all of us,
Deeper than all the noise of the parade,
The thing the haters never understand
And never will, the habit of the free.

Out of the flesh, out of the minds and hearts
Of thousand upon thousand common men,
Cranks, martyrs, starry-eyed enthusiasts
Slow-spoken neighbors, hard to push around,
Women whose hands were gentle with their kids
And men with a cold passion for mere justice.
We made this thing, this dream.
This land unsatisfied by little ways,
Open to every man who brought good will,
This peaceless vision, groping for the stars,
Not as a huge devouring machine
Rolling and clanking with remorseless force
Over submitted bodies and the dead
But as live earth where anything could grow,
Your crankiness, my notions and his dream,
Grow and be looked at, grow and live or die.
But get their chance of growing and the sun.
We made it and we make it and it's ours.
We shall maintain it. It shall be sustained.

ALL VOICES UP:

WE SHALL MAINTAIN IT. IT SHALL BE SUSTAINED.
(MUSIC UP TO CLIMAX)
(CURTAIN)

SELECTED WORKS OF
Stephen Vincent Benét

• • •

VOLUME TWO: PROSE

CONTENTS VOLUME TWO

STORIES OF AMERICAN HISTORY

Stories of American History

JACOB AND THE INDIANS

I<small>T GOES BACK</small> to the early days—may God profit all who lived then—and the ancestors.

Well, America, you understand, in those days was different. It was a nice place, but you wouldn't believe it if you saw it today. Without busses, without trains, without states, without Presidents, nothing!

With nothing but colonists and Indians and wild woods all over the country and wild animals to live in the wild woods. Imagine such a place! In these days, you children don't even think about it; you read about it in the schoolbooks, but what is that? And I put in a call to my daughter, in California, and in three minutes I am saying "Hello, Rosie," and there it is Rosie and she is telling me about the weather, as if I wanted to know! But things were not always that way. I remember my own days, and they were different. And in the times of my grandfather's grandfather, they were different still. Listen to the story.

My grandfather's grandfather was Jacob Stein, and he came from Rettelsheim, in Germany. To Philadelphia he came, an orphan in a sailing ship, but not a common man. He had learning —he had been to the *chedar*—he could have been a scholar among the scholars. Well, that is the way things happen in this bad world. There was a plague and a new grand duke—things are always so. He would say little of it afterward—they had left his teeth in his mouth, but he would say little of it. He did not have to say—we are children of the Dispersion—we know a black day when it comes.

Yet imagine—a young man with fine dreams and learning, a scholar with a pale face and narrow shoulders, set down in those early days in such a new country. Well, he must work, and he did. It was very fine, his learning, but it did not fill his mouth. He

3

must carry a pack on his back and go from door to door with it. That was no disgrace; it was so that many began. But it was not expounding the Law, and at first he was very homesick. He would sit in his room at night, with the one candle, and read the preacher Koheleth, till the bitterness of the preacher rose in his mouth. Myself, I am sure that Koheleth was a great preacher, but if he had had a good wife he would have been a more cheerful man. They had too many wives in those old days—it confused them. But Jacob was young.

As for the new country where he had come, it was to him a place of exile, large and frightening. He was glad to be out of the ship, but, at first, that was all. And when he saw his first real Indian in the street—well, that was a day! But the Indian, a tame one, bought a ribbon from him by signs, and after that he felt better. Nevertheless, it seemed to him at times that the straps of the pack cut into his very soul, and he longed for the smell of the *chedar* and the quiet streets of Rettelsheim and the good smoked goose-breast pious housewives keep for the scholar. But there is no going back—there is never any going back.

All the same, he was a polite young man, and a hardworking. And soon he had a stroke of luck—or at first it seemed so. It was from Simon Ettelsohn that he got the trinkets for his pack, and one day he found Simon Ettelsohn arguing a point of the Law with a friend, for Simon was a pious man and well thought of in the Congregation Mikveh Israel. Our grandfather's grandfather stood by very modestly at first—he had come to replenish his pack and Simon was his employer. But finally his heart moved within him, for both men were wrong, and he spoke and told them where they erred. For half an hour he spoke, with his pack still upon his shoulders, and never has a text been expounded with more complexity, not even by the great Reb Samuel. Till, in the end, Simon Ettelsohn threw up his hands and called him a young David and a candle of learning. Also, he allowed him a more profitable route of trade. But, best of all, he invited young Jacob to his house, and there Jacob ate well for the first time since he had come to Philadelphia. Also he laid eyes upon Miriam Ettelsohn for the first time, and she was Simon's youngest daughter and a rose of Sharon.

After that, things went better for Jacob, for the protection of the strong is like a rock and a well. But yet things did not go

4

Jacob and the Indians

altogether as he wished. For, at first, Simon Ettelsohn made much of him, and there was stuffed fish and raisin wine for the young scholar, though he was a peddler. But there is a look in a man's eyes that says "H'm? Son-in-law?" and that look Jacob did not see. He was modest—he did not expect to win the maiden over-night, though he longed for her. But gradually it was borne in upon him what he was in the Ettelsohn house—a young scholar to be shown before Simon's friends, but a scholar whose learning did not fill his mouth. He did not blame Simon for it, but it was not what he had intended. He began to wonder if he would ever get on in the world at all, and that is not good for any man.

Nevertheless, he could have borne it, and the aches and pains of his love, had it not been for Meyer Kappelhuist. Now, there was a pushing man! I speak no ill of anyone, not even of your Aunt Cora, and she can keep the De Groot silver if she finds it in her heart to do so; who lies down in the straw with a dog, gets up with fleas. But this Meyer Kappelhuist! A big, red-faced fellow from Holland with shoulders the size of a barn door and red hair on the backs of his hands. A big mouth for eating and drinking and telling schnorrer stories—and he talked about the Kappelhuists, in Holland, till you'd think they were made of gold. The crane says, "I am really a peacock—at least on my mother's side." And yet, a thriving man—that could not be denied. He had started with a pack, like our grandfather's grandfather, and now he was trading with the Indians and making money hand over fist. It seemed to Jacob that he could never go to the Ettelsohn house without meeting Meyer and hearing about those Indians. And it dried the words in Jacob's mouth and made his heart burn.

For, no sooner would our grandfather's grandfather begin to expound a text or a proverb, than he would see Meyer Kappel-huist looking at the maiden. And when Jacob had finished his expounding, and there should have been a silence, Meyer Kappel-huist would take it upon himself to thank him, but always in a tone that said: "The Law is the Law and the Prophets are the Prophets, but prime beaver is also prime beaver, my little scholar!" It took the pleasure from Jacob's learning and the joy of the maiden from his heart. Then he would sit silent and burn-ing, while Meyer told a great tale of Indians, slapping his hands on his knees. And in the end he was always careful to ask Jacob how many needles and pins he had sold that day; and when

5

Jacob told him, he would smile and say very smoothly that all things had small beginnings, till the maiden herself could not keep from a little smile. Then, desperately, Jacob would rack his brains for more interesting matter. He would tell of the wars of the Maccabees and the glory of the Temple. But even as he told them, he felt they were far away. Whereas Meyer and his accursed Indians were there, and the maiden's eyes shone at his words.

Finally he took his courage in both hands and went to Simon Ettelsohn. It took much for him to do it, for he had not been brought up to strive with men, but with words. But it seemed to him now that everywhere he went he heard of nothing but Meyer Kappelhuist and his trading with the Indians, till he thought it would drive him mad. So he went to Simon Ettelsohn in his shop.

"I am weary of this narrow trading in pins and needles," he said, without more words.

Simon Ettelsohn looked at him keenly; for while he was an ambitious man, he was kindly as well.

"*Nu*," he said. "A nice little trade you have and the people like you. I myself started in with less. What would you have more?"

"I would have much more," said our grandfather's grandfather stiffly. "I would have a wife and a home in this new country. But how shall I keep a wife? On needles and pins?"

"*Nu*, it has been done," said Simon Ettelsohn, smiling a little. "You are a good boy, Jacob, and we take an interest in you. Now, if it is a question of marriage, there are many worthy maidens. Asher Levy, the baker, has a daughter. It is true that she squints a little, but her heart is of gold." He folded his hands and smiled.

"It is not of Asher Levy's daughter I am thinking," said Jacob, taken aback. Simon Ettelsohn nodded his head and his face grew grave.

"*Nu*, Jacob," he said. "I see what is in your heart. Well, you are a good boy, Jacob, and a fine scholar. And if it were in the old country, I am not saying. But here, I have one daughter married to a Seixas and one to a Da Silva. You must see that makes a difference." And he smiled the smile of a man well pleased with his world.

Jacob and the Indians

"And if I were such a one as Meyer Kappelhuist?" said Jacob bitterly.

"Now—well, that is a little different," said Simon Ettelsohn sensibly. "For Meyer trades with the Indians. It is true, he is a little rough. But he will die a rich man."

"I will trade with the Indians too," said Jacob, and trembled. Simon Ettelsohn looked at him as if he had gone out of his mind. He looked at his narrow shoulders and his scholar's hands.

"Now, Jacob," he said soothingly, "do not be foolish. A scholar you are, and learned, not an Indian trader. Perhaps in a store you would do better. I can speak to Aaron Copras. And sooner or later we will find you a nice maiden. But to trade with Indians—well, that takes a different sort of man. Leave that to Meyer Kappelhuist."

"And your daughter, that rose of Sharon? Shall I leave her, too, to Meyer Kappelhuist?" cried Jacob.

Simon Ettelsohn looked uncomfortable.

"*Nu*, Jacob," he said. "Well, it is not settled, of course. But—"

"I will go forth against him as David went against Goliath," said our grandfather's grandfather wildly. "I will go forth into the wilderness. And God should judge the better man!"

Then he flung his pack on the floor and strode from the shop. Simon Ettelsohn called out after him, but he did not stop for that. Nor was it in his heart to go and seek the maiden. Instead, when he was in the street, he counted the money he had. It was not much. He had meant to buy his trading goods on credit from Simon Ettelsohn, but now he could not do that. He stood in the sunlit street of Philadelphia, like a man bereft of hope.

Nevertheless, he was stubborn—though how stubborn he did not yet know. And though he was bereft of hope, he found his feet taking him to the house of Raphael Sanchez.

Now, Raphael Sanchez could have bought and sold Simon Ettelsohn twice over. An arrogant old man he was, with fierce black eyes and a beard that was whiter than snow. He lived apart, in his big house with his granddaughter, and men said he was very learned, but also very disdainful, and that to him a Jew was not a Jew who did not come of the pure sephardic strain.

Jacob had seen him, in the Congregation Mikveh Israel, and to Jacob he had looked like an eagle, and fierce as an eagle. Yet

7

now, in his need, he found himself knocking at that man's door. It was Raphael Sanchez himself who opened. "And what is for sale today, peddler?" he said, looking scornfully at Jacob's jacket where the pack straps had worn it.

"A scholar of the Law is for sale," said Jacob in his bitterness, and he did not speak in the tongue he had learned in this country, but in Hebrew.

The old man stared at him a moment.

"Now am I rebuked," he said. "For you have the tongue. Enter, my guest," and Jacob touched the scroll by the doorpost and went in.

They shared the noon meal at Raphael Sanchez's table. It was made of dark, glowing mahogany, and the light sank into it as sunlight sinks into a pool. There were many precious things in that room, but Jacob had no eyes for them. When the meal was over and the blessing said, he opened his heart and spoke, and Raphael Sanchez listened, stroking his beard with one hand. When the young man had finished, he spoke.

"So, Scholar," he said, though mildly, "you have crossed an ocean that you might live and not die, and yet all you see is a girl's face."

"Did not Jacob serve seven years for Rachel?" said our grandfather's grandfather.

"Twice seven, Scholar," said Raphael Sanchez dryly, "but that was in the blessed days." He stroked his beard again. "Do you know why I came to this country?" he said.

"No," said Jacob Stein.

"It was not for the trading," said Raphael Sanchez. "My house has lent money to kings. A little fish, a few furs—what are they to my house? No, it was for the promise—the promise of Penn—that this land should be an habitation and a refuge, not only for the Gentiles. Well, we know Christian promises. But so far, it has been kept. Are you spat upon in the street here, Scholar of the Law?"

"No," said Jacob. "They call me Jew, now and then. But the Friends, though Gentile, are kind."

"It is not so in all countries," said Raphael Sanchez, with a terrible smile.

"No," said Jacob quietly, "it is not."

The old man nodded. "Yes, one does not forget that," he

8

Jacob and the Indians

said. "The spittle wipes off the cloth, but one does not forget. One does not forget the persecutor or the persecuted. That is why they think me mad, in the Congregation Mikveh Israel, when I speak what is in my mind. For, look you"—and he pulled a map from a drawer—"here is what we know of these colonies, and here and here our people make a new beginning, in another air. But here is New France—see it?—and down the great river come the French traders and their Indians."

"Well?" said Jacob in puzzlement.

"Well?" said Raphael Sanchez. "Are you blind? I do not trust the King of France—the king before him drove out the Huguenots, and who knows what he may do? And if they hold the great rivers against us, we shall never go westward."

"We?" said Jacob in bewilderment.

"We," said Raphael Sanchez. He struck his hand on the map. "Oh, they cannot see it in Europe—not even their lords in parliament and their ministers of state," he said. "They think this is a mine, to be worked as the Spaniards worked Potosi, but it is not a mine. It is something beginning to live, and it is faceless and nameless yet. But it is our lot to be part of it—remember that in the wilderness, my young scholar of the Law. You think you are going there for a girl's face, and that is well enough. But you may find something there you did not expect to find."

He paused and his eyes had a different look.

"You see, it is the trader first," he said. "Always the trader, before the settled man. The Gentiles will forget that, and some of our own folk too. But one pays for the land of Canaan; one pays in blood and sweat."

Then he told Jacob what he would do for him and dismissed him, and Jacob went home to his room with his head buzzing strangely. For at times it seemed to him that the Congregation Mikveh Israel was right in thinking Raphael Sanchez half mad. And at other times it seemed to him that the old man's words were a veil, and behind them moved and stirred some huge and unguessed shape. But chiefly he thought of the rosy cheeks of Miriam Ettelsohn.

It was with the Scotchman, McCampbell, that Jacob made his first trading journey. A strange man was McCampbell, with grim features and cold blue eyes, but strong and kindly, though silent, except when he talked of the Ten Lost Tribes of Israel.

9

Stephen Vincent Benét

For it was his contention that they were the Indians beyond the Western Mountains, and on this subject he would talk endlessly. Indeed, they had much profitable conversation, McCampbell quoting the doctrines of a rabbi called John Calvin, and our grandfather's grandfather replying with Talmud and Torah till McCampbell would almost weep that such a honey-mouthed scholar should be destined to eternal damnation. Yet he did not treat our grandfather's grandfather as one destined to eternal damnation, but as a man, and he, too, spoke of cities of refuge as a man speaks of realities, for his people had also been persecuted.

First they left the city behind them, and then the outlying towns and, soon enough, they were in the wilderness. It was very strange to Jacob Stein. At first he would wake at night and lie awake listening, while his heart pounded, and each rustle in the forest was the step of a wild Indian, and each screech of an owl in the forest the whoop before the attack. But gradually this passed. He began to notice how silently the big man, McCampbell, moved in the woods; he began to imitate him. He began to learn many things that even a scholar of the Law, for all his wisdom, does not know—the girthing of a packsaddle and the making of fires, the look of dawn in the forest and the look of evening. It was all very new to him, and sometimes he thought he would die of it, for his flesh weakened. Yet always he kept on.

When he saw his first Indians—in the woods, not in the town —his knees knocked together. They were there as he had dreamt of them in dreams, and he thought of the spirit, Iggereth-beth-Mathlan, and her seventy-eight dancing demons, for they were painted and in skins. But he could not let his knees knock together, before heathens and a Gentile, and the first fear passed. Then he found they were grave men, very ceremonious and silent at first, and then when the silence had been broken, full of curiosity. They knew McCampbell, but him they did not know, and they discussed him and his garments with the frankness of children, till Jacob felt naked before them, and yet not afraid. One of them pointed to the bag that hung at Jacob's neck—the bag in which, for safety's sake, he carried his phylactery—then McCampbell said something and the brown hand dropped quickly, but there was a buzz of talk.

Later on, McCampbell explained to him that they, too, wore

10

Jacob and the Indians

little bags of deerskin and inside them sacred objects—and they thought, seeing his, that he must be a person of some note. It made him wonder. It made him wonder more to eat deer meat with them, by a fire.

It was a green world and a dark one that he had fallen in—dark with the shadow of the forest, green with its green. Through it ran trails and paths that were not yet roads or highways—that did not have the dust and smell of the cities of men, but another scent, another look. These paths Jacob noted carefully, making a map, for that was one of the instructions of Raphael Sanchez. It seemed a great labor and difficult and for no purpose; yet, as he had promised, so he did. And as they sank deeper and deeper into the depths of the forest, and he saw pleasant streams and wide glades, untenanted but by the deer, strange thoughts came over him. It seemed to him that the Germany he had left was very small and crowded together; it seemed to him that he had not known there was so much width to the world.

Now and then he would dream back—dream back to the quiet fields around Rettelsheim and the red-brick houses of Philadelphia, to the stuffed fish and the raisin wine, the chanting in the *chedar* and the white twisted loaves of calm Sabbath, under the white cloth. They would seem very close for the moment, then they would seem very far away. He was eating deer's meat in a forest and sleeping beside embers in the open night. It was so that Israel must have slept in the wilderness. He had not thought of it as so, but it was so.

Now and then he would look at his hands—they seemed tougher and very brown, as if they did not belong to him any more. Now and then he would catch a glimpse of his own face, as he drank at a stream. He had a beard, but it was not the beard of a scholar—it was wild and black. Moreover, he was dressed in skins, now; it seemed strange to be dressed in skins at first, and then not strange.

Now all this time, when he went to sleep at night, he would think of Miriam Ettelsohn. But, queerly enough, the harder he tried to summon up her face in his thoughts, the vaguer it became.

He lost track of time—there was only his map and the trading and the journey. Now it seemed to him that they should surely turn back, for their packs were full. He spoke of it to McCamp-

Stephen Vincent Benét

bell, but McCampbell shook his head. There was a light in the Scotchman's eyes now—a light that seemed strange to our grandfather's grandfather—and he would pray long at night, sometimes too loudly. So they came to the banks of the great river, brown and great, and saw it, and the country beyond it, like a view across Jordan. There was no end to that country—it stretched to the limits of the sky and Jacob saw it with his eyes. He was almost afraid at first, and then he was not afraid.

It was there that the strong man, McCampbell, fell sick, and there that he died and was buried. Jacob buried him on a bluff overlooking the river and faced the grave to the west. In his death sickness, McCampbell raved of the Ten Lost Tribes again and swore they were just across the river and he would go to them. It took all Jacob's strength to hold him—if it had been at the beginning of the journey, he would not have had the strength. Then he turned back, for he, too, had seen a Promised Land, not for his seed only, but for nations yet to come.

Nevertheless, he was taken by the Shawnees, in a season of bitter cold, with his last horse dead. At first, when misfortune began to fall upon him, he had wept for the loss of the horses and the good beaver. But, when the Shawnees took him, he no longer wept; for it seemed to him that he was no longer himself, but a man he did not know.

He was not concerned when they tied him to the stake and piled the wood around him, for it seemed to him still that it must be happening to another man. Nevertheless he prayed, as was fitting, chanting loudly; for Zion in the wilderness he prayed. He could smell the smell of the *chedar* and hear the voices that he knew—Reb Moses and Reb Nathan, and through them the curious voice of Raphael Sanchez, speaking in riddles. Then the smoke took him and he coughed. His throat was hot. He called for drink, and though they could not understand his words, all men know the sign of thirst, and they brought him a bowl filled. He put it to his lips eagerly and drank, but the stuff in the bowl was scorching hot and burned his mouth. Very angry then was our grandfather's grandfather, and without so much as a cry he took the bowl in both hands and flung it straight in the face of the man who had brought it, scalding him. Then there was a cry and a murmur from the Shawnees and, after some moments, he felt himself unbound and knew that he lived.

12

Jacob and the Indians

It was flinging the bowl at the man while yet he stood at the stake that saved him, for there is an etiquette about such matters. One does not burn a madman, among the Indians; and to the Shawnees, Jacob's flinging the bowl proved that he was mad, for a sane man would not have done so. Or so it was explained to him later, though he was never quite sure that they had not been playing cat-and-mouse with him, to test him. Also they were much concerned by his chanting his death song in an unknown tongue and by the phylactery that he had taken from its bag and bound upon brow and arm for his death hour, for these they thought strong medicine and uncertain. But in any case they released him, though they would not give him back his beaver, and that winter he passed in the lodges of the Shawnees, treated sometimes like a servant and sometimes like a guest, but always on the edge of peril. For he was strange to them, and they could not quite make up their minds about him, though the man with the scalded face had his own opinion, as Jacob could see.

Yet when the winter was milder and the hunting better than it had been in some seasons, it was he who got the credit of it, and the holy phylactery also; and by the end of the winter he was talking to them of trade, though diffidently at first. Ah, our grandfather's grandfather, *selig*, what woes he had! And yet it was not all woe, for he learned much woodcraft from the Shawnees and began to speak in their tongue.

Yet he did not trust them entirely; and when spring came and he could travel, he escaped. He was no longer a scholar then, but a hunter. He tried to think what day it was by the calendar, but he could only remember the Bee Moon and the Berry Moon. Yet when he thought of a feast he tried to keep it, and always he prayed for Zion. But when he thought of Zion, it was not as he had thought of it before—a white city set on a hill—but a great and open landscape, ready for nations. He could not have said why his thought had changed, but it had.

I shall not tell all, for who knows all? I shall not tell of the trading post he found deserted and the hundred and forty French louis in the dead man's money belt. I shall not tell of the half-grown boy, McGillvray, that he found on the fringes of settle-ment—the boy who was to be his partner in the days to come—and how they traded again with the Shawnees and got much beaver. Only this remains to be told, for this is true.

13

It was a long time since he had even thought of Meyer Kappel-huist—the big pushing man with red hairs on the backs of his hands. But now they were turning back toward Philadelphia, he and McGillvray, their packhorses and their beaver; and as the paths began to grow familiar, old thoughts came into his mind. Moreover, he would hear now and then, in the outposts of the wilderness, of a red-haired trader. So when he met the man himself, not thirty miles from Lancaster, he was not surprised.

Now, Meyer Kappelhuist had always seemed a big man to our grandfather's grandfather. But he did not seem such a big man, met in the wilderness by chance, and at that Jacob was amazed. Yet the greater surprise was Meyer Kappelhuist's, for he stared at our grandfather's grandfather long and puzzledly before he cried out, "But it's the little scholar!" and clapped his hand on his knee. Then they greeted each other civilly and Meyer Kappelhuist drank liquor because of the meeting, but Jacob drank nothing. For, all the time, they were talking, he could see Meyer Kappelhuist's eyes fixed greedily upon his packs of beaver, and he did not like that. Nor did he like the looks of the three tame Indians who traveled with Meyer Kappelhuist and, though he was a man of peace, he kept his hand on his arms, and the boy, McGillvray, did the same.

Meyer Kappelhuist was anxious that they should travel on together, but Jacob refused, for, as I say, he did not like the look in the red-haired man's eyes. So he said he was taking another road and left it at that.

"And the news you have of Simon Ettelsohn and his family—it is good, no doubt, for I know you are close to them," said Jacob, before they parted.

"Close to them?" said Meyer Kappelhuist, and he looked black as thunder. Then he laughed a forced laugh. "Oh, I see them no more," he said. "The old rascal has promised his daughter to a cousin of the Seixas, a greeny, just come over, but rich, they say. But to tell you the truth, I think we are well out of it, Scholar —she was always a little too skinny for my taste," and he laughed coarsely.

"She was a rose of Sharon and a lily of the valley," said Jacob respectfully, and yet not with the pang he would have expected at such news, though it made him more determined than ever not to travel with Meyer Kappelhuist. And with that they parted

14

and Meyer Kappelhuist went his way. Then Jacob took a fork in the trail that McGillvray knew of and that was as well for him. For when he got to Lancaster, there was news of the killing of a trader by the Indians who traveled with him; and when Jacob asked for details, they showed him something dried on a willow hoop. Jacob looked at the thing and saw the hairs upon it were red.

"Sculped all right, but we got it back," said the frontiersman, with satisfaction. "The red devil had it on him when we caught him. Should have buried it, too, I guess, but we'd buried him already and it didn't seem feasible. Thought I might take it to Philadelphy, sometime—might make an impression on the governor. Say, if you're going there, you might—after all, that's where he come from. Be a sort of memento to his folks."

"And it might have been mine, if I had traveled with him," said Jacob. He stared at the thing again, and his heart rose against touching it. Yet it was well the city people should know what happened to men in the wilderness, and the price of blood. "Yes, I will take it," he said.

Jacob stood before the door of Raphael Sanchez, in Philadelphia. He knocked at the door with his knuckles, and the old man himself peered out at him.

"And what is your business with me, Frontiersman?" said the old man, peering.

"The price of blood for a country," said Jacob Stein. He did not raise his voice, but there was a note in it that had not been there when he first knocked at Raphael Sanchez's door.

The old man stared at him soberly. "Enter, my son," he said at last, and Jacob touched the scroll by the doorpost and went in.

He walked through the halls as a man walks in a dream. At last he was sitting by the dark mahogany table. There was nothing changed in the room—he wondered greatly that nothing in it had changed.

"And what have you seen, my son?" said Raphael Sanchez.

"I have seen the land of Canaan, flowing with milk and honey," said Jacob, Scholar of the Law. "I have brought back grapes from Eshcol, and other things that are terrible to behold," he cried, and even as he cried he felt the sob rise in his throat. He choked it down. "Also there are eighteen packs of prime beaver at the warehouse and a boy named McGillvray, a Gentile, but very trusty," he said. "The beaver is very good and the boy under my protection. And McCampbell died by the great river, but he had seen the land and I think he rests well. The map is not made as I would have it, but it shows new things. And we must trade with the Shawnees. There are three posts to be established —I have marked them on the map—and later, more. And beyond the great river there is country that stretches to the end of the world. That is where my friend McCampbell lies, with his face turned west. But what is the use of talking? You would not understand."

He put his head on his arms, for the room was too quiet and peaceful, and he was very tired. Raphael Sanchez moved around the table and touched him on the shoulder.

"Did I not say, my son, that there was more than a girl's face to be found in the wilderness?" he said.

"A girl's face?" said Jacob. "Why, she is to be married and, I hope, will be happy, for she was a rose of Sharon. But what are girls' faces beside this?" and he flung something on the table. It rattled dryly on the table, like a cast snakeskin, but the hairs upon it were red.

"It was Meyer Kappelhuist," said Jacob childishly, "and he was a strong man. And I am not strong, but a scholar. But I have seen what I have seen. And we must say Kaddish for him."

"Yes, yes," said Raphael Sanchez. "It will be done. I will see to it."

"But you do not understand," said Jacob. "I have eaten deer's meat in the wilderness and forgotten the month and the year. I have been a servant to the heathen and held the scalp of my enemy in my hand. I will never be the same man."

"Oh, you will be the same," said Sanchez. "And no worse a scholar, perhaps. But this is a new country."

"It must be for all," said Jacob. "For my friend McCampbell died also, and he was a Gentile."

"Let us hope," said Raphael Sanchez and touched him again upon the shoulder. Then Jacob lifted his head and he saw that the light had declined and the evening was upon him. And even as he looked, Raphael Sanchez's granddaughter came in to light the candles for Sabbath. And Jacob looked upon her, and she was a dove, with dove's eyes.

A TOOTH FOR PAUL REVERE

Some say it all happened because of Hancock and Adams (said the old man, pulling at his pipe), and some put it back to the Stamp Act and before. Then there's some hold out for Paul Revere and his little silver box. But the way I heard it, it broke loose because of Lige Butterwick and his tooth.

What's that? Why, the American Revolution, of course. What else would I be talking about? Well, your story about the land down South that they had to plough with alligators reminded me.

No, this is a true story—or at least that's how I heard it told. My great-aunt was a Butterwick and I heard it from her. And, every now and then, she'd write it out and want to get it put in the history books. But they'd always put her off with some trifling sort of excuse. Till, finally, she got her dander up and wrote direct to the President of the United States. Well, no, he didn't answer himself exactly—the President's apt to be a pretty busy man. But the letter said he'd received her interesting communication and thanked her for it, so that shows you. We've got it framed, in the trailer—the ink's a little faded, but you can make out the man's name who signed it. It's either Bowers or Thorpe and he wrote a very nice hand.

You see, my great-aunt, she wasn't very respectful to the kind of history that does get into the books. What she liked was the queer corners of it and the tales that get handed down in families. Take Paul Revere, for instance—all most folks think about, with him, is his riding a horse. But when she talked about Paul Revere —why, you could just see him in his shop, brewing the American Revolution in a silver teapot and waiting for it to settle. Oh yes, he was a silversmith by trade—but she claimed he was something more. She claimed there was a kind of magic in that quick, skillful hand of his—and that he was one of the kind of folks that can see just a little bit farther into a millstone than most. But it was when she got to Lige Butterwick that she really turned herself loose.

For she claimed that it took all sorts to make a country—and that meant the dumb ones, too. I don't mean ijits or nincompoops —just the ordinary folks that live along from day to day. And

17

that day may be a notable day in history—but it's just Tuesday to them, till they read all about it in the papers. Oh, the heroes and the great men—they can plan and contrive and see ahead. But it isn't till the Lige Butterwicks get stirred up that things really start to happen. Or so she claimed. And the way that they do get stirred up is often curious, as she'd tell this story to prove.

For, now you take Lige Butterwick—and, before his tooth started aching, he was just like you and me. He lived on a farm about eight miles from Lexington, Massachusetts, and he was a peaceable man. It was troubled times in the American colonies, what with British warships in Boston Harbor and British soldiers in Boston and Sons of Liberty hooting the British soldiers—not to speak of Boston tea parties and such. But Lige Butterwick, he worked his farm and didn't pay much attention. There's lots of people like that, even in troubled times.

When he went into town, to be sure, there was high talk at the tavern. But he bought his goods and came home again—he had ideas about politics, but he didn't talk about them much. He had a good farm and it kept him busy—he had a wife and five children and they kept him humping. The young folks could argue about King George and Sam Adams—he wondered how the corn was going to stand that year. Now and then, if somebody said that this and that was a burning shame, he'd allow as how it might be, just to be neighborly. But, inside, he was wondering whether next year he mightn't make an experiment and plant the west field in rye.

Well, everything went along for him the way that it does for most folks with good years and bad years, till one April morning, in 1775, he woke up with a toothache. Being the kind of man he was, he didn't pay much attention to it at first. But he mentioned it that evening, at supper, and his wife got a bag of hot salt for him. He held it to his face and it seemed to ease him, but he couldn't hold it there all night, and, next morning, the tooth hurt worse than ever.

Well, he stood it the next day and the next, but it didn't improve any. He tried tansy tea and other remedies—he tried tying a string to it and having his wife slam the door. But, when it came to the pinch, he couldn't quite do it. So, finally, he took the horse and rode into Lexington town to have it seen to. Mrs. Butterwick made him—she said it might be an expense, but any-

A Tooth for Paul Revere

thing was better than having him act as if he wanted to kick the cat across tne room every time she put her feet down hard.

When he got into Lexington, he noticed that folks there seemed kind of excited. There was a lot of talk about muskets and powder and a couple of men called Hancock and Adams who were staying at Parson Clarke's. But Lige Butterwick had his own business to attend to—and, besides, his tooth was jumping so he wasn't in any mood for conversation. He set off for the local barber's, as being the likeliest man he knew to pull a tooth.

The barber took one look at it and shook his head.

"I can pull her, Lige," he said. "Oh, I can pull her, all right. But she's got long roots and strong roots and she's going to leave an awful gap when she's gone. Now, what you really need," he said, kind of excited, for he was one of those perky little men who's always interested in the latest notion, "what you really need—though it's taking away my business—is one of these-here artificial teeth to go in the hole."

"Artificial teeth!" said Lige. "It's flying in the face of Nature!"

The barber shook his head. "No, Lige," he said, "that's where you're wrong. Artificial teeth is all the go these days, and Lexington ought to keep up with the times. It would do me good to see you with an artificial tooth—it would so."

"Well, it might do *you* good," said Lige, rather crossly, for his tooth was jumping, "but, supposing I did want one—how in tunket will I get one in Lexington?"

"Now you just leave that to me," said the barber, all excited, and he started to rummage around. "You'll have to go to Boston for it, but I know just the man." He was one of those men who can always tell you where to go and it's usually wrong. "See here," he went on. "There's a fellow called Revere in Boston that fixes them and they say he's a boss workman. Just take a look at this prospectus"—and he started to read from a paper: " 'Whereas many persons are so unfortunate as to lose their fore-teeth'—that's you, Lige—'to their great detriment, not only in looks but in speaking, both in public and private, this is to inform all such that they may have them replaced by artificial ones'—see? —'that look as well as the natural and answer the end of speaking to all intents'—and then he's got his name—Paul Revere, gold-smith, near the head of Dr. Clarke's wharf, Boston."

"Sounds well enough," said Lige, "but what's it going to cost?"

"Oh, I know Revere," said the barber, swelling up like a robin. "Comes through here pretty often, as a matter of fact. And he's a decent fellow, if he is a pretty big bug in the Sons of Liberty. You just mention my name."

"Well, it's something I hadn't thought of," said Lige, as his tooth gave another red-hot jounce, "but in for a penny, in for a pound. I've missed a day's work already and that tooth's got to come out before I go stark, staring mad. But what sort of man is this Revere, anyway?"

"Oh, he's a regular wizard!" said the barber. "A regular wizard with his tools."

"Wizard!" said Lige. "Well, I don't know about wizards. But if he can fix my tooth I'll call him one."

"You'll never regret it," said the barber—and that's the way folks always talk when they're sending someone else to the dentist. So Lige Butterwick got on his horse again and started out for Boston. A couple of people shouted at him as he rode down the street, but he didn't pay any attention. And, going by Parson Clarke's, he caught a glimpse of two men talking in the Parson's front room. One was a tallish, handsomish man in pretty fine clothes and the other was shorter and untidy, with a kind of bulldog face. But they were strangers to him and he didn't really notice them—just rode ahead.

II

But as soon as he got into Boston he started to feel queer—and it wasn't only his tooth. He hadn't been there in four years and he'd expected to find it changed, but it wasn't that. It was a clear enough day and yet he kept feeling there was thunder in the air. There'd be knots of people, talking and arguing, on street corners, and then, when you got closer to them, they'd kind of melt away. Or, if they stayed, they'd look at you, out of the corners of their eyes. And there, in the Port of Boston, were the British warships, black and grim. He'd known they'd be there, of course, but it was different, seeing them. It made him feel queer to see their guns pointed at the town. He'd known there was trouble and dispute, in Boston, but the knowledge had passed over him like rain and hail. But now here he was in

A Tooth for Paul Revere

the middle of it—and it smelt like earthquake weather. He couldn't make head or tail of it, but he wanted to be home.

All the same, he'd come to get his tooth fixed, and, being New England, he was bound to do it. But first he stopped at a tavern for a bite and a sup, for it was long past his dinnertime. And there, it seemed to him, things got even more curious.

"Nice weather we're having, these days," he said, in a friendly way, to the barkeep.

"It's bitter weather for Boston," said the barkeep, in an unfriendly voice, and a sort of low growl went up from the boys at the back of the room and every eye fixed on Lige.

Well, that didn't help the toothache any, but, being a sociable person, Lige kept on.

"May be, for Boston," he said, "but out in the country we'd call it good planting weather."

The barkeep stared at him hard.

"I guess I was mistaken in you," he said. "It *is* good planting weather—for some kinds of trees."

"And what kind of trees were you thinking of?" said a sharp-faced man at Lige's left and squeezed his shoulder.

"There's trees and trees, you know," said a red-faced man at Lige's right, and gave him a dig in the ribs.

"Well, now that you ask me—" said Lige, but he couldn't even finish before the red-faced man dug him hard in the ribs again.

"The liberty tree!" said the red-faced man. "And may it soon be watered in the blood of tyrants!"

"The royal oak of England!" said the sharp-faced man. "And God save King George and loyalty!"

Well, with that it seemed to Lige Butterwick as if the whole tavern kind of riz up at him. He was kicked and pummeled and mauled and thrown into a corner and yanked out of it again, with the red-faced man and the sharp-faced man and all the rest of them dancing quadrilles over his prostrate form. Till, finally, he found himself out in the street with half his coat gone galley-west.

"Well," said Lige to himself, "I always heard city folks were crazy. But politics must be getting serious in these American colonies when they start fighting about trees!"

Then he saw the sharp-faced man was beside him, trying to

shake his hand. He noticed with some pleasure that the sharp-faced man had the beginnings of a beautiful black eye.

"Nobly done, friend," said the sharp-faced man, "and I'm glad to find another true-hearted loyalist in this pestilent, rebellious city."

"Well, I don't know as I quite agree with you about that," said Lige. "But I came here to get my tooth fixed, not to talk politics. And as long as you've spoken so pleasant, I wonder if you could help me out. You see, I'm from Lexington way—and I'm looking for a fellow named Paul Revere—"

"Paul Revere!" said the sharp-faced man, as if the name hit him like a bullet. Then he began to smile again—not a pleasant smile.

"Oh, it's Paul Revere you want, my worthy and ingenuous friend from the country," he said. "Well, I'll tell you how to find him. You go up to the first British soldier you see and ask the way. But you better give the password first."

"Password?" said Lige Butterwick, scratching his ear.

"Yes," said the sharp-faced man, and his smile got wider. "You say to that British soldier, 'Any lobsters for sale today?' Then you ask about Revere."

"But why do I talk about lobsters first?" said Lige Butterwick, kind of stubborn.

"Well, you see," said the sharp-faced man, "the British soldiers wear red coats. So they like being asked about lobsters. Try it and see." And he went away, with his shoulders shaking.

Well, that seemed queer to Lige Butterwick, but no queerer than the other things that had happened that day. All the same, he didn't quite trust the sharp-faced man, so he took care not to come too close to the British patrol when he asked them about the lobsters. And it was lucky he did, for no sooner were the words out of his mouth than the British soldiers took after him and chased him clear down to the wharves before he could get away. At that, he only managed it by hiding in an empty tar-barrel, and when he got out he was certainly a sight for sore eyes.

"Well, I guess that couldn't have been the right password," he said to himself, kind of grimly, as he tried to rub off some of the tar. "All the same, I don't think soldiers ought to act like that when you ask them a civil question. But, city folks or soldiers, they can't make a fool out of me. I came here to get my tooth fixed and get it fixed I will, if I have to surprise the whole British Empire to do it."

And just then he saw a sign on a shop at the end of the wharf. And, according to my great-aunt, this was what was on the sign. It said "PAUL REVERE, SILVERSMITH" at the top, and then, under it, in smaller letters, "Large and small bells cast to order, engraving and printing done in job lots, artificial teeth sculptured and copper boilers mended, all branches of goldsmith and silversmith work and revolutions put up to take out. Express Service, Tuesdays and Fridays, to Lexington, Concord and Points West."

"Well," said Lige Butterwick, "kind of a Jack-of-all-trades. Now maybe I can get my tooth fixed." And he marched up to the door.

III

Paul Revere was behind the counter when Lige came in, turning a silver bowl over and over in his hands. A man of forty-odd he was, with a quick, keen face and snapping eyes. He was wearing Boston clothes, but there was a French look about him—for his father was Apollos Rivoire from the island of Guernsey, and good French Huguenot stock. They'd changed the name to Revere when they crossed the water.

It wasn't such a big shop, but it had silver pieces in it that people have paid thousands for, since. And the silver pieces weren't all. There were prints and engravings of the Port of Boston and caricatures of the British and all sorts of goldsmith work, more than you could put a name to. It was a crowded place, but shipshape. And Paul Revere moved about it, quick and keen, with his eyes full of life and hot temper—the kind of man who knows what he wants to do and does it the next minute.

There were quite a few customers there when Lige Butterwick first came in—so he sort of scrooged back in a corner and waited his chance. For one thing, after the queer sign and the barber's calling him a wizard, he wanted to be sure about this fellow, Revere, and see what kind of customers came to his shop.

Well, there was a woman who wanted a christening mug for a baby and a man who wanted a print of the Boston Massacre. And then there was a fellow who passed Revere some sort of message, under cover—Lige caught the whisper, "powder" and

23

Stephen Vincent Benét

"Sons of Liberty," though he couldn't make out the rest. And, finally, there was a very fine silk-dressed lady who seemed to be giving Revere considerable trouble. Lige peeked at her round the corner of his chair, and, somehow or other, she reminded him of a turkey-gobbler, especially the strut.

She was complaining about some silver that Paul Revere had made for her—expensive silver it must have been. And "Oh, Master Revere, I'm so disappointed!" she was saying. "When I took the things from the box, I could just have cried!"

Revere drew himself up a little at that, Lige noticed, but his voice was pleasant.

"It is I who am disappointed, madam," he said, with a little bow. "But what was the trouble? It must have been carelessly packed. Was it badly dented? I'll speak to my boy."

"Oh no, it wasn't dented," said the turkey-gobbler lady. "But I wanted a really impressive silver service—something I can use when the Governor comes to dinner with us. I certainly *paid* for the best. And what have you given me?"

Lige waited to hear what Paul Revere would say. When he spoke, his voice was stiff.

"I have given you the best work of which I am capable, madam," he said. "It was in my hands for six months—and I think they are skillful hands."

"Oh," said the woman, and rustled her skirts. "I know you're a competent artisan, Master Revere—"

"Silversmith, if you please—" said Paul Revere, and the woman rustled again.

"Well, I don't care what you call it," she said, and then you could see her fine accent was put on like her fine clothes. "But I know I wanted a real service—something I could show my friends. And what have you given me? Oh, it's silver, if you choose. But it's just as plain and simple as a picket fence!"

Revere looked at her for a moment and Lige Butterwick thought he'd explode.

"Simple?" he said. "And plain? You pay me high compliments, madam!"

"Compliments indeed!" said the woman, and now she was getting furious. "I'm sending it back tomorrow! Why, there isn't as much as a lion or a unicorn on the cream jug. And I told you I wanted the sugar bowl covered with silver grapes! But you've

24

A Tooth for Paul Revere

given me something as bare as the hills of New England! And I won't stand it, I tell you! I'll send to England instead."

Revere puffed his cheeks and blew, but his eyes were dangerous.

"Send away, madam," he said. "We're making new things in this country—new men—new silver—perhaps, who knows, a new nation. Plain, simple, bare as the hills and rocks of New England—graceful as the boughs of her elm trees—if my silver were only like that indeed! But that is what I wish to make it. And, as for you, madam,"—he stepped toward her like a cat,—"with your lions and unicorns and grape leaves and your nonsense of bad ornament done by bad silversmiths—your imported bad taste and your imported British manners—puff!" And he blew at her, just the way you blow at a turkey-gobbler, till she fairly picked up her fine silk skirts and ran. Revere watched her out of the door and turned back, shaking his head.

"William!" he called to the boy who helped him in the shop. "Put up the shutters—we're closing for the day. And William—no word yet from Dr. Warren?"

"Not yet, sir," said the boy, and started to put up the shutters. Then Lige Butterwick thought it was about time to make his presence known.

So he coughed, and Paul Revere whirled and Lige Butterwick felt those quick, keen eyes boring into his. He wasn't exactly afraid of them, for he was stubborn himself, but he knew this was an unexpected kind of man.

"Well, my friend," said Revere, impatiently, "and who in the world are you?"

"Well, Mr. Revere," said Lige Butterwick. "It is Mr. Revere, isn't it? It's kind of a long story. But, closing or not, you've got to listen to me. The barber told me so."

"The barber!" said Revere, kind of dumbfounded.

"Uh-huh," said Lige, and opened his mouth. "You see, it's my tooth."

"Tooth!" said Revere, and stared at him as if they were both crazy. "You'd better begin at the beginning. But wait a minute. You don't talk like a Boston man. Where do you come from?"

"Oh, around Lexington way," said Lige. "And, you see—"

But the mention of Lexington seemed to throw Revere into a regular excitement. He fairly shook Lige by the shoulders.

25

"Lexington!" he said. "Were you there this morning?"

"Of course I was," said Lige. "That's where the barber I told you about—"

"Never mind the barber!" said Revere. "Were Mr. Hancock and Mr. Adams still at Parson Clarke's?"

"Well, they might have been, for all I know," said Lige. "But I couldn't say."

"Great heaven!" said Revere. "Is there a man in the American colonies who doesn't know Mr. Hancock and Mr. Adams?"

"There seems to be me," said Lige. "But, speaking of strangers —there *was* two of them staying at the parsonage, when I rode past. One was a handsomish man and the other looked more like a bulldog—"

"Hancock and Adams!" said Revere. "So they are still there." He took a turn or two up and down the room. "And the British ready to march!" he muttered to himself. "Did you see many soldiers as you came to my shop, Mr. Butterwick?"

"See them?" said Lige. "They chased me into a tar-barrel. And there was a whole passel of them up by the Common with guns and flags. Looked as if they meant business."

Revere took his hand and pumped it up and down.

"Thank you, Mr. Butterwick," he said. "You're a shrewd observer. And you have done me—and the colonies—an invaluable service."

"Well, that's nice to know," said Lige. "But, speaking about this tooth of mine—"

Revere looked at him and laughed, while his eyes crinkled.

"You're a stubborn man, Mr. Butterwick," he said. "All the better. I like stubborn men. I wish we had more of them. Well, one good turn deserves another—you've helped me and I'll do my best to help you. I've made artificial teeth—but drawing them is hardly my trade. All the same, I'll do what I can for you."

So Lige sat down in a chair and opened his mouth.

"Whew!" said Revere, with his eyes dancing. His voice grew solemn. "Mr. Butterwick," he said, "it seems to be a compound, agglutinated infraction of the upper molar. I'm afraid I can't do anything about it tonight."

"But—" said Lige.

"But here's a draught—that will ease the pain for a while,"

A Tooth for Paul Revere

said Revere, and poured some medicine into a cup. "Drink!" he said, and Lige drank. The draught was red and spicy, with a queer, sleepy taste, but pungent. It wasn't like anything Lige had ever tasted before, but he noticed it eased the pain.

"There," said Revere. "And now you go to a tavern and get a good night's rest. Come back to see me in the morning—I'll find a tooth-drawer for you, if I'm here. And—oh yes—you'd better have some liniment."

He started to rummage in a big cupboard at the back of the shop. It was dark now, with the end of day and the shutters up, and whether it was the tooth, or the tiredness, or the draught Paul Revere had given him, Lige began to feel a little queer. There was a humming in his head and a lightness in his feet. He got up and stood looking over Paul Revere's shoulder, and it seemed to him that things moved and scampered in that cupboard in a curious way, as Revere's quick fingers took down this box and that. And the shop was full of shadows and murmurings.

"It's a queer kind of shop you've got here, Mr. Revere," he said, glad to hear the sound of his own voice.

"Well, some people think so," said Revere—and that time Lige was almost sure he saw something move in the cupboard. He coughed. "Say—what's in that little bottle?" he said, to keep his mind steady.

"That?" said Paul Revere, with a smile, and held the bottle up. "Oh, that's a little chemical experiment of mine. I call it Essence of Boston. But there's a good deal of East Wind in it."

"Essence of Boston," said Lige, with his eyes bulging. "Well, they did say you was a wizard. It's gen-u-wine magic, I suppose?"

"Genuine magic, of course," said Revere, with a chuckle. "And here's the box with your liniment. And here—"

He took down two little boxes—a silver and a pewter one—and placed them on the counter. But Lige's eyes went to the silver one—they were drawn to it, though he couldn't have told you why.

"Pick it up," said Paul Revere, and Lige did so and turned it in his hands. It was a handsome box. He could make out a growing tree and an eagle fighting a lion. "It's mighty pretty work," he said.

27

"It's my own design," said Paul Revere. "See the stars around the edge—thirteen of them? You could make a very pretty design with stars—for a new country, say—if you wanted to—I've sometimes thought of it."

"But what's in it?" said Lige.

"What's in it?" said Paul Revere, and his voice was light but steely. "Why, what's in the air around us? Gunpowder and war and the making of a new nation. But the time isn't quite ripe yet —not quite ripe."

"You mean," said Lige, and he looked at the box very respectful, "that this-here revolution folks keep talking about—"

"Yes," said Paul Revere, and he was about to go on. But just then his boy ran in, with a letter in his hand.

"Master!" he said. "A message from Dr. Warren!"

IV

Well, with that Revere started moving, and, when he started to move, he moved fast. He was calling for his riding boots in one breath and telling Lige Butterwick to come back tomorrow in another—and, what with all the bustle and confusion, Lige Butterwick nearly went off without his liniment after all. But he grabbed up a box from the counter, just as Revere was practically shoving him out of the door—and it wasn't till he'd got to his tavern and gone to bed for the night that he found out he'd taken the wrong box.

He found it out then because, when he went to bed, he couldn't get to sleep. It wasn't his tooth that bothered him—that had settled to a kind of dull ache and he could have slept through that. But his mind kept going over all the events of the day— the two folks he'd seen at Parson Clarke's and being chased by the British and what Revere had said to the turkey-gobbler woman—till he couldn't get any peace. He could feel something stirring in him, though he didn't know what it was.

" 'Tain't right to have soldiers chase a fellow down the street," he said to himself. "And 'tain't right to have people like that woman run down New England. No, it ain't. Oh me—I better look for that liniment of Mr. Revere's."

So he got up from his bed and went over and found his coat.

28

A Tooth for Paul Revere

Then he reached his hand in the pocket and pulled out the silver box.

Well, at first he was so flustrated that he didn't know rightly what to do. For here, as well as he could remember it, was gunpowder and war and the makings of a new nation—the revolution itself, shut up in a silver box by Paul Revere. He mightn't have believed there could be such things before he came to Boston. But now he did.

The draught was still humming in his head, and his legs felt a mite wobbly. But, being human, he was curious. "Now, I wonder what *is* inside that box," he said.

He shook the box and handled it, but that seemed to make it warmer, as if there was something alive inside it, so he stopped that mighty quick. Then he looked all over it for a keyhole, but there wasn't any keyhole, and, if there had been, he didn't have a key.

Then he put his ear to the box and listened hard. And it seemed to him that he heard, very tiny and far away, inside the box, the rolling fire of thousands of tiny muskets and the tiny, faraway cheers of many men. "Hold your fire!" he heard a voice say. "Don't fire till you're fired on—but, if they want a war, let it begin here!" And then there was a rolling of drums and a squeal of fifes. It was small, still, and far away, but it made him shake all over, for he knew he was listening to something in the future —and something that he didn't have a right to hear. He sat down on the edge of his bed, with the box in his hands.

"Now, what am I going to do with this?" he said. "It's too big a job for one man."

Well, he thought, kind of scared, of going down to the river and throwing the box in, but, when he thought of doing it, he knew he couldn't. Then he thought of his farm near Lexington and the peaceful days. Once the revolution was out of the box, there'd be an end to that. But then he remembered what Revere had said when he was talking with the woman about the silver— the thing about building a new country and building it clean and plain. "Why, I'm not a Britisher," he thought. "I'm a New Englander. And maybe there's something beyond that—something people like Hancock and Adams know about. And, if it has to come with a revolution—well, I guess it has to come. We can't stay Britishers forever, here in this country."

29

He listened to the box again, and now there wasn't any shooting in it—just a queer tune played on a fife. He didn't know the
name of the tune, but it lifted his heart.

He got up, sort of slow and heavy. "I guess I'll have to take
this back to Paul Revere," he said.

Well, the first place he went was Dr. Warren's, having heard
Revere mention it, but he didn't get much satisfaction there. It
took quite a while to convince them that he wasn't a spy, and,
when he did, all they'd tell him was that Revere had gone over
the river to Charlestown. So he went down to the waterfront
to look for a boat. And the first person he met was a very angry
woman.

"No," she said, "you don't get any boats from me. There was
a crazy man along here an hour ago and he wanted a boat, too,
and my husband was crazy enough to take him. And then, do you
know what he did?"

"No, mam," said Lige Butterwick.

"He made my husband take my best petticoat to muffle the
oars so they wouldn't make a splash when they went past that
Britisher ship," she said, pointing out where the man-of-war
Somerset lay at anchor. "My best petticoat, I tell you! And when
my husband comes back he'll get a piece of my mind!"

"Was his name Revere?" said Lige Butterwick. "Was he a
man of forty-odd, keen-looking and kind of Frenchy?"

"I don't know what his right name is," said the woman, "but
his name's mud with me. My best petticoat tore into strips and
swimming in that nasty river!" And that was all he could get
out of her.

All the same, he managed to get a boat at last—the story doesn't
say how—and row across the river. The tide was at young flood
and the moonlight bright on the water, and he passed under the
shadow of the *Somerset*, right where Revere had passed. When
he got to the Charlestown side, he could see the lanterns in
North Church, though he didn't know what they signified. Then
he told the folks at Charlestown he had news for Revere and
they got him a horse and so he started to ride. And, all the while,
the silver box was burning his pocket.

Well, he lost his way more or less, as you well might in the
darkness, and it was dawn when he came into Lexington by a

side road. The dawn in that country's pretty, with the dew still on the grass. But he wasn't looking at the dawn. He was feeling the box burn his pocket and thinking hard.

Then, all of a sudden, he reined up his tired horse. For there, on the side road, were two men carrying a trunk—and one of them was Paul Revere.

They looked at each other and Lige began to grin. For Revere was just as dirty and mud-splashed as he was—he'd warned Hancock and Adams all right, but then, on his way to Concord, he'd got caught by the British and turned loose again. So he'd gone back to Lexington to see how things were there—and now he and the other fellow were saving a trunk of papers that Hancock had left behind, so they wouldn't fall into the hands of the British.

Lige swung off his horse. "Well, Mr. Revere," he said, "you see, I'm on time for that little appointment about my tooth. And, by the way, I've got something for you." He took the box from his pocket. And then he looked over toward Lexington Green and caught his breath. For, on the Green, there was a little line of Minute Men—neighbors of his, as he knew—and, in front of them, the British regulars. And, even as he looked, there was the sound of a gunshot, and, suddenly, smoke wrapped the front of the British line and he heard them shout as they ran forward.

Lige Butterwick took the silver box and stamped on it with his heel. And with that the box broke open—and there was a dazzle in his eyes for a moment and a noise of men shouting— and then it was gone.

"Do you know what you've done?" said Revere. "You've let out the American Revolution!"

"Well," said Lige Butterwick, "I guess it was about time. And I guess I'd better be going home, now. I've got a gun on the wall there. And I'll need it."

"But what about your tooth?" said Paul Revere.

"Oh, a tooth's a tooth," said Lige Butterwick. "But a country's a country. And, anyhow, it's stopped aching."

All the same, they say Paul Revere made a silver tooth for him, after the war. But my great-aunt wasn't quite sure of it, so I won't vouch for that.

31

THE DEVIL AND DANIEL WEBSTER

It's a story they tell in the border country, where Massachusetts joins Vermont and New Hampshire.

Yes, Dan'l Webster's dead—or, at least, they buried him. But every time there's a thunderstorm around Marshfield, they say you can hear his rolling voice in the hollows of the sky. And they say that if you go to his grave and speak loud and clear, "Dan'l Webster—Dan'l Webster!" the ground'll begin to shiver and the trees begin to shake. And after a while you'll hear a deep voice saying, "Neighbor, how stands the Union?" Then you better answer the Union stands as she stood, rock-bottomed and copper-sheathed, one and indivisible, or he's liable to rear right out of the ground. At least, that's what I was told when I was a youngster.

You see, for a while, he was the biggest man in the country. He never got to be President, but he was the biggest man. There were thousands that trusted in him right next to God Almighty, and they told stories about him that were like the stories of patriarchs and such. They said, when he stood up to speak, stars and stripes came right out in the sky, and once he spoke against a river and made it sink into the ground. They said, when he walked the woods with his fishing rod, Killall, the trout would jump out of the streams right into his pockets, for they knew it was no use putting up a fight against him; and, when he argued a case, he could turn on the harps of the blessed and the shaking of the earth underground. That was the kind of man he was, and his big farm up at Marshfield was suitable to him. The chickens he raised were all white meat down through the drumsticks, the cows were tended like children, and the big ram he called Goliath had horns with a curl like a morning-glory vine and could butt through an iron door. But Dan'l wasn't one of your gentlemen farmers; he knew all the ways of the land, and he'd be up by candlelight to see that the chores got done. A man with a mouth like a mastiff, a brow like a mountain and eyes like burning anthracite—that was Dan'l Webster in his prime. And the biggest case he argued never got written down in the books, for he argued it against the devil, nip and tuck and no holds barred. And this is the way I used to hear it told.

The Devil and Daniel Webster

There was a man named Jabez Stone, lived at Cross Corners, New Hampshire. He wasn't a bad man to start with, but he was an unlucky man. If he planted corn, he got borers; if he planted potatoes, he got blight. He had good-enough land, but it didn't prosper him; he had a decent wife and children, but the more children he had, the less there was to feed them. If stones cropped up in his neighbor's field, boulders boiled up in his; if he had a horse with the spavins, he'd trade it for one with the staggers and give something extra. There's some folks bound to be like that, apparently. But one day Jabez Stone got sick of the whole business.

He'd been plowing that morning and he'd just broke the plowshare on a rock that he could have sworn hadn't been there yesterday. And, as he stood looking at the plowshare, the off horse began to cough—that ropy kind of cough that means sickness and horse doctors. There were two children down with the measles, his wife was ailing, and he had a whitlow on his thumb. It was about the last straw for Jabez Stone. "I vow," he said, and he looked around him kind of desperate—"I vow it's enough to make a man want to sell his soul to the devil! And I would, too, for two cents!"

Then he felt a kind of queerness come over him at having said what he'd said; though, naturally, being a New Hampshireman, he wouldn't take it back. But, all the same, when it got to be evening and, as far as he could see, no notice had been taken, he felt relieved in his mind, for he was a religious man. But notice is always taken, sooner or later, just like the Good Book says. And, sure enough, next day, about suppertime, a softspoken, dark-dressed stranger drove up in a handsome buggy and asked for Jabez Stone.

Well, Jabez told his family it was a lawyer, come to see him about a legacy. But he knew who it was. He didn't like the looks of the stranger, nor the way he smiled with his teeth. They were white teeth, and plentiful—some say they were filed to a point, but I wouldn't vouch for that. And he didn't like it when the dog took one look at the stranger and ran away howling, with his tail between his legs. But having passed his word, more or less, he stuck to it, and they went out behind the barn and made their bargain. Jabez Stone had to prick his finger to sign, and the stranger lent him a silver pin. The wound healed clean, but it left a little white scar.

After that, all of a sudden, things began to pick up and prosper for Jabez Stone. His cows got fat and his horses sleek, his crops were the envy of the neighborhood, and lightning might strike all over the valley, but it wouldn't strike his barn. Pretty soon, he was one of the prosperous people of the county; they asked him to stand for selectman, and he stood for it; there began to be talk of running him for state senate. All in all, you might say the Stone family was as happy and contented as cats in a dairy. And so they were, except for Jabez Stone.

He'd been contented enough, the first few years. It's a great thing when bad luck turns; it drives most other things out of your head. True, every now and then, especially in rainy weather, the little white scar on his finger would give him a twinge. And once a year, punctual as clockwork, the stranger with the handsome buggy would come driving by. But the sixth year, the stranger lighted, and, after that, his peace was over for Jabez Stone.

The stranger came up through the lower field, switching his boots with a cane—they were handsome black boots, but Jabez Stone never liked the look of them, particularly the toes. And, after he'd passed the time of day, he said, "Well, Mr. Stone, you're a hummer! It's a very pretty property you've got here, Mr. Stone."

"Well, some might favor it and others might not," said Jabez Stone, for he was a New Hampshireman.

"Oh, no need to decry your industry!" said the stranger, very easy, showing his teeth in a smile. "After all, we know what's been done, and it's been according to contract and specifications. So when—ahem—the mortgage falls due next year, you shouldn't have any regrets."

"Speaking of that mortgage, mister," said Jabez Stone, and he looked around for help to the earth and the sky, "I'm beginning to have one or two doubts about it."

"Doubts?" said the stranger, not quite so pleasantly.

"Why, yes," said Jabez Stone. "This being the U.S.A. and me always having been a religious man." He cleared his throat and got bolder. "Yes, sir," he said, "I'm beginning to have considerable doubts as to that mortgage holding in court."

34

The Devil and Daniel Webster

"There's courts and courts," said the stranger, clicking his teeth. "Still, we might as well have a look at the original document." And he hauled out a big black pocketbook, full of papers. "Sherwin, Slater, Stevens, Stone," he muttered. "I, Jabez Stone, for a term of seven years—— Oh, it's quite in order, I think." But Jabez Stone wasn't listening, for he saw something else flutter out of the black pocketbook. It was something that looked like a moth, but it wasn't a moth. And as Jabez Stone stared at it, it seemed to speak to him in a small sort of piping voice, terrible small and thin, but terrible human. "Neighbor Stone!" it squeaked. "Neighbor Stone! Help me! For God's sake, help me!"

But before Jabez Stone could stir hand or foot, the stranger whipped out a big bandanna handkerchief, caught the creature in it, just like a butterfly, and started tying up the ends of the bandanna.

"Sorry for the interruption," he said. "As I was saying——"

But Jabez Stone was shaking all over like a scared horse.

"That's Miser Stevens' voice!" he said, in a croak. "And you've got him in your handkerchief!"

The stranger looked a little embarrassed.

"Yes, I really should have transferred him to the collecting box," he said with a simper, "but there were some rather unusual specimens there and I didn't want them crowded. Well, well, these little contretemps will occur."

"I don't know what you mean by contertan," said Jabez Stone, "but that was Miser Stevens' voice! And he ain't dead! You can't tell me he is! He was just as spry and mean as a woodchuck, Tuesday!"

"In the midst of life—" said the stranger, kind of pious. "Listen!" Then a bell began to toll in the valley and Jabez Stone listened, with the sweat running down his face. For he knew it was tolled for Miser Stevens and that he was dead.

"These long-standing accounts," said the stranger with a sigh; "one really hates to close them. But business is business."

He still had the bandanna in his hand, and Jabez Stone felt sick as he saw the cloth struggle and flutter.

"Are they all as small as that?" he asked hoarsely.

"Small?" said the stranger. "Oh, I see what you mean. Why, they vary." He measured Jabez Stone with his eyes, and his teeth showed. "Don't worry, Mr. Stone," he said. "You'll go with

35

a very good grade. I wouldn't trust you outside the collecting box. Now, a man like Dan'l Webster, of course—well, we'd have to build a special box for him, and even at that, I imagine the wing spread would astonish you. But, in your case, as I was saying——"

"Put that handkerchief away!" said Jabez Stone, and he began to beg and to pray. But the best he could get at the end was a three years' extension, with conditions.

But till you make a bargain like that, you've got no idea of how fast four years can run. By the last months of those years, Jabez Stone's known all over the state and there's talk of running him for governor—and it's dust and ashes in his mouth. For every day, when he gets up, he thinks, "There's one more night gone," and every night when he lies down, he thinks of the black pocketbook and the soul of Miser Stevens, and it makes him sick at heart. Till, finally, he can't bear it any longer, and, in the last days of the last year, he hitches up his horse and drives off to seek Dan'l Webster. For Dan'l was born in New Hampshire, only a few miles from Cross Corners, and it's well known that he has a particular soft spot for old neighbors.

It was early in the morning when he got to Marshfield, but Dan'l was up already, talking Latin to the farm hands and wrestling with the ram, Goliath, and trying out a new trotter and working up speeches to make against John C. Calhoun. But when he heard a New Hampshireman had come to see him, he dropped everything else he was doing, for that was Dan'l's way. He gave Jabez Stone a breakfast that five men couldn't eat, went into the living history of every man and woman in Cross Corners, and finally asked him how he could serve him.

Jabez Stone allowed that it was a kind of mortgage case.

"Well, I haven't pleaded a mortgage case in a long time, and I don't generally plead now, except before the Supreme Court," said Dan'l, "but if I can, I'll help you."

"Then I've got hope for the first time in ten years," said Jabez Stone, and told him the details.

Dan'l walked up and down as he listened, hands behind his back, now and then asking a question, now and then plunging his eyes at the floor, as if they'd bore through it like gimlets. When Jabez Stone had finished, Dan'l puffed out his cheeks and blew. Then he turned to Jabez Stone and a smile broke over his face like the sunrise over Monadnock.

"You've certainly given yourself the devil's own row to hoe, Neighbor Stone," he said, "but I'll take your case."

"You'll take it?" said Jabez Stone, hardly daring to believe.

"Yes," said Dan'l Webster. "I've got about seventy-five other things to do and the Missouri Compromise to straighten out, but I'll take your case. For if two New Hampshiremen aren't a match for the devil, we might as well give the country back to the Indians."

Then he shook Jabez Stone by the hand and said, "Did you come down here in a hurry?"

"Well, I admit I made time," said Jabez Stone.

"You'll go back faster," said Dan'l Webster, and he told 'em to hitch up Constitution and Constellation to the carriage. They were matched grays with one white forefoot, and they stepped like greased lightning.

Well, I won't describe how excited and pleased the whole Stone family was to have the great Dan'l Webster for a guest, when they finally got there. Jabez Stone had lost his hat on the way, blown off when they overtook a wind, but he didn't take much account of that. But after supper he sent the family off to bed, for he had most particular business with Mr. Webster. Mrs. Stone wanted them to sit in the front parlor, but Dan'l Webster knew front parlors and said he preferred the kitchen. So it was there they sat, waiting for the stranger, with a jug on the table between them and a bright fire on the hearth—the stranger being scheduled to show up on the stroke of midnight, according to specifications.

Well, most men wouldn't have asked for better company than Dan'l Webster and a jug. But with every tick of the clock Jabez Stone got sadder and sadder. His eyes roved round, and though he sampled the jug you could see he couldn't taste it. Finally, on the stroke of 11:30 he reached over and grabbed Dan'l Webster by the arm.

"Mr. Webster, Mr. Webster!" he said, and his voice was shaking with fear and a desperate courage. "For God's sake, Mr. Webster, harness your horses and get away from this place while you can!"

37

"You've brought me a long way, neighbor, to tell me you don't like my company," said Dan'l Webster, quite peaceable, pulling at the jug.

"Miserable wretch that I am!" groaned Jabez Stone. "I've brought you a devilish way, and now I see my folly. Let him take me if he wills. I don't hanker after it, I must say, but I can stand it. But you're the Union's stay and New Hampshire's pride! He mustn't get you, Mr. Webster! He mustn't get you!"

Dan'l Webster looked at the distracted man, all gray and shaking in the firelight, and laid a hand on his shoulder.

"I'm obliged to you, Neighbor Stone," he said gently. "It's kindly thought of. But there's a jug on the table and a case in hand. And I never left a jug or a case half finished in my life."

And just at that moment there was a sharp rap on the door.

"Ah," said Dan'l Webster, very coolly, "I thought your clock was a trifle slow, Neighbor Stone." He stepped to the door and opened it. "Come in!" he said.

The stranger came in—very dark and tall he looked in the firelight. He was carrying a box under his arm—a black, japanned box with little air holes in the lid. At the sight of the box, Jabez Stone gave a low cry and shrank into a corner of the room.

"Mr. Webster, I presume," said the stranger, very polite, but with his eyes glowing like a fox's deep in the woods.

"Attorney of record for Jabez Stone," said Dan'l Webster, but his eyes were glowing too. "Might I ask your name?"

"I've gone by a good many," said the stranger carelessly. "Perhaps Scratch will do for the evening. I'm often called that in these regions."

Then he sat down at the table and poured himself a drink from the jug. The liquor was cold in the jug, but it came steaming into the glass.

"And now," said the stranger, smiling and showing his teeth, "I shall call upon you, as a law-abiding citizen, to assist me in taking possession of my property."

Well, with that the argument began—and it went hot and heavy. At first, Jabez Stone had a flicker of hope, but when he saw Dan'l Webster being forced back at point after point, he just scrunched in his corner, with his eyes on that japanned box. For there wasn't any doubt as to the deed or the signature— that was the worst of it. Dan'l Webster twisted and turned

The Devil and Daniel Webster

and thumped his fist on the table, but he couldn't get away from that. He offered to compromise the case; the stranger wouldn't hear of it. He pointed out the property had increased in value, and state senators ought to be worth more; the stranger stuck to the letter of the law. He was a great lawyer, Dan'l Webster, but we know who's the King of Lawyers, as the Good Book tells us, and it seemed as if, for the first time, Dan'l Webster had met his match.

Finally, the stranger yawned a little. "Your spirited efforts on behalf of your client do you credit, Mr. Webster," he said, "but if you have no more arguments to adduce, I'm rather pressed for time"—and Jabez Stone shuddered.

Dan'l Webster's brow looked dark as a thundercloud.

"Pressed or not, you shall not have this man!" he thundered. "Mr. Stone is an American citizen, and no American citizen may be forced into the service of a foreign prince. We fought England for that in '12 and we'll fight all hell for it again!"

"Foreign?" said the stranger. "And who calls me a foreigner?"

"Well, I never yet heard of the dev—of your claiming American citizenship," said Dan'l Webster with surprise.

"And who with better right?" said the stranger, with one of his terrible smiles. "When the first wrong was done to the first Indian, I was there. When the first slaver put out for the Congo, I stood on her deck. Am I not in your books and stories and beliefs, from the first settlements on? Am I not spoken of, still, in every church in New England? 'Tis true the North claims me for a Southerner and the South for a Northerner, but I am neither. I am merely an honest American like yourself—and of the best descent—for, to tell the truth, Mr. Webster, though I don't like to boast of it, my name is older in this country than yours."

"Aha!" said Dan'l Webster, with the veins standing out in his forehead. "Then I stand on the Constitution! I demand a trial for my client!"

"The case is hardly one for an ordinary court," said the stranger, his eyes flickering. "And, indeed, the lateness of the hour——"

"Let it be any court you choose, so it is an American judge and an American jury!" said Dan'l Webster in his pride. "Let it be the quick or the dead; I'll abide the issue!"

39

"You have said it," said the stranger, and pointed his finger at the door. And with that, and all of a sudden, there was a rushing of wind outside and a noise of footsteps. They came, clear and distinct, through the night. And yet, they were not like the footsteps of living men.

"In God's name, who comes by so late?" cried Jabez Stone, in an ague of fear.

"The jury Mr. Webster demands," said the stranger, sipping at his boiling glass. "You must pardon the rough appearance of one or two; they will have come a long way."

And with that the fire burned blue and the door blew open and twelve men entered, one by one.

If Jabez Stone had been sick with terror before, he was blind with terror now. For there was Walter Butler, the loyalist, who spread fire and horror through the Mohawk Valley in the times of the Revolution; and there was Simon Girty, the renegade, who saw white men burned at the stake and whooped with the Indians to see them burn. His eyes were green, like a catamount's, and the stains on his hunting shirt did not come from the blood of the deer. King Philip was there, wild and proud as he had been in life, with the great gash in his head that gave him his death wound, and cruel Governor Dale, who broke men on the wheel. There was Morton of Merry Mount, who so vexed the Plymouth Colony, with his flushed, loose, handsome face and his hate of the godly. There was Teach, the bloody pirate, with his black beard curling on his breast. The Reverend John Smeet, with his strangler's hands and his Geneva gown, walked as daintily as he had to the gallows. The red print of the rope was still around his neck, but he carried a perfumed handkerchief in one hand. One and all, they came into the room with the fires of hell still upon them, and the stranger named their names and their deeds as they came, till the tale of twelve was told. Yet the stranger had told the truth—they had all played a part in America.

"Are you satisfied with the jury, Mr. Webster?" said the stranger mockingly, when they had taken their places.

The sweat stood upon Dan'l Webster's brow, but his voice was clear.

"Quite satisfied," he said. "Though I miss General Arnold from the company."

The Devil and Daniel Webster

"Benedict Arnold is engaged upon other business," said the stranger, with a glower. "Ah, you asked for a justice, I believe." He pointed his finger once more, and a tall man, soberly clad in Puritan garb, with the burning gaze of the fanatic, stalked into the room and took his judge's place.

"Justice Hathorne is a jurist of experience," said the stranger. "He presided at certain witch trials once held in Salem. There were others who repented of the business later, but not he."

"Repent of such notable wonders and undertakings?" said the stern old justice. "Nay, hang them—hang them all!" And he muttered to himself in a way that struck ice into the soul of Jabez Stone.

Then the trial began, and, as you might expect, it didn't look anyways good for the defense. And Jabez Stone didn't make much of a witness in his own behalf. He took one look at Simon Girty and screeched, and they had to put him back in his corner in a kind of swoon.

It didn't halt the trial, though; the trial went on, as trials do. Dan'l Webster had faced some hard juries and hanging judges in his time, but this was the hardest he'd ever faced, and he knew it. They sat there with a kind of glitter in their eyes, and the stranger's smooth voice went on and on. Every time he'd raise an objection, it'd be "Objection sustained," but whenever Dan'l objected, it'd be "Objection denied." Well, you couldn't expect fair play from a fellow like this Mr. Scratch.

It got to Dan'l in the end, and he began to heat, like iron in the forge. When he got up to speak he was going to flay that stranger with every trick known to the law, and the judge and jury too. He didn't care if it was contempt of court or what would happen to him for it. He didn't care any more what happened to Jabez Stone. He just got madder and madder, thinking of what he'd say. And yet, curiously enough, the more he thought about it, the less he was able to arrange his speech in his mind.

Till, finally, it was time for him to get up on his feet, and he did so, all ready to bust out with lightnings and denunciations. But before he started he looked over the judge and jury for a moment, such being his custom. And he noticed the glitter in their eyes was twice as strong as before, and they all leaned forward. Like hounds just before they get the fox, they looked, and the blue mist of evil in the room thickened as he watched

41

Stephen Vincent Benét

them. Then he saw what he'd been about to do, and he wiped his forehead, as a man might who's just escaped falling into a pit in the dark.

For it was him they'd come for, not only Jabez Stone. He read it in the glitter of their eyes and in the way the stranger hid his mouth with one hand. And if he fought them with their own weapons, he'd fall into their power; he knew that, though he couldn't have told you how. It was his own anger and horror that burned in their eyes; and he'd have to wipe that out or the case was lost. He stood there for a moment, his black eyes burning like anthracite. And then he began to speak.

He started off in a low voice, though you could hear every word. They say he could call on the harps of the blessed when he chose. And this was just as simple and easy as a man could talk. But he didn't start out by condemning or reviling. He was talking about the things that make a country a country, and a man a man.

And he began with the simple things that everybody's known and felt—the freshness of a fine morning when you're young, and the taste of food when you're hungry, and the new day that's every day when you're a child. He took them up and he turned them in his hands. They were good things for any man. But without freedom, they sickened. And when he talked of those enslaved, and the sorrows of slavery, his voice got like a big bell. He talked of the early days of America and the men who had made those days. It wasn't a spread-eagle speech, but he made you see it. He admitted all the wrong that had ever been done. But he showed how, out of the wrong and the right, the suffering and the starvations, something new had come. And everybody had played a part in it, even the traitors.

Then he turned to Jabez Stone and showed him as he was—an ordinary man who'd had hard luck and wanted to change it. And, because he'd wanted to change it, now he was going to be punished for all eternity. And yet there was good in Jabez Stone, and he showed that good. He was hard and mean, in some ways, but he was a man. There was sadness in being a man, but it was a proud thing too. And he showed what the pride of it was till you couldn't help feeling it. Yes, even in hell, if a man was a man, you'd know it. And he wasn't pleading for any

42

The Devil and Daniel Webster

one person any more, though his voice rang like an organ. He was telling the story and the failures and the endless journey of mankind. They got tricked and trapped and bamboozled, but it was a great journey. And no demon that was ever foaled could know the inwardness of it—it took a man to do that.

The fire began to die on the hearth and the wind before morning to blow. The light was getting gray in the room when Dan'l Webster finished. And his words came back at the end to New Hampshire ground, and the one spot of land that each man loves and clings to. He painted a picture of that, and to each one of that jury he spoke of things long forgotten. For his voice could search the heart, and that was his gift and his strength. And to one, his voice was like the forest and its secrecy, and to another like the sea and the storms of the sea; and one heard the cry of his lost nation in it, and another saw a little harmless scene he hadn't remembered for years. But each saw something. And when Dan'l Webster finished he didn't know whether or not he'd saved Jabez Stone. But he knew he'd done a miracle. For the glitter was gone from the eyes of judge and jury, and, for the moment, they were men again, and knew they were men.

"The defense rests," said Dan'l Webster, and stood there like a mountain. His ears were still ringing with his speech, and he didn't hear anything else till he heard Judge Hathorne say, "The jury will retire to consider its verdict."

Walter Butler rose in his place and his face had a dark, gay pride on it.

"The jury has considered its verdict," he said, and looked the stranger full in the eye. "We find for the defendant, Jabez Stone."

With that, the smile left the stranger's face, but Walter Butler did not flinch.

"Perhaps 'tis not strictly in accordance with the evidence," he said, "but even the damned may salute the eloquence of Mr. Webster."

With that, the long crow of a rooster split the gray morning sky, and judge and jury were gone from the room like a puff of smoke and as if they had never been there. The stranger turned to Dan'l Webster, smiling wryly.

43

"Major Butler was always a bold man," he said. "I had not thought him quite so bold. Nevertheless, my congratulations, as between two gentlemen."

"I'll have that paper first, if you please," said Dan'l Webster, and he took it and tore it into four pieces. It was queerly warm to the touch. "And now," he said, "I'll have you!" and his hand came down like a bear trap on the stranger's arm. For he knew that once you bested anybody like Mr. Scratch in fair fight, his power on you was gone. And he could see that Mr. Scratch knew it too.

The stranger twisted and wriggled, but he couldn't get out of that grip. "Come, come, Mr. Webster," he said, smiling palely. "This sort of thing is ridic—ouch!—is ridiculous. If you're worried about the costs of the case, naturally, I'd be glad to pay——"

"And so you shall!" said Dan'l Webster, shaking him till his teeth rattled. "For you'll sit right down at that table and draw up a document, promising never to bother Jabez Stone nor his heirs or assigns nor any other New Hampshireman till doomsday! For any hades we want to raise in this state, we can raise ourselves, without assistance from strangers."

"Ouch!" said the stranger. "Ouch! Well, they never did run very big to the barrel, but—ouch!—I agree!"

So he sat down and drew up the document. But Dan'l Webster kept his hand on his coat collar all the time.

"And, now, may I go?" said the stranger, quite humble, when Dan'l'd seen the document was in proper and legal form.

"Go?" said Dan'l, giving him another shake. "I'm still trying to figure out what I'll do with you. For you've settled the costs of the case, but you haven't settled with me. I think I'll take you back to Marshfield," he said, kind of reflective. "I've got a ram there named Goliath that can butt through an iron door. I'd kind of like to turn you loose in his field and see what he'd do."

Well, with that the stranger began to beg and to plead. And he begged and he pled so humble that finally Dan'l, who was naturally kindhearted, agreed to let him go. The stranger seemed terrible grateful for that and said, just to show they were friends, he'd tell Dan'l's fortune before leaving. So Dan'l agreed to that, though he didn't take much stock in fortune-tellers ordinarily. But, naturally, the stranger was a little different.

Well, he pried and he peered at the lines in Dan'l's hands. And he told him one thing and another that was quite remarkable. But they were all in the past.

"Yes, all that's true, and it happened," said Dan'l Webster. "But what's to come in the future?"

The stranger grinned, kind of happily, and shook his head.

"The future's not as you think it," he said. "It's dark. You have a great ambition, Mr. Webster."

"I have," said Dan'l firmly, for everybody knew he wanted to be President.

"It seems almost within your grasp," said the stranger, "but you will not attain it. Lesser men will be made President and you will be passed over."

"And, if I am, I'll still be Daniel Webster," said Dan'l. "Say on."

"You have two strong sons," said the stranger, shaking his head. "You look to found a line. But each will die in war and neither reach greatness."

"Live or die, they are still my sons," said Dan'l Webster. "Say on."

"You have made great speeches," said the stranger. "You will make more."

"Ah," said Dan'l Webster.

"But the last great speech you make will turn many of your own against you," said the stranger. "They will call you Ichabod; they will call you by other names. Even in New England, some will say you have turned your coat and sold your country, and their voices will be loud against you till you die."

"So it is an honest speech, it does not matter what men say," said Dan'l Webster. Then he looked at the stranger and their glances locked.

"One question," he said. "I have fought for the Union all my life. Will I see that fight won against those who would tear it apart?"

"Not while you live," said the stranger, grimly, "but it will be won. And after you are dead, there are thousands who will fight for your cause, because of words that you spoke."

"Why, then, you long-barreled, slab-sided, lantern-jawed, fortune-telling note shaver!" said Dan'l Webster, with a great roar of laughter, "be off with you to your own place before I put my mark on you! For, by the thirteen original colonies, I'd go to the Pit itself to save the Union!"

And with that he drew back his foot for a kick that would have stunned a horse. It was only the tip of his shoe that caught the stranger, but he went flying out of the door with his collecting box under his arm.

"And now," said Dan'l Webster, seeing Jabez Stone beginning to rouse from his swoon, "let's see what's left in the jug, for it's dry work talking all night. I hope there's pie for breakfast, Neighbor Stone."

But they say that whenever the devil comes near Marshfield, even now, he gives it a wide berth. And he hasn't been seen in the state of New Hampshire from that day to this. I'm not talking about Massachusetts or Vermont.

FREEDOM'S A HARD-BOUGHT THING

A long time ago, in times gone by, in slavery times, there was a man named Cue. I want you to think about him. I've got a reason.

He got born like the cotton in the boll or the rabbit in the pea patch. There wasn't any fine doings when he got born, but his mammy was glad to have him. Yes. He didn't get born in the Big House, or the overseer's house, or any place where the bearing was easy or the work light. No, Lord. He came out of his mammy in a field hand's cabin one sharp winter, and about the first thing he remembered was his mammy's face and the taste of a piece of bacon rind and the light and shine of the pitch-pine fire up the chimney. Well, now, he got born and there he was.

His daddy worked in the fields and his mammy worked in the fields when she wasn't bearing. They were slaves; they chopped the cotton and hoed the corn. They heard the horn blow before the light came and the horn blow that meant the day's work was done. His daddy was a strong man—strong in his back and his arms. The white folks called him Cuffee. His mammy was a good woman, yes, Lord. The white folks called her Sarah, and she was gentle with her hands and gentle wih her voice. She had a voice like the river going by in the night, and at night when she wasn't too tired she'd sing songs to little Cue. Some had foreign words in them—African words. She couldn't remember what some of them meant, but they'd come to her down out of time.

Now, how am I going to describe and explain about that time when that time's gone? The white folks lived in the Big House and they had many to tend on them. Old Marster, he lived there like Pharaoh and Solomon, mighty splendid and fine. He had his flocks and his herds, his butler and his baker; his fields ran from the river to the woods and back again. He'd ride around the fields each day on his big horse, Black Billy, just like thunder and lightning, and evenings he'd sit at his table and drink his wine. Man, that was a sight to see, with all the silver knives and the silver forks, the glass decanters, and the gentlemen and ladies from all over. It was a sight to see. When Cue was young, it seemed to him that Old Marster must own the whole world, right up to the edge of the sky. You can't blame him for thinking that.

There were things that changed on the plantation, but it didn't change. There were bad times and good times. There was the time young Marse Edward got bit by the snake, and the time Big Rambo ran away and they caught him with the dogs and brought him back. There was a swivel-eyed overseer that beat folks too much, and then there was Mr. Wade, and he wasn't so bad. There was hog-killing time and Christmas and springtime and summertime. Cue didn't wonder about it or why things happened that way; he didn't expect it to be different. A bee in a hive don't ask you how there come to be a hive in the beginning. Cue grew up strong; he grew up smart with his hands. They put him in the blacksmith shop to help Daddy Jake; he didn't like it, at first, because Daddy Jake was mighty cross-tempered. Then he got to like the work; he learned to forge iron and shape it; he learned to shoe a horse and tire a wagon wheel, and everything a blacksmith does. One time they let him shoe Black Billy, and he shod him light and tight and Old Marster praised him in front of Mr. Wade. He was strong; he was black as night; he was proud of his back and his arms.

Now, he might have stayed that way—yes, he might. He heard freedom talk, now and then, but he didn't pay much mind to it.

He wasn't a talker or a preacher; he was Cue and he worked in the blacksmith shop. He didn't want to be a field hand, but he didn't want to be a house servant either. He'd rather be Cue than poor white trash or owned by poor white trash. That's the way he felt; I'm obliged to tell the truth about that way.

Then there was a sickness came and his mammy and his daddy died of it. Old Miss got the doctor for them, but they died just the same. After that, Cue felt lonesome.

He felt lonesome and troubled in his mind. He'd seen his daddy and his mammy put in the ground and new slaves come to take their cabin. He didn't repine about that, because he knew things had to be that way. But when he went to bed at night, in the loft over the blacksmith shop, he'd keep thinking about his mammy and his daddy—how strong his daddy was and the songs that his mammy sang. They'd worked all their lives and had children, though he was the only one left, but the only place of their own they had was the place in the burying ground. And yet they'd been good and faithful servants, because Old Marster said so, with his hat off, when he buried them. The Big House stayed, and the cotton and the corn, but Cue's mammy and daddy were gone like last year's crop. It made Cue wonder and trouble.

He began to take notice of things he'd never noticed. When the horn blew in the morning for the hands to go to the fields, he'd wonder who started blowing that horn, in the first place. It wasn't like thunder and lightning; somebody had started it. When he heard Old Marster say, when he was talking to a friend, "This damned epidemic! It's cost me eight prime field hands and the best-trained butler in the state. I'd rather have lost the Flyaway colt than Old Isaac," Cue put that down in his mind and pondered it. Old Marster didn't mean it mean, and he'd sat up with Old Isaac all night before he died. But Isaac and Cue and the Flyaway colt, they all belonged to Old Marster and he owned them, hide and hair. He owned them, like money in his pockets. Well, Cue had known that all his life, but because he was troubled now, it gave him a queer feeling.

Well, now, he was shoeing a horse for young Marster Shepley one day, and he shod it light and tight. And when he was through, he made a stirrup for young Marster Shepley, and young Marster Shepley mounted and threw him a silver bit, with a laughing word. That shouldn't have bothered Cue, because gentlemen sometimes did that. And Old Marster wasn't mean; he didn't object. But all night Cue kept feeling the print of young Marster Shepley's heel in his hands. And yet he liked young Marster Shepley. He couldn't explain it at all.

Finally, Cue decided he must be conjured. He didn't know who had done it or why they'd done it. But he knew what he had to do. He had to go see Aunt Rachel.

Aunt Rachel was an old, old woman, and she lived in a cabin by herself, with her granddaughter, Sukey. She'd seen Old Marster's father and his father, and the tale went she'd seen George Washington with his hair all white, and General Lafayette in his gold-plated suit of clothes that the King of France gave him to fight in. Some folks said she was a conjure and some folks said she wasn't, but everybody on the plantation treated her mighty respectful, because, if she put her eye on you, she mightn't take it off. Well, his mammy had been friends with Aunt Rachel, so Cue went to see her.

She was sitting alone in her cabin by the low light of a fire. There was a pot on the fire, and now and then you could hear it bubble and chunk, like a bullfrog chunking in the swamp, but that was the only sound. Cue made his obleegances to her and asked her about the misery in her back. Then he gave her a chicken he happened to bring along. It was a black rooster, and she seemed pleased to get it. She took it in her thin black hands and it fluttered and clucked a minute. So she drew a chalk line from its beak along a board, and then it stayed still and frozen. Well, Cue had seen that trick done before. But it was different, seeing it done in Aunt Rachel's cabin, with the big pot chunking on the fire. It made him feel uneasy and he jingled the bit in his pocket for company.

After a while, the old woman spoke. "Well, Son Cue," said she, "that's a fine young rooster you've brought me. What else did you bring me, Son Cue?"

"I brought you trouble," said Cue, in a husky voice, because that was all he could think of to say.

She nodded her head as if she'd expected that. "They mostly brings me trouble," she said. "They mostly brings trouble to Aunt Rachel. What kind of trouble, Son Cue? Man trouble or woman trouble?"

49

"It's my trouble," said Cue, and he told her the best way he could. When he'd finished, the pot on the fire gave a bubble and a croak, and the old woman took a long spoon and stirred it.

"Well, Son Cue, son of Cuffee, son of Shango," she said, "you've got a big trouble, for sure."

"Is it going to kill me dead?" said Cue.

"I can't tell you right about that," said Aunt Rachel. "I could give you lies and prescriptions. Maybe I would, to some folks. But your Granddaddy Shango was a powerful man. It took three men to put the irons on him, and I saw the irons break his heart. I won't lie to you, Son Cue. You've got a sickness."

"Is it a bad sickness?" said Cue.

"It's a sickness in your blood," said Aunt Rachel. "It's a sickness in your liver and your veins. Your daddy never had it that I knows of—he took after his mammy's side. But his daddy was a Corromantee, and they is bold and free, and you takes after him. It's the freedom sickness, Son Cue."

"The freedom sickness?" said Cue.

"The freedom sickness," said the old woman, and her little eyes glittered like sparks. "Some they break and some they tame down," she said, "and some is neither to be tamed or broken. Don't I know the signs and the sorrow—me, that come through the middle passage on the slavery ship and seen my folks scattered like sand? Ain't I seen it coming, Lord—O Lord, ain't I seen it coming?"

"What's coming?" said Cue.

"A darkness in the sky and a cloud with a sword in it," said the old woman, stirring the pot, "because they hold our people and they hold our people."

Cue began to tremble. "I don't want to get whipped," he said. "I never been whipped—not hard."

"They whipped your Granddaddy Shango till the blood ran twinkling down his back," said the old woman, "but some you can't break or tame."

"I don't want to be chased by dogs," said Cue. "I don't want to hear the dogs belling and the paterollers after me."

The old woman stirred the pot.

"Old Marster, he's a good marster," said Cue. "I don't want to do him no harm. I don't want no trouble or projecting to get me into trouble."

Freedom's a Hard-Bought Thing

The old woman stirred the pot and stirred the pot.

"O God, I want to be free," said Cue. "I just ache and hone to be free. How I going to be free, Aunt Rachel?"

"There's a road that runs underground," said the old woman. "I never seen it, but I knows of it. There's a railroad train that runs, sparking and snorting, underground through the earth. At least that's what they tell me. But I wouldn't know for sure," and she looked at Cue.

Cue looked back at her bold enough, for he'd heard about the Underground Railroad himself—just mentions and whispers. But he knew there wasn't any use asking the old woman what she wouldn't tell.

"How I going to find that road, Aunt Rachel?" he said.

"You look at the rabbit in the brier and you see what he do," said the old woman. "You look at the owl in the woods and you see what he do. You look at the star in the sky and you see what she do. Then you come back and talk to me. Now I'm going to eat, because I'm hungry."

That was all the words she'd say to him that night; but when Cue went back to his loft, her words kept boiling around in his mind. All night he could hear that train of railroad cars, snorting and sparking underground through the earth. So, next morning, he ran away.

He didn't run far or fast. How could he? He'd never been more than twenty miles from the plantation in his life; he didn't know the roads or the ways. He ran off before the horn, and Mr. Wade caught him before sundown. Now, wasn't he a stupid man, that Cue?

When they brought him back, Mr. Wade let him off light, because he was a good boy and never run away before. All the same, he got ten, and ten laid over the ten. Yellow Joe, the head driver, laid them on. The first time the whip cut into him, it was just like a fire on Cue's skin, and he didn't see how he could stand it. Then he got to a place where he could.

After it was over, Aunt Rachel crope up to his loft and had her granddaughter, Sukey, put salve on his back. Sukey, she was sixteen, and golden-skinned and pretty as a peach on a peach tree. She worked in the Big House and he never expected her to do a thing like that.

"I'm mighty obliged," he said, though he kept thinking it was

Aunt Rachel got him into trouble and he didn't feel as obliged as he might.

"Is that all you've got to say to me, Son Cue?" said Aunt Rachel, looking down at him. "I told you to watch three things. Did you watch them?"

"No'm," said Cue. "I run off in the woods just like I was a wild turkey. I won't never do that no more."

"You're right, Son Cue," said the old woman. "Freedom's a hard-bought thing. So, now you've been whipped, I reckon you'll give it up."

"I been whipped," said Cue, "but there's a road running underground. You told me so. I been whipped, but I ain't beaten."

"Now you're learning a thing to remember," said Aunt Rachel, and went away. But Sukey stayed behind for a while and cooked Cue's supper. He never expected her to do a thing like that, but he liked it when she did.

When his back got healed, they put him with the field gang for a while. But then there was blacksmith work that needed to be done and they put him back in the blacksmith shop. And things went on for a long time just the way they had before. But there was a difference in Cue. It was like he'd lived up till now with his ears and his eyes sealed over. And now he began to open his eyes and his ears.

He looked at the rabbit in the brier and he saw it could hide. He looked at the owl in the woods and he saw it went soft through the night. He looked at the star in the sky and he saw she pointed north. Then he began to figure.

He couldn't figure things fast, so he had to figure things slow. He figure the owl and the rabbit got wisdom the white folks don't know about. But he figure the white folks got wisdom he don't know about. They got reading and writing wisdom, and it seem mighty powerful. He ask Aunt Rachel if that's so, and she say it's so.

That's how come he learned to read and write. He ain't supposed to. But Sukey, she learned some of that wisdom, along with the young misses, and she teach him out of a little book she tote from the Big House. The little book, it's all about bats and rats and cats, and Cue figure whoever wrote it must be sort of touched in the head not to write about things folks would want to know, instead of all those trifling animals. But he put himself to it and he

Freedom's a Hard-Bought Thing

learn. It almost bust his head, but he learn. It's a proud day for him when he write his name, "Cue," in the dust with the end of a stick and Sukey tell him that's right.

Now he began to hear the first rumblings of that train running underground—that train that's the Underground Railroad. Oh, children, remember the names of Levi Coffin and John Hansen! Remember the Quaker saints that hid the fugitive! Remember the names of all those that helped set our people free!

There's a word dropped here and a word dropped there and a word that's passed around. Nobody know where the word come from or where it goes, but it's there. There's many a word spoken in the quarters that the Big House never hears about. There's a heap said in front of the fire that never flies up the chimney. There's a name you tell to the grapevine that the grapevine don't tell back.

There was a white man, one day, came by, selling maps and pictures. The quality folks, they looked at his maps and pictures and he talked with them mighty pleasant and respectful. But while Cue was tightening a bolt on his wagon, he dropped a word and a word. The word he said made that underground train come nearer.

Cue meet that man one night, all alone, in the woods. He's a quiet man with a thin face. He hold his life in his hands every day he walk about, but he don't make nothing of that. Cue's seen bold folks and bodacious folks, but it's the first time he's seen a man bold that way. It makes him proud to be a man. The man ask Cue questions and Cue give him answers. While he's seeing that man, Cue don't just think about himself any more. He think about all his people that's in trouble.

The man say something to him; he say, "No man own the earth. It's too big for one man." He say, "No man own another man; that's too big a thing too." Cue think about those words and ponder them. But when he gets back to his loft, the courage drains out of him and he sits on his straw tick, staring at the wall. That's the time the darkness comes to him and the shadow falls on him.

He aches and he hones for freedom, but he aches and he hones for Sukey too. And Long Ti's cabin is empty, and it's a good cabin. All he's got to do is to go to Old Marster and take Sukey with him. Old Marster don't approve to mix the field hand with the house servant, but Cue's different; Cue's a blacksmith. He can see the way Sukey would look, coming back to her in the evening. He can see the way she'd be in the morning before the horn. He can see all that. It ain't freedom, but it's what he's used to. And the other way's long and hard and lonesome and strange.

"O Lord, why you put this burden on a man like me?" say Cue. Then he listen a long time for the Lord to tell him, and it seem to him, at last, that he get an answer. The answer ain't in any words, but it's a feeling in his heart.

So when the time come and the plan ripe and they get to the boat on the river and they see there's one too many for the boat, Cue know the answer. He don't have to hear the quiet white man say, "There's one too many for the boat." He just pitch Sukey into it before he can think too hard. He don't say a word or a groan. He know it's that way and there's bound to be a reason for it. He stand on the bank in the dark and see the boat pull away, like Israel's children. Then he hear the shouts and the shot. He know what he's bound to do then, and the reason for it. He know it's the paterollers, and he show himself. When he get back to the plantation, he's worn and tired. But the paterollers, they've chased him, instead of the boat.

He creep by Aunt Rachel's cabin and he see the fire at her window. So he scratch at the door and go in. And there she is, sitting by the fire, all hunched up and little.

"You looks poorly, Son Cue," she say, when he come in, though she don't take her eye off the pot.

"I'm poorly, Aunt Rachel," he say. "I'm sick and sorry and distressed."

"What's the mud on your jeans, Son Cue?" she say, and the pot, it bubble and croak.

"That's the mud of the swamp where I hid from the paterollers," he say.

"What's the hole in your leg, Son Cue?" she say, and the pot, it croak and bubble.

"That's the hole from the shot they shot at me," say Cue. "The blood most nearly dried, but it make me lame. But Israel's children, they's safe."

"They's across the river?" say the old woman.

"They's across the river," say Cue. "They ain't room for no more in the boat. But Sukey, she's across."

Freedom's a Hard-Bought Thing

"And what will you do now, Son Cue?" say the old woman. "For that was your chance and your time, and you give it up for another. And tomorrow morning, Mr. Wade, he'll see that hole in your leg and he'll ask questions. It's a heavy burden you've laid on yourself, Son Cue."

"It's a heavy burden," say Cue, "and I wish I was shut of it. I never asked to take no such burden. But freedom's a hard-bought thing."

The old woman stand up sudden, and for once she look straight and tall. "Now bless the Lord!" she say. "Bless the Lord and praise him! I come with my mammy in the slavery ship—I come through the middle passage. There ain't many that remember that, these days, or care about it. There ain't many that remember the red flag that witched us on board or how we used to be free. Many thousands gone, and the thousands of many thousands that lived and died in slavery. But I remember. I remember them all. Then they took me into the Big House—me that was a Mandingo and a witch woman—and the way I live in the Big House, that's between me and my Lord. If I done wrong, I done paid for it— I paid for it with weeping and sorrow. That's before Old Miss' time and I help raise up Old Miss. They sell my daughter to the South and my son to the West, but I raise up Old Miss and tend on her. I ain't going to repine of that. I count the hairs on Old Miss' head when she's young, and she turn to me, weak and help-less. And for that there'll be a kindness between me and the Big House—a kindness that folks will remember. But my children's children shall be free."

"You do this to me," say Cue, and he look at her, and he look dangerous. "You do this to me, old woman," he say, and his breath come harsh in his throat, and his hands twitch.

"Yes," she say, and look him straight in the eyes. "I do to you what I never even do for my own. I do it for your Granddaddy Shango, that never turn to me in the light of the fire. He turn to that soft Eboe woman, and I have to see it. He roar like a lion in the chains, and I have to see that. So, when you come, I try you and I test you, to see if you fit to follow after him. And because you fit to follow after him, I put freedom in your heart, Son Cue."

"I never going to be free," say Cue, and look at his hands. "I done broke all the rules. They bound to sell me now."

"You'll be sold and sold again," say the old woman. "You'll know the chains and the whip. I can't help that. You'll suffer for your people and with your people. But while one man's got freedom in his heart, his children bound to know the tale."

She put the lid on the pot and it stop bubbling.

"Now I come to the end of my road," she say, "but the tale don't stop there. The tale go backward to Africa and it go forward, like clouds and fire. It go, laughing and grieving forever, through the earth and the air and the waters—my people's tale."

Then she drop her hands in her lap and Cue creep out of the cabin. He know then he's bound to be a witness, and it make him feel cold and hot. He know then he's bound to be a witness and tell that tale. O Lord, it's hard to be a witness, and Cue know that. But it help him in the days to come.

Now, when he get sold, that's when Cue feel the iron in his heart. Before that, and all his life, he despise bad servants and bad marsters. He live where the marster's good; he don't take much mind of other places. He's a slave, but he's Cue, the blacksmith, and Old Marster and Old Miss, they tend to him. Now he know the iron in his heart and what it's like to be a slave.

He know that on the rice fields in the hot sun. He know that, working all day for a handful of corn. He know the bad marsters and the cruel overseers. He know the bite of the whip and the gall of the iron on the ankle. Yes, Lord, he know tribulation. He know his own tribulation and the tribulation of his people. But all the time, somehow, he keep freedom in his heart. Freedom mighty hard to root out when it's in the heart.

He don't know the day or the year, and he forget, half the time, there ever was a gal named Sukey. All he don't forget is the noise of the train in his ears, the train snorting and sparking underground. He think about it at nights till he dream it carry him away. Then he wake up with the horn. He feel ready to die then, but he don't die. He live through the whip and the chain; he live through the iron and the fire. And finally he get away.

When he get away, he ain't like the Cue he used to be—not even back at Old Marster's place. He hide in the woods like a rabbit; he slip through the night like an owl. He go cold and hungry, but the star keep shining over him and he keep his eyes on the star. They set the dogs after him and he hear the dogs belling and yipping through the woods.

Freedom's a Hard-Bought Thing

He's scared when he hear the dogs, but he ain't scared like he used to be. He ain't more scared than any man. He kill the big dog in the clearing—the big dog with the big voice—and he do it with his naked hands. He cross water three times after that to kill the scent, and he go on.

He got nothing to help him—no, Lord—but he got a star. The star shine in the sky and the star shine—the star point north with its shining. You put that star in the sky, O Lord; you put it for the prisoned and the humble. You put it there—you ain't never going to blink it out.

He hungry and he eat green corn and cowpeas. He thirsty and he drink swamp water. One time he lie two days in the swamp, too puny to get up on his feet, and he know they hunting around him. He think that's the end of Cue. But after two days he lift his head and his hand. He kill a snake with a stone, and after he's cut out the poison bag, he eat the snake to strengthen him, and go on.

He don't know what the day is when he come to the wide, cold river. The river yellow and foaming, and Cue can't swim. But he hide like a crawdad on the bank; he make himself a little raft with two logs. He know this time's the last time and he's obliged to drown. But he put out on the raft and it drift him to the freedom side. He mighty weak by then.

He mighty weak, but he careful. He know tales of Billy Shea, the slave catcher; he remember those tales. He slide into the town by night, like a shadow, like a ghost. He beg broken victuals at a door; the woman give them to him, but she look at him suspicious. He make up a tale to tell her, but he don't think she believe the tale. In the gutter he find a newspaper; he pick it up and look at the notices. There's a notice about a runaway man named Cue. He look at it and it make the heart beat in his breast.

He patient; he mighty careful. He leave that town behind. He got the name of another town, Cincinnati, and a man's name in that town. He don't know where it is; he have to ask his way, but he do it mighty careful. One time he ask a yellow man directions; he don't like the look on the yellow man's face. He remember Aunt Rachel; he tell the yellow man he conjure his liver out if the yellow man tell him wrong. Then the yellow man scared and tell him right. He don't hurt the yellow man; he don't blame him for not wanting trouble. But he make the yellow man change pants with him, because his pants mighty ragged.

He patient; he very careful. When he get to the place he been told about, he look all about that place. It's a big house; it don't look right. He creep around to the back—he creep and he crawl. He look in a window; he see white folks eating their supper. They just look like any white folks. He expect them to look different. He feel mighty bad. All the same, he rap at the window the way he been told. They don't nobody pay attention and he just about to go away. Then the white man get up from the table and open the back door a crack. Cue breathe in the darkness.

"God bless the stranger the Lord sends us," say the white man in a low, clear voice, and Cue run to him and stumble, and the white man catch him. He look up and it's a white man, but he ain't like thunder and lightning.

He take Cue and wash his wounds and bind them up. He feed him and hide him under the floor of the house. He ask him his name and where he's from. Then he send him on. O Lord, remember thy tried servant, Asaph Brown! Remember his name!

They send him from there in a wagon, and he's hidden in the straw at the bottom. They send him from the next place in a closed cart with six others, and they can't say a word all night. One time a tollkeeper ask them what's in the wagon, and the driver say, "Southern calico," and the tollkeeper laugh. Cue always recollect that.

One time they get to big water—so big it look like the ocean. They cross that water in a boat; they get to the other side. When they get to the other side, they sing and pray, and white folks look on, curious. But Cue don't even feel happy; he just feel he want to sleep.

He sleep like he never sleep before—not for days and years. When he wake up, he wonder; he hardly recollect where he is. He lying in the loft of a barn. Ain't nobody around him. He get up and go out in the air. It's a fine sunny day.

He get up and go out. He say to himself, *I'm free*, but it don't take hold yet. He say to himself, *This is Canada and I'm free*, but it don't take hold. Then he start to walk down the street.

The first white man he meet on the street, he scrunch up in

himself and start to run across the street. But the white man don't pay him any mind. Then he know.

He say to himself in his mind, *I'm free. My name's Cue—John H. Cue. I got a strong back and strong arms. I got freedom in my heart. I got a first name and a last name and a middle name. I never had them all before.*

He say to himself, *My name's Cue—John H. Cue. I got a name and a tale to tell. I got a hammer to swing. I got a tale to tell my people. I got recollection. I call my first son 'John Freedom Cue.' I call my first daughter 'Come-Out-of-the-Lion's-Mouth.'*

Then he walk down the street, and he pass a blacksmith shop. The blacksmith, he's an old man and he lift the hammer heavy. Cue look in that shop and smile.

He pass on; he go his way. And soon enough he see a girl like a peach tree—a girl named Sukey—walking free down the street.

O'HALLORAN'S LUCK

They were strong men built the Big Road, in the early days of America, and it was the Irish did it.

My grandfather, Tim O'Halloran, was a young man then, and wild. He could swing a pick all day and dance all night, if there was a fiddler handy; and if there was a girl to be pleased he pleased her, for he had the tongue and the eye. Likewise, if there was a man to be stretched, he could stretch him with the one blow.

I saw him later on in years when he was thin and white-headed, but in his youth he was not so. A thin, white-headed man would have had little chance, and they driving the Road to the West. It was two-fisted men cleared the plains and bored through the mountains. They came in the thousands to do it from every county in Ireland; and now the names are not known. But it's over their graves you pass, when you ride in the Pullmans. And Tim O'Halloran was one of them, six feet high and solid as the Rock of Cashel when he stripped to the skin.

He needed to be all of that, for it was not easy labor. 'Twas

Stephen Vincent Benét

a time of great booms and expansions in the railroad line, and they drove the tracks north and south, east and west, as if the devil was driving behind. For this they must have the boys with shovel and pick, and every immigrant ship from Ireland was crowded with bold young men. They left famine and England's rule behind them—and it was the thought of many they'd pick up gold for the asking in the free States of America, though it's little gold that most of them ever saw. They found themselves up to their necks in the water of the canals, and burnt black by the suns of the prairie—and that was a great surprise to them. They saw their sisters and their mothers made servants that had not been servants in Ireland, and that was a strange change too. Eh, the death and the broken hopes it takes to make a country! But those with the heart and the tongue kept the tongue and the heart.

Tim O'Halloran came from Clonmelly, and he was the fool of the family and the one who listened to tales. His brother Ignatius went for a priest and his brother James for a sailor, but they knew he could not do those things. He was strong and biddable and he had the O'Halloran tongue; but there came a time of famine, when the younger mouths cried for bread and there was little room in the nest. He was not entirely wishful to emigrate, and yet, when he thought of it, he was wishful. 'Tis often enough that way, with a younger son. Perhaps he was the more wishful because of Kitty Malone.

'Tis a quiet place, Clonmelly, and she'd been the light of it to him. But now the Malones had gone to the States of America —and it was well known that Kitty had a position there the like of which was not to be found in all Dublin Castle. They called her a hired girl, to be sure, but did not she eat from gold plates, like all the citizens of America? And when she stirred her tea, was not the spoon made of gold? Tim O'Halloran thought of this, and of the chances and adventures that a bold young man might find, and at last he went to the boat. There were many from Clonmelly on that boat, but he kept himself to himself and dreamed his own dreams.

The more disillusion it was to him, when the boat landed him in Boston and he found Kitty Malone there, scrubbing the stairs of an American house with a pail and brush by her side. But that did not matter, after the first, for her cheeks still had the

60

O'Halloran's Luck

rose in them and she looked at him in the same way. 'Tis true there was an Orangeman courting her—conductor he was on the horsecars, and Tim did not like that. But after Tim had seen her, he felt himself the equal of giants; and when the call came for strong men to work in the wilds of the West, he was one of the first to offer. They broke a sixpence between them before he left—it was an English sixpence, but that did not matter greatly to them. And Tim O'Halloran was going to make his fortune, and Kitty Malone to wait for him, though her family liked the Orangeman best.

Still and all, it was cruel work in the West, as such work must be, and Tim O'Halloran was young. He liked the strength and the wildness of it—he'd drink with the thirstiest and fight with the wildest—and that he knew how to do. It was all meat and drink to him—the bare tracks pushing ahead across the bare prairie and the fussy cough of the wood-burning locomotives and the cold blind eyes of a murdered man, looking up at the prairie stars. And then there was the cholera and the malaria— and the strong man you'd worked on the grade beside, all of a sudden gripping his belly with the fear of death on his face and his shovel falling to the ground.

Next day he would not be there and they'd scratch a name from the pay roll. Tim O'Halloran saw it all.

He saw it all and it changed his boyhood and hardened it. But, for all that, there were times when the black fit came upon him, as it does to the Irish, and he knew he was alone in a strange land. Well, that's a hard hour to get through, and he was young. There were times when he'd have given all the gold of the Americas for a smell of Clonmelly air or a glimpse of Clonmelly sky. Then he'd drink or dance or fight or put a black word on the foreman, just to take the aching out of his mind. It did not help him with his work and it wasted his pay; but it was stronger than he, and not even the thought of Kitty Malone could stop it. 'Tis like that, sometimes.

Well, it happened one night he was coming back from the place where they sold the potheen, and perhaps he'd had a trifle more of it than was advisable. Yet he had not drunk it for that, but to keep the queer thoughts from his mind. And yet, the more that he drank, the queerer were the thoughts in his head. For he kept thinking of the Luck of the O'Hallorans and the

61

tales his grandda had told about it in the old country—the tales about pookas and banshees and leprechauns with long white beards.

"And that's a queer thing to be thinking and myself at labor with a shovel on the open prairies of America," he said to himself. "Sure, creatures like that might live and thrive in the old country—and I'd be the last to deny it—but 'tis obvious they could not live here. The first sight of Western America would scare them into conniptions. And as for the Luck of the O'Hallorans, 'tis little good I've had of it, and me not even able to rise to foreman and marry Kitty Malone. They called me the fool of the family in Clonmelly, and I misdoubt but they were right. Tim O'Halloran, you're a worthless man, for all your strong back and arms." It was with such black, bitter thoughts as these that he went striding over the prairie. And it was just then that he heard the cry in the grass.

'Twas a strange little piping cry, and only the half of it human. But Tim O'Halloran ran to it, for in truth he was spoiling for a fight. "Now this will be a beautiful young lady," he said to himself as he ran, "and I will save her from robbers; and her father, the rich man, will ask me—but, wirra, 'tis not her I wish to marry, 'tis Kitty Malone. Well, he'll set me up in business, out of friendship and gratitude, and then I will send for Kitty—"

But by then he was out of breath, and by the time he had reached the place where the cry came from he could see that it was not so. It was only a pair of young wolf cubs, and they chasing something small and helpless and playing with it as a cat plays with a mouse. Where the wolf cub is the old wolves are not far, but Tim O'Halloran felt as bold as a lion. "Be off with you!" he cried and he threw a stick and a stone. They ran away into the night, and he could hear them howling—a lonesome sound. But he knew the camp was near, so he paid small attention to that but looked for the thing they'd been chasing.

It scuttled in the grass but he could not see it. Then he stooped down and picked something up, and when he had it in his hand he stared at it unbelieving. For it was a tiny shoe, no bigger than a child's. And more than that, it was not the kind of shoe that is made in America. Tim O'Halloran stared and stared at it—and at the silver buckle upon it—and still he could not believe.

"If I'd found this in the old country," he said to himself, half

62

O'Halloran's Luck

aloud, "I'd have sworn that it was a leprechaun's and looked for the pot of gold. But here, there's no chance of that—"

"I'll trouble you for the shoe," said a small voice close by his feet.

Tim O'Halloran stared round him wildly. "By the piper that played before Moses!" he said. "Am I drunk beyond comprehension? Or am I mad? For I thought that I heard a voice."

"So you did, silly man," said the voice again, but irritated, "and I'll trouble you for my shoe, for it's cold in the dewy grass."

"Honey," said Tim O'Halloran, beginning to believe his ears, "honey dear, if you'll but show yourself—"

"I'll do that and gladly," said the voice; and with that the grasses parted, and a little old man with a long white beard stepped out. He was perhaps the size of a well-grown child, as O'Halloran could see clearly by the moonlight on the prairie; moreover, he was dressed in the clothes of antiquity, and he carried cobbler's tools in the belt at his side.

"By faith and belief, but it *is* a leprechaun!" cried O'Halloran, and with that he made a grab for the apparition. For you must know, in case you've been ill brought up, that a leprechaun is a sort of cobbler fairy and each one knows the whereabouts of a pot of gold. Or it's so they say in the old country. For they say you can tell a leprechaun by his long white beard and his cobbler's tools; and once you have the possession of him, he must tell you where his gold is hid.

The little old man skipped out of reach as nimbly as a cricket. "Is this Clonmelly courtesy?" he said with a shake in his voice, and Tim O'Halloran felt ashamed.

"Sure, I didn't mean to hurt your worship at all," he said, "but if you're what you seem to be, well, then, there's the little matter of a pot of gold—"

"Pot of gold!" said the leprechaun, and his voice was hollow and full of scorn. "And would I be here today if I had that same? Sure, it all went to pay my sea passage, as you might expect."

"Well," said Tim O'Halloran, scratching his head, for that sounded reasonable enough, "that may be so or again it may not be so. But—"

"Oh, 'tis bitter hard," said the leprechaun, and his voice was weeping, "to come to the waste, wild prairies all alone, just for

63

the love of Clonmelly folk—and then to be disbelieved by the first that speaks to me! If it had been an Ulsterman now, I might have expected it. But the O'Hallorans wear the green."

"So they do," said Tim O'Halloran, "and it shall not be said of an O'Halloran that he denied succor to the friendless. I'll not touch you."

"Do you swear it?" said the leprechaun.

"I swear it," said Tim O'Halloran.

"Then I'll just creep under your coat," said the leprechaun, "for I'm near destroyed by the chills and damps of the prairie. Oh, this weary emigrating!" he said, with a sigh like a furnace. " 'Tis not what it's cracked up to be."

Tim O'Halloran took off his own coat and wrapped it around him. Then he could see him closer—and it could not be denied that the leprechaun was a pathetic sight. He'd a queer little boy-ish face, under the long white beard, but his clothes were all torn and ragged and his cheeks looked hollow with hunger.

"Cheer up!" said Tim O'Halloran and patted him on the back. "It's a bad day that beats the Irish. But tell me first how you came here—for that still sticks in my throat."

"And would I be staying behind with half Clonmelly on the water?" said the leprechaun stoutly. "By the bones of Finn, what sort of a man do you think I am?"

"That's well said," said Tim O'Halloran. "And yet I never heard of the Good People emigrating before."

"True for you," said the leprechaun. "The climate here's not good for most of us and that's a fact. There's a boggart or so that came over with the English, but then the Puritan ministers got after them and they had to take to the woods. And I had a word or two, on my way West, with a banshee that lives by Lake Superior—a decent woman she was, but you could see she'd come down in the world. For even the bits of children wouldn't believe in her; and when she let out a screech, sure they thought it was a steamboat. I misdoubt she's died since then—she was not in good health when I left her.

"And as for the native spirits—well, you can say what you like, but they're not very comfortable people. I was captive to some of them a week and they treated me well enough, but they whooped and danced too much for a quiet man, and I did not like the long, sharp knives on them. Oh, I've had the adventures

O'Halloran's Luck

on my way here," he said, "but they're over now, praises be, for I've found a protector at last," and he snuggled closer under O'Halloran's coat.

"Well," said O'Halloran, somewhat taken aback, "I did not think this would be the way of it when I found O'Halloran's Luck that I'd dreamed of so long. For, first I save your life from the wolves; and now, it seems, I must be protecting you further. But in the tales it's always the other way round."

"And is the company and conversation of an ancient and experienced creature like myself nothing to you?" said the leprechaun fiercely. "Me that had my own castle at Clonmelly and saw O'Sheen in his pride? Then St. Patrick came—wirra, wirra!—and there was an end to it all. For some of us—the Old Folk of Ireland—he baptized, and some of us he chained with the demons of hell. But I was Lazy Brian, betwixt and between, and all I wanted was peace and a quiet life. So he changed me to what you see—me that had six tall harpers to harp me awake in the morning—and laid a doom upon me for being betwixt and between. I'm to serve Clonmelly folk and follow them wherever they go till I serve the servants of servants in a land at the world's end. And then, perhaps, I'll be given a Christian soul and can follow my own inclinations."

"Serve the servants of servants?" said O'Halloran. "Well, that's a hard riddle to read."

"It is that," said the leprechaun, "for I never once met the servant of a servant in Clonmelly, all the time I've been looking. I doubt but that was in St. Patrick's mind."

"If it's criticizing the good saint you are, I'll leave you here on the prairie," said Tim O'Halloran.

"I'm not criticizing him," said the leprechaun with a sigh, "but I wish he'd been less hasty. Or more specific. And now, what do we do?"

"Well," said O'Halloran, and he sighed, too, " 'tis a great responsibility, and one I never thought to shoulder. But since you've asked for help, you must have it. Only there's just this to be said. There's little money in my pocket."

"Sure, 'tis not for your money I've come to you," said the leprechaun joyously. "And I'll stick closer than a brother."

"I've no doubt of that," said O'Halloran with a wry laugh. "Well, clothes and food I can get for you—but if you stick with

65

me, you must work as well. And perhaps the best way would be for you to be my young nephew, Rory, run away from home to work on the railroad."

"And how would I be your young nephew, Rory, and me with a long white beard?"

"Well," said Tim O'Halloran with a grin, "as it happens, I've got a razor in my pocket."

And with that you should have heard the leprechaun. He stamped and he swore and he pled—but it was no use at all. If he was to follow Tim O'Halloran, he must do it on Tim O'Halloran's terms and no two ways about it. So O'Halloran shaved him at last, by the light of the moon, to the leprechaun's great horror, and when he got him back to the construction camp and fitted him out in some old duds of his own—well, it wasn't exactly a boy he looked, but it was more like a boy than anything else. Tim took him up to the foreman the next day and got him signed on for a water boy, and it was a beautiful tale he told the foreman. As well, too, that he had the O'Halloran tongue to tell it with, for when the foreman first looked at young Rory you could see him gulp like a man that's seen a ghost.

"And now what do we do?" said the leprechaun to Tim when the interview was over.

"Why, you work," said Tim with a great laugh, "and Sundays you wash your shirt."

"Thank you for nothing," said the leprechaun with an angry gleam in his eye. "It was not for that I came here from Clonmelly."

"Oh, we've all come here for great fortune," said Tim, "but it's hard to find that same. Would you rather be with the wolves?"

"Oh, no," said the leprechaun.

"Then drill, ye tarrier, drill!" said Tim O'Halloran and shouldered his shovel, while the leprechaun trailed behind.

At the end of the day the leprechaun came to him.

"I've never done mortal work before," he said, "and there's no bone in my body that's not a pain and an anguish to me."

"You'll feel better after supper," said O'Halloran. "And the night's made for sleep."

"But where will I sleep?" said the leprechaun.

66

O'Halloran's Luck

"In the half of my blanket," said Tim, "for are you not young Rory, my nephew?"

It was not what he could have wished, but he saw he could do no otherwise. Once you start a tale, you must play up to the tale.

But that was only the beginning, as Tim O'Halloran soon found out. For Tim O'Halloran had tasted many things before, but not responsibility, and now responsibility was like a bit in his mouth. It was not so bad the first week, while the leprechaun was still ailing. But when, what with the food and the exercise, he began to recover his strength, 'twas a wonder Tim O'Halloran's hair did not turn gray overnight. He was not a bad creature, the leprechaun, but he had all the natural mischief of a boy of twelve and, added to that, the craft and knowledge of generations.

There was the three pipes and the pound of shag the leprechaun stole from McGinnis—and the dead frog he slipped in the foreman's tea—and the bottle of potheen he got hold of one night when Tim had to hold his head in a bucket of water to sober him up. A fortunate thing it was that St. Patrick had left him no great powers, but at that he had enough to put the jumping rheumatism on Shaun Kelly for two days—and it wasn't till Tim threatened to deny him the use of his razor entirely that he took off the spell.

That brought Rory to terms, for by now he'd come to take a queer pleasure in playing the part of a boy and he did not wish to have it altered.

Well, things went on like this for some time, and Tim O'Halloran's savings grew; for whenever the drink was running he took no part in it, for fear of mislaying his wits when it came to deal with young Rory. And as it was with the drink, so was it with other things—till Tim O'Halloran began to be known as a steady man. And then, as it happened one morning, Tim O'Halloran woke up early. The leprechaun had finished his shaving and was sitting cross-legged, chuckling to himself.

"And what's your source of amusement so early in the day?" said Tim sleepily.

"Oh," said the leprechaun, "I'm just thinking of the rare hard work we'll have when the line's ten miles farther on."

"And why should it be harder there than it is here?" said Tim.

"Oh, nothing," said the leprechaun, "but those fools of surveyors have laid out the line where there's hidden springs of water. And when we start digging, there'll be the devil to pay."

"Do you know that for a fact?" said Tim.

"And why wouldn't I know it?" said the leprechaun. "Me that can hear the waters run underground."

"Then what should we do?" said Tim.

"Shift the line half a mile to the west and you'd have a firm roadbed," said the leprechaun.

Tim O'Halloran said no more at the time. But for all that, he managed to get to the assistant engineer in charge of construction at the noon hour. He could not have done it before, but now he was known as a steady man. Nor did he tell where he got the information—he put it on having seen a similar thing in Clonmelly.

Well, the engineer listened to him and had a test made—and sure enough, they struck the hidden spring. "That's clever work, O'Halloran," said the engineer. "You've saved us time and money. And now how would you like to be foreman of a gang?"

"I'd like it well," said Tim O'Halloran.

"Then you boss Gang Five from this day forward," said the engineer. "And I'll keep my eye on you. I like a man that uses his head."

"Can my nephew come with me," said Tim, "for, 'troth, he's my responsibility?"

"He can," said the engineer, who had children of his own.

So Tim got promoted and the leprechaun along with him. And the first day on the new work, young Rory stole the gold watch from the engineer's pocket, because he liked the tick of it, and Tim had to threaten him with fire and sword before he'd put it back.

Well, things went on like this for another while, till finally Tim woke up early on another morning and heard the leprechaun laughing.

"And what are you laughing at?" he said.

"Oh, the more I see of mortal work, the less reason there is to it," said the leprechaun. "For I've been watching the way they get the rails up to us on the line. And they do it thus and so.

But if they did it so and thus, they could do it in half the time with half the work."

"Is that so indeed?" said Tim O'Halloran, and he made him explain it clearly. Then, after he'd swallowed his breakfast, he was off to his friend the engineer.

"That's a clever idea, O'Halloran," said the engineer. "We'll try it." And a week after that, Tim O'Halloran found himself with a hundred men under him and more responsibility than he'd ever had in his life. But it seemed little to him beside the responsibility of the leprechaun, and now the engineer began to lend him books to study and he studied them at nights while the leprechaun snored in its blanket.

A man could rise rapidly in those days—and it was then Tim O'Halloran got the start that was to carry him far. But he did not know he was getting it, for his heart was near broken at the time over Kitty Malone. She'd written him a letter or two when he first came West, but now there were no more of them and at last he got a word from her family telling him he should not be disturbing Kitty with letters from a laboring man. That was bitter for Tim O'Halloran, and he'd think about Kitty and the Orangeman in the watches of the night and groan. And then, one morning, he woke up after such a night and heard the leprechaun laughing.

"And what are you laughing at now?" he said sourly. "For my heart's near burst with its pain."

"I'm laughing at a man that would let a cold letter keep him from his love, and him with pay in his pocket and the contract ending the first," said the leprechaun.

Tim O'Halloran struck one hand in the palm of the other.

"By the piper, but you've the right of it, you queer little creature!" he said. " 'Tis back to Boston we go when this job's over."

It was laborer Tim O'Halloran that had come to the West, but it was Railroadman Tim O'Halloran that rode back East in the cars like a gentleman, with a free pass in his pocket and the promise of a job on the railroad that was fitting a married man. The leprechaun, I may say, gave some trouble in the cars, more particularly when he bit a fat woman that called him a dear little boy; but what with giving him peanuts all the way, Tim O'Halloran managed to keep him fairly quieted.

When they got to Boston he fitted them both out in new

clothes from top to toe. Then he gave the leprechaun some money and told him to amuse himself for an hour or so while he went to see Kitty Malone.

He walked into the Malones' flat as bold as brass, and there sure enough, in the front room, were Kitty Malone and the Orangeman. He was trying to squeeze her hand, and she refusing, and it made Tim O'Halloran's blood boil to see that. But when Kitty saw Tim O'Halloran she let out a scream.

"Oh, Tim!" she said. "Tim! And they told me you were dead in the plains of the West!"

"And a great pity that he was not," said the Orangeman, blowing out his chest with the brass buttons on it, "but a bad penny always turns up."

"Bad penny is it, you brass-buttoned son of iniquity," said Tim O'Halloran. "I have but the one question to put you. Will you stand or will you run?"

"I'll stand as we stood at Boyne Water," said the Orangeman, grinning ugly. "And whose backs did we see that day?"

"Oh, is that the tune?" said Tim O'Halloran. "Well, I'll give you a tune to match it. Who fears to speak of Ninety-Eight?"

With that he was through the Orangeman's guard and stretched him at the one blow, to the great consternation of the Malones. The old woman started to screech and Pat Malone to talk of policemen, but Tim O'Halloran silenced the both of them.

"Would you be giving your daughter to an Orangeman that works on the horsecars, when she might be marrying a future railroad president?" he said. And with that he pulled his savings out of his pocket and the letter that promised the job for a married man. That quieted the Malones a little and, once they got a good look at Tim O'Halloran, they began to change their tune. So, after they'd got the Orangeman out of the house—and he did not go willing, but he went as a whipped man must—Tim O'Halloran recounted all of his adventures.

The tale did not lose in the telling, though he did not speak of the leprechaun, for he thought that had better be left to a later day; and at the end Pat Malone was offering him a cigar. "But I find none upon me," said he with a wink at Tim, "so I'll just run down to the corner."

"And I'll go with you," said Kitty's mother, "for if Mr.

O'Halloran's Luck

O'Halloran stays to supper—and he's welcome—there's a bit of shopping to be done."

So the old folks left Tim O'Halloran and his Kitty alone. But just as they were in the middle of their planning and contriving for the future, there came a knock on the door.

"What's that?" said Kitty, but Tim O'Halloran knew well enough and his heart sank within him. He opened the door—and sure enough, it was the leprechaun.

"Well, Uncle Tim," said the creature, grinning, "I'm here."

Tim O'Halloran took a look at him as if he saw him for the first time. He was dressed in new clothes, to be sure, but there was soot on his face and his collar had thumbmarks on it already. But that wasn't what made the difference. New clothes or old, if you looked at him for the first time, you could see he was an unchancy thing, and not like Christian souls.

"Kitty," he said, "Kitty darlint, I had not told you. But this is my young nephew, Rory, that lives with me."

Well, Kitty welcomed the boy with her prettiest manners, though Tim O'Halloran could see her giving him a side look now and then. All the same, she gave him a slice of cake, and he tore it apart with his fingers; but in the middle of it he pointed to Kitty Malone.

"Have you made up your mind to marry my Uncle Tim?" he said. "Faith, you'd better, for he's a grand catch."

"Hold your tongue, young Rory," said Tim O'Halloran angrily, and Kitty blushed red. But then she took the next words out of his mouth.

"Let the gossoon be, Tim O'Halloran," she said bravely. "Why shouldn't he speak his mind? Yes, Roryeen—it's I that will be your aunt in the days to come—and a proud woman too."

"Well, that's good," said the leprechaun, cramming the last of the cake in his mouth, "for I'm thinking you'll make a good home for us, once you're used to my ways."

"Is that to be the way of it, Tim?" said Kitty Malone very quietly, but Tim O'Halloran looked at her and knew what was in her mind. And he had the greatest impulse in the world to deny the leprechaun and send him about his business. And yet, when he thought of it, he knew that he could not do it, not even if it meant the losing of Kitty Malone.

71

"I'm afraid that must be the way of it, Kitty," he said with a groan.

"Then I honor you for it," said Kitty, with her eyes like stars. She went up to the leprechaun and took his hard little hand. "Will you live with us, young Rory?" she said. "For we'd be glad to have you."

"Thank you kindly, Kitty Malone—O'Halloran to be," said the leprechaun. "And you're lucky, Tim O'Halloran—lucky yourself and lucky in your wife. For if you had denied me then, your luck would have left you—and if she had denied me then, 'twould be but half luck for you both. But now the luck will stick to you the rest of your lives. And I'm wanting another piece of cake," said he.

"Well, it's a queer lad you are," said Kitty Malone, but she went for the cake. The leprechaun swung his legs and looked at Tim O'Halloran. "I wonder what keeps my hands off you," said the latter with a groan.

"Fie!" said the leprechaun, grinning, "and would you be lifting the hand to your one nephew? But tell me one thing, Tim O'Halloran, was this wife you're to take ever in domestic service?"

"And what if she was?" said Tim O'Halloran, firing up. "Who thinks the worse of her for that?"

"Not I," said the leprechaun, "for I've learned about mortal labor since I came to this country—and it's an honest thing. But tell me one thing more. Do you mean to serve this wife of yours and honor her through the days of your wedded life?"

"Such is my intention," said Tim, "though what business it is of—"

"Never mind," said the leprechaun. "Your shoelace is undone, bold man. Command me to tie it up."

"Tie up my shoe, you black-hearted, villainous little anatomy!" thundered Tim O'Halloran, and the leprechaun did so. Then he jumped to his feet and skipped about the room.

"Free! Free!" he piped. "Free at last! For I've served the servants of servants and the doom has no power on me longer. Free, Tim O'Halloran! O'Halloran's Luck is free!"

Tim O'Halloran stared at him, dumb; and even as he stared, the creature seemed to change. He was small, to be sure, and boyish—but you could see the unchancy look leave him and the

Christian soul come into his eyes. That was a queer thing to be seen, and a great one too.

"Well," said Tim O'Halloran in a sober voice, "I'm glad for you, Rory. For now you'll be going back to Clonmelly, no doubt—and faith, you've earned the right."

The leprechaun shook his head.

"Clonmelly's a fine, quiet place," said he, "but this country's bolder. I misdoubt it's something in the air—you will not have noticed it, but I've grown two inches and a half since first I met you, and I feel myself growing still. No, it's off to the mines of the West I am, to follow my natural vocation—for they say there are mines out there you could mislay all Dublin Castle in—and wouldn't I like to try! But speaking of that, Tim O'Halloran," he said, "I was not quite honest with you about the pot of gold. You'll find your share behind the door when I've gone. And now good day and long life to you!"

"But, man dear," said Tim O'Halloran, " 'tis not good-by!" For it was then he realized the affection that was in him for the queer little creature.

"No, 'tis not good-by," said the leprechaun. "When you christen your first son, I'll be at his cradle, though you may not see me—and so with your sons' sons and their sons, for O'Halloran's luck's just begun. But we'll part for the present now. For now I'm a Christian soul, I've work to do in the world."

"Wait a minute," said Tim O'Halloran. "For you would not know, no doubt, and you such a new soul. And no doubt you'll be seeing the priest—but a layman can do it in an emergency and I think this is one. I dare not have you leave me—and you not even baptized."

And with that he made the sign of the cross and baptized the leprechaun. He named him Rory Patrick.

" 'Tis not done with all the formalities," he said at the end, "but I'll defend the intention."

"I'm grateful to you," said the leprechaun. "And if there was a debt to be paid, you've paid it back and more."

And with that he was gone somehow, and Tim O'Halloran was alone in the room. He rubbed his eyes. But there was a little sack behind the door, where the leprechaun had left it—and Kitty was coming in with a slice of cake on a plate.

"Well, Tim," she said, "and where's that young nephew of yours?"

So he took her into his arms and told her the whole story. And how much of it she believed, I do not know. But there's one remarkable circumstance. Ever since then, there's always been one Rory O'Halloran in the family, and that one luckier than the lave. And when Tim O'Halloran got to be a railroad president, why, didn't he call his private car "The Leprechaun"? For that matter, they said, when he took his business trips there'd be a small boyish-looking fellow would be with him now and again. He'd turn up from nowhere, at some odd stop or other, and he'd be let in at once, while the great of the railroad world were kept waiting in the vestibule. And after a while, there'd be singing from inside the car.

THE DIE-HARD

Where was a town called Shady, Georgia, and a time that's gone, and a boy named Jimmy Williams who was curious about things. Just a few years before the turn of the century it was, and that seems far away now. But Jimmy Williams was living in it, and it didn't seem far away to him.

It was a small town, Shady, and sleepy, though it had two trains a day and they were putting through a new spur to Vickery Junction.

They'd dedicated the War Memorial in the Square, but, on market days, you'd still see oxcarts on Main Street. And once, when Jimmy Williams was five, there'd been a light fall of snow and the whole town had dropped its business and gone out to see it. He could still remember the feel of the snow in his hands, for it was the only snow he'd ever touched or seen.

He was a bright boy—maybe a little too bright for his age. He'd think about a thing till it seemed real to him—and that's a dangerous gift. His father was the town doctor, and his father would try to show him the difference, but Doctor Williams was a right busy man. And the other Williams children were a good deal younger and his mother was busy with them. So Jimmy

The Die-Hard

had more time to himself than most boys—and youth's a dreamy time.

I reckon it was that got him interested in Old Man Cappalow, in the first place. Every town has its legends and characters, and Old Man Cappalow was one of Shady's. He lived out of town, on the old Vincey place, all alone except for a light-colored Negro named Sam that he'd brought from Virginia with him; and the local Negroes wouldn't pass along that road at night. That was partly because of Sam, who was supposed to be a conjur, but mostly on account of Old Man Cappalow. He'd come in the troubled times, right after the end of the war, and ever since then he'd kept himself to himself. Except that once a month he went down to the bank and drew money that came in a letter from Virginia. But how he spent it, nobody knew. Except that he had a treasure—every boy in Shady knew that.

Now and then, a gang of them would get bold and they'd rattle sticks along the sides of his fence and yell, "Old Man Cappalow! Where's your money?" But then the light-colored Negro, Sam, would come out on the porch and look at them, and they'd run away. They didn't want to be conjured, and you couldn't be sure. But on the way home, they'd speculate and wonder about the treasure, and each time they speculated and wondered, it got bigger to them.

Some said it was the last treasure of the Confederacy, saved right up to the end to build a new *Alabama*, and that Old Man Cappalow had sneaked it out of Richmond when the city fell and kept it for himself; only now he didn't dare spend it, for the mark of Cain was on every piece. And some said it came from the sea islands, where the pirates had left it, protected by h'ants and devils, and Old Man Cappalow had had to fight devils for it six days and six nights before he could take it away. And if you looked inside his shirt, you could see the long white marks where the devils had clawed him. Well, sir, some said one thing and some said another. But they all agreed it was there, and it got to be a byword among the boys of the town.

It used to bother Jimmy Williams tremendously. Because he knew his father worked hard, and yet sometimes he'd only get fifty cents a visit, and often enough he'd get nothing. And he knew his mother worked hard, and that most folks in Shady

75

weren't rich. And yet, all the time, there was that treasure, sitting out at Old Man Cappalow's. He didn't mean to steal it exactly. I don't know just what he did intend to do about it. But the idea of it bothered him and stayed at the back of his mind. Till, finally, one summer when he was turned thirteen, he started making expeditions to the Cappalow place.

He'd go in the cool of the morning or the cool of the afternoon, and sometimes he'd be fighting Indians and Yankees on the way, because he was still a boy, and sometimes he was thinking what he'd be when he grew up, for he was starting to be a man. But he never told the other boys what he was doing—and that was the mixture of both. He'd slip from the road, out of sight of the house, and go along by the fence. Then he'd lie down in the grass and the weeds, and look at the house.

It had been quite a fine place once, but now the porch was sagging and there were mended places in the roof and paper pasted over broken windowpanes. But that didn't mean much to Jimmy Williams; he was used to houses looking like that. There was a garden patch at the side, neat and well-kept, and sometimes he'd see the Negro, Sam, there, working. But what he looked at mostly was the side porch. For Old Man Cappalow would be sitting there.

He sat there, cool and icy-looking, in his white linen suit, on his cane chair, and now and then he'd have a leather-bound book in his hand, though he didn't often read it. He didn't move much, but he sat straight, his hands on his knees and his black eyes alive. There was something about his eyes that reminded Jimmy Williams of the windows of the house. They weren't blind, indeed they were bright, but there was something living behind them that wasn't usual. You didn't expect them to be so black, with his white hair. Jimmy Williams had seen a governor once, on Memorial Day, but the governor didn't look half as fine. This man was like a man made of ice—ice in the heat of the South. You could see he was old, but you couldn't tell how old, or whether he'd ever die.

Once in a great while he'd come out and shoot at a mark. The mark was a kind of metal shield, nailed up on a post, and it had been painted once, but the paint had worn away. He'd hold the pistol very steady, and the bullets would go "whang, whang" on the metal, very loud in the stillness. Jimmy Williams would watch him and wonder if that was the way he'd fought with his devils, and speculate about all kinds of things.

All the same, he was only a boy, and though it was fun and scary, to get so near Old Man Cappalow without being seen, and he'd have a grand tale to tell the others, if he ever decided to tell it, he didn't see any devils or any treasure. And probably he'd have given the whole business up in the end, boylike, if something hadn't happened.

He was lying in the weeds by the fence, one warm afternoon, and, boylike, he fell asleep. And he was just in the middle of a dream where Old Man Cappalow was promising him a million dollars if he'd go to the devil to get it, when he was wakened by a rustle in the weeds and a voice that said, "White boy."

Jimmy Williams rolled over and froze. For there, just half a dozen steps away from him, was the light-colored Negro, Sam, in his blue jeans, the way he worked in the garden patch, but looking like the butler at the club for all that.

I reckon if Jimmy Williams had been on his feet, he'd have run. But he wasn't on his feet. And he told himself he didn't mean to run, though his heart began to pound.

"White boy," said the light-colored Negro, "Marse John see you from up at the house. He send you his obleegances and say will you step that way." He spoke in a light, sweet voice, and there wasn't a thing in his manners you could have objected to. But just for a minute, Jimmy Williams wondered if he was being conjured. And then he didn't care. Because he was going to do what no boy in Shady had ever done. He was going to walk into Old Man Cappalow's house and not be scared. He wasn't going to be scared, though his heart kept pounding.

He scrambled to his feet and followed the line of the fence till he got to the driveway, the light-colored Negro just a little behind him. And when they got near the porch, Jimmy Williams stopped and took a leaf and wiped off his shoes, though he couldn't have told you why. The Negro stood watching while he did it, perfectly at ease. Jimmy Williams could see that the Negro thought better of him for wiping off his shoes, but not much. And that made him mad, and he wanted to say, "I'm no white trash. My father's a doctor," but he knew better than to say it. He just wiped his shoes and the Negro stood and waited.

Then the Negro took him around to the side porch, and there was Old Man Cappalow, sitting in his cane chair.

"White boy here, Marse John," said the Negro in his low, sweet voice.

The old man lifted his head, and his black eyes looked at Jimmy Williams. It was a long stare and it went to Jimmy Williams' backbone.

"Sit down, boy," he said, at last, and his voice was friendly enough, but Jimmy Williams obeyed it. "You can go along, Sam," he said, and Jimmy Williams sat on the edge of a cane chair and tried to feel comfortable. He didn't do very well at it, but he tried.

"What's your name, boy?" said the old man, after a while.

"Jimmy Williams, sir," said Jimmy Williams. "I mean James Williams, Junior, sir."

"Williams," said the old man, and his black eyes glowed. "There was a Colonel Williams with the Sixty-fifth Virginia—or was it the Sixty-third? He came from Fairfax County and was quite of my opinion that we should have kept to primogeniture, in spite of Thomas Jefferson. But I doubt if you are kin."

"No, sir," said Jimmy Williams. "I mean, Father was with the Ninth Georgia. And he was a private. They were aiming to make him a corporal, he says, but they never got around to it. But he fit—he fought lots of Yankees. He fit tons of 'em. And I've seen his uniform. But now he's a doctor instead."

The old man seemed to look a little queer at that. "A doctor?" he said. "Well, some very reputable gentlemen have practiced medicine. There need be no loss of standing."

"Yes, sir," said Jimmy Williams. Then he couldn't keep it back any longer: "Please, sir, were you ever clawed by the devil?" he said.

"Ha-hrrm!" said the old man, looking startled. "You're a queer boy. And suppose I told you I had been?"

"I'd believe you," said Jimmy Williams, and the old man laughed. He did it as if he wasn't used to it, but he did it.

"Clawed by the devil!" he said. "Ha-hrrm! You're a bold boy. I didn't know they grew them nowadays. I'm surprised." But he didn't look angry, as Jimmy Williams had expected him to.

"Well," said Jimmy Williams, "if you had been, I thought

maybe you'd tell me about it. I'd be right interested. Or maybe let me see the clawmarks. I mean, if they're there."

"I can't show you those," said the old man, "though they're deep and wide." And he stared fiercely at Jimmy Williams. "But you weren't afraid to come here and you wiped your shoes when you came. So I'll show you something else." He rose and was tall. "Come into the house," he said.

So Jimmy Williams got up and went into the house with him. It was a big, cool, dim room they went into, and Jimmy Williams didn't see much at first. But then his eyes began to get used to the dimness.

Well, there were plenty of houses in Shady where the rooms were cool and dim and the sword hung over the mantelpiece and the furniture was worn and old. It wasn't that made the difference. But stepping into this house was somehow like stepping back into the past, though Jimmy Williams couldn't have put it that way. He just knew it was full of beautiful things and grand things that didn't quite fit it, and yet all belonged together. And they knew they were grand and stately, and yet there was dust in the air and a shadow on the wall. It was peaceful enough and handsome enough, yet it didn't make Jimmy Williams feel comfortable, though he couldn't have told you why.

"Well," said the old man, moving about among shadows, "how do you like it, Mr. Williams?"

"It's—I never saw anything like it," said Jimmy Williams.

The old man seemed pleased. "Touch the things, boy," he said. "Touch the things. They don't mind being touched."

So Jimmy Williams went around the room, staring at the miniatures and the pictures, and picking up one thing or another and putting it down. He was very careful and he didn't break anything. And there were some wonderful things. There was a game of chess on a table—carved-ivory pieces—a game that people had started, but hadn't finished. He didn't touch those, though he wanted to, because he felt the people might not like it when they came back to finish their game. And yet, at the same time, he felt that if they ever did come back, they'd be dead, and that made him feel queerer. There were silver-mounted pistols, long-barreled, on a desk by a big silver inkwell; there was a quill pen made of a heron's feather, and a silver sandbox beside it—there were all sorts of curious and interesting things. Finally Jimmy Williams stopped in front of a big, tall clock.

"I'm sorry, sir," he said, "but I don't think that's the right time."

"Oh, yes, it is," said the old man. "It's always the right time."

"Yes, sir," said Jimmy Williams, "but it isn't running."

"Of course not," said the old man. "They say you can't put the clock back, but you can. I've put it back and I mean to keep it back. The others can do as they please. I warned them—I warned them in 1850, when they accepted the Compromise. I warned them there could be no compromise. Well, they would not be warned."

"Was that bad of them, sir?" asked Jimmy Williams.

"It was misguided of them," said the old man. "Misguided of them all." He seemed to be talking more to himself than to Jimmy, but Jimmy Williams couldn't help listening. "There can be no compromise with one's class or one's breeding or one's sentiments," the old man said. "Afterwards—well, there were gentlemen I knew who went to Guatemala or elsewhere. I do not blame them for it. But mine is another course." He paused and glanced at the clock. Then he spoke in a different voice. "I beg your pardon," he said. "I fear I was growing heated. You will excuse me. I generally take some refreshment around this time in the afternoon. Perhaps you will join me, Mr. Williams?"

It didn't seem to Jimmy Williams as if the silver hand bell in the old man's hand had even stopped ringing before the Negro, Sam, came in with a tray. He had a queer kind of old-fashioned long coat on now, and a queer old-fashioned cravat, but his pants were the pants of his blue jeans. Jimmy Williams noticed that, but Old Man Cappalow didn't seem to notice.

"Yes," he said, "there are many traitors. Men I held in the greatest esteem have betrayed their class and their system. They have accepted ruin and domination in the name of advancement. But we will not speak of them now." He took the frosted silver cup from the tray and motioned to Jimmy Williams that the small fluted glass was for him. "I shall ask you to rise, Mr. Williams," he said. "We shall drink a toast." He paused for a moment, standing straight. "To the Confederate States of America and damnation to all her enemies!" he said.

The Die-Hard

Jimmy Williams drank. He'd never drunk any wine before, except blackberry cordial, and this wine seemed to him powerfully thin and sour. But he felt grown up as he drank it, and that was a fine feeling.

"Every night of my life," said the old man, "I drink that toast. And usually I drink it alone. But I am glad of your company, Mr. Williams."

"Yes, sir," said Jimmy Williams, but all the same, he felt queer. For drinking the toast, somehow, had been very solemn, almost like being in church. But in church you didn't exactly pray for other people's damnation, though the preacher might get right excited over sin.

Well, then the two of them sat down again, and Old Man Cappalow began to talk of the great plantation days and the world as it used to be. Of course, Jimmy Williams had heard plenty of talk of that sort. But this was different. For the old man talked of those days as if they were still going on, not as if they were past. And as he talked, the whole room seemed to join in, with a thousand, sighing, small voices, stately and clear, till Jimmy Williams didn't know whether he was on his head or his heels and it seemed quite natural to him to look at the fresh, crisp Richmond newspaper on the desk and see it was dated "June 14, 1859" instead of "June 14, 1897." Well, maybe it was the wine, though he'd only had a thimbleful. But when Jimmy Williams went out into the sun again, he felt changed, and excited too. For he knew about Old Man Cappalow now, and he was just about the grandest person in the world.

The Negro went a little behind him, all the way to the gate, on soft feet. When they got there, the Negro opened the gate and spoke.

"Young marster," he said, "I don't know why Marse John took in his head to ask you up to the house. But we lives private, me and Marse John. We lives very private." There was a curious pleading in his voice.

"I don't tell tales," said Jimmy Williams, and kicked at the fence.

"Yes, sir," said the Negro, and he seemed relieved. "I knew you one of the right ones. I knew that. But we'se living very private till the big folks come back. We don't want no tales spread before. And then we'se going back to Otranto, the way we should."

"I know about Otranto. He told me," said Jimmy Williams, catching his breath.

"Otranto Marse John's plantation in Verginny," said the Negro, as if he hadn't heard. "He owns the river and the valley, the streams and the hills. We got four hundred field hands at Otranto and stables for sixty horses. But we can't go back there till the big folks come back. Marse John say so, and he always speak the truth. But they's goin' to come back, a-shootin' and pirootin', they pistols at they sides. And every day I irons his Richmond paper for him and he reads about the old times. We got boxes and boxes of papers down in the cellar." He paused. "And if he say the old days come back, it bound to be so," he said. Again his voice held that curious pleading, "You remember, young marster," he said. "You remember, white boy."

"I told you I didn't tell tales," said Jimmy Williams. But after that, things were different for him. Because there's one thing about a boy that age that most grown people forget. A boy that age can keep a secret in a way that's perfectly astonishing. And he can go through queer hells and heavens you'll never hear a word about, not even if you got him or bore him.

It was that way with Jimmy Williams; it mightn't have been for another boy. It began like a game, and then it stopped being a game. For, of course, he went back to Old Man Cappalow's. And the Negro, Sam, would show him up to the house and he'd sit in the dim room with the old man and drink the toast in the wine. And it wasn't Old Man Cappalow any more; it was Col. John Leonidas Cappalow, who'd raised and equipped his own regiment and never surrendered. Only, when the time was ripe, he was going back to Otranto, and the old days would bloom again, and Jimmy Williams would be part of them.

When he shut his eyes at night, he could see Otranto and its porches, above the rolling river, great and stately; he could hear the sixty horses stamping in their stalls. He could see the pretty girls, in their wide skirts, coming down the glassy, proud staircases; he could see the fine, handsome gentlemen who ruled the earth and the richness of it without a thought of care. It was all like a storybook to Jimmy Williams—a storybook come true.

The Die-Hard

And more than anything he'd ever wanted in his life, he wanted to be part of it.

The only thing was, it was hard to fit the people he really knew into the story. Now and then Colonel Cappalow would ask him gravely if he knew anyone else in Shady who was worthy of being trusted with the secret. Well, there were plenty of boys like Bob Miller and Tommy Vine, but somehow you couldn't see them in the dim room. They'd fit in, all right, when the great days came back—they'd have to—but meanwhile—well, they might just take it for a tale. And then there was Carrie, the cook. She'd have to be a slave again, of course, and though Jimmy Williams didn't imagine that she'd mind, now and then he had just a suspicion that she might. He didn't ask her about it, but he had the suspicion.

It was even hard to fit Jimmy's father in, with his little black bag and his rumpled clothes and his laugh. Jimmy couldn't quite see his father going up the front steps of Otranto—not because he wasn't a gentleman or grand enough, but because it just didn't happen to be his kind of place. And then, his father didn't really hate anybody, as far as Jimmy knew. But you had to hate people a good deal, if you wanted to follow Colonel Cappalow. You had to shoot at the mark and feel you were really shooting the enemy's colors down. You had to believe that even people like General Lee had been wrong, because they hadn't held out in the mountains and fought till everybody died. Well, it was hard to believe a wrong thing of General Lee, and Jimmy Williams didn't quite manage it. He was willing to hate the Yankees and the Republicans—hate them hot and hard—but there weren't any of them in Shady. Well, come to think of it, there was Mr. Rosen, at the dry-goods store, and Mr. Ailey, at the mill. They didn't look very terrible and he was used to them, but he tried to hate them all he could. He got hold of the Rosen boy one day and rocked him home, but the Rosen boy cried, and Jimmy felt mean about it. But if he'd ever seen a real live Republican, with horns and a tail, he'd have done him a mortal injury—he felt sure he would.

And so the summer passed, and by the end of the summer Jimmy didn't feel quite sure which was real—the times now or the times Colonel Cappalow talked about. For he'd dream about

Otranto at night and think of it during the day. He'd ride back there on a black horse, at Colonel Cappalow's left, and his saber would be long and shining. But if there was a change in him, there was a change in Colonel Cappalow too. He was a lot more excitable than he used to be, and when he talked to Jimmy sometimes, he'd call him by other names, and when he shot at the mark with the enemy's colors on it, his eyes would blaze. So by that, and by the news he read out of the old papers, Jimmy suddenly got to know that the time was near at hand. They had the treasure all waiting, and soon they'd be ready to rise. And Colonel Cappalow filled out Jimmy Williams' commission as captain in the army of the New Confederate States of America and presented it to him, with a speech. Jimmy Williams felt very proud of that commission, and hid it under a loose brick in his fireplace chimney, where it would be safe.

Well, then it came to the plans, and when Jimmy Williams first heard about them, he felt a little surprised. There were maps spread all over the big desk in the dim room now, and Colonel Cappalow moved pins and showed Jimmy strategy. And that was very exciting, and like a game. But first of all, they'd have to give a signal and strike a blow. You had to do that first, and then the country would rise. Well, Jimmy Williams could see the reason in that.

They were going into Shady and capture the post office first, and then the railroad station and, after that, they'd dynamite the railroad bridge to stop the trains, and Colonel Cappalow would read a proclamation from the steps of the courthouse. The only part Jimmy Williams didn't like about it was killing the postmaster and the station agent, in case they resisted. Jimmy Williams felt pretty sure they would resist, particularly the station agent, who was a mean customer. And, somehow, killing people you knew wasn't quite like killing Yankees and Republicans. The thought of it shook something in Jimmy's mind and made it waver. But after that they'd march on Washington, and everything would be all right.

All the same, he'd sworn his oath and he was a commissioned officer in the army of the New Confederate States. So, when Colonel Cappalow gave him the pistol that morning, with the bullets and the powder, and explained how he was to keep watch at the door of the post office and shoot to kill if he had to,

The Die-Hard

Jimmy said, "I shall execute the order, sir," the way he'd been taught. After that, they'd go for the station agent and he'd have a chance for a lot more shooting. And it was all going to be for noon the next day.

Somehow, Jimmy Williams couldn't quite believe it was going to be for noon the next day, even when he was loading the pistol in the woodshed of the Williams house, late that afternoon. And yet he saw, with a kind of horrible distinctness, that it was going to be. It might sound crazy to some, but not to him—Colonel Cappalow was a sure shot; he'd seen him shoot at the mark. He could see him shooting, now, and he wondered if a bullet went "whang" when it hit a man. And, just as he was fumbling with the bullets, the woodshed door opened suddenly and there was his father.

Well, naturally, Jimmy dropped the pistol and jumped. The pistol didn't explode, for he'd forgotten it needed a cap. But with that moment something seemed to break inside Jimmy Williams. For it was the first time he'd really been afraid and ashamed in front of his father, and now he was ashamed and afraid. And then it was like waking up out of an illness, for his father saw his white face and said, "What's the matter, son?" and the words began to come out of his mouth.

"Take it easy, son," said his father, but Jimmy couldn't take it easy. He told all about Otranto and Old Man Cappalow and hating the Yankees and killing the postmaster, all jumbled up and higgledy-piggledy. But Doctor Williams made sense of it. At first he smiled a little as he listened, but after a while he stopped smiling, and there was anger in his face. And when Jimmy was quite through, "Well, son," he said, "I reckon we've let you run wild. But I never thought . . ." He asked Jimmy a few quick questions, mostly about the dynamite, and he seemed relieved when Jimmy told him they were going to get it from the men who were blasting for the new spur track.

"And now, son," he said, "when did you say this massacre was going to start?"

"Twelve o'clock at the post office," said Jimmy. "But we weren't going to massacre. It was just the folks that resisted—"

Doctor Williams made a sound in his throat. "Well," he said, "you and I are going to take a ride in the country, Jimmy. No, we won't tell your mother, I think."

Stephen Vincent Benét

It was the last time Jimmy Williams went out to Old Man Cappalow's, and he remembered that. His father didn't say a word all the way, but once he felt in his back pocket for something he'd taken out of the drawer of his desk, and Jimmy remembered that too.

When they drove up in front of the house, his father gave the reins to Jimmy. "Stay in the buggy, Jimmy," he said. "I'll settle this."

Then he got out of the buggy, a little awkwardly, for he was a heavy man, and Jimmy heard his feet scrunch on the gravel. Jimmy knew again, as he saw him go up the steps, that he wouldn't have fitted in Otranto, and somehow he was glad.

The Negro, Sam, opened the door.

"Tell Colonel Cappalow Doctor Williams wishes to speak with him," said Jimmy's father, and Jimmy could see that his father's neck was red.

"Colonel Cappalow not receivin'," said Sam, in his light sweet voice, but Jimmy's father spoke again.

"Tell Colonel Cappalow," he said. He didn't raise his voice, but there was something in it that Jimmy had never heard in that voice before. Sam looked for a moment and went inside the house.

Then Colonel Cappalow came to the door himself. There was red from the evening sun on his white suit and his white hair, and he looked tall and proud. He looked first at Jimmy's father and then at Jimmy. And his voice said, quite coldly, and reasonably and clearly, "Traitor! All traitors!"

"You'll oblige me by leaving the boy out of it," said Jimmy's father heavily. "This is 1897, sir, not 1860," and for a moment there was something light and heady and dangerous in the air between them. Jimmy knew what his father had in his pocket then, and he sat stiff in the buggy and prayed for time to change and things to go away.

Then Colonel Cappalow put his hand to his forehead. "I beg your pardon, sir," he said, in an altered voice. "You mentioned a date?"

"I said it was 1897," said Doctor Williams, standing square and stocky, "I said Marse Robert's dead—God bless him!—and Jefferson Davis too. And before he died, Marse Robert said we ought to be at peace. The ladies can keep up the war as long as

The Die-Hard

they see fit—that's their privilege. But men ought to act like men."
He stared for a moment at the high-chinned, sculptural face.
"Why, damn your soul!" he said, and it was less an oath than
a prayer. "I was with the Ninth Georgia; I went through three
campaigns. We fought till the day of Appomattox and it was
we-uns' fight." Something rough and from the past had slipped
back into his speech—something, too, that Jimmy Williams had
never heard in it before. "We didn't own niggers or plantations—
the men I fought with. But when it was over, we reckoned it
was over and we'd build up the land. Well, we've had a hard time
to do it, but we're hoeing corn. We've got something better to
do than fill up a boy with a lot of magnolious notions and aim
to shoot up a postmaster because there's a Republican President.
My God," he said, and again it was less an oath than a prayer,
"it was bad enough getting licked when you thought you couldn't
be—but when I look at you—well, hate stinks when it's kept too
long in the barrel, no matter how you dress it up and talk fine
about it. I'm warning you. You keep your hands off my boy.
Now, that's enough."
  "Traitors," said the old man vaguely, "all traitors." Then a
change came over his face and he stumbled forward as if he had
stumbled over a stone. The Negro and the white man both sprang
to him, but it was the Negro who caught him and lowered him
to the ground. Then Jimmy Williams heard his father calling
for his black bag, and his limbs were able to move again.

Doctor Williams came out of the bedroom, drying his hands
on a towel. His eyes fell upon Jimmy Williams, crouched in
front of the chessboard.
  "He's all right, son," he said. "At least—he's not all right. But
he wasn't in pain."
  Jimmy Williams shivered a little. "I heard him talking," he
said difficultly. "I heard him calling people things."
  "Yes," said his father. "Well, you mustn't think too much of
that. You see, a man—" He stopped and began again, "Well, I've
no doubt he was considerable of a man once. Only—well, there's
a Frenchman calls it a fixed idea. You let it get a hold of you . . .
and the way he was brought up. He got it in his head, you see
—he couldn't stand it that he might have been wrong about any-

87

thing. And the hate—well, it's not for a man. Not when it's like that. Now, where's that Nigra?"

Jimmy Williams shivered again; he did not want Sam back in the room. But when Sam came, he heard the Negro answer, politely.

"H'm," said Doctor Williams. "Twice before. He should have had medical attention."

"Marse John don't believe in doctors," said the low, sweet voice.

"He wouldn't," said Doctor Williams briefly. "Well, I'll take the boy home now. But I'll have to come back. I'm coroner for this county. You understand about that?"

"Yes, sir," said the low, sweet voice, "I understand about that." Then the Negro looked at the doctor. "Marse Williams," he said, "I wouldn't have let him do it. He thought he was bound to. But I wouldn't have let him do it."

"Well," said the doctor. He thought, and again said, "Well." Then he said, "Are there any relatives?"

"I take him back to Otranto," said the Negro. "It belongs to another gentleman now, but Marse John got a right to lie there. That's Verginny law, he told me."

"So it is," said the doctor. "I'd forgotten that."

"He don't want no relatives," said the Negro. "He got nephews and nieces and all sorts of kin. But they went against him and he cut them right out of his mind. He don't want no relatives." He paused. "He cut everything out of his mind but the old days," he said. "He start doing it right after the war. That's why we come here. He don't want no part nor portion of the present days. And they send him money from Verginny, but he only spend it the one way—except when we buy this place." He smiled as if at a secret.

"But how?" said the doctor, staring at furniture and pictures.

"Jus' one muleload from Otranto," said the Negro, softly. "And I'd like to see anybody cross Marse John in the old days." He coughed. "They's just one thing, Marse Williams," he said, in his suave voice. "I ain't skeered of sittin' up with Marse John. I always been with him. But it's the money."

"What money?" said Doctor Williams. "Well, that will go through the courts—"

"No, sir," said the Negro patiently. "I mean Marse John's spe-

The Die Hard

cial money that he spend the other money for. He got close to
a millyum dollars in that blind closet under the stairs. And nobody dare come for it, as long as he's strong and spry. But now
I don't know. I don't know."

"Well," said Doctor Williams, receiving the incredible fact,
"I suppose we'd better see."

It was as the Negro had said—a blind closet under the stairs,
opened by an elementary sliding catch.

"There's the millyum dollars," said the Negro as the door
swung back. He held the cheap glass lamp high—the wide roomy
closet was piled from floor to ceiling with stacks of printed
paper.

"H'm," said Doctor Williams. "Yes, I thought so. . . . Have
you ever seen a million dollars, son?"

"No, sir," said Jimmy Williams.

"Well, take a look," said his father. He slipped a note from a
packet, and held it under the lamp.

"It says 'One Thousand Dollars,'" said Jimmy Williams. "Oh!"

"Yes," said his father gently. "And it also says 'Confederate
States of America'. . . . You don't need to worry, Sam. The
money's perfectly safe. Nobody will come for it. Except, maybe,
museums."

"Yes, Marse Williams," said Sam unquestioningly, accepting
the white man's word, now he had seen and judged the white
man. He shut the closet.

On his way out, the doctor paused for a moment and looked
at the Negro. He might have been thinking aloud—it seemed that
way to Jimmy Williams.

"And why did you do it?" he said. "Well, that's something
we'll never know. And what are you going to do, once you've
taken him back to Otranto?"

"I got my arrangements, thank you, sir," said the Negro.

"I haven't a doubt of it," said Jimmy Williams' father. "But I
wish I knew what they were."

"I got my arrangements, gentlemen," the Negro repeated, in
his low, sweet voice. Then they left him, holding the lamp, with
his tall shadow behind him.

"Maybe I oughtn't to have left him," said Jimmy Williams'
father, after a while, as the buggy jogged along. "He's perfectly

89

capable of setting fire to the place and burning it up as a sort of a funeral pyre. And maybe that wouldn't be a bad thing," he added, after a pause. Then he said, "Did you notice the chessmen? I wonder who played that game. It was stopped in the middle." Then, after a while, he said, "I remember the smell of the burning woods in the Wilderness. And I remember Reconstruction. But Marse Robert was right, all the same. You can't go back to the past. And hate's the most expensive commodity in the world. It's never been anything else, and I've seen a lot of it. We've got to realize that—got too much of it, still, as a nation."

But Jimmy Williams was hardly listening. He was thinking it was good to be alone with his father in a buggy at night and good they didn't have to live in Otranto after all.

JOHNNY PYE AND THE FOOL-KILLER

You don't hear so much about the Fool-Killer these days, but when Johnny Pye was a boy there was a good deal of talk about him. Some said he was one kind of person, and some said another, but most people agreed that he came around fairly regular. Or, it seemed so to Johnny Pye. But then, Johnny was an adopted child, which is, maybe, why he took it so hard.

The miller and his wife had offered to raise him, after his own folks died, and that was a good deed on their part. But, as soon as he lost his baby teeth and started acting the way most boys act, they began to come down on him like thunder, which wasn't so good. They were good people, according to their lights, but their lights were terribly strict ones, and they believed that the harder you were on a youngster, the better and brighter he got. Well, that may work with some children, but it didn't with Johnny Pye.

He was sharp enough and willing enough—as sharp and willing as most boys in Martinsville. But, somehow or other, he never seemed to be able to do the right things or say the right words— at least when he was home. Treat a boy like a fool and he'll act like a fool, I say, but there's some folks need convincing. The miller and his wife thought the way to smarten Johnny was to treat him like a fool, and finally they got so he pretty much believed it himself.

And that was hard on him, for he had a boy's imagination, and maybe a little more than most. He could stand the beatings and he did. But what he couldn't stand was the way things went at the mill. I don't suppose the miller intended to do it. But, as long as Johnny Pye could remember, whenever he heard of the death of somebody he didn't like, he'd say, "Well, the Fool-Killer's come for so-and-so," and sort of smack his lips. It was, as you might say, a family joke, but the miller was a big man with a big red face, and it made a strong impression on Johnny Pye. Till, finally, he got a picture of the Fool-Killer, himself. He was a big man, too, in a checked shirt and corduroy trousers, and he went walking the ways of the world, with a hickory club that had a lump of lead in the end of it. I don't know how Johnny Pye got that picture so clear, but, to him, it was just as plain as the face of any human being in Martinsville. And, now and then, just to test it, he'd ask a grown-up person, kind of timidly, if that was the way the Fool-Killer looked. And, of course, they'd generally laugh and tell him it was. Then Johnny would wake up at night, in his room over the mill, and listen for the Fool-Killer's step on the road and wonder when he was coming. But he was brave enough not to tell anybody that.

Finally, though, things got a little more than he could bear. He'd done some boy's trick or other—let the stones grind a little fine, maybe, when the miller wanted the meal ground coarse— just carelessness, you know. But he'd gotten two whippings for it, one from the miller and one from his wife, and, at the end of it, the miller had said, "Well, Johnny Pye, the Fool-Killer ought to be along for you most any day now. For I never did see a boy that was such a fool." Johnny looked to the miller's wife to see if she believed it, too, but she just shook her head and looked serious. So he went to bed that night, but he couldn't sleep, for every time a bough rustled or the mill wheel creaked, it seemed to him it must be the Fool-Killer. And, early next morning, before anybody was up, he packed such duds as he had in a bandanna handkerchief and ran away.

He didn't really expect to get away from the Fool-Killer very long—as far as he knew, the Fool-Killer got you wherever you went. But he thought he'd give him a run for his money, at least. And when he got on the road, it was a bright spring morning, and the first peace and quiet he'd had in some time. So his spirits rose, and he chunked a stone at a bullfrog as he went along, just to show he was Johnny Pye and still doing business.

He hadn't gone more than three or four miles out of Martinsville, when he heard a buggy coming up the road behind him. He knew the Fool-Killer didn't need a buggy to catch you, so he wasn't afraid of it, but he stepped to the side of the road to let it pass. But it stopped, instead, and a black-whiskered man with a stovepipe hat looked out of it.

"Hello, bub," he said. "Is this the road for East Liberty?"

"My name's John Pye and I'm eleven years old," said Johnny, polite but firm, "and you take the next left fork for East Liberty. They say it's a pretty town—I've never been there myself." And he sighed a little, because he thought he'd like to see the world before the Fool-Killer caught up with him.

"H'm," said the man. "Stranger here, too, eh? And what brings a smart boy like you on the road so early in the morning?"

"Oh," said Johnny Pye, quite honestly, "I'm running away from the Fool-Killer. For the miller says I'm a fool and his wife says I'm a fool and almost everybody in Martinsville says I'm a fool except little Susie Marsh. And the miller says the Fool-Killer's after me—so I thought I'd run away before he came."

The black-whiskered man sat in his buggy and wheezed for a while. When he got his breath back, "Well, jump in, bub," he said. "The miller may say you're a fool, but I think you're a right smart boy to be running away from the Fool-Killer all by yourself. And I don't hold with small-town prejudices and I need a right smart boy, so I'll give you a lift on the road."

"But, will I be safe from the Fool-Killer, if I'm with you?" said Johnny. "For, otherwise, it don't signify."

"Safe?" said the black-whiskered man, and wheezed again. "Oh, you'll be safe as houses. You see, I'm a herb doctor—and some folks think, a little in the Fool-Killer's line of business, myself. And I'll teach you a trade worth two of milling. So jump in, bub."

"Sounds all right the way you say it," said Johnny, "but my name's John Pye," and he jumped into the buggy. And they went rattling along toward East Liberty with the herb doctor talking

Johnny Pye and the Fool-Killer

and cutting jokes till Johnny thought he'd never met a pleasanter man. About half a mile from East Liberty, the doctor stopped at a spring.

"What are we stopping here for?" said Johnny Pye.

"Wait and see," said the doctor, and gave him a wink. Then he got a haircloth trunk full of empty bottles out of the back of the buggy and made Johnny fill them with spring water and label them. Then he added a pinch of pink powder to each bottle and shook them up and corked them and stowed them away.

"What's that?" said Johnny, very interested.

"That's Old Doctor Waldo's Unparalleled Universal Remedy," said the doctor, reading from the label.

"Made from the purest snake oil and secret Indian herb, it cures rheumatism, blind staggers, headache, malaria, five kinds of fits, and spots in front of the eyes. It will also remove oil or grease stains, clean knives and silver, polish brass, and is strongly recommended as a general tonic and blood purifier. Small size, one dollar—family bottle, two dollars and a half."

"But I don't see any snake oil in it," said Johnny, puzzled, "or any secret Indian herbs."

"That's because you're not a fool," said the doctor, with another wink. "The Fool-Killer wouldn't, either. But most folks will."

And, that very same night, Johnny saw. For the doctor made his pitch in East Liberty and he did it handsome. He took a couple of flaring oil torches and stuck them on the sides of the buggy; he put on a diamond stickpin and did card tricks and told funny stories till he had the crowd goggle-eyed. As for Johnny, he let him play on the tambourine. Then he started talking about Doctor Waldo's Universal Remedy, and, with Johnny to help him, the bottles went like hot cakes. Johnny helped the doctor count the money afterward, and it was a pile.

"Well," said Johnny, "I never saw money made easier. You've got a fine trade, Doctor."

"It's cleverness does it," said the doctor, and slapped him on the back.

"Now a fool's content to stay in one place and do one thing, but the Fool-Killer never caught up with a good pitchman yet."

"Well, it's certainly lucky I met up with you," said Johnny, "and, if it's cleverness does it, I'll learn the trade or bust."

So he stayed with the doctor quite a while—in fact, till he could make up the remedy and do the card tricks almost as good as the doctor. And the doctor liked Johnny, for Johnny was a biddable boy. But one night they came into a town where things didn't go as they usually did. The crowd gathered as usual, and the doctor did his tricks. But, all the time, Johnny could see a sharp-faced little fellow going through the crowd and whispering to one man and another. Till, at last, right in the middle of the doctor's spiel, the sharp-faced fellow gave a shout of "That's him all right! I'd know them whiskers anywhere!" and, with that, the crowd growled once and began to tear slats out of the nearest fence. Well, the next thing Johnny knew, he and the doctor were being ridden out of town on a rail, with the doctor's long coattails flying at every jounce.

They didn't hurt Johnny particular—him only being a boy. But they warned 'em both never to show their faces in that town again, and then they heaved the doctor into a thistle patch and went their ways.

"Owoo!" said the doctor, "ouch!" as Johnny was helping him out of the thistle patch. "Go easy with those thistles! And why didn't you give me the office, you blame little fool?"

"Office?" said Johnny. "What office?"

"When that sharp-nosed man started snooping around," said the doctor. "I thought that infernal main street looked familiar—I was through there two years ago, selling solid gold watches for a dollar apiece."

"But the works to a solid gold watch would be worth more than that," said Johnny.

"There weren't any works," said the doctor, with a groan, "but there was a nice lively beetle inside each case and it made the prettiest tick you ever heard."

"Well, that certainly was a clever idea," said Johnny. "I'd never have thought of that."

"Clever?" said the doctor. "Ouch—it was ruination! But who'd have thought the fools would bear a grudge for two years? And now we've lost the horse and buggy, too—not to speak of the bottles and the money. Well, there's lots more tricks to be played and we'll start again."

But, though he liked the doctor, Johnny began to feel dubious.

Johnny Pye and the Fool-Killer

For it occurred to him that, if all the doctor's cleverness got him was being ridden out of town on a rail, he couldn't be so far away from the Fool-Killer as he thought. And, sure enough, as he was going to sleep that night, he seemed to hear the Fool-Killer's footsteps coming after him—step, step, step. He pulled his jacket up over his ears, but he couldn't shut it out. So, when the doctor had got in the way of starting business over again, he and Johnny parted company. The doctor didn't bear any grudge; he shook hands with Johnny and told him to remember that cleverness was power. And Johnny went on with his running away.

He got to a town, and there was a store with a sign in the window, BOY WANTED, so he went in. There, sure enough, was the merchant, sitting at his desk, and a fine, important man he looked, in his black broadcloth suit.

Johnny tried to tell him about the Fool-Killer, but the merchant wasn't interested in that. He just looked Johnny over and saw that he looked biddable and strong for his age. "But, remember, no fooling around, boy!" said the merchant sternly, after he'd hired him.

"No fooling around?" said Johnny, with the light of hope in his eyes.

"No," said the merchant, meaningly. "We've no room for fools in this business, I can tell you! You work hard, and you'll rise. But, if you've got any foolish notions, just knock them on the head and forget them."

Well, Johnny was glad enough to promise that, and he stayed with the merchant a year and a half. He swept out the store, and he put the shutters up and took them down; he ran errands and wrapped up packages and learned to keep busy twelve hours a day. And, being a biddable boy and an honest one, he rose, just like the merchant had said. The merchant raised his wages and let him begin to wait on customers and learn accounts. And then, one night, Johnny woke up in the middle of the night. And it seemed to him he heard, far away but getting nearer, the steps of the Fool-Killer after him—tramping, tramping.

He went to the merchant next day and said, "Sir, I'm sorry to tell you this, but I'll have to be moving on."

"Well, I'm sorry to hear that, Johnny," said the merchant, "for you've been a good boy. And, if it's a question of salary—"

"It isn't that," said Johnny, "but tell me one thing, sir, if you don't mind my asking. Supposing I did stay with you—where would I end?"

The merchant smiled. "That's a hard question to answer," he said, "and I'm not much given to compliments. But I started, myself, as a boy, sweeping out the store. And you're a bright youngster with lots of go-ahead. I don't see why, if you stuck to it, you shouldn't make the same kind of success that I have."

"And what's that?" said Johnny.

The merchant began to look irritated, but he kept his smile.

"Well," he said, "I'm not a boastful man, but I'll tell you this. Ten years ago I was the richest man in town. Five years ago, I was the richest man in the county. And five years from now— well, I aim to be the richest man in the state."

His eyes kind of glittered as he said it, but Johnny was looking at his face. It was sallow-skinned and pouchy, with the jaw as hard as a rock. And it came upon Johnny that moment that, though he'd known the merchant a year and a half, he'd never really seen him enjoy himself except when he was driving a bargain.

"Sorry, sir," he said, "but, if it's like that, I'll certainly have to go. Because, you see, I'm running away from the Fool-Killer, and if I stayed here and got to be like you, he'd certainly catch up with me in no—"

"Why, you impertinent young cub!" roared the merchant, with his face gone red all of a sudden. "Get your money from the cashier!" and Johnny was on the road again before you could say "Jack Robinson." But, this time, he was used to it, and walked off whistling.

Well, after that, he hired out to quite a few different people, but I won't go into all of his adventures. He worked for an inventor for a while, and they split up because Johnny happened to ask him what would be the good of his patent, self-winding, perpetual-motion machine, once he did get it invented. And, while the inventor talked big about improving the human race and the beauties of science, it was plain he didn't know. So that night, Johnny heard the steps of the Fool-Killer, far off but coming closer, and, next morning, he went away. Then he stayed with a minister for a while, and he certainly hated to leave him, for the minister was a good man. But they got talking one evening

96

and, as it chanced, Johnny asked him what happened to people who didn't believe in his particular religion. Well, the minister was broad-minded, but there's only one answer to that. He admitted they might be good folks—he even admitted they mightn't exactly go to hell—but he couldn't let them into heaven, no, not the best and the wisest of them, for there were the specifications laid down by creed and church, and, if you didn't fulfill them, you didn't.

So Johnny had to leave him, and, after that, he went with an old drunken fiddler for a while. He wasn't a good man, I guess, but he could play till the tears ran down your cheeks. And, when he was playing his best, it seemed to Johnny that the Fool-Killer was very far away. For, in spite of his faults and his weaknesses, while he played, there was might in the man. But he died drunk in a ditch, one night, with Johnny to hold his head, and, while he left Johnny his fiddle, it didn't do Johnny much good. For, while Johnny could play a tune, he couldn't play like the fiddler—it wasn't in his fingers.

Then it chanced that Johnny took up with a company of soldiers. He was still too young to enlist, but they made a kind of pet of him, and everything went swimmingly for a while. For the captain was the bravest man Johnny had ever seen, and he had an answer for everything, out of regulations and the Articles of War. But then they went West to fight Indians and the same old trouble cropped up again. For one night the captain said to him, "Johnny, we're going to fight the enemy tomorrow, but you'll stay in camp."

"Oh, I don't want to do that," said Johnny; "I want to be in on the fighting."

"It's an order," said the captain, grimly. Then he gave Johnny certain instructions and a letter to take to his wife.

"For the colonel's a copper-plated fool," he said, "and we're walking straight into an ambush."

"Why don't you tell him that?" said Johnny.

"I have," said the captain, "but he's the colonel."

"Colonel or no colonel," said Johnny, "if he's a fool, somebody ought to stop him."

"You can't do that, in an army," said the captain. "Orders are orders." But it turned out the captain was wrong about it, for, next day, before they could get moving, the Indians attacked and got badly licked. When it was all over, "Well, it was a good fight," said the captain, professionally. "All the same, if they'd waited and laid in ambush, they'd have had our hair. But, as it was, they didn't stand a chance."

"But why didn't they lay in ambush?" said Johnny.

"Well," said the captain, "I guess they had their orders too. And now, how would you like to be a soldier?"

"Well, it's a nice outdoors life, but I'd like to think it over," said Johnny. For he knew the captain was brave and he knew the Indians had been brave—you couldn't find two braver sets of people. But, all the same, when he thought the whole thing over, he seemed to hear steps in the sky. So he soldiered to the end of the campaign and then he left the army, though the captain told him he was making a mistake.

By now, of course, he wasn't a boy any longer; he was getting to be a young man with a young man's thoughts and feelings. And, half the time, nowadays, he'd forget about the Fool-Killer except as a dream he'd had when he was a boy. He could even laugh at it now and then, and think what a fool he'd been to believe there was such a man.

But, all the same, the desire in him wasn't satisfied, and something kept driving him on. He'd have called it ambitiousness, now, but it came to the same thing. And with every new trade he tried, sooner or later would come the dream—the dream of the big man in the checked shirt and corduroy pants, walking the ways of the world with his hickory stick in one hand. It made him angry to have that dream, now, but it had a singular power over him. Till, finally, when he was turned twenty or so, he got scared.

"Fool-Killer or no Fool-Killer," he said to himself. "I've got to ravel this matter out. For there must be some one thing a man could tie to, and be sure he wasn't a fool. I've tried cleverness and money and half a dozen other things, and they don't seem to be the answer. So now I'll try book learning and see what comes of that."

So he read all the books he could find, and whenever he'd seem to hear the steps of the Fool-Killer coming for the authors—and that was frequent—he'd try and shut his ears. But some books said one thing was best and some another, and he couldn't rightly decide.

Johnny Pye and the Fool-Killer

"Well," he said to himself, when he'd read and read till his head felt as stuffed with book learning as a sausage with meat, "it's interesting, but it isn't exactly contemporaneous. So I think I'll go down to Washington and ask the wise men there. For it must take a lot of wisdom to run a country like the United States, and if there's people who can answer my questions, it's there they ought to be found."

So he packed his bag and off to Washington he went. He was modest for a youngster, and he didn't intend to try and see the President right away. He thought probably a congressman was about his size. So he saw a congressman, and the congressman told him the thing to be was an upstanding young American and vote the Republican ticket—which sounded all right to Johnny Pye, but not exactly what he was after.

Then he went to a senator, and the senator told him to be an upstanding young American and vote the Democratic ticket—which sounded all right, too, but not what he was after, either. And, somehow, though both men had been impressive and affable, right in the middle of their speeches he'd seemed to hear steps—you know.

But a man has to eat, whatever else he does, and Johnny found he'd better buckle down and get himself a job. It happened to be with the first congressman he struck, for that one came from Martinsville, which is why Johnny went to him in the first place. And, in a little while, he forgot his search entirely and the Fool-Killer, too, for the congressman's niece came East to visit him, and she was the Susie Marsh that Johnny had sat next in school. She'd been pretty then, but she was prettier now, and as soon as Johnny Pye saw her, his heart gave a jump and a thump.

"And don't think we don't remember you in Martinsville, Johnny Pye," she said, when her uncle had explained who his new clerk was. "Why, the whole town'll be excited when I write home. We've heard all about your killing Indians and inventing perpetual motion and traveling around the country with a famous doctor and making a fortune in dry goods and—oh, it's a wonderful story!"

"Well," said Johnny, and coughed, "some of that's just a little bit exaggerated. But it's nice of you to be interested. So they don't think I'm a fool any more, in Martinsville?"

Stephen Vincent Benét

"I never thought you were a fool," said Susie with a little smile, and Johnny felt his heart give another bump.

"And I always knew you were pretty, but never how pretty till now," said Johnny, and coughed again. "But, speaking of old times, how's the miller and his wife? For I did leave them right sudden, and while there were faults on both sides, I must have been a trial to them too."

"They've gone the way of all flesh," said Susie Marsh, "and there's a new miller now. But he isn't very well-liked, to tell the truth, and he's letting the mill run down."

"That's a pity," said Johnny, "for it was a likely mill." Then he began to ask her more questions and she began to remember things too. Well, you know how the time can go when two youngsters get talking like that.

Johnny Pye never worked so hard in his life as he did that winter. And it wasn't the Fool-Killer he thought about—it was Susie Marsh. First he thought she loved him and then he was sure she didn't, and then he was betwixt and between, and all perplexed and confused. But, finally, it turned out all right and he had her promise, and Johnny Pye knew he was the happiest man in the world. And that night, he waked up in the night and heard the Fool-Killer coming after him—step, step, step.

He didn't sleep much after that, and he came down to breakfast hollow-eyed. But his uncle-to-be didn't notice that—he was rubbing his hands and smiling.

"Put on your best necktie, Johnny!" he said, very cheerful, "for I've got an appointment with the President today, and, just to show I approve of my niece's fiancé, I'm taking you along."

"The President!" said Johnny, all dumbfounded.

"Yes," said Congressman Marsh, "you see, there's a little bill—well, we needn't go into that. But slick down your back hair, Johnny—we'll make Martinsville proud of us this day!"

Then a weight seemed to go from Johnny's shoulders and a load from his heart. He wrung Mr. Marsh's hand.

"Thank you, Uncle Eben!" he said. "I can't thank you enough." For, at last, he knew he was going to look upon a man that was bound to be safe from the Fool-Killer—and it seemed to him if he could just once do that, all his troubles and searchings would be ended.

100

Johnny Pye and the Fool-Killer

Well, it doesn't signify which President it was—you can take it from me that he was President and a fine-looking man. He'd just been elected, too, so he was lively as a trout, and the saddle galls he'd get from Congress hadn't even begun to show. Anyhow, there he was, and Johnny feasted his eyes on him. For if there was anybody in the country the Fool-Killer couldn't bother, it must be a man like this.

The President and the congressman talked politics for a while, and then it was Johnny's turn.

"Well, young man," said the President, affably, "and what can I do for you—for you look to me like a fine, upstanding young American."

The congressman cut in quick before Johnny could open his mouth.

"Just a word of advice, Mr. President," he said. "Just a word in season. For my young friend's led an adventurous life, but now he's going to marry my niece and settle down. And what he needs most of all is a word of ripe wisdom from you."

"Well," said the President, looking at Johnny rather keenly, "if that's all he needs, a short horse is soon curried. I wish most of my callers wanted as little."

But, all the same, he drew Johnny out, as such men can, and before Johnny knew it, he was telling his life story.

"Well," said the President, at the end, "you certainly have been a rolling stone, young man. But there's nothing wrong in that. And, for one of your varied experience there's one obvious career. Politics!" he said, and slapped his fist in his hand.

"Well," said Johnny, scratching his head, "of course, since I've been in Washington, I've thought of that. But I don't know that I'm rightly fitted."

"You can write a speech," said Congressman Marsh, quite thoughtful, "for you've helped me with mine. You're a likeable fellow too. And you were born poor and worked up—and you've even got a war record—why, hell! Excuse me, Mr. President!— he's worth five hundred votes just as he stands!"

"I—I'm more than honored by you two gentlemen," said Johnny, abashed and flattered, "but supposing I did go into politics—where would I end up?"

The President looked sort of modest.

"The Presidency of the United States," said he, "is within the legitimate ambition of every American citizen. Provided he can get elected, of course."

"Oh," said Johnny, feeling dazzled, "I never thought of that. Well, that's a great thing. But it must be a great responsibility too."

"It is," said the President, looking just like his pictures on the campaign buttons.

"Why, it must be an awful responsibility!" said Johnny. "I can't hardly see how a mortal man can bear it. Tell me, Mr. President," he said, "may I ask you a question?"

"Certainly," said the President, looking prouder and more responsible and more and more like his picture on the campaign buttons every minute.

"Well," said Johnny, "it sounds like a fool question, but it's this: This is a great big country of ours, Mr. President, and it's got the most amazing lot of different people in it. How can any President satisfy all those people at one time? Can you yourself, Mr. President?"

The President looked a bit taken aback for a minute. But then he gave Johnny Pye a statesman's glance.

"With the help of God," he said, solemnly, "and in accordance with the principles of our great party, I intend . . ."

But Johnny didn't even hear the end of the sentence. For, even as the President was speaking, he heard a step outside in the corridor and he knew, somehow, it wasn't the step of a secretary or a guard. He was glad the President had said "with the help of God" for that sort of softened the step. And when the President finished, Johnny bowed.

"Thank you, Mr. President," he said; "that's what I wanted to know. And now I'll go back to Martinsville, I guess."

"Go back to Martinsville?" said the President, surprised.

"Yes, sir," said Johnny. "For I don't think I'm cut out for politics."

"And is that all you have to say to the President of the United States?" said his uncle-to-be, in a fume.

But the President had been thinking, meanwhile, and he was a bigger man than the congressman.

"Wait a minute, Congressman," he said. "This young man's honest, at least, and I like his looks. Moreover, of all the people who've come to see me in the last six months, he's the only one who hasn't wanted something—except the White House cat, and I guess she wanted something, too, because she meowed. You don't want to be President, young man—and, confidentially, I don't blame you. But how would you like to be postmaster at Martinsville?"

"Postmaster at Martinsville?" said Johnny. "But—"

"Oh, it's only a tenth-class post office," said the President, "but, for once in my life, I'll do something because I want to, and let Congress yell its head off. Come—is it yes or no?"

Johnny thought of all the places he'd been and all the trades he'd worked at. He thought, queerly enough, of the old drunk fiddler dead in the ditch, but he knew he couldn't be that. Mostly, though, he thought of Martinsville and Susie Marsh. And, though he'd just heard the Fool-Killer's step, he defied the Fool-Killer.

"Why, it's yes, of course, Mr. President," he said, "for then I can marry Susie."

"That's as good a reason as you'll find," said the President. "And now, I'll just write a note."

Well, he was as good as his word, and Johnny and his Susie were married and went back to live in Martinsville. And, as soon as Johnny learned the ways of postmastering, he found it as good a trade as most. There wasn't much mail in Martinsville, but, in between whiles, he ran the mill, and that was a good trade too. And all the time, he knew, at the back of his mind, that he hadn't quite settled accounts with the Fool-Killer. But he didn't much care about that, for he and Susie were happy. And after a while they had a child, and that was the most remarkable experience that had ever happened to any young couple, though the doctor said it was a perfectly normal baby.

One evening, when his son was about a year old, Johnny Pye took the river road, going home. It was a mite longer than the hill road, but it was the cool of the evening, and there's times when a man likes to walk by himself, fond as he may be of his wife and family.

He was thinking of the way things had turned out for him, and they seemed to him pretty astonishing and singular, as they do to most folks, when you think them over. In fact, he was thinking so hard that, before he knew it, he'd almost stumbled over an old scissors grinder who'd set up his grindstone and tools by the side of the road. The scissors grinder had his cart with him, but he'd turned the horse out to graze—and a lank, old, white horse it was, with every rib showing. And he was very busy, putting an edge on a scythe.

"Oh, sorry," said Johnny Pye. "I didn't know anybody was camping here. But you might come around to my house tomorrow—my wife's got some knives that need sharpening."

Then he stopped, for the old man gave him a long, keen look. "Why, it's you, Johnny Pye," said the old man. "And how do you do, Johnny Pye! You've been a long time coming—in fact, now and then, I thought I'd have to fetch you. But you're here at last."

Johnny Pye was a grown man now, but he began to tremble. "But it isn't you!" he said, wildly. "I mean you're not him! Why, I've known how he looks all my life! He's a big man, with a checked shirt, and he carries a hickory stick with a lump of lead in one end."

"Oh, no," said the scissors grinder, quite quiet. "You may have thought of me that way, but that's not the way I am." And Johnny Pye heard the scythe go whet-whet-whet on the stone. The old man ran some water on it and looked at the edge. Then he shook his head as if the edge didn't quite satisfy him. "Well, Johnny, are you ready?" he said, after a while.

"Ready?" said Johnny, in a hoarse voice. "Of course I'm not ready."

"That's what they all say," said the old man, nodding his head, and the scythe went whet-whet on the stone.

Johnny wiped his brow and started to argue it out.

"You see, if you'd found me earlier," he said, "or later. I don't want to be unreasonable, but I've got a wife and a child."

"Most has wives and many has children," said the old man, grimly, and the scythe went whet-whet on the stone as he pushed the treadle. And a shower of sparks flew, very clear and bright, for the night had begun to fall.

"Oh, stop that damn racket and let a man think for a minute!" said Johnny, desperate. "I can't go, I tell you. I won't. It isn't time. It's—"

The old man stopped the grindstone and pointed with the scythe at Johnny Pye.

"Tell me one good reason," he said. "There's men would be

missed in the world, but are you one of them? A clever man might be missed, but are you a clever man?"

"No," said Johnny, thinking of the herb doctor. "I had a chance to be clever, but I gave it up."

"One," said the old man, ticking off on his fingers. "Well, a rich man might be missed—by some. But you aren't rich, I take it."

"No," said Johnny, thinking of the merchant, "nor wanted to be."

"Two," said the old man. "Cleverness—riches—they're done. But there's still martial bravery and being a hero. There might be an argument to make, if you were one of those."

Johnny Pye shuddered a little, remembering the way that battlefield had looked, out West, when the Indians were dead and the fight over.

"No," he said, "I've fought, but I'm not a hero."

"Well, then, there's religion," said the old man, sort of patient, "and science, and—but what's the use? We know what you did with those. I might feel a trifle of compunction if I had to deal with a President of the United States. But—"

"Oh, you know well enough I ain't President," said Johnny, with a groan. "Can't you get it over with and be done?"

"You're not putting up a very good case," said the old man, shaking his head. "I'm surprised at you, Johnny. Here you spend your youth running away from being a fool. And yet, what's the first thing you do, when you're man grown? Why, you marry a girl, settle down in your home town, and start raising children when you don't know how they'll turn out. You might have known I'd catch up with you, then—you just put yourself in my way."

"Fool I may be," said Johnny Pye in his agony, "and if you take it like that, I guess we're all fools. But Susie's my wife, and my child's my child. And, as for work in the world—well, somebody has to be postmaster, or folks wouldn't get the mail."

"Would it matter much if they didn't?" said the old man, pointing his scythe.

"Well, no, I don't suppose it would, considering what's on the post cards," said Johnny Pye. "But while it's my business to sort it, I'll sort it as well as I can."

The old man whetted his scythe so hard that a long shower of sparks flew out on the grass.

"Well," he said, "I've got my job, too, and I do it likewise. But I'll tell you what I'll do. You're coming my way, no doubt of it, but, looking you over, you don't look quite ripe yet. So I'll let you off for a while. For that matter," said he, "if you'll answer one question of mine—how a man can be a human being and not be a fool—I'll let you off permanent. It'll be the first time in history," he said, "but you've got to do something on your own hook, once in a while. And now you can walk along, Johnny Pye."

With that he grounded the scythe till the sparks flew out like the tail of a comet and Johnny Pye walked along. The air of the meadow had never seemed so sweet to him before.

All the same, even with his relief, he didn't quite forget, and sometimes Susie had to tell the children not to disturb father because he was thinking. But time went ahead, as it does, and pretty soon Johnny Pye found he was forty. He'd never expected to be forty, when he was young, and it kind of surprised him. But there it was, though he couldn't say he felt much different, except now and then when he stooped over. And he was a solid citizen of the town, well-liked and well-respected, with a growing family and a stake in the community, and when he thought those things over, they kind of surprised him too. But, pretty soon, it was as if things had always been that way.

It was after his eldest son had been drowned out fishing that Johnny Pye met the scissors grinder again. But this time he was bitter and distracted, and, if he could have got to the old man, he'd have done him a mortal harm. But, somehow or other, when he tried to come to grips with him, it was like reaching for air and mist. He could see the sparks fly from the ground scythe, but he couldn't even touch the wheel.

"You coward!" said Johnny Pye. "Stand up and fight like a man!" But the old man just nodded his head and the wheel kept grinding and grinding.

"Why couldn't you have taken me?" said Johnny Pye, as if those words had never been said before. "What's the sense in all this? Why can't you take me now?"

Then he tried to wrench the scythe from the old man's hands,

Johnny Pye and the Fool-Killer

but he couldn't touch it. And then he fell down and lay on the grass for a while.

"Time passes," said the old man, nodding his head. "Time passes."

"It will never cure the grief I have for my son," said Johnny Pye.

"It will not," said the old man, nodding his head. "But time passes. Would you leave your wife a widow and your other children fatherless for the sake of your grief?"

"No, God help me!" said Johnny Pye. "That wouldn't be right for a man."

"Then go home to your house, Johnny Pye," said the old man. And Johnny Pye went, but there were lines in his face that hadn't been there before.

And time passed, like the flow of the river, and Johnny Pye's children married and had houses and children of their own. And Susie's hair grew white, and her back grew bent, and when Johnny Pye and his children followed her to her grave, folks said she'd died in the fullness of years, but that was hard for Johnny Pye to believe. Only folks didn't talk as plain as they used to, and the sun didn't heat as much, and sometimes, before dinner, he'd go to sleep in his chair.

And once, after Susie had died, the President of those days came through Martinsville and Johnny Pye shook hands with him and there was a piece in the paper about his shaking hands with two Presidents, fifty years apart. Johnny Pye cut out the clipping and kept it in his pocketbook. He liked this President all right, but, as he told people, he wasn't a patch on the other one fifty years ago. Well, you couldn't expect it—you didn't have Presidents these days, not to call them Presidents. All the same, he took a lot of satisfaction in the clipping.

He didn't get down to the river road much any more—it wasn't too long a walk, of course, but he just didn't often feel like it. But, one day, he slipped away from the granddaughter that was taking care of him, and went. It was kind of a steep road, really —he didn't remember its being so steep.

"Well," said the scissors grinder, "and good afternoon to you, Johnny Pye."

"You'll have to talk a little louder," said Johnny Pye. "My hearing's perfect, but folks don't speak as plain as they used to. Stranger in town?"

"Oh, so that's the way it is," said the scissors grinder.

"Yes, that's the way it is," said Johnny Pye. He knew he ought to be afraid of this fellow, now he'd put on his spectacles and got a good look at him, but for the life of him, he couldn't remember why.

"I know just who you are," he said, a little fretfully. "Never forgot a face in my life, and your name's right on the tip of my tongue—"

"Oh, don't bother about names," said the scissors grinder. "We're old acquaintances. And I asked you a question, years ago —do you remember that?"

"Yes," said Johnny Pye, "I remember." Then he began to laugh—a high, old man's laugh. "And of all the fool questions I ever was asked," he said, "that certainly took the cake."

"Oh?" said the scissors grinder.

"Uh-huh," said Johnny Pye. "For you asked me how a man could be a human being and yet not be a fool. And the answer is—when he's dead and gone and buried. Any fool would know that."

"That so?" said the scissors grinder.

"Of course," said Johnny Pye. "I ought to know. I'll be ninety-two next November, and I've shook hands with two Presidents. The first President I shook—"

"I'll be interested to hear about that," said the scissors grinder, "but we've got a little business, first. For, if all human beings are fools, how does the world get ahead?"

"Oh, there's lots of other things," said Johnny Pye, kind of impatient. "There's the brave and the wise and the clever—and they're apt to roll it ahead as much as an inch. But it's all mixed in together. For, Lord, it's only some fool kind of creature that would have crawled out of the sea to dry land in the first place —or got dropped from the Garden of Eden, if you like it better that way. You can't depend on the kind of folks people think they are—you've got to go by what they do. And I wouldn't give much for a man that some folks hadn't thought was a fool, in his time."

"Well," said the scissors grinder, "you've answered my question—at least as well as you could, which is all you can expect of a man. So I'll keep my part of the bargain."

"And what was that?" said Johnny. "For, while it's all straight in my head, I don't quite recollect the details."

"Why," said the scissors grinder, rather testy, "I'm to let you go, you old fool! You'll never see me again till the Last Judgment. There'll be trouble in the office about it," said he, "but you've got to do what you like, once in a while."

"Phew!" said Johnny Pye. "That needs thinking over!" And he scratched his head.

"Why?" said the scissors grinder, a bit affronted. "It ain't often I offer a man eternal life."

"Well," said Johnny Pye, "I take it very kind, but, you see, it's this way." He thought for a moment. "No," he said, "you wouldn't understand. You can't have touched seventy yet, by your looks, and no young man would."

"Try me," said the scissors grinder.

"Well," said Johnny Pye, "it's this way," and he scratched his head again. "I'm not saying—if you'd made the offer forty years ago, or even twenty. But, well, now, let's just take one detail. Let's say 'teeth.' "

"Well, of course," said the scissors grinder, "naturally—I mean you could hardly expect me to do anything about that."

"I thought so," said Johnny Pye. "Well, you see, these are good, bought teeth, but I'm sort of tired of hearing them click. And spectacles, I suppose, the same?"

"I'm afraid so," said the scissors grinder. "I can't interfere with time, you know—that's not my department. And, frankly, you couldn't expect, at a hundred and eighty, let's say, to be quite the man you was at ninety. But still, you'd be a wonder!"

"Maybe so," said Johnny Pye, "but, you see—well, the truth is, I'm an old man now. You wouldn't think it to look at me, but it's so. And my friends—well, they're gone—and Susie and the boy—and somehow you don't get as close to the younger people, except the children. And to keep on just going and going till Judgment Day, with nobody around to talk to that had real horse sense—well, no, sir, it's a handsome offer but I just don't feel up to accepting it. It may not be patriotic of me, and I feel sorry for Martinsville. It'd do wonders for the climate and the chamber of commerce to have a leading citizen live till Judgment Day. But a man's got to do as he likes, at least once in his life." He stopped and looked at the scissors grinder. "I'll admit, I'd kind of like to beat out Ike Leavis," he said. "To hear him talk, you'd think nobody had ever pushed ninety before. But I suppose—"

"I'm afraid we can't issue a limited policy," said the scissors grinder.

"Well," said Johnny Pye, "I just thought of it. And Ike's all right." He waited a moment. "Tell me," he said, in a low voice. "Well, you know what I mean. Afterwards. I mean, if you're likely to see"—he coughed—"your friends again. I mean, if it's so —like some folks believe."

"I can't tell you that," said the scissors grinder. "I only go so far."

"Well, there's no harm in asking," said Johnny Pye, rather humbly. He peered into the darkness; a last shower of sparks flew from the scythe, then the whir of the wheel stopped.

"H'm," said Johnny Pye, testing the edge. "That's a well-ground scythe. But they used to grind 'em better in the old days." He listened and looked, for a moment, anxiously. "Oh, Lordy!" he said, "there's Helen coming to look for me. She'll take me back to the house."

"Not this time," said the scissors grinder. "Yes, there isn't bad steel in that scythe. Well, let's go, Johnny Pye."

SPANISH BAYONET

Spanish Bayonet

PRELUDE: THE BARBARY APE

THEY were dancing in the streets of Port Mahon.
The time was shortly after Easter in the year of our
Lord, 1769. Christ had died and risen again in the Cathedral, with
flowers and candleflame and the songs of Easter Eve, when stroll-
ers pass through the narrow, rocky streets, singing the Fromajar-
dis—the sorrows of Mary—and receive through opened lattice and
shutter, small sanctified gifts of sweetmeats and pastry from hands
blurred by the dusk. This year the sweetmeats had been few and
poor, for the scanty crops of Minorca had failed for the third
successive season, and all Lent the Vicar-General had excused his
afflicted children from their duty of abstinence, so pinched were
the times. But now, with the resurrection of the earth and the
grave twilights of April, there was hope in the air, and the tiled
and terrace-roofed houses that clung together in a town against
the rock, like the nests of swallows upon a chimney of stone,
knew again the music of the guitar.

Below, in the famous harbor where all the fleets of Europe
might ride at anchor, lay the ships which had brought that hope.
Minorca had too many children to feed from a narrow and indurate breast—the ships would take some away, over the ocean,
to a new country, where the British flag flew from the top of a
palm-tree in the Floridas of America, and, after four years of
labor for the master of the expedition, a man might claim his own
fifty acres of fertile ground and take his siesta at noon in the
shadow of his own trees.

Sebastian Zafortezas, looking down at the harbor through the
clear darkness, made out the riding-lights of those ships, and pondered the strange benevolencies of the English. Quick, loud-
voiced, red-faced men who swore without punctilio and prayed
without courtesy, who bathed themselves unnecessarily in frigid

waters as a preparation for future torments of incessant fire, they nevertheless displayed an extraordinary unwillingness to let newly-reconquered subjects die quietly of starvation. They were all a little mad, of course, and the master of the ships in the harbor no doubt as mad as any.

A doctor they called him, but Sebastian could hardly believe it. He was not like Spanish doctors, seemly and mournful, as befits one who immediately precedes the priest and the undertaker, but spry and perpetually smiling with clean hands and a gentleman's wig. Moreover the English governor had received him with much honor, which even an English governor would hardly show to one whose avouched occupation was not much better than that of a burier-beetle. Ah well, it was all one, thought Sebastian—doctor or prince, he had given the word of an Englishman as to the rewards which might be gained by those who embarked with him as colonists for the distant country—and the word of an Englishman, no matter how mad, was good. Minorca had learned that in her last fifty years of shuttlecocking between the Powers —and the hearts of her people cherished few romantic yearnings for reunion with Spain.

Spain was well enough, but they were the people of the islands. They had given sailors to Carthage and slingers to Rome, their rocks held deserted altars to gods forgotten before the Cross. Their pilots had known the sea when Prince Henry the Navigator was a royal doll in swaddling-clothes, and it was said of them on the mainland that the poorest fisherman of the islands was prouder than three grandees.

As Sebastian gazed at the harbor, he felt a wave of unexpected sickness strike at his heart at the thought of never seeing it again nor any of the streamless island of doves and eagles, but it soon passed. At the age of fifteen he was admittedly a man and men did not suffer from homesickness. Besides, there was nothing else to do. His uncle could not keep him in Port Mahon any longer; there were enough mouths in that house already. And the hut near the Altar of the Gentiles, in the boulders of Fererias, where he had been born and lived till a year ago, had been picked clean before his mother died. He had her rosary of sea-snail shells and his father's knife; that was all one could expect.

Moreover, his adventure would not be a lonely one. When the ships passed out by St. Philip's Castle next week, on the track

Spanish Bayonet

the beaten Almojarife had travelled toward Barbary with his people, his books of magic, his Moorish gowns and his fifty swords, more than a thousand Mahonese would be aboard, men, women and children, pet lizards, pots and scapulars. Sebastian saw himself in the future for an instant, gazing out over the foreign landscape of his fifty acres with a burst ripe fig half-eaten in his hand and a child making scrawls with a stick in the dust before his doorstep. Then he turned away from his post of musing with a smile on his mouth.

He had made his confession at Easter and been absolved—the past was balanced, the future incomprehensible,—but tonight he could dance with a free heart. He followed the clue of the music along mazy alleyways, his body a little giddy at times from weeks of undernourishment, but his mind at peace. At last he came out where the wider street was crowded with the grave dancers and the throb of the guitars echoed like silver blood in the dark veins of heaven. He stood for a moment, observing the scene.

The street was lit by torches—occasionally one of them would sputter and send up a shower of tiny golden bees in the still air. Beneath them the dissolving patterns of the dance formed and broke and reformed again like a shower of the colored petals of flowers stirred by light wind. The women danced discreetly, their eyes cast on the ground; the men were more extravagant in their gestures; but in the faces of both, the eyes were large with starvation and solemn with joy. The rebozillas pinned about the heads of the women did not hide the faint hollows in their cheeks—hunger had given them a new and extenuate beauty—their feet seemed lighter to them and a little mad. The red worsted girdles of the men were drawn tighter about their bodies, their cheeks showed the play of hunger too, but their broad flat shoes of white leather slapped gallantly on the stones; and in a corner of shadows the musicians plucked at their ribboned instruments yet more swiftly and the dance went on and on, without beginning or end.

Occasionally, without apparent reason, the musicians would give in unison a short sonorous cry, and the bystanders would call out at once "Long live the dancers!" in reticent approval, to be echoed by a low, soft murmur from the dancers of "Long live the lookers-on!" Such was the courtesy of Minorca, and to Sebastian, as he watched, the murmurous call and response turned

115

to the perpetual cooing of the ringdoves in the sea-caves where his father had been drowned and the red of worsted girdle and Phrygian cap was the blood of the sun sinking into the waters of evening above the Altar of the Gentiles, and music touched at the heart, and an island was hard to leave. But presently he found himself dancing, too—aloofly and arrogantly as befits a man of fifteen.

He hardly noticed his partner—the torches threw confusing shadows, her eyes were averted, her mouth hidden behind her black fan. Presently one of the bystanders called out to him gayly in the permissible words, "Say a word to her! Say a word to her!" He responded mechanically in the set and ancient compliment, "What would you have me say to her but that she has the face of a rose?" and there was a clapping of hands. But her face, as the fan drooped aside for an instant in acknowledgment, was not like that of a rose but a darker and more barbarous flower. He sought idly for the name of such a flower for a moment, then the thought passed from his mind and the pattern of the dance took its place. "Ha! Ha!" cried the musicians and stamped their feet—"Spain! Spain!" twanged the strings of the guitars.

It was some time later and Sebastian was wholly absorbed in the flow of the dance, when the little ape on the roof of one of the houses overlooking the street, decided that there might be pickings down among men if he were bold enough to go and look for them. He was very hungry but equally terrified and the more recent events of his life had given him little confidence in humanity. Bought from a Barbary Jew by the master of a Spanish merchantman and sold again in Mahon harbor to a drunken private of the Royal Irish Foot, he had tasted the characteristics of three different nations of mankind in the last few weeks and found each as bitter and strange as the cold, stinging waters of the sea. He was a young, uninstructed ape, smaller than most of his tail-less species—and his disposition normally inclined toward the cheerful. But his heart was gloomy now, and the fur of his body miserable.

There were neither proper victuals nor people of his race in this stony region and he could not forget the fight between his latest master and another bellowing, red-furred giant which had given him his liberty some hours ago. The sergeant had made suggestions anent the succulent qualities of roasted monkey which the other had not treated with due respect—but a knowledge of this was spared the cause of the combat who regarded all the various, inexplicable noises emitted by the human race with the same timid disdain. Their occupations, too, seemed both futile and mysterious, he thought as he shivered on his rooftop, watching the dance. One never could expect anything of them but curious pawings and tweakings and a series of imprisonments in places that smelt indelicately of humanity. But his hunger drove him, and presently he slipped down the wall of the house to crouch a moment in the shadows at its foot, peering about with quick, startled, melancholy eyes.

The dancers did not observe him but a boy half-asleep in a doorway did, came awake abruptly and ran, shouting and waving his arms. Quite distraught with terror at once, the monkey lost his wits completely and darted blindly between the feet of the dancers. Great jostling bodies trampled all about him and his nostrils were full of the unpleasing odor of man. He ran this way and that confusedly for an instant while everyone shouted and pointed, and then suddenly leaped for refuge at something tall and stationary which, if Fate were really a monkey, might prove to be some new sort of tree. It was not a tree but a man, and he knew it while he was yet in the air, but at least he was off the dangerous ground. He clung to the man's shirt, half-dead and hardly daring to breathe. But the man stayed perfectly still, and, after a while, the monkey felt a finger rubbing his fur the right way.

The incident had only halted the dance for a moment. It continued now; the boy, his brief excitement forgotten, fell asleep in his doorway again; "Say a word to her! Say a word to her!" called the loungers by the walls to another dancer; the music caught new fire from crafty hands. Sebastian was the only person much affected—he had dropped out of the dance and stood a little removed now, gently stroking the monkey's back.

He could not have said why he had protected the little creature—the Latin has no great native tenderness for animals, and while monkeys were a rarity in Minorca, no one but a mad Englishman would buy such a thing. But as he looked into the wrinkled and mournful face of the animal clinging at his breast, he knew that he intended to keep it if he could, even take it with

117

him on his travels. It was bad to refuse shelter to the shelterless, and, though this petitioner had no soul, he came dressed as a friar and so deserved the hospitality of a Christian—but those were not the real reasons, "Besides, we are both alone in the world," thought Sebastian—but that was no reason, either, for a world where many were alone. What the true springs of his action had been, he could not have said.

"You shall have a little gold collar and sit on a perch when I have my fifty acres," he confided to the monkey. The monkey, hearing a new noise, thought he was to be beaten and looked up prepared to bite—so it seemed to Sebastian as if he had understood. After a moment Sebastian fumbled a piece of cord from his pocket and tied one end about the monkey's neck—an attention the latter accepted with passive resignation—at least this latest owner seemed quieter than the others. "There," said Sebastian. "No, you must not bite at the cord—we are going to the Floridas, monkey, you and I—we shall be rich there, monkey," and he pulled his coat around further so the monkey should be warm. Then his eyes turned away from his new possession and lost themselves in watching the dance—and presently the girl who had been his partner and whose face was like some flower more savage than the rose came over and stood near him, her fan moving in a slow regular beat that ruffled the soft black fur on the top of the monkey's head.

PART ONE:

THE PRIDE OF THE COLONIES

Some five years later, the merchantman, "Pride of the Colonies," bound out of New York for St. Augustine, was running before a fresh breeze down the blue, sparkling plain of the Atlantic. The single passenger she carried, a young man named Andrew Beard, was seated in a sort of improvised chair by the lee-rail, watching the milk-streaked ribbon of her wake dwindle out continually along the broad, endless back of the sea, with that idle, rather pleasant monotony of mind which comes to those who have been many days on the water without much active occupation. A small, brown, dumpy copy of Mr. Pope's translation of the Iliad lay in his lap, and his forefinger mechanically kept the place where he had left off reading. He had been drawn from the book by a certain, inert curiosity as to whether the color of the waters of any ocean might fitly be compared with the color of wine—and having decided, sleepily, that not even the palest vintages of the Rhine, beheld through green Venetian glass, could match the occasional streaks of lucid emerald where the trace of the ship's wake grew faint as the imprint of a feather on velvet, had excused himself from further concern at present with the doings of the well-greaved Achaeans.

He had never felt either so well or so lazy and New York and the life he had led till this voyage began seemed very small and distant—a diminutive red city with paper snow on its gables, imprisoned in a glass bubble that the sea had washed away. Tomorrow, Captain Stout had said, they were likely to sight the lighthouse on Anastasia Island, and journey's end—but at the moment the journey still seemed infinite. It was impossible to think that in a little while the last sound in his head as he fell asleep at night would not be the strain of the breeze in the cordage and the complaint of wood against wind and water or that he would ever rise again in the morning to look out upon a solid and unfluctuating world. Nevertheless, these things would be so, and swiftly. It behooved him, against his will, to think of what lay in store for him beyond the horizon, and why he had lived all this time with a seashell held close to his ear.

A series of inconsecutive pictures passed before his eyes. He was a little boy, stiffly seated in a high, banister-backed chair before a gleaming mirror, his eyes sober with excitement, as that most impressive of men, his father's barber, who lived in a shop full of sweet-smelling bottles with a great gold basin hung over the front door, arranged upon his shorn head with deft, pale, long fingers the tiny, marvellous wig that had come in a box from London, and, wonder of wonders, crowned it at last with a little laced hat, just like his older brother's even to its Kevenhuller cock.

He smiled—how proud he had been of that ridiculous wig and what a fight he had had with the butcher's boy who had asked him jeeringly if old Sandy Beard was setting up for a Lord. Fashions had changed, and little boys could wear their own hair now, even when their fathers were as important merchants as Alexander Beard. The thought called up an image of his father's huge, cool storehouses down by the water and a gang of Negroes, singing together in rich, deep, mournful voices, as they unloaded merchandise consigned to Alexander Beard and Son from a ship just come to port from strangely-painted corners of the map. Wherever the commerce of New York Colony voyaged, Alexander Beard's name was known and his signature good.

The storehouses disappeared, and in their place, for some reason, Andrew saw the silver-sanded floor of a Dutch kitchen. He was munching an oelykoek and Gerrit Jans was telling him stolidly of the wonders of St. Nicholas who stuffed the wooden shoes of godly little boys in Holland with crullers and toy windmills and silver skates on his name-day. . . . The heavy, flowery scent of the catalpa-trees outside the King's Arms, on Broadway between Crown and Little Prince Streets, where the officers came from Fort George, mixed, somehow, with the odor of mignonette and sweet-william in his mother's garden in the country. She was walking along the bricked path on a hot, Spring morning, with her green calash shading her stern, fine face, and a small painted basket of seeds in her hand.

Then he was one of a group of boys running home past the Fort on a chill, green winter evening, not daring to look aside lest Governor Sir Danvers Osborne, who had hanged himself on the palisade after five days of office, should suddenly be dangling there to appall them, with his silk-handkerchief noosed around his neck . . . he was sitting on his brother Lucius' knees watching the historic cockfight out on the Germantown road when Massachusetts Boy had beaten and killed Mr. Signet's long-undefeated Cock of the North . . . he was walking with his father underneath the arches of the Exchange, unspeakably proud at being allowed to hold his father's gold-headed cane and see him converse with the great ones of the city.

The images faded. He sighed, lazily. Boyhood had been a good time. If he had never been as dashing as Lucius, he had always admired Lucius far too much to envy him and had been well content to take second place. As for Peggy, poor child, he certainly did not envy her—with her stiff, buckram stays clamped on her round, adolescent body, and the long needle stuck upright in the front of her dress for an hour each day to teach her to

Spanish Bayonet

hold her chin erect as a young girl of quality should. Somewhere
among his baggage he had the letter case stitched with red and
green silk that had been her damp, parting gift to him—and how
she had begged him to bring her home a little alligator from the
Floridas! He smiled amusedly. He felt quite old enough to be
Peggy's grandfather, now that he was travelling alone on important business for his father—though he was only twenty-one
and she was fourteen.

By the way, he must look at his new case of pistols again. He
had been warned particularly against letting the sea-air rust
them. But the thought of the pistols brought up the troubled
state of the times to his mind, and his eyes narrowed. It seemed
to him that through all the years of his boyhood, New York had
been in a constant turmoil of celebrations and protests and placards on the walls. The Stamp Act—the Liberty poles—the repeal
of the Stamp Act and the new gilded statue of a togaed King
George ramping upon a fat, embarrassed charger in the Bowling
Green—the liberty boys with their rowdy songs and their continual scuffles with the soldiers—this tea business, now. Lucius, too
—he knew that his father suspected Lucius, for all his dandyism,
of secret affiliations with the more fashionable wing of the so-
called Friends of Liberty—young Gouverneur Morris and some
of the Livingston set. He himself did not care so much for young
Gouverneur Morris. His celebrated King's College oration upon
Wit and Beauty might be of as marbled an elegance as the conversation of Rasselas, Prince of Abyssinia—but he wore a conscious little air of prodigy that irked Andrew's soul.

Andrew stirred, uneasily, and wondered what the latest news
was from the madmen in Boston. He remembered his father's
bitter description of that troublesome John Hancock—"a rattle-
tongued spendthrift who has wasted two fortunes on fine clothes
and sedition"—mincing along the streets at noonday in a scarlet
velvet cap, red morocco slippers and a blue damask gown. It
would have been fun, if you had been unlucky enough to be born
in Boston, to paint yourself up like an Indian and dump tea
chests into gray water. But it was a boy's exploit, for all that,
hardly worth the attention of a level-headed New Yorker. When
the New York tea-ship arrived, the world would see how a really
civilized colony dealt with such matters. He was sorry to be out
of it all—the meeting of protest at the City Hall had been most

121

impressive, though noisy. Still, it was quite unthinkable that the present tangle would lead to anything really serious. They would repeal the tea-tax as they had repealed the Stamp Act—such pushing Massachusetts gentry as Hancock and Sam Adams would be taught a lesson—the Livingston faction sing smaller for a while—and people drive out in Italian chaises to Turtle Bay for fish-suppers to the end of time.

He yawned, and turning his head, took in the steady eyes and the broad, leathery chest of the helmsman of the ship. For a boyish moment he envied the man completely the easy strength of his hands, and the blue tail of the tattooed mermaid disappearing under his shirt. Then he told himself sternly that he had pistols in his cabin, and at twenty-one, was already the master of an errand that could command the bodies of a dozen such able seamen. He tried over a phrase or two of textbook Spanish in his mind and then, sailor and errand alike dismissed for the moment, settled back to reading Mr. Pope's Homer at the passage where Hector bids Andromache farewell in the choicest of Addisonian English.

2.

Nevertheless, in the privacy of his cabin that night, as he lay on one arm, staring out through the open porthole at stars that seemed already tropical and soft in a languid heaven, certain fragments of his last long conversation with his father recurred to his mind to trouble it obscurely. For one thing, not one of the many excellent reasons for his present journey to the South had seemed particularly urgent till the trouble over the tea-tax grew to a head.

He had suffered from colds and occasional fever for some two winters, and the doctor had diagnosed a weakness of the lungs and recommended a sea-voyage toward warmer climates—that was true enough. And it was undoubtedly true that, since his health had not permitted him to finish his course of studies at King's College, he should begin to learn the ins and outs of the great merchant-house of Alexander Beard and Son. But there had been something in his father's eyes, when they talked together of the trip, that had disquieted him. For one thing he had never conceived before that his father might be uncertain of or puzzled by anything on earth.

He had started out firmly enough with, "Andrew—how's your cough?"

"About the same, sir," said Andrew, coughing.

"H'm—sit down, lad—I thought so. Well, my son, you'll be rid of it shortly, if Dr. Summerall knows his business. Can you sail on the 'Pride of the Colonies' for St. Augustine two weeks from now—on my business?"

"Yes sir," said Andrew, at once dumbfounded and very flattered. It was the first time in his life that his father had treated him entirely as an equal.

"Good son," said Alexander Beard and played with the feathers of a goose-quill a moment. "It may be business of weight, Andrew. I would go myself if," he hesitated, "if times were more settled, d'ye see?—yes—I might go myself—but as things are—" He frowned and lost himself in staring at something dubious he seemed to see in the wood of the table. After a while, "You may think it strange I don't send your brother," he said.

Here was something that Andrew, in the innocence of his heart, had never even considered. The glittering Lucius seemed to him far too splendid an adornment of the house of Beard to be spared for any such errand. He said something of the sort.

"Your obleeged servant sir, I'm sure, but Lucius is a damned macaroni!" said Alexander Beard abruptly, then, as Andrew grew rigid with loyalty, "Sorry, boy—I lost my temper then—but your brother, Lucius—if you can inform me why your brother Lucius" (the goose-quill rapped on his knuckles) "makes such friends of the pack of ranting Mohocks that set up barber's poles to Liberty all over the town—"

"My brother, sir," said Andrew, stiffly, "has his own political opinions, but—"

"But, but, but," said his father impatiently. "Oh your brother's a damned fine fellow—but he'll marry that Livingston wench before he's done and set the De Lanceys against him for good and all—if he doesn't do worse and go to bed with some Boston madam who thinks Sam Adams is God Almighty because he talks like a codfish. A plague on them all, I say—a plague out of Egypt—" He threw the snapped goose-quill aside.

Andrew was silent—his father's tempers were rare, but when they came, they had to run their course. He tried not to hear what his father was saying about the Livingstons and the De Lanceys. His father's passionate reverence for James De Lancey, the dead ex-Governor, had always irked him queerly, and he had never been able to see the great, stately family coach roll by behind its famous white horses without a secret feeling of discontent. He remembered the time it had drawn up before their own door and the arrogant, courteous, languid gentleman who was carried like a phial of holywater inside it had descended to take a glass of Malaga with an Alexander Beard whose hands and manner were suddenly and definitely obsequious. That had happened when Andrew was only a small boy, but the imprint of it had remained on his mind. He had not been sorry, a little later, to stand in the crowd and watch the long black worm of the funeral procession wind slowly, with its gilt-escutcheoned hearse, toward Trinity Church, while the minute guns from Copsey Battery tolled out the fifty-seven years of the dead man's life.

"A great gentleman," his father was saying. He sighed. "And yet one that would drink his glass of wine in my house and never once—" He checked himself.

Andrew stirred rebelliously. "Father! But why should not even a gentleman like Governor De Lancey take wine in our house?"

"Why not indeed?" said his father, and smiled. "Why not indeed?"

The words were gently-spoken, but at their implication, Andrew felt the steady world rock under his feet.

"But, Father, we—we've always been—gentle—haven't we?"

"Gentle enough, of a surety," said his father, with eyes averted. "Or why should my eldest son be able to carry a sword?"

"But—the Beards of Westmoreland, sir—" said Andrew, horrified. Somehow, he had always taken gentility for granted. Now, in a brief moment, the very fabric of pleasant existence grew infirm.

"Aye," said his father, quietly. "The Beards of Westmoreland. Of a truth no one can say that there are not Beards in Westmoreland," and he actually chuckled. For an instant Andrew was appalled to find himself almost hating him. In his mind, he had walked through the green, English park of that Westmoreland estate a thousand times—he had rubbed the brown dust away with his finger from the names of the tombs in the chapel that ran back before Elizabeth. And yet, now that he came to think of it, park and manor-house and chapel alike had all been built of the insubstantial stuff of his own imagination. His father had never told him one word about his people. Now, suspicion once awake, he could see those imaginary ancestors and their signs of honor, crumble slowly to ash before him—leaving only a shopkeeper's family, uneasy with new-got riches, their backs supple whenever a gentleman passed in the street—and he felt naked and ashamed.

Something of what he felt and thought must have been written in his face, for "Dinna hurt yourself so, laddie," said his father now, his speech slipped suddenly back to the burr of the countryman. "That's the benefit of a new country. A man starts more even. And your mother's folk are gentle—and—well—we can all say with right that we're gentle, now. But nevertheless— no, ye wouldn't understand—but when Governor De Lancey came to my house—"

He left the words in the air, seeing their uselessness. What he said was true. Andrew could not understand. He could not look back through the years and see what his father saw—the little boy in the rough fur cap and the blue-yarn stockings staring round-eyed from the door of the catchpenny shop to see the fine gentleman's coach whirl past in a glory of gilt and glass and trampling white horses—the lank, burningly-ambitious, young man with ink on his fingers who had found in James De Lancey a patron worthy of worship. The little boy and young man had come a long and hazardous way to the impressive new house on the right side of Wall Street, with its fashionable cupola and the Turkey carpets on its floors—but the stages of that epic were hidden from Andrew, and father and son looked at each other across a barrier that would not fall.

"Well, sir," said his father at last, breaking the deep silence, "as to this matter of the Floridas—"

The ensuing conversation helped Andrew back on his feet again at the time, though, remembered, certain things rose in a cloud of silver bubbles to fret him. He had always known his father's business interests wide, but now, for the first time, he saw them unroll before him like a parti-colored map on the dark table, and it made him proud. Even down in that strange, hot, spicy peninsula so lately Spain's, his father's eyes saw the long rows of indigo, cut down in the moment of flowering, and counted the profit of traffic with swamp Indians, hidden like alligators in the marshes, and the yield of fields of sugar cane he had never seen in the flesh.

It appeared that his father had had some dealings already with this Scotch Dr. Hilary Gentian who had brought his mixed cargo of Minorcans, Greeks and Italians to colonize the hammock-lands below St. Augustine. "An ingenious man, sir, but pressed for money—and the men in London never understand that. They think a colony grows as easily as a thistle patch, once it's seeded—'tis more like an asparagus-bed—you can't expect returns for the first few years." Yet there had been some returns already—the indigo alone had brought in three thousand pounds during the last year. "Then there are his sugar works—and the hemp and maize and barilla. But they began with over two thousand souls to feed and were much harassed by sickness, I understand. You must be free with your glass, boy, when you reach there—they say a free glass wards off the fevers."

Andrew listened dazzled, seeing the strange landscape rise before him with its blue sea and its tufted palms and its smell of alien blossoms. And yet the deep-seated reason, if there were one, for his immediate departure remained unexplained to him. Dr. Gentian had been warned of his probable arrival—that made Andrew blink a little—his father had never really mentioned the project before. He was to remain at New Sparta for a number of months at least—half-guest, half-apprentice in the ways of such a plantation, always his father's agent. "I would have you write me most fully of all that comes to your mind—particularly as to whether such a venture as Dr. Gentian's might be profitably copied by other gentlemen of sufficient fortune."

Now what had his father meant by that? Surely he could not be thinking of transferring part of his interests to the distant Floridas? But there was more. "Also, sir, and most particularly, I would have you note the temper of the colony toward these scatterbrains your brother admires so greatly. I have heard that of all the colonies the Floridas alone feel no whistle-belly grievance against the Crown. If that be so—and these Gadarene swine that call themselves sons of Liberty start running their path to the sea—"

Spanish Bayonet

"But, sir, you cannot really think that—"

"I do not know," said his father, sombrely, "I do not know. God knows there's no reason—but there. I only know where the De Lanceys will stand—if it comes to more than speechifying. And their interest is mine."

"But why must your interest go with any other man's interest?" said Andrew, touchily—the sting still in the old wound his father had reopened.

"Because it must, boy. The one sure loser in any conflict is your neutral—and we're not patroons. It's lucky the Patroon's a minor—they'll be out of it whatever happens. They'd think me mad at the Coffee House if I told them what's at the back of my mind, but let a few years pass and—if your mother could see it as plain as I do and were better able to stomach the trials of a new venture—But 'tis little use talking of that and things may better somehow—You'll need a new fowling-piece and some light sort of gear—they say the sun is hot, though not deadly as it is in India—"

So the conversation had flickered out into a discussion of Andrew's wardrobe and the climate, leaving him with a feeling of mingled insecurity and pride. The abrupt extinction of those long-cherished kinsfolk, the Beards of Westmoreland, rankled now and then, but he could feel no scornful challenge to the accepted dignity of the house of Beard in the air of the city; and a fowling-piece with silver mounts soon wiped out the freshness of the hurt. On the whole he was too anxious to acquit himself well and too awed by the vague magnitude of his responsibilities, to give excessive thought to the gentility of his lineage, or the lack of it.

It occurred to him more than once that his father might be sending him away on a pretext to keep him from mixing too intimately with those friends of Lucius' who met every Thursday to drink toasts of a porcupine saddle, a cobweb pair of breeches and a long gallop to all enemies of Liberty. But even if the queer constraint of Lucius' farewell seemed to bear this theory out— he could not really believe in it when he thought it over. And it was equally impossible to believe with reason that his father actually considered abandoning the house on Wall Street and the cavernous storehouses by the docks for a palmetto-hut by a white-shawled strip of sand just because a row of wigs in a vague

House of Parliament over the water had decided to impose a duty on certain, small, black dried leaves. And yet—

The days of the voyage gave him time to follow many such speculations to no conclusion. Of only one thing could he be sure. The fabric of life had always seemed secure and definite before —now he felt it give under his feet like a floor of fresh pine-boughs and saw things begin to grow unfamiliar that had always been familiar as water and light.

He gave the problem up and began to wonder drowsily just what he would find at New Sparta. Dr. Gentian had a Greek wife and a pair of daughters—or was it a daughter? He saw a tall, high-breasted girl with the face of Nausicaä—then her features sharpened—feathers came on her arms—was she harpy or eagle?— He did not know, but there was a soft thunder of wings about him for an instant, that passed away into the rumble of a cart over the paving-stones, a cart bringing sweet water to the house from the Tea-Water Pump—a blackamoor got out of it, dressed in his brother Lucius' best scarlet coat and was offering him a basket of indigo in the name of Liberty as he fell asleep.

3.

The rumble of the cart was in his ears again as he woke, but he translated it swiftly into accustomed sounds. Bare feet ran on the deck above him to the piping whine of the bosun's whistle—cries answered a bawling voice. He jumped out of his bunk and felt something knock at his heart. Through the round porthole, like a picture held in the circle of a spyglass, was the white stone thumb of a lighthouse and a crawling line of foam on a beach—then, across more water, the vivid green of unex-pected pines and the solid bones of land. The land had been an indented, meaningless line to starboard before, vanishing and re-appearing again like a casual, evanescent mark scrawled hastily on the surface of the universal sea—now it lay broad across the path in a continent, and the sea shrank back again from the illimitable and savage world into measurable blue water, fretting the sides of a cup of rock and sand. He dressed hastily, in a mounting excitement and ran up on deck.

"Have to anchor outside the bar, sir," said Captain Stout. "The

Spanish Bayonet

Pride's a lady—she draws more'n eight feet of water, she does—
Now if she was one of your nasty little French baggages, *which*
she ain't—"

Andrew nodded sagely, paying little attention. Now the actual
land lay so plump before them, he felt a vast, unreasonable impatience at the various petty motions that must be gone through
before they could set foot on it. The air seemed to him to smell
of oranges already and he stared through the captain's spyglass
feverishly, as if doing so would transport him at once to the
shore.

"That's the Fort," said the Captain, pointing, "Spanishy-look-
ing affair, *I* call it—see the lobster-back walking post? Cathedral's
over there—don't know as you can make it out—" He chuckled,
"Queer souls, Spaniards, and that's a fact," he confided. "No spit
and polish about them—no, sir. Don't even have any Christian
sort of a bellringer in the church—just a lame old codger to
rattle the bells with a stick."

Andrew turned to him with a thousand questions on his
tongue.

"How soon before we—"

"Oh, they know we're here," said the Captain, chuckling again.
"See that boat, Mr. Beard? Shouldn't be surprised if Dr. Gentian
was aboard her." His throat suddenly became a leather trumpet.
"*Aye, Mister Mate?*" he roared. He turned away.

The black, struggling bug in the waves jumped into a long-
boat as Andrew put the glass to his eye again. He could see the
sweat start on the backs of the eight Negro rowers as their oars
rose and fell in thrashing dumb-show. But the figure in the stern-
sheets was what held his gaze—if it could be Doctor Gentian.

He had expected such a different personage. A Scotch army-
surgeon turned planter suggested, somehow, a tall, rawboned,
iron-mouthed dragoon in patched kilts and a palmetto hat. This
spruce, erect little figure with the chin and eyes of Caesar was
dressed in black superfine broadcloth, with Mechlin ruffles at the
throat and wrists. His wig was freshly powdered, his gold-laced
hat cocked in the fine extreme of fashion—even Lucius, Andrew
thought, might have been a little awed by the sombre perfection
of his attire. Andrew suddenly realized the incongruity of his
own apparel with a start. He had dressed hastily, in the clothes

he had worn during most of the voyage. After one glance through the spyglass at his host, the glazed hat borrowed from a sailor on his own head, the loose shirt and wide breeches he had thought so aptly nautical, made him feel as if he had strolled into White's in London painted like a Seneca chief. He cast a wild glance around him, but it was too late. They were lowering the Jacob's ladder already. In a moment Dr. Gentian would be aboard.

"Ahoy, Pride of the Colonies!" came a sharp clear voice from the water. "Ahoy, Captain Stout!"

"Ahoy sir!" called the Captain. "Stand by the ladder for Dr. Gentian, you sons of sweeps, or by God I'll—We've a passenger aboard for ye, Doctor!"

The spruce little Caesar in black broadcloth called back something that the wind blew away. Then he was coming up the Jacob's ladder as nimbly as a fly. Andrew shivered with annoyance and embarrassment. Why hadn't the Captain told him the Doctor was like this?

"Mr. Beard?" said the man whom Andrew had visualized as a kilted dragoon. There was a fresh breeze blowing, but not a drop of spray seemed to have spotted his black silk stockings and he stepped across the spattered deck with the quick daintiness of a cat. "Your obliged, obedient servant, Mr. Beard." A ring winked on his outstretched hand.

"Nay, yours, sir," said Andrew, diffidently, and stood staring. He liked Dr. Gentian at first sight—there was something very merry about his mouth. Moreover, he had obviously taken in Andrew's strange attire at one rapid glance, and yet the sight had not perceptibly increased his merriment.

Captain Stout came bumbling up in a sort of respectful fury. "Servant, Doctor Gentian—so you've met your passenger?— good, sir. You'll find him a bit broadened out since he started to voyage with us—none of your night-sweats now, eh, Mr. Beard?— and if you could have seen him set to his victuals after the first natteral squeamishness, sir—By God, the first day out, I thought he'd puke the very anchor up—but after that—"

Andrew felt with abhorrence that his ears were reddening, but Dr. Gentian saved him.

"The sea plays odd tricks on the best of us," he said easily, "I have seen an Admiral of the Blue hold his head in his cabin and wish himself a turnip-patch back on land—the first day out."

He turned to Andrew, "I am glad to hear our good captain is so excellent a victualler. Do you snuff, Mr. Beard?"

"Thank you, sir," said Andrew gratefully, his fingers fumbling at fine rappee in a gold-and-tortoise shell box. The little act somehow set himself and Dr. Gentian apart from the effusive Captain in a world where the immodest allusions of such captains to nausea and victuals were the permitted liberties of old family servants.

"A weakness of mine, I fear," sighed Dr. Gentian, after an elegantly-managed sneeze. Andrew's sneezes had been far less elegant but he noted gratefully that Dr. Gentian had not been critical. Now, though, he grew a little brisk.

"But we must have you ashore, Mr. Beard, as soon as may suit your convenience. Have you breakfasted?"

"Not yet," said Andrew, suddenly conscious that he wished to very much.

Dr. Gentian put his palms together softly. "Excellent. Then you must do me the honor of breakfasting with me at Judge Willo's—we must set out for New Sparta, tomorrow, I fear, but meanwhile it is only fit you should meet some of the gentry of the town. Perhaps Captain Stout would favor us, also—"

"Thankee, Doctor." Somehow the captain had deflated in the last few minutes and seemed awkwardly aware of it. "But I shan't get ashore much before noon, you know—"

"You deprive us of a pleasure, I assure you." The Doctor was smiling again, "Mr. Beard, I venture to hope, will not be so harsh."

"Delighted—certainly—Doctor Gentian," stammered Andrew confusedly, "but—my luggage—"

"I am sure our good captain can send what you find most necessary with us—the heavier luggage can follow later. I have already settled for the services of a barber for you, in case you should need him. A sea-voyage is always trying to one's razors. If there is anything else—you have only to command me—I have a little business to transact with the captain—but if you could be ready to go ashore with your small baggage in half an hour—Your servant till then, sir."

"Yours," said a slightly bewildered but flattered Andrew, and stumbled down below to strip himself hastily of the glazed hat in which he had taken such pride and to thank his stars that he had abandoned the transient idea of having the bosun tattoo the Royal Arms of Great Britain in blue across his chest.

4.

The evening air was light with the frail sweetness of crepe-myrtle; a little wind stirred in the trees like the ghost of a humming-bird. In Judge Willo's dining-room, the cloth had long been drawn and the branched silver candlesticks at either end of the table cast shadowy pools of light that seemed to sink into the grain of the dark mahogany. The wreck of the dessert lay scattered like the relics of a battlefield—a great china punchbowl of bombo had succeeded the St. Lucar wine and gentlemen were beginning to be flushed and loquacious. Andrew, seated between Judge Willo and Dr. Gentian in the post of honor, sipped slowly at the cool deceptive compound of grated nutmeg, sugared water and Antigua rum, and felt a great indefinite affection for all humanity in general and the Floridas in particular rise in his heart.

He was wearing his best India-muslin cravat, his hair was clubbed and powdered, he felt clean and gay and at ease. Already he loved this little, lazy city whose trees were hung with the golden balls of oranges and whose houses were built of a multitude of tiny seashells weathered into stone. He would be sorry to leave it in the morning—the projecting balconies of the old Spanish dwellings had printed their shape on his heart. Many times, in the dreams before dawn, in the cold hour, he would wander the narrow swept streets, for years unmarred by the track of any wheeled vehicle, where the Spanish ladies in the old time had walked in their satin ball-slippers, at evening, with a languid grace.

He finished his glass of bombo with an air of wise melancholy—life was like that. The glass was refilled—he drank again, abstractedly, using on the world. Life was like that, yes. Life was an orange-tree—an orange-tree in flower—and he was getting a little drunk.

Only two things marred his perfect content—his interview with the Governor and the fact that his best shoe-buckles had been slightly tarnished by the sea-air. The Governor was a petulant, worried person who had treated him like a boy. But Dr. Gentian had behaved to the man with freezing civility and apologized for him to Andrew later. "An honest gentleman, Mr. Beard, but alas, no friend of mine." "Then no friend of mine, sir, I'll warrant you!" Andrew had cried sagaciously and Dr. Gentian had thanked him gravely and explained. It appeared that the best of St. Augustine was with them in lacking the Governor's approval.

The candles were growing very bright. Judge Willo's voice in his ear besought him to tell the company again the ridiculous tale of Governor Tryon's escape in his shirt from his burning house and how only the heavy snow on the roofs of the city had saved New York from a general conflagration that winter. It was an effort to find the proper words, but when he did, he was well repaid, for all the gentlemen laughed like thunder and Dr. Gentian clapped him on the back and called him a very Harry Fielding for choiceness of wit. Then he tried to repeat some verse of Phillis Wheatley's, the young Negro poetess who had just made such a stir, but broke down in the middle and only saved himself by saying that he hoped they understood he had meant no disrespect to Governor Tryon by his story.

"Governor Tryon's worthy gentleman," he heard himself repeating. "They called him the Black Wolf in the Carolinas—but he's for the King! And we're all for the King here, aren't we—and damnation to liberty-boys? Who isn't for the King here?" he asked uncertainly, but his query was drowned in a roar of applause as they all stood up and drank to the King. Andrew, drinking too, felt the tears come to his eyes at the thought of such splendid loyalty to the King. He tried to picture the King to himself—he felt he should—but the features kept getting more and more uncertain.

A second bowl of bombo succeeded the first and, some time later, Andrew found himself by a window, gazing out into the garden. His legs seemed subject to occasional, inexplicable wabblings, but the night air, cool on his forehead, was a great refreshment. He glanced back at the room—a stertorous huddle of scarlet on the floor must be that pleasant Major from the garrison, succumbed at last to bombo and the force of gravity—the gentleman in plum-colored velvet whose name he could not remember was asleep with his head in a bowl of nuts—Judge Willo seemed to be making indefinite attempts at song. Andrew felt a great pride that he was still soberly on his feet.

"They say our moonlight here is brighter than yours in the North," said the serene voice of Dr. Gentian in his ear.

" 'Tis very bright, in all conscience," said Andrew a little thickly. The Doctor's glass had been filled as often as any, but he seemed as yet quite untouched by the revel. The small, demure, merry mouth was composed and peaceful, the calm face showed only a tinge of added color, the slight pressure of the fingers on Andrew's elbow was firm and springy as a vise of tough, light whalebone.

"Shall we stroll in the garden a moment and let the air freshen us?"

Andrew assented, with an effort, but a fuddled cry of "Gentian! One moment, Gentian!" called the Doctor away for a moment and Andrew remained at the window, gazing up at the sky and trying to keep a sparkling wheel from whirring about in his head.

The moonlight was bright indeed, the moon huge and pale, the garden crowded with silver trees and flowers. At its foot grew a single bush of Spanish bayonet which seemed to Andrew, as he stared, the most beautiful thing he had ever seen, for it too was in flower, and the single stalk of waxen petals rose out of the green spikes of the plant like a cold plume set upon a barbarous crest. Andrew filled his eyes with the sight of it—it seemed to him, suddenly, as if he had run his hand into the very soil of this new country and touched its heart. Not even the orange-groves could so explain the nature of the land, for they were fruitful and, after a fashion, tamed, but this bush of thorns gave nothing to man but a single bloom of moonlight, serene, careless and wholly pure. More northern latitudes could not suffer such a creation—only in the hot night of the south could the ivory frond arise from among edged blades to challenge a tropic star.

As Andrew considered this, he felt just on the edge of some great discovery—some immense understanding—some gift of tongues—but Dr. Gentian's hand was lightly imperious on his arm again, and he was being led outside to have his eyes dazzled by the moon. The half-made discovery slipped away—the gift of tongues was forgotten. There remained only a leaden body and a flight of stairs unnaturally steep and limitless, up which he was being assisted to lie down at last in a bed that whirled into spinning darkness.

5.

Three days later the events of that evening were forgotten phantasmagoria, and only the shape of the Spanish bayonet stood out distinct and fruitful in Andrew's memory. To have been drunk in good company was nothing to be ashamed of—but the long next day in the saddle had been torment, in spite of all Dr. Gentian's solicitude—and the following one had found Andrew sober enough, but stiff and sore. The third day, however, almost made him regret that they would reach the end of their journey at evening. The air had been flawless since dawn, his first saddle-weariness had abated a little, and he had begun to notice the details of the land.

All morning they had ridden through low barrens, smelling of pine-needles—then the road had turned to swampier country, where red cane fringed the edge of the spongy bay-galls and a thrown stone went in with a sucking sound. Over languid creeks bridged with cedar-planking the road took its way—past swamps where mosquitoes buzzed and alligators slept and rotting ancient trees were hung with Spanish moss like witches' hair—then wound up into the woods again.

They had passed a woodrat's disorderly house of sticks and seen the rat run chattering up a tree with a young rat hanging to its tail. They had slept in the green russell chamber of a manor-house whose furnishings would not have shamed the Patroon and whose master entertained them with music upon the German flute; they had plucked dwarf wild-oranges from stunted, untended trees and ridden, at evening, up a grassy avenue heavy with the sweetness of magnolia-bloom; and once Andrew had seen a cinnamon-colored Indian stare at them for a moment out of the tangled underbrush with eyes black as obsidian beads, to vanish among the leaves as noiselessly as a puff of dandelion seed. Now the shadows were long with late afternoon, the road skirted the river, and New Sparta was near.

"There," said Dr. Gentian as they came to a fork in the road.

Andrew followed the line of his hand and made out a clot of white among distant trees. "The upper road is ours, Mr. Beard— the lower goes down to the colony itself. You shall see it soon enough. For the present," he smiled, "I imagine you have ridden hard enough these last days to postpone the pleasure. The best lands are farther down the river—that is why you see no signs of our industry here."

"I thought you lived in the colony itself, sir," said Andrew, making conversation.

"Not precisely," Dr. Gentian was very amiable. "My own house is over a mile from the wharves—you see, indigo needs space and we have more than a thousand souls in the settlement itself— there were more at first but one always loses a number when men are transplanted to a new climate—"

He chatted on, describing his newly-finished sugar-mill and the system of irrigation he had recently completed. Andrew fell more and more under the spell of that easy, Caesarean voice. Beside this man, with his tales of strange travel in the Indies and the Greek Islands, with his casual chat of the great ones of London and Paris, even Alexander Beard began to seem a little provincial. Now he quoted a passage from the Georgics to illustrate a point in husbandry, and turned from that to a discussion as to whether Dr. Goldsmith's "She Stoops to Conquer," witty though it was, might fitly be compared to the best of the comedies of Plautus. Andrew felt his own mammoth ignorance descend upon him like a heavy velvet pall and thought humbly that Lucius should have come in his place. He resolved to write to Lucius for the best edition of Plautus procurable at Garret Noel's bookshop before the week was out.

He was so engaged in trying to listen intelligently that he did not notice how the road stole away from the river again; and the goal of their three days' ride was almost upon him before he realized it. The great, white coquina house stood on a slight rise of ground, its stables and outbuildings massed behind it. There were lights in its windows, for twilight had fallen, and as the tired horses pricked their ears and whinnied at the thought of oats, servants came running out with lanterns and hubbub. Andrew knew suddenly that he was very tired and struggled from his saddle at last with the stiff awkwardness of a marionette. He was glad to throw the horse's reins to a grinning little boy, but too weary to pay much attention to the bustle about him.

"My dear," said Dr. Gentian and kissed a tall woman with a proud nose and a secret mouth delicately upon the cheek.

136

Spanish Bayonet

"This is our young friend from New York, Mr. Beard, my dear," and Andrew made his manners dutifully to a worn comely hand and words of greeting that had a foreign slur in them. Then there was another hand, warm and pleasant to touch, and he was being introduced to a yellow-haired girl with eyes gray and changing as winter cloud—"My daughter—Miss Sparta Gentian." But she was not at all like his image of Nausicáa and Andrew felt vaguely disappointed. Then he only knew that he was hobbling up the steps of the porch in a disgracefully ungenteel manner, but he could not help it for each of his boots was made of solid stone.

Strength and curiosity returned to him with food and wine, and at last, seated alone with Dr. Gentian while the Madeira passed between them the way of the sun, he began to appraise the circumstances of his new environment.

"You will find we live in simple rusticity, Mr. Beard," Dr. Gentian had said—but if these were Florida notions of simple rusticity! It was true that the servants were not in livery and that the dress of the Gentian ladies was not quite in the latest mode, but otherwise, from the old silver plate on the sideboard to the new forte-piano with Lord Kelly's Overtures upon it in the drawing-room, Andrew might have thought himself enjoying the famous hospitality of a Philipse or a William Walton the elder. That was certainly a fruit-piece by Vandermoulen on the wall, and the Indian chintz hangings of his own bedroom could not have been bettered at the fashionable upholsterer, Joseph Cox's.

His eye was caught by the flash of a green stone on Dr. Gentian's finger. There was cold, precious light in the stone like the light at the bottom of the eyes of a great cat.

"A quaint setting," said his host, politely, "I had it when I served in India. The Begum happened to think me a practitioner in the black arts." He rose, "Shall we join the ladies?"

In the flowered drawing-room, the tall woman with the proud nose and the secret mouth was embroidering upon catgut-gauze with a needle tiny as a fairy's spear and the gray-eyed girl who was not like Nausicáa was seated at the forte-piano, playing. She broke off as they came in.

"I beg you will not cease your playing, Miss Gentian," said Andrew, awkwardly. "I am devoted to the forte-piano," he added, feeling the words were foolish as soon as they were out of his mouth.

"Then I shan't dare continue," said the girl carelessly. "My strumming must sound like a rigadoon on a milkpan to the ears of such a connoisseur—from New York—"

"Miss Gentian—I implore you," said Andrew, embarrassed.

"Oh, if you'll promise me no criticism, I'll play, sir—or sing perhaps—'tis too hot for playing alone—the piano sounds like a locust in August—heat—heat—heat—" she drummed it out on the keys, impatiently. "But sing, sing, what shall I sing? Shall it be Charley over the Water, father, to remind you of the Forty-Five —or let me see—'Bobby Shaftoe,' for Mr. Beard—'Bobby Shaftoe's come from sea—Silver buckles on his—shoon—" she hummed with gipsy impertinence and Andrew winced as he saw her eyes fixed mockingly on his shoe-buckles—"Come, fine ladies and gentlemen —what d'ye lack—lack—"

"Sing 'Beauty Retire,' daughter," said her father quietly. His eyes were intent upon hers and it seemed to Andrew as if he were witnessing some obscure and inaudible struggle of wills between them—a struggle watched by the tall woman in the chair with great weariness of mind.

"That old thing? Oh, very well—I'm a dutiful daughter. You'll pardon our rusticity, Mr. Beard—we have none of your New York novelties here in songs or ladies—" She struck a chord on the forte-piano as if she hated it, and began to sing.

"Beauty retire—retire—" she sang,

> "Retire—retire, thou dost my pity move
> Believe my pity and then trust my love—"

Her voice was extraordinarily pure and moving. Andrew, listening, thought of skeins of rock-crystal, flecked through and through with tiny flakes of the softest gold—of a golden box where a crystal bird beat and beat its wings in trammelled, scornful delight. Her face had turned grave as she sang, and a little drowsy, as if some excess of vitality came to her through the act of singing and suffused the veins of her heart with a sleepy power. She was like a child now, Andrew thought—a beautiful, daunting child—

Spanish Bayonet

The song ceased, and Andrew, back in his chair again, stammered some sort of compliment. But she would not sing again. Instead she professed an interest in paduasoys and cordova-water and the genuineness of the reported mode in sage-green cloaks trimmed with ermine. Andrew, trying vainly to remember the cut of the sleeves on the last fashion doll from London, made but heavy weather of it. But he did not mind, for the girl seemed to have forgotten her obvious first intention of being rude to him, and he was able to watch the play of her smooth hands as she talked. Her foreign strain came out in that, he thought—no New York girl of his acquaintance would have gestured with such fluid deftness. He saw her hands for a moment as separate and living creatures, molding Tanagra clay to the shape of a precious urn.

Then at last Dr. Gentian was offering him a candlestick and he was bidding them all good night. He happened to say good night to the daughter last of all and the warm touch of her hand went with him all the way up the stairs, as if he had dipped his fingers in quicksilver for an instant and seen them come out silvered. Dr. Gentian accompanied him to his door.

"Good night, Mr. Beard. You will find the mosquito-net at the foot of your bed a necessity. We are not so much troubled with them here as down at the colony—but they have a particular passion for strangers."

"Many thanks for the warning, sir," Andrew smiled. "Good night."

The smiling little Caesar in black broadcloth passed down the long corridor with a wavering flame in his hand and disappeared. Andrew turned toward his own door, yawning. A spot of hot wax fell on the back of his hand—he swore and dropped his candle, which fuffed and went out. He groped blindly for it in the sudden pitch a moment and then stood up. Another will-o'-the-wisp of light trembled far down the corridor, and came nearer. He waited—perhaps the Doctor had noted his misadventure and was coming back with a new candle for him.

The will-o'-the-wisp grew and became a candle held in the hands of a girl. For a moment he thought, with a beat in his heart, that it might be Sparta Gentian, but it was not. This girl seemed about Miss Gentian's age and height but the faint, deceptive flame she carried illuminated dark brows and darker eyes, a skin tinctured with the sun, a mouth ripened by it. Seen thus, in a weak halo of light which defined no more than head and shoulders and hands, the features were startlingly like those of some worn young Madonna of olivewood in the stone niche of a Spanish church, and Andrew excused himself easily enough for watching from his dark doorway.

No, she was not beautiful as Sparta Gentian was, in the way of a golden rose, but she had her qualities. The face was at once more reticent and more untamed—the manner had an odd dignity as of one who lives in oppression but is not afraid. He thought of the Spanish bayonet, in flower in Judge Willo's garden, under the swimming moon. Then he realized with a little shock, as the girl drew nearer, that from her dress she must be a servant in the house, and stepped forward abruptly to borrow light from her taper.

"Can you—" he began, but got no further, for the girl saw him suddenly, cried out, and dropped her candle, which went out instantly, leaving the corridor a pit of black velvet. He heard footsteps running away from him and called again, but there was no reply. He stayed futilely in the corridor for some time, cursing himself for forgetting that any serving-wench might well be frightened at a strange voice speaking suddenly out of gloom, and waiting for sounds that would tell him his idiocy had aroused the house. But the running footsteps ceased after a brief moment as if they had plunged into quicksand, and were followed by no sound at all. At first he was more than glad of this—then the continued quiet began to finger at his spine.

The girl had made noise enough to wake any ordinary set of sleepers, yet no one seemed to have stirred. And why had she cried out just once, when he first spoke to her and not again— a frightened maid in most houses would have screamed her throat dry. He stood uneasily in his doorway till doing so began to seem ridiculous, of a sudden feeling insecure and a stranger in a soft and hostile night. Then he went into his room and shut his door very carefully as if to shut out entirely the deeper darkness in the corridor. But he had an uncanny feeling that it seeped in after him, and would have given a gold Johannes to be able to find his tinder-box. Presently, though, his eyes became more accustomed to the gloom. He thought of the clear stream of Sparta Gentian's voice as it flowed over golden sand in "Beauty Retire" and hummed to himself as he undressed in the dark.

6.

The morning was so bright and calm, that he could afford to laugh at his fears of the night. He found one of the light striped-cotton suits that Mr. Windlestraw at the Sign of the Needle and Shears had assured him were all the fashion in the Southern Colonies and put it on. From his window he could see Dr. Gentian walking about his garden. The merry-mouthed Doctor seemed all content this morning, he was whistling a tune as he walked and now and then paused to smell at a flower or chirrup to a bird. He wore a broad leaf-hat and a flowered dressing-gown and looked more comfortably like the planter of Andrew's imagination. When Andrew bade him good morning, he found him observing a hedged-in patch of cactus on which tiny, red and brown insects crawled like baby ladybugs.

"Observe an industry that shames lazy fellows like you and myself, Mr. Beard," he called gayly as Andrew came up to him. "Those are cochineal insects—they have but two ends in life—to eat and make dye for our garments. I am experimenting with them now—perhaps next year we can produce the dye in quantities worth your London merchants' notice. Strange, is it not, that a little bug should carry royal colors in its belly?"

He delicately shook a few of the insects in his cupped palm and extended it for Andrew's inspection. They ran about it like tiny drops of blood, in an intent, blind busyness. Andrew looked at them with interest, feeling it strange that they did not stain the Doctor's white hand. The man was certainly a compound of the most diverse interests. Now one of the insects fell from the enclosing hand. The Doctor set his foot on it, idly. Andrew shivered.

"After breakfast you shall make the grand tour of our settlement," promised the Doctor, replacing the other insects on their fleshy green feeding-place with exquisite care.

Two things stuck in Andrew's mind particularly from that first confused trip of inspection—the babbling sound of water in the network of irrigation-canals that made New Sparta like a tropical Venice of palmetto and coquina—and the stink of the rotting indigo in the great vats in the fields where it was steeped and beaten and settled. He had never encountered such an overpowering and all-pervasive stench or such clouds of flies. "You may understand now, why my own house is built some distance from the fields," said the Doctor, offering Andrew the gilt pomander he carried in his hand, and Andrew, putting it gratefully to his nose, understood indeed.

"I don't see how your men endure it," he confessed.

"Oh—they grow accustomed," said the Doctor, carelessly. He addressed a question in lilting Italian to a bronzed statue whose naked neck crawled with flies. The statue grinned nervously with white teeth and replied.

"He says it stinks no worse than a Minorcan," translated the Doctor, smiling. "You would think that when men came to a new country they might give up the narrower prejudices of race—but not so. My Italians hate my Minorcans and my Greeks hate them both. There is always bad blood between one or the other. Of course they intermarry, too, but that only makes things worse."

He spoke casually, as of a herd of serviceable but unruly animals, and Andrew sympathized with him. The headship of a mixed colony such as this, must be a constant balancing upon thorns, though the Doctor did not seem bowed down. He walked among his men with the easy grace of a beast-tamer, and yet, Andrew noticed, with the same alert and penetrating eye.

"But which are the Minorcans?" said Andrew, vaguely looking for some odd, distinctive type of body or skull, as they passed along.

The Doctor smiled. "There is one," he said, pointing. "That fellow testing the vat. I forget his name."

Andrew looked. Four men with their trousers rolled above their knees and their legs stained with dye-water were churning the liquor in the beating-vat with a lever that had two bottomless square buckets at either end; and a younger man, at the side, was stooping over occasionally to dip out some of the liquor in a wooden cup and test it. Andrew caught his breath as he looked at this man; he thought he had never seen so fine a human creature. The fellow was of the middle height and seemed of Andrew's years—but so perfectly and aptly proportioned was he that Andrew felt himself clumsy and rudely-fashioned in comparison. The sun, which had fairly blackened the skins of many of the colonists, had only browned him to the deep tawniness of fine Spanish leather, his face wore the aloof dignity of a sombre prince, and every movement of his body was as deft as a gymnast's. Andrew could have visualized him far more easily dispensing justice from a stone chair of state or riding a horse to war clad in antique armor, than stirring indigo-muck. He said something of the sort.

"A good man, though sullen like most of them," Dr. Gentian agreed. "All the Mahonese are a fine-looking lot. Meaninglessly fine. The Greeks are much sharper. But that fellow knows his business. Few of them can judge a test rightly—and judgment's the secret of indigo-culture—for if the beating and churning there is stopped too soon some of the dye-matter stays in solution and if beat too long it begins to dissolve again. Either way you get bad indigo. This is the second cutting now—we hope for five cuttings this season if all goes well. The profit will mean we can finish our fort and add to the sugar-works. The fort will lie over there—it commands the wharves and the storehouses—"

Andrew looked across fields checkered with irrigation and beheld vast raw foundations of coquina.

"I should not have thought you needed so large a defensive work in a peaceable colony," he said, somewhat astonished. He had already noted the colony's guard-house with its garrison of eight bored soldiers—but this new work would hold a company, at least, and was planned for cannon.

"We had trouble here two years ago," said Dr. Gentian briefly. "The ringleaders were hanged in St. Augustine. And then—most of the Indians are peaceable enough—but Cowkeeper, the Creek Chief, is a mischief-maker. Ah, Mr. Cave," as a heavy-set man in his thirties, with a red, sweating face and odd, crumpled-looking ears, came toward them with his broad hat in his hand.

"This is Mr. Beard, Mr. Cave—the young gentleman I was speaking of before I went to St. Augustine. Mr. Cave, our chief overseer, Mr. Beard—"

"Servant, I'm sure," grunted Mr. Cave in a piggy voice and stared at Andrew intently. His eyes were a dull, hard blue, with reddened rings about them, and Andrew felt uncomfortable under their gaze.

Stephen Vincent Benét

"Mr. Cave comes from an English family," said Dr. Gentian pleasantly. "He is my right hand."

He laid his fingers on Mr. Cave's bare forearm, as if in acknowledgment of Mr. Cave's abilities, and Andrew saw the muscles twitch an instant under that light touch.

"Dr. Gentian's very kind," said Mr. Cave defiantly. "He knows how to treat a man, Dr. Gentian does."

"Mr. Cave flatters me sadly," said the Doctor, sniffing his pomander. "He is aware how indispensable he is to us all. You and Mr. Cave must be better acquainted, Mr. Beard. We must have Mr. Cave to supper—tonight, perhaps," he continued reflectively. "Will you sup with us tonight, Mr. Cave?"

"Thank you sir. You're very kind indeed," said Mr. Cave, again with that strange rebelliousness in his voice. Andrew thought him a queer, ungenteel sort of person and wondered at the Doctor's tolerance of his eccentricities. But doubtless he made a good chief-overseer.

"And, by the way," said Dr. Gentian, amiably, "you must be provided with a body-servant, Mr. Beard—I grieve I did not think of it before. Perhaps Mr. Cave would recommend us one. Shall it be a Greek, Mr. Cave—or an Italian—or one of your favorite Mahonese?"

"Don't ask me, sir," growled Mr. Cave with a bull-like shake of his head. "They all look alike to me—the lot of them. Not one of them's worth a sucked sugar cane, if you want my advice."

"Come, come, Mr. Cave, we must not belittle our good colonists," said the Doctor in light reproof that made Mr. Cave's muscles twitch anew. He turned to Andrew. "What preference have you, Mr. Beard?"

"I am confident that anyone Mr. Cave recommends," said Andrew, a little puzzled. Mr. Cave gave a brief, uncivil bark of laughter. "But I did not understand—I thought they were all free colonists—I mean—I did not think they would be willing to do body-service for a—"

"Oh, we'll have no trouble with that," said Dr. Gentian, briskly. "All free colonists, of course—but lazy fellows, you know, Mr. Beard—lazy fellows like most of us—" he chirruped in tones of mock condemnation. "Any one of them would be only too glad to get out of the fields for a while and take life easy in the cool of the big house. I admit it was not my first intention to use them

144

for such work. I had a shipload of Negroes on the way—but the ship was wrecked," he sighed, "and the sea ate up my poor blackamoors—a pity—a great pity—I've not felt justified in expending further monies on slaves since then, so we've had to scratch along as best we could. By the way," he continued airily, "I understand you had an encounter with my daughter's maid last night—she's a Mahonese."

"I beg to assure you sir—it was very clumsy of me—" said Andrew, flushing.

"Not at all," said Dr. Gentian, "don't trouble your mind with it further, I beg of you. The poor silly girl was frightened and took you for a ghost—they're very superstitious. I assure you she won't behave in such a foolish manner again." He tapped his pomander and looked at Andrew.

"A hot, dogged wench—that Minorca piece," said Mr. Cave with ugly abruptness, and Andrew decided then and there that he definitely disliked Mr. Cave.

His behavior at supper that evening did not make Andrew like him any better, though it did produce a certain tinge of contemptuous pity for him. The man fumbled absurdly with his food, through the meal, in a dour silence, his reddened brow bent on his plate, in spite of all the genial Doctor's attempts to draw him out. Occasionally he would steal a queer, hostile glance at Miss Gentian and address a few loutish words to her to be repaid with an iced gentility. Andrew could not blame Miss Gentian for her aloofness, but he felt sorry for Mr. Cave nevertheless. He himself was in fine feather and described the hanging of Lieutenant Governor Colden in effigy, during the Stamp Act riots, with the devil whispering in his ear, and the unparalleled musical clock but recently exhibited in Hull's assembly rooms, in a manner to win the concerted smiles of both the Gentian ladies.

After supper they retired to the drawing room again, and again Sparta Gentian's voice breathed gold through a crystal instrument in the strains of "Beauty Retire." The occasion was marred for Andrew only by the fact that Mr. Cave had obviously taken too much wine in the interval before joining the ladies, and now sat in a brooding, red-browed silence like a stupefied bear, with his drooping-lidded eyes stupidly intent upon Sparta Gentian's averted face. When the song was ended he got up abruptly, almost overturning his chair, and without a word went over to the open window at the other end of the room and remained standing there with his back to the company.

Andrew seemed to read a message in Dr. Gentian's face—he rose too, and went over to the window himself. He stood for a moment at Mr. Cave's side—the man was staring out into darkness and did not notice him. Then he laid his hand lightly on Mr. Cave's arm to attract his attention, as he had seen Dr. Gentian do that morning.

All Mr. Cave's stolid composure dropped from him on the instant.

"Don't touch me!" he said in a fierce whisper, shaking off Andrew's hand as if it stung him, "Don't touch me, I tell you!"

"But my dear sir—" said Andrew astounded. Then he paused, for he had seen the man's eyes, and the watery madness in them. For an instant Andrew felt on his body the impact of a blow that was not given—a blow like a hammerstroke. Then the bloody color died from Mr. Cave's eyes and his mouth ceased to quiver like an angry child's.

"I—I am very sorry, Mr. Beard," he said, recovering himself with visible effort, "the heat—and Miss Gentian's singing—I am not very well with the heat and I—I cannot endure to have a stranger touch me suddenly—don't think too hardly of me because of it, Mr. Beard—"

He was almost fawning now. Andrew did not know which aspect of the man he found more distasteful—the sudden, lunatic rage of a minute ago or this present and horrible obsequiousness.

"Pray think no more of it," said Andrew, haughtily, trying to copy Dr. Gentian's tone, "Miss Gentian is about to sing again—shall we hear her?" He led the way back into the room. But he was relieved when, after Mr. Cave had taken his bearish departure, Dr. Gentian explained the reason for his singular behavior.

"You have my thanks for treating Mr. Cave so courteously," he said gravely. "A strange, bitter creature, Cave—but loyal and devoted, so we must put up with his strangeness." He lowered his voice, "He comes of good enough stock—but you see it's by the left hand—and that frets him, whenever he's in company."

"If he had his rights he'd be rich. Rich," said Sparta Gentian suddenly in her thrilling voice.

"You were going to play us something of Handel's, my dear,"

said her father, and the girl turned back to the forte-piano with
an impatient jerk of her head. Under cover of the music, Dr.
Gentian went on in snatches.

"I found him in London—what an exquisite passage, my pet—
very bitter against the world. Well, I'd known his father. A hard
man. I thought perhaps in a country where nobody knew the
story—but I fear the wound is too old and deep. One cannot
blame him too much. In his place, who would not be strange? Ah,
bravo, daughter!" and he clapped his hands.

Surely, thought Andrew, here was a gentleman of the most
comprehensive benevolence and understanding, and as he looked
at the beauty of Sparta Gentian's face, a little flushed now from
the exertion of playing, he resolved that the morrow would find
him more than courteous to unlucky Mr. Cave.

7.

The morrow came—and other morrows. A month slipped down
the curve of the year without Andrew's realizing how quickly it
had vanished—the indigo was in its third cutting—then in its
fourth. Soon it was time for hoarfrost to whiten the doorstep of
the house on Wall Street and autumn to gild and redden the trees
on the Boston road. Here it was hard to believe in snow feathering
from a leaden caldron of sky and the cries of skaters on the black
ice of Lispenard's Pond. The news from the North was scant
and disturbing, but its message, to Andrew, very tiny and far
away, a troubled voice hardly heard through heavy glass, the
faint disturbance of cannon and drums on a ship anchored beyond the horizon.

The tea-ships had been sent back from New York in orderly
protest—ships along the Northern seaboard hoisted their colors
at halfmast when the news of the closing of the port of Boston
came, and in Philadelphia, the bells of the churches were muffled and tolled all day. In the city Andrew had left, the Committee of Fifty-One was organized and began to quarrel internally
at once. The call for the First Continental Congress went forth,
and from all the colonies but Georgia the delegates began to
assemble. Dust-powdered riders jogged along bad roads, north
and south, to Philadelphia—John Adams and the other delegates
from defiant Massachusetts were received along their way with

the state and circumstance of dukes or convicted felons. The Congress sat and deliberated—adopted a declaration of rights—resolved to import no British merchandise after the first of December—ended with a stately but ineffective petition to the king. John Adams found the Philadelphia ladies charming but deplored the general extravagance of the city—the Congress dissolved, to meet again the following May, having made its gesture.

A cloud formed in the sky and grew—behind it a masked and indifferent figure of chaos sharpened certain lightnings and saw that his thunders were in voice. But cloud and figure were alike unperceived by the plump, stupid king who still thought of his obedient subjects of New York Colony, and by those subjects who still stood ready to drink his health in broken glass on his birthday and wish him better advised. Only Chatham in the increasing weakness of his age saw a little—and a few men in America who had helped push a stone to the edge of a steep slope, perceived now where that bounding missile would strike in the valley, and caught their breath. But Andrew was not one of those few.

He was honestly concerned at the tone of his father's letters, however. At first they were stiff and a little magniloquent, now they grew hasty and brief, with odd gaps in them as if the writer were too constantly fretted in mind to drive quill along paper for long at a time. One strange, sparse missive had come from Lucius—he had left the house on Wall Street and the business of Alexander Beard and Son, and remained Andrew's affectionate brother, with no address. Andrew had written him at once, asking for the details of the estrangement, but had got no reply except a bundle of the more violent manifestoes of the Sons of Liberty, which he had read with a queer detachment. Lucius' name dropped abruptly out of his father's letters and was not alluded to again, while every letter was full of eager, almost querulous queries as to the details of plantation-management. Andrew pictured his father as a man at sword's-points with an invisible enemy, forced back and back into a shadow. He took his courage in both hands and wrote him formally for permission to come home—sons did that, then. But the letter he got in answer was even briefer and stranger than the rest, and adjured Andrew, by every tie of filial duty, to remain where he was for a time. "My dear Son—I implore you by all I hold most holy to remain yet a while in the Floridas—I have reasons for this request you know not of, my Dear Son—and if you would be the Staff of my Age, I conjure you to obey me in this—. Your Mother is not Well and I am everywhere beset by difficulty—"

So it ran, in part, and Andrew, perplexed and sorry, could not but obey. Besides, there were other reasons for his staying. He had fallen deeply in love with Sparta Gentian and as deeply in hate with the uncouth Mr. Cave.

The first complete passion of the heart may be written in water for its permanency, but it leaves a cicatrice few care to have the wind blow on, even when iron has grown over the scar. Andrew had known women before, or their flesh, as a part of his coming of age—a circumstance of as definite, physical importance as the acquisition of a new watch by Green of London or the ability to curse a servant adequately. But the fashionable bawdy-house by the docks which he had visited a trifle shrinkingly in Lucius' company, with its ton of syrup-voiced female meat who rapped her trollops' knuckles with an iron key-ring to make them be civil to the young gentlemen, had as little to do with this present fever as the stiff exchange of high compliment with suitably marriageable daughters, minikin-mouthed, in green lutestring gowns. This was burning and ague at once, an arrow in the veins, a bitter gold in the mind.

He had realized it first some weeks ago, overseeing a gang of Greeks sickle the tall indigo with shining, leisurely strokes while the flies buzzed and the mown swathe gave out a scent of crushed herb. An incongruous moment, but most high moments are incongruous. Something had passed before his eyes like the shadow of a sea-gull in flight; then he knew; and the rest of the afternoon he had let his Greeks soldier as they would, while he stared at a visionary image through eyes that saw the field he stood in and the men who worked in that field as meaningless silhouettes cut out of colored paper.

Then he went back to the house and, after washing the smell of the fields from his body with unusual thoroughness, descended to supper and was tongue-tied and inept whenever he looked at Sparta. But gradually the first sheer bedazzlement passed, and he began to think and suffer.

He was so thoroughly acclimated to New Sparta by now that at times it seemed as if he never had led any other life. He could test the indigo in the beating vats as expertly as Dr. Gentian himself; and knew why no sun must fall upon it while it lies in the drying-shed; and the differences between the light, pure indigo called flotant or flora, the *gorge-de-pigeon* sort, and the copper-colored, heavier stuff that is used for dyeing woolens and the coarser fabrics. The smell of the rotting plant no longer revolted him, he had become inured to it, and if not inured, accustomed at least to the mosquitoes and flies in the fields.

He had long ago acquired his body-servant—a slim, silent, olive Minorcan lad with melancholy eyes. Also, he had begun to take a considerable interest in many of the other men and see the colony much more clearly as a whole. Some things he saw made him wince—but it was a hard-handed age, and he gradually fell into the way men have of overlooking little uncomfortable incidents that would have given him pause six months before. Whatever happened, Dr. Gentian was never to blame. The Doctor could not be everywhere, and if, occasionally he seemed to overlook occurrences that made Andrew hot behind the eyes, the abundant, evident prosperity of the settlement was ample testimony for the general wisdom and justice of his policy. Besides, and always now, he was Sparta's father.

Mr. Cave, though, was a brute and an unpleasant one. In regard to him, Andrew could not but feel that Dr. Gentian carried a point of generosity too far. The friction between himself and Mr. Cave had begun the very morning after the scene between them at the window. Mr. Cave was giving him his first lesson in the ways of the plantation, and Andrew had certainly intended all scrupulous courtesy towards him. But after an hour or so of contemptuous, ursine explanations on Mr. Cave's part and eager questions on Andrew's, Mr. Cave stopped suddenly as they were crossing a field together.

"What did he tell you about me, last night, after I was gone, hey?" he said hoarsely, jerking his thumb in the general direction of the great house.

Andrew felt trapped. "I do not recall that we discussed any one of your qualities in particular," he said finally. The man galled him, but he was resolved to be civil.

"Qualities!" said Mr. Cave, scornfully. "Qualities, hell. He told you I was a bastard—didn't he now? A London lawyer's bastard without even a decent name to his back?" His voice was vinegary. He looked Andrew up and down with red, peering eyes.

"I assure you Mr. Cave," said Andrew, still grasping at civility, "that even if Dr. Gentian did happen to refer to the—the unhappy circumstances of your birth—"

"Listen to me!" said Mr. Cave with sudden violence, "You can't talk fine to me—I don't want any of your stinking New York sop! I'm a bastard, all right—I knew he'd tell you—well, if I am—" he beat his fist in his palm, "I don't want any damn cocked-hat pity from you or him neither—savvy? I take care of myself—savvy? I could stake the two of you out in the sun to dry there for boucan—savvy? All right—now you go and snigger about me with him over your wine as much as you damn well want to!"

The hoarse, brief explosion of his rage left Andrew stunned for an instant. He felt as if he had stretched out his hand in the dark and put it upon a toad.

"Oh—go to the devil!" he said, rather impotently, and started to walk away in a fog of anger. But already the man's fit had passed and he was running after him with apologies.

"Mr. Beard! Mr. Beard! I didn't mean anything, sir—I swear I didn't! I get a fit like that every now and then—Dr. Gentian knows it—he never pays any attention to it. You aren't going to tell him, Mr. Beard? You aren't going to—"

The tawdry tears were actually running down his cheeks. It took some time for Andrew, loathing them both, to quiet him with promises and assurances. Then the man relapsed into his usual heavy sullenness and the tour of instruction proceeded. But even the crowded months since then had not been able to obliterate the shoddy scene from Andrew's memory.

Then there was the time, a month or so later, when Mr. Cave had been about to take the whip to the Minorcan. The Minorcan was the fine-looking fellow whom Andrew had noticed on his first day at New Sparta, and Andrew had stopped the projected whipping in short order, for he was used to his work by then, and conscious of Dr. Gentian's favor. But again, he would not easily forget the Minorcan's clenched face as Mr. Cave had whistled the rawhide lash in his hands in preparation to strike, nor Mr. Cave's dull fury when Andrew had intervened.

That matter had gone up to Dr. Gentian and Mr. Cave had been cautioned, though, as Dr. Gentian explained, there were times when the whip—"A new colony must live its first decade under what, to all purposes, is martial law, Mr. Beard, if it is to survive. Take away the punitive power—even the power of life and death—from its governors and—well, you've heard of the first days at Jamestown—"

Andrew agreed. Dr. Gentian, as usual, had reason and experience on his side. But he thought Mr. Cave should be discharged and said so.

"Some time, perhaps—if I could find him another post," mused Dr. Gentian, gravely. "But just now—well—we are short of men, Mr. Beard, and after all, if I did discharge him, where would the wretched fellow go? I could not turn him out naked to pig it with the Indians."

Andrew saw the justice of that, and the air cleared again. At least, he thought, the incident had been of some value, for it won him the friendship of the Minorcan concerned and he began to be popular among the palmetto-huts.

The Minorcan's name was Sebastian Zafortezas, and Andrew discovered, with that curious pleasure the mind takes in tiny coincidences, that they had been born in the same year. He began to visit Sebastian's hut, now and then—it was on the edge of the Minorcan quarter and cleaner and better kept than those of his Greek neighbors. As the acquaintanceship grew, Sebastian began to teach him Mahonese Spanish—hesitatingly at first, for he had only a little English to begin on. But soon they were really able to talk to each other—and Andrew began to learn about the deserted hut near the Altar of the Gentiles and the long sick voyage from Port Mahon.

Gradually, Andrew slipped into the way of frequenting Sebastian's hut as often as circumstance allowed. Conversation with Dr. Gentian was always instructive—but he found that at times he missed the fellowship of men near his own age more than he had thought—and Mr. Cave was the only other possibility. Colonial and Mahonese exchanged knives and minor confidences and began to feel secure in each other's company. Andrew discovered that Sebastian was passionately fond of tobacco and repaid his language lessons with pipefuls of rank Virginia, while the two chatted and the blue smoke wavered in the evening air, and the Barbary ape that Sebastian was so proud of bringing alive from Minorca chattered to itself in a corner. Andrew thought a dozen times of transferring Sebastian from the fields to the coquina house, as his body servant, but something held him back —he suspected his friend of a pride of race as great as any De Lancey's and feared to wound him.

They were seated so, one afternoon in early March when work was over, smoking in comparative silence, for both were tired. Andrew was thinking that it was nearly a year since he had sailed from New York, that he had had no news from home for almost two months now, and that the little hollow at the base of Sparta Gentian's throat was the most lovely of all created things.

He had long ago confided his passion to Sebastian and had received a grave, laconic sympathy in return. Sometimes he wondered at himself for revealing the most hidden trouble of his heart so easily to a foreign laborer—but that ghost of snobbery was quickly laid. His friend understood him, that was enough. But he wondered sometimes, if he understood his friend.

The other had told him many things—he could see the barren island of ringdoves and eagles rise before him out of the sea, in Sebastian's words, like a city long-drowned—he could hear the soft slur of the dancers' feet in the rocky streets of Mahon—but the secret springs of Sebastian's mind remained unrevealed. Occasionally, in a chance word or a casual idiom, he could catch a glimpse of some alien, resolved purpose, hidden under the surface of Sebastian's talk like the gleam of a fish, seen far down, in very deep water, but that was all. Still, Andrew decided, he did not like Sebastian any the less for it. He shook out the dottel from his pipe, stretched his arms, and spoke.

"She is beautiful as a golden rose," he said in Spanish. "Beautiful. Is she not beautiful, my friend?"

Sebastian nodded gravely. "All women are beautiful, but only one to a lover," he said, reflectively. "It is well, so. When do you speak to her father, amigo?"

"Soon," said Andrew. "As soon as I have any notion there is hope for me in her mind."

"You must serenade her more often," said Sebastian smiling.

"No." Andrew smiled, too. "I have told you we have not the custom of the serenade."

"That is bad," said Sebastian seriously. "Guitar-music comes like a child to a woman's heart—it can enter where a man must stay out in the darkness. I would get you a guitar, my friend, if you had need of it. Tonight is a night for love and the guitar."

"That is true," said Andrew, nodding. "But you, Sebastian— how do you know? Have you never been in love?"

Sebastian regarded the bowl of his pipe.

"Yes. I have been in love," he said.

"But I've never seen you with a girl."

"No," said Sebastian. "You have never seen me with a girl." His face was masked.

"And yet—what happened, Sebastian?—Are you still, per-haps—"

"It is possible," said Sebastian, smiling. "Let us talk no more of it, my friend. Let us talk of your love instead—and wish you good fortune."

Andrew felt rebuffed, but he respected the other's reticence. Besides, it was so very much more interesting to pour his own doubts and fears in Sebastian's sympathetic ear.

"Perhaps, I will find my rose tonight," he said, tossing a pebble idly in his hand, "perhaps."

"May you wear it many years," said Sebastian with courteous dignity.

"Dr. Gentian sets out for St. Augustine soon," went on Andrew, thinking aloud. "He will be gone some time. If I do not speak before then—"

"Ah," said Sebastian and muttered something to himself in Spanish.

"*Que?*" said Andrew, eagerly. He had not caught the words.

"I said nothing," said Sebastian, holding out his hand before the door of his hut to try the direction of the wind. "The air is heavy. We will have rain before morning. Rain and thunder."

"Nonsense, Sebastian," said Andrew and laughed. "The sky's as clear as a bell and it rained only two days ago."

"Perhaps," said Sebastian, staring into a distance. His eyes were veiled. "But for all that, we will have rain soon enough, and thunder. There is thunder in the air, my friend—thunder coming up from the sea."

PART TWO:

THE DAZZLING NET

The strangeness of his friend's last speech bothered Andrew a little, on his way back to the house, but not long. The gradual veils of dusk blue, patched with silver, that evening drew solemnly across the sky were too calm and gentle to be flowered with anything more sullen than the palest stripes of Spring rain —a cool air blew from the inlet like a promise given in a whisper —it was, indeed, a night for love and the guitar. Andrew came up the grassy avenue that led to the house with that promise clutched tight in his hand like a Spanish coin.

Tonight, he told himself as he had told himself so often, he would find out the color of his fortune, black or gold. In the interval after supper, when the Gentian ladies had withdrawn, he would speak to his surgeon Caesar, and know his fate there, at least. Admitted, the Doctor was too liberal and modern a father to give away his daughter against her will—etiquette was etiquette —and it must never be said in the Floridas that a New Yorker lacked proper punctilio. But even if the Doctor did approve— what of Sparta herself? Andrew sifted a thousand little incidents of the past few months between his fingers like grains of sparkling sand. Here she had certainly smiled, yes—and there thanked him most graciously for turning over the leaves of her new song. But there she had been distant as a ghost, and there again, definitely satiric. This balanced that, and left him in troubled confusion. He was so absorbed in love-stricken calculations that he nearly ran into one of the servants, on the stairs, before he realized where he was.

"Ten thousand dev—," he began, in irritation, then, seeing it was Sparta's Minorcan maid, changed his tune abruptly. If this girl were not divinity itself, she was blessed at least by the service of divinity, and he stared at her hungrily, as if he expected to see a golden collar, with godhead's name upon it, around her throat. He had noticed the wench very little after that first awkward encounter in the corridor—she went about her duties as unobtrusively as a spirit—but tonight she seemed to him, somehow, a precious object, and he spoke to her on impulse.

"Is anything wrong?" he said, for now that he came to observe her, she seemed more sombre than usual and her face was a trifle drawn.

"Nothing, *señor*," said the girl quietly. "Supper will be ready in half an hour." She stood aside for him to pass. He lingered, feeling, in the folly of a lover, that her presence might have some sort of augury for him, if he could only puzzle it out.

"But—there is something the matter, Caterina," he went on, with vague kindliness. "You really look very tired—and the fever-season's coming on. You should go to Dr. Gentian and have him give you a powder of cinchona."

"No, *gracias*, I am quite well, *señor*," said the girl, and sucked in her breath. A dark glow came into her eyes for a second, like the soul of a flame in an obscured mirror, and died again. For some reason, Andrew felt, momentarily, as he had that evening in the corridor when her footsteps had died away so suddenly and left him alone in the very belly of night. The sensation was so acute that he almost put out a hand to steady himself against an assault of shadows. Then he remembered.

"Of course," he said rather aimlessly, "of course—but still, you don't look very well, Caterina,—and really, now, if you went to—"

"I am quite well," the girl repeated steadily, but he saw a sob rise in her throat. It broke now, and tore her. "But the Minorcans will never have their lands, now—the Minorcans will never have their lands!" she cried, passionately, in a deep, shaken voice, and then pushing him aside with a child's gesture of impotent pain, ran sobbing down the stairs. Andrew gazed after her helplessly, reflecting that Minorcans were very peculiar. One got just so far with them—and then one came up against a blind wall of silence or an inexplicable grief. Her words were meaningless, of course, but coming, as they did, after Sebastian's talk about the thunder, they jarred him and set the pattern of the evening awry. He went to his room with a prickle in his mind, and was not pleased, when he got there, to hear, through the open window, the mutter of other voices in irritated discussion.

He was about to go out and silence the debate—the room next his was a store-room and generally only frequented by servants —when the voices rose higher, and he caught one sentence clearly.

"You've been at that wench, again," said a dry, passionless

accent which Andrew was horrified to recognize as Mrs. Gentian's. "I'll not suffer it, Hilary. I'll not suffer it any more."

A low rasping murmur replied. The other voice fell to meet it, and Andrew found himself gripping the back of a chair with a clenched hand. Mrs. Gentian was so taciturn at the best of times that he had come to think of her as a statue rather than a woman—a statue whose worn, fine hands busied themselves interminably with flowers of lace and needlework, but whose memorial mouth was as dedicated to silence as the mouth of a buried nun. Now, though, those lips had opened, and a voice, arid and clear as the rattle of dry palm-branches in the wind, spoke out a hate so weary and long enduring that it hurt the mind.

Andrew closed the window as quickly as he could but he could not shut out the sour, tearless repetition of the words, "I will not suffer it, Hilary. I will not suffer it again," or the hard rasp of the Doctor's voice in reply. He felt very sorry for Dr. Gentian—Mrs. Gentian had the wreck of what must have been a great beauty. The beauty had gone, but its jealousy, apparently, remained—acrid as the dregs of spoilt incense. Andrew had heard, in books, of the lengths to which such ingrown jealousy may lead very worthy women, and shook his head in wise acknowledgment of the strangeness of existence. It was worse, somehow, that Sparta's mother should yield to such a failing. He could not restrain a natural pity for the unhappy lady, but he felt that in combining Sparta's mother with a jealous wife, she had committed, at the least, a serious breach of taste.

He was relieved to find no traces of the quarrel lingering in the air when he came down to the supper-table. Dr. Gentian was pleasanter than usual, if anything, and Mrs. Gentian very composed. He marvelled anew at the deceptiveness of all women but Sparta—he could hardly believe that the cool, terse accents which asked him politely for his verdict on the salad of hearts of cabbage-palm, belonged to the same woman whose voice had been so sere with an exhausted flame a little while ago. Then he was left alone with Dr. Gentian, and it was time for him to put his question. Only now, when the time had come, in spite of any fortification of wine, the question stuck in his throat.

"Shall we take our wine into my study?" said Dr. Gentian and rose. "There is a new herbal I should like to show you—the author has some ingenious ideas upon the domestication of the mulberry-tree in these parts."

Andrew assented gratefully, grasping at the moment's relief. Besides he took it as a good omen that on this night of all nights, Dr. Gentian should invite him to the seldom-visited chamber which he had always visualized as the hidden brain of the plantation.

He took in its details now with care, as if some one of them might give him a clue to his future. The fantastic yet effective diversity of its master's character was displayed in the chamber almost to excess. It was a long, oval, high-ceiled room, hung in blue and gold leather—the domed ceiling was blue, as well, and powdered with small gold stars. There were books and chemical apparatus, a set of chessmen whose kings rode ivory elephants, a foreign dagger with beryls set in the blade. An herbarium stood in a corner beside the articulated skeleton of a child—a violin lay on a carved wooden chest, neighbored by a case of surgical instruments, a pair of dividers and an azimuth. Yet in spite of this litter of incompatible objects and interests, the room gave an impression of neatness and order as precise as that of a captain's cabin on a shipshape frigate. Andrew felt that Dr. Gentian could go blindfold to any single thing in the room and put his hand upon it—and also, that the room was, in a measure, an extension of the soul of its master, and should he die, would be haunted forever by a light, sure footstep and a tight, Roman smile. He turned over the leaves of the herbal—the plates made a blur of color in his eyes and Dr. Gentian was saying something about mulberries that he should listen to, but his mind was racked, and he could not attend.

"I intended the ceiling as a planetary map, showing roughly the movements of the various heavenly bodies and the transit of the moon," said his host, politely, as Andrew's eyes strayed from the herbal to the ceiling, "but the work was never completed." He sighed. "Perhaps some day, we can manage it."

"It is a splendid chamber, sir," said Andrew, thinking of Sparta.

"It is my retreat," Dr. Gentian confided. "You may not have noticed—but there is deadening in the walls, and when I am secluded here, there are orders I shall not be disturbed. I even have my own staircase to the upper part of the house."

"Really?" said Andrew, marshalling the facts of his birth and

worldly circumstances in proper order to present to a father.
"Yes, indeed," said Dr. Gentian. He rose and opened a door
at the side—a door flush with the wall. "Would you like to see
it—the workmanship is truly ingenious."

He led the way up a short, winding stair, chatting. At a landing, he paused. "We are behind the ceiling now," he said. He
slid a little panel back with an oily click. "When I planned my
planetary map, I thought to place my moon here and light it
with a concealed lamp—a childish fancy enough, but what's life
without vagaries? Then I thought my toy might burn the roof
down over my head some fine night and gave up the plan. As it
is, my moon makes an excellent Judas-hole if I had need of one."
He stepped aside. Andrew came forward and peered through a
small round opening directly down into the room which they had
just left. He muttered something about an interesting device.

"Only a toy," said Dr. Gentian, "and a costly one. I fear I
am too fond of toys." He shut the panel with a smooth sound,
and waved into the gloom. "The stair there leads direct to the
main corridor—I find it convenient, but I will not make you
climb any further beyond the moon." He chuckled and led the
way down again. "I have always hankered after oddities—'tis my
greatest defect. I never realize how I may fatigue others with my
hobbies—as I fear I have fatigued you, this evening, Mr. Beard, by
your face—"

"Not at all, sir," said Andrew, untruthfully, seated in his chair
again. He cleared his throat desperately. "Dr. Gentian—" he said.

"Yes, Mr. Beard?—the bottle lies with you, I think—thank you."
The little gurgle of the Doctor's wine into his glass put Andrew
off unaccountably. For a moment he thoroughly wished himself
heartwhole and a thousand miles away. But he set his teeth and
brought up an image of Sparta to aid him.

"Dr. Gentian—" he began again, with an unfortunate sense
of repetition.

"Pardon me," interrupted the smiling Doctor politely, "but
your glass is already full. You may not have observed it." And
Andrew discovered to his horror that he was spilling a red stream
on the table from an overflowing glass.

"Sorry, I'm sure," he mumbled.

"It is nothing," the Doctor assured him. "But I chance to have
a peculiar affection for certain years of Madeira. Pray continue,

Mr. Beard—you will find it a trifle difficult to rest the bottle on a walnut—I mention it, merely—pray continue—"

Andrew silently placed the bottle as far from him as possible and wetted his lips.

"Dr. Gentian," he said for the third time, "I crave—I wish— May I humbly crave, sir, your permission to—"

"You may certainly have my most willing permission to pay your addresses to my daughter, Sparta," said the Doctor, briskly snipping Andrew's disjoined stammerings in two. Then, seeing Andrew's stupefied face, he threw back his head and burst into a shout of laughter.

"Why, you silly boy," he said, laughing and wiping the tears of laughter from his eyes, "d'you suppose I haven't seen where your heart's been drifting this last half-year? But the blindest worm in the ground's a crystal-gazer to a young man in love. Here, lad—" and he gave his hand to Andrew across the table. "Shake hands and don't look so solemn. You can have her if you can win her. I can say no more than that, for I won't force her—but that I'll say with a good conscience."

"I can never thank you enough, sir," said Andrew, solemnly, shaking hands.

"Well then—don't thank me at all—that's far the best course for both of us," said the Doctor, cheerfully. "I'll say this, too— the girl has no other attachment I know of, and I'll be glad to give her to you, should she be agreeable. But a word on other matters." He grew serious now. "I am not a young man, Mr. Beard, and somewhat loath to part with my one chick for the few years left me. So I must ask you this—should you marry my daughter, sir, would you intend to remain in the Floridas or return to New York?"

Andrew felt himself unable to think of such petty matters.

"I have grown much attached to the Floridas," he said smiling. "So much that I should not think of quitting them, if—"

"Good," said the Doctor. "Then we're agreed. I confess—I'd feel a wrench were it to be otherwise. Well, sir—I think that is all I wished to say. The settlements—of course I speak merely in the eventuality, Mr. Beard—had best be discussed between your father and myself—I might even make the voyage North in case —though in these uneasy times—"

"My father is much interested in the Floridas," Andrew blurted out. "It is even possible my father might remove some of his interests here—" He half-regretted the words once they were spoken, but Dr. Gentian had behaved with such admirable candor that it surely behooved him to do likewise.

"Indeed?" said the Doctor quietly. "That is very interesting." He reflected. "Your father is a wise man," he said. "No one knows what this stir in the North may lead to—but the Floridas will stand by the Crown. And should your father—well, well," he broke off. "There'll be time enough to talk of that later. At present, no doubt you're already busy with a sonnet to my daughter's eyebrow and aching for the sight of her. Ah, youth— what a heat in the mind it is, and how we cool when it's over. By the way," he went on more practically, "as you know, I must visit St. Augustine in a month or so, and be gone some time. If this matter we have discussed might be settled before I leave—"

"But sir—I—I—Miss Gentian—" said Andrew, his mind topsy-turvy.

Dr. Gentian laid a paternal hand on his shoulder.

"There, lad—I don't mean to press you—or you her—but take my word for it, the swiftest love is often the surest and lastingest —and your bold, rapid lover is wedded and bedded and got his child on the maid while Sir Timothy Shilly-Shally is still sighing outside her door."

Andrew felt this last advice a trifle frank in tone—but it was an unsqueamish age, and he could hardly quibble with so amiable a prospective father-in-law over niceties of language. He went out of the study, with the other's hand on his shoulder and a bronze call, like the call of a centaur's hunting-horn, in his heart.

2.

He was alone with Sparta in the garden, and his hour was upon him. The opportunity had come so swiftly and easily that he felt bewildered. A word from Dr. Gentian as to the beauty of that strange plant, the cereus, which blooms only at night. A sigh from Sparta that the house was close and she would risk any treachery of the night air for a breath of cool from the river. She had put a light shawl about her shoulders, impatiently, at her mother's insistence. In the white shine of the stars its vivid flowers were darkened and strange, it wrapped her shoulders in a pale fleece, marked obscurely with the imprint of blossoms sprung from fields on the dark side of the moon. Andrew had never seen her more beautiful or less attainable. Her composed face seemed to have no room for thoughts of him or any other man, her eyes were lighted at an indifferent planet, her mouth was a shut flower.

They had seen the cereus and marvelled—the night-flower that blooms when heaven is dark and dies in the sun, showing only the secret hours of the risen planets the perfection of its whiteness, cool, sterile and lovely as a blossom congealed from some metal slighter than foam. They had talked of a dozen, indifferent things as they strolled about. Andrew had long ago discovered that Sparta was very curious of New York and of cities in general. Her childish years were a confused memory of long sea-voyages and strange nurses. The one glimpse of London, seen when she was eleven and her roving father had been interesting Lord Hillsborough in his projects, was hugged like the ghost of a jewel to her breast. She remembered Vauxhall passionately—and the very sprigs on the dresses of the fine ladies in panniered silk who came there in sedan-chairs with a train of tame wits and sniffing lapdogs.

"Sometimes, I confess, Mr. Beard—I must have a foolish heart—I'd rather be an orange girl in the meanest London playhouse than an empress in these exiled Floridas. But then I remember, when I was a child my sole ambition was to be a midshipman on one of His Majesty's frigates so I could carry a dirk and kill Frenchmen—and I calm myself."

Andrew longed to tell her, that he would give her London, a chicken-skin fan, and a lapdog with the arrogant nose of a Chinese god—but his promise to Dr. Gentian held him back. At least, he thought, she should be an empress in the Floridas, if he could make her one. He glanced up the sky—the change Sebastian had predicted was beginning. Clouds hurried across the stars like trotting black sheep—a rampart of darkness built itself up steadily in the glittering wake of the moon. He chose a particular cloud. When it blotted the moon he would speak.

"Mr. Beard—Mr. Beard—is my company so wearisome? You have not honored me with a word these five minutes past." Her shoe tapped on the path. Her face was amused. He stared at her in silence, waiting for his omen. It came at last. The cloud blotted the moon and darkness fell on them both.

"Miss Gentian—Sparta—" he said with a crack in his throat. Then all his elaborate prologue of speech forgotten, he put shaking hands on her shoulders and drew her to him.

"Sparta? You'll marry me?" he said, in that same, cracked, violent voice. She was very near, now. He could see her eyes in the darkness, the gray had gone out of them, they were black as opals, and in each was a tiny gleaming image of his face. She looked at him steadily, for an instant, without replying. Then, "Yes, I'll marry you," she said, the crystal bell of her voice untroubled by doubt or surprise. Then his arms went round her and she kissed him full on the mouth, and he felt his heart stop in his body for that instant of felicity as if the pointed blade of the Spanish bayonet had run him through and through with a golden thorn.

Through the further events of the evening, Andrew moved like a man in trance. There were Sparta's kisses in the garden, which were real, though incredible, and there was the formal reception of their betrothal by Dr. and Mrs. Gentian, which, while equally real no doubt, seemed in memory, vague as a painting upon a dream. He could hear the words on Sparta's lips clearly enough, "Mr. Beard has asked for me in marriage, Father, and I have accepted him, subject to your consent," but of the practical conversation which followed he had little recollection. Dr. Gentian had drunk his health and called him son—he had drunk Dr. Gentian's health—Mrs. Gentian had been terse but agreeable—he was going to marry Sparta—that remained, unbelievable though it might be, the one steadfast fact in a rocking world. He tried to recall what Mrs. Gentian had said to him— her congratulations had certainly not erred on the side of loquacity.

He was sure she had said no more than, "So you are to marry our daughter, Mr. Beard? I wish you much joy," while she looked at him curiously. But then he had taken her hand to kiss it in acknowledgment and had been surprised to find it trembling. Obviously a lady of deep, if hidden, feeling—and certainly Dr. Gentian's cheery talkativeness more than made up for any curtness of hers.

He must tell Sebastian, in the morning. He had forgotten all about Sebastian till now, he realized with a start. No—not quite forgotten. He had paused an instant as Sparta and he were about to reënter the house, and glancing about idly, had seen two indistinct shapes, a woman's and a man's, part from each other in the shadows of the outbuildings. He suspected them of being lovers, and had felt friendship for them because he was now happy in love. Now he suspected more—that one shape had been Sebastian's and the other that of Caterina, the Minorcan maid. The thought pleased him extraordinarily—he was in that benevolent state when we are generous enough to wish all our friends a bliss only slightly less than our own. He gave Sebastian a suitable wedding, engaged him as chief-overseer on his new plantation and stood godfather to his first child, before he fell asleep to the rushing of light, fierce rain on the roof above his head.

3.

About the time that Andrew and his divinity were first observing the mystery of the cereus, the monkey in Sebastian's hut gave over its attempts to capture a peculiarly elusive flea and began to consider other means of diversion. Its master was away —fleas ceased to interest after a certain time—life in general was a sucked cocoanut and obedience a rusty chain about the body that kept one from all sorts of pleasantly destructive occupations. If the chain could only be got rid of somehow—but there the monkey had never had the slightest success before and hoped for little now. Still, it was worth trying, and the monkey bit at it a couple of times for luck and then squatted down sailorwise and tugged at it till it rattled, delightfully.

To his surprise, it seemed to give a little—Sebastian had hammered the staple in a new place that morning without noticing the rottenness of the wood. The monkey, encouraged, tried again and again, with less result, and was about to give it up and go to sleep, when one last jerk pulled the staple loose and set him free. He bounded instantly upon Sebastian's bed and sat there chattering triumphantly. There were so many breakable objects within easy reach that he did not know quite where to begin. He started by hammering Sebastian's red clay pipe against a stone. It smashed very satisfactorily in a moment or two and he amused himself for some time by carefully distributing the bits inside Sebastian's blankets. Then that too palled and he scuttled over to the door, his chain jingling behind him. The night seemed very large and interesting. There were trees in it. He had not climbed a tree in a long time.

He remedied the lack immediately, but the tree he chose wasn't much of a tree at that—it had no fruit on it to suck and throw away, with a squash, at other men or monkeys. Still, it was good to be independent again, at last. He said so at length, to the surrounding world, and set out upon his travels.

The joys of independence lasted till the first large drops of rain began to soak into his fur. Then they grew a trifle dubious. After all, he had become used to living in a house with a roof on it, and the society of mankind, while often tedious, had its compensations. He had had an adventurous outing and smelled and bitten at all sorts of new and interesting substances. He had proven himself a monkey of ingenuity and initiative. Now, the hut on the edge of the Minorcan quarter seemed snug and warm, and the food he shared with Sebastian more filling, on the whole, than what one could forage for oneself. He would go back—but he had come a considerable distance in his careless rambling and was not quite sure of his bearings.

He looked around him—ah, there was a house with a light in the window. That meant man and warmth and shelter. A different master, perhaps—but he had been so long with Sebastian that he had quite forgotten his first unpleasant experiences with masters.

He slipped down to the ground and jangled over toward the lighted house, shivering as he ran. It was really raining now, and he hated rain like a cat.

Mr. Cave, alone in colloquy with a half-emptied bottle of spirits, heard a sudden ghostly clanking through the dripping pour of the rain, and looking up, saw the Devil in person standing in his doorway with a chain wrapped around his middle. He rubbed horrified eyes and began to pray in a whisper. Then his mind righted itself and he sank back in his chair, muttering. It was only that impudent Minorcan's draggled pet-ape—but it had given him a start, and he did not like being startled when he was in liquor.

Stephen Vincent Benét

The wet monkey had jumped on the table now and sat opposite him, grinning and looking at the bottle of spirits. He grinned back at it. It would be funny to give the miserable little beast some liquor and get it drunk. You could get a chicken drunk on corn soaked in brandy but a drunken monkey would be even more amusing.

"Here," he said, splashed some liquor into a glass and held it out to the monkey. If the monkey behaved itself and proved entertaining when intoxicated, he might even keep it. The Minorcan fellow set a good deal of store by it and laborers had no business keeping pets.

The monkey took the glass trustingly—Sebastian had taught it how to drink from a glass, in the useless way men had. Now it swallowed a gulp of what was inside the glass. The raw liquor stung its throat—it coughed and spat in quaint loathing. Mr. Cave roared—this was even more diverting than he had expected. Then he felt the monkey's sharp teeth almost meet in his thumb, gave a squeal of pain, and struck at it blindly with the bottle.

Even so, the monkey might have escaped, if it had not been for its chain. But the chain tangled its feet as it dodged away—and Mr. Cave's second blow was better aimed than his first.

He stood looking at the dead animal, stupidly. It bled like a man. He hadn't really meant to kill it. But he had—and that Minorcan who owned it was a sullen devil. Well, he'd just have to face it out, if the ugly little swine tried any tricks on him.

He took the limp body of the monkey gingerly by one leg and threw it out of the door. It was raining hard, now—the rain would wash some of the blood off, he thought, inanely. He shivered. Killing an animal wasn't much, but he wished its hands hadn't looked like a dead baby's when he picked it up. He shut the door carefully, bolted it, and returned to his bottle. Now and then he cast an uneasy glance at the window. If the damn little brute hadn't bitten—it should have known he had a quick temper and wouldn't stand biting—His thoughts trailed off uneasily, into a mist the color of liquor.

Sebastian got back to his hut just before the rain broke, and, finding the monkey vanished, started to search for it at once. At first he did not imagine that it could have gone very far and stood in the doorway, calling, "Amigo! Amigo!" in a crooning voice, for some time. But when no chattering answered from the darkness, he became disturbed and started out to visit the huts nearest him. Even the Greeks answered pleasantly enough—the monkey was quite a favorite in the colony—but none had any news. A Minorcan woman said that she had been awakened by the rattling of a chain outside her window, but that was all.

The rain soaked Sebastian to the skin, as he proceeded on his quest, but he did not notice it. He grew increasingly distraught and cursed himself for not having seen that the monkey was securely chained, before he left the hut. "Amigo! Amigo!" he called again and again, with a dry throat, and promised his namesaint a candle for every arrow that had stuck in his flesh. But there was no answer from either saint or monkey.

He did not know what impulse drove him at last to Mr. Cave's cottage, save that he hated the man and knew the man hated him. It was there, however, in the dripping weeds near the house of his enemy, that he stumbled at last upon the body of his friend. He took it up silently, the head was still bloody in spite of the rain, and the wrinkled face stiff and sad. Then, still in silence, with the dead animal in his arms, he made the complete circuit of the cottage, trying every door and window, noiselessly. But the doors and windows were fastened and the house was dark.

He sat down upon the ground then, still holding the monkey, and burst into a fit of dry sobbing, while the rain beat on him. Then he returned to his hut.

When he got back, he lit two scraps of candle and placed the monkey's body between them. Then he stripped himself to the waist, and, going to the wooden chest that held his few possessions, took out of it a small brass medal, tarnished green by the damp. On it was the image of the Mother of God. Her face was quiet—she had seven swords in her heart. This, together with the knife that Andrew had given him, he also put on the table between the candles. He then knelt and began to pray in Mahonese. The form of prayer was one peculiar to the men of the islands and unacknowledged by Rome. Andrew would have thought him even too alien, if he had seen him then—the muscles of his stripped body trembled with the vehemence of his supplication —he was dedicating Andrew's knife to Our Lady of Vengeance. After a time had passed, he rose again, put on his soaked shirt, and went stiffly out to dig the childish grave.

4.

Next morning, in spite of Andrew's resolve, the two friends did not meet. Instead, Sparta had a wish to go riding through the new-washed and freshly-scented countryside, and when they returned, Dr. Gentian, a cloud on his brow, was dismissing a deputation of the elder Minorcans from his study. He turned to Andrew sharply, the moment he saw him.

"Was your ride a pleasant one, lad?" he said, abstractedly. "Come with me a moment—there is something I would have your advice on."

"Certainly, sir," said Andrew, pleased at being consulted. He turned to Sparta. "You'll excuse me, mistress?" he said lightly.

"I shall excuse you sir," said Sparta smiling, her fingers playing with the lash of her riding-whip.

Dr. Gentian shut the door of his study. "The Minorcans are making trouble," he said without preface. "I thought it best you should know."

"Making trouble?" said Andrew, jarred. He somehow felt that trouble at this time was an insult to his happiness and Sparta's.

"Yes," said Dr. Gentian. He hesitated. " 'Tis a long story. The gist of it's this. They say they've served their time for their lands, under our agreement. Now they want them."

Andrew's mind reverted to his encounter with Caterina on that yesterday that seemed so distant. "The Minorcans will never have their lands now," she had said.

"Well, sir—" he began judicially.

Dr. Gentian cut him off. "Yes—that was the agreement," he admitted. "Three years. But there's the religious difficulty. They're Catholics, every man jack of them—Roman Catholics. Now listen to me," he tapped his thumb on the table. "When I first took them on my ships—would they have made conditions then? No. They were starving. I took them because they were starving. I didn't think then—They let me take the Greeks because the Greek Church to our mind's a Protestant church—but if I'd proposed transporting twelve hundred Catholics to the Floridas as settlers—giving them lands—the men at Whitehall would have cracked my whole project like an egg. I had to dissemble a little—how could I refuse starving men?—I thought once they were settled here—but the present governor's my enemy, as you know—"

"Even so, sir—" said Andrew, trying to put in a word.

"See here, lad," said Dr. Gentian, very firmly and gently, "Spain's still plotting to recover the Floridas. If I yield to these men's demands and give them their lands now—the governor can make a mare's nest out of it—enough to link me up with any kind of a trumpery Spanish plot he can bogy the men in England with. Then all New Sparta falls to the ground—and who gains by it? Your friends, the Minorcans? No. I must put them off for the present—till we have a new governor—or—"

"I can see the logic in everything you say, sir," said Andrew, a trifle stubbornly, "but nevertheless—"

The green stone in Dr. Gentian's ring flashed as he stretched out his hand to Andrew.

"Have I treated you like a son, Andrew—yes or no?" he said quite simply, and Andrew felt touched and humbled, but a little trapped as well. After all, whether or not Dr. Gentian had treated him like a son had little to do with his treatment of the Minorcans.

"You have always treated me most kindly, sir," he said, a bit grudgingly, yet hating himself for being grudging. "And yet—"

Dr. Gentian looked hurt. He dropped his hand.

"And yet you are unwilling to take my word on this—even when I assure you that one of my reasons for going to St. Augustine will be my wish to remedy the matter with the governor?"

"Of course, I must take your word, sir—if you put it like that," said Andrew, in a sudden glow of self-reproach.

"Ah," said Dr. Gentian, and laid a hand on his elbow. "Ah—that's my good lad!"

5.

Nevertheless, a tiny crack had come in the polished lacquer of his relation with Dr. Gentian. Dr. Gentian's course of action might be dictated by an expediency entirely honorable—but there must be a Minorcan side, if only a mistaken one. Andrew respected the Minorcans—they had great patience—he could not think of them as lightly aroused. He intended to find out their side—have a long talk with Sebastian—discuss things with some of the elders of the colony. Indeed, he intended much, and as people will, remained satisfied with the intent, while time drifted away, like a bough of wild peaches floating on a lazy stream.

The bright retiarius had caught and bound him in a dazzling net—now its trident poised above him and he did not fear the stroke. His servitude was too happy—why should he be free?— he ran at a golden heel.

He did not go so often to the fields, now, or to Sebastian's hut. For one thing, Dr. Gentian thought he should begin to take up the accounting and governing side of the plantation. Besides, there were expeditions for turtle, down the inlet, to be made in Sparta's company—she handled a boat like a man. There were rides through the green woods and sandy pine-barrens, and once, a dance at a neighboring plantation a day's journey away, where he saw divinity move through the stately patterns of louvre and minuet with a jealous joy. This was no New York courtship, done up in packthread stays, but something hardy and wild as a journey up the face of a crag to take the eggs from the nest of a mountain-eagle, and he rejoiced that it could be so.

Yet it seemed to him, often enough, that now, in betrothal, he was less sure of her heart than ever before. Before, she had seemed strange since she could never be his; now she was to be his indeed, but she still was strange. He could touch the hand, kiss the lips, hear the voice speak love, but in the eyes something remained aloof, a spectator who watched all that befell them both like an enchanter shut in a tower of clouded glass, without love or hate or sin, with only a dispassionate interest in the certain working of a spell. If he could once break that glass with the silver hammer of his desire—perhaps it would come with marriage and the incantation of the flesh. But the days passed, and the enchanter watched, and the glass remained unbroken.

Dr. Gentian went to St. Augustine at last. Andrew would hardly have noticed his departure, save for one thing. The Pride of the Colonies was expected with long-delayed mail from the North and might even bring an answer to the letter he had written his father about his betrothal. The letter had been written in March and it was nearly the end of May now. Then he came back to the house, one evening, after a day at the vats, as Dr. Gentian's deputy, to find his head heavy and thick, and his hands hot. He had caught a little fever, somehow, and was ill for several days.

The illness, after the first bad night had passed, gave him a chance to consider a number of things he had not thought of for some while. Sparta sent her maid to help nurse him, but did not come often herself. He was glad of that—he did not want her to see him with cracked lips and fever in his face. The maid was very quiet and deft—she had cool hands, and moved without little irritating creakings and rustlings, unlike most women.

They talked, now and then. She reminded him of Sebastian. He had been remiss about Sebastian. Sebastian's monkey was dead— he remembered that, now. He had gone to Sebastian to tell him the great news and, while Sebastian had been appreciative enough, Andrew saw that he was sad. He had asked about the monkey.

"Yes, Amigo is dead," said Sebastian, but would say no more, though he looked at a little brass medal that hung around his neck on a cord, and Andrew, who was bursting with talk, had felt rebuffed. He asked the maid about Sebastian now.

"He is well, I think," said the maid, holding a cup to his lips. Andrew drank of the bitter infusion within it gratefully.

"Don't you ever see him?" he said, smiling, when the cup had been taken away.

"He asks for you often. He hopes you will be better soon." She avoided the direct reply.

"Oh, I'll be up and around in no time," said Andrew. "Thanks to your nursing," he added.

"I am glad if my nursing has helped you," said the maid, rather haltingly, as if she had to hunt for the English words. "You are a friend of the Minorcans—or you have been."

"Tell me," said Andrew suddenly. "What did you mean that time in the corridor when you said the Minorcans would never get their lands? Dr. Gentian is going to give them their lands as soon as the governor lets him."

"They will never have their lands," said the girl, sombrely. Her eyes fixed him. "Sometimes Dr. Gentian sits in his tall room with a gold cap on his head," she said, abruptly. "He sits there like a king—he thinks he is a king—*el rey—el rey—*" Her voice rose. "When he thinks that—men are taken into the woods to have their backs combed with steel as the coat of a horse is curried by its servant. That has not happened since you have been here, but it has happened. He had a madness in him, then

—a madness that hides—the madness of a drunken king. That is why the Minorcans will never have their lands."

Andrew stared at her, wonderingly. The picture she presented was wholly fantastic, but he could not doubt the sincerity in her face.

"You're mad!" he said, finally. "Mad or—where did you ever hear such a crazy tale?"

"I should not have spoken," said the girl, relapsing into her amazing calm. "You are going to marry my mistress. I should not have spoken."

"What about Mr. Cave?" said Andrew, on impulse. "What do you Minorcans think of Mr. Cave?"

The girl shrugged her shoulders. "He is a dog," she said, quietly enough, though a bitterness colored her voice like rust. "He is mad, too—but only with the madness of a dog."

"You're not very cheerful today," said Andrew, with invalid peevishness. "And where you ever got such a farrago of nonsense —God knows I hate Cave as much as any of you can—but you make everything sound cruel."

She shrugged again. "What do you want me to say?" she said, with that even bitterness. "Life is cruel. Men that are cruel do no more than copy life."

"Don't," said Andrew, wincing, "I'm sorry you're so unhappy. You oughtn't to be so unhappy if you're Sebastian's sweetheart."

"So I am Sebastian's sweetheart?" said the girl and smiled.

"Well—aren't you?"

"Am I? I don't know. How do you know? You are a boy, sometimes—a little, little boy. You must take your medicine."

"I don't want it," complained Andrew, childishly. "You just gave it to me, anyhow."

"You must take it often." She approached him with the cup. "It takes away the fever. See, you are much cooler, this afternoon." She laid a hand on his forehead—the light touch was cool and firm as if she had brushed his brow with a ringdove's feather, fallen upon cool stones. "There now. Go to sleep. Sleep mends the fever, too."

"Why do you say such things about Dr. Gentian?" said Andrew, impatiently, but she turned away with her finger on her lips and sat down again in her chair. He watched her through half-closed eyes, seeing again the dark Madonna in the niche of the Spanish church. A single lamp burned before it—the face was calm and secret—the face of a gypsy saint—a mystery hung above it like a dove in chains. He could feel the touch of fingers upon his brow, cool as the roots of lilies, bathed in water from the hills. He lay for a long time silent, half-drowsing, thinking of Dr. Gentian in a gold cap and a lamp before an image, and the roots of lilies steeped in a clear, cold stream.

Next morning the fever had gone; his body felt weak, but no longer possessed. He lay alone all morning feeling his strength return to him and listening with mild curiosity to the various noises of the house. The day was hot and sultry, he could feel that inside his skin, but his room was cool and he did not mind. He had a convalescent's desire for visitors and talk, but the only person he saw till noon was the body-servant who brought his breakfast, and the boy slipped away before he could question him much.

He asked for Sparta—Miss Gentian was well, but occupied, she sent her regrets at not being able to visit him till later. Then he asked for the Minorcan maid. The boy stammered and said that she was occupied too, on some work for Mrs. Gentian. He noticed that the boy seemed uneasy and as if he were listening for something in the pauses of his speech, but laid it to the heat. "Here," said Andrew, feeling generous, and getting his purse from under his pillow, tossed him one of the Spanish dollars that still passed current the boy was a good servant and deserved an occasional coin. The boy murmured his thanks, pouched the dollar quickly, and disappeared, leaving Andrew to idleness and musing.

After a while he fell asleep and woke much refreshed. The house was very quiet and he began to consider getting up. He looked at his watch—it had stopped—but, by the light in the room, it must be mid-afternoon. A tray with food was beside him on the table—someone must have come and gone without rousing him. He was disturbed at the thought that it might have been Sparta. He called for his boy, and no one answered. Then he gave it up and set to his lunch with the first real hunger he had known in some days.

Later, he was wakened from another nap by an indefinite sound like the soft closing of the door of his room. He stared at the door—the curtains near it still moved, but if there had been a visitor, the visitor had departed. He could have sworn that, in the first confused instant of waking, he had seen a face staring in through the closing crack of the door—a face like Sparta's, but not hers, for the eyes in this face were hostile. A dream, probably —the shadows had changed again and the air of the room was charged with a heavy, groping twilight. But as soon as he was fully awake, his decision to get up was taken. The bed had grown wrinkled and uncomfortable, besides, he wanted to find out why nobody had been near him all day.

He dressed clumsily, taking a long time. He was not as well as he had thought, he found—the fever had made him lax, and sweat came on his hands when he bent to put on his shoes. However, he managed things at last, and went over to look at himself in the mirror. His cheeks were a little sunken, and his hair lanker than he would have liked, but otherwise he seemed much as usual. The effort it was to control his body properly did not tell in the glass. He would go downstairs now. He would go down and surprise Sparta with the news of his recovery.

It would be more difficult to get downstairs than he had supposed. The main staircase looked long and formidable—he looked at it and wondered. Then he remembered the other, easier staircase, at the bottom of the corridor, that led directly to Dr. Gentian's high-ceiled study. He found it and started going down—it was dark and winding, but the steps were shorter. He went gingerly and quietly, for fear of falling. At the landing he paused, remembering, with a smile, Dr. Gentian's disquisition on the proposed planetary map for the ceiling. The panel that slid back behind the moon, must be about here—yes. His fingers found the catch. Mechanically, he slid it open and peered through the little round opening into the room below.

What he saw made his fingers shake on the latch of the panel. Sparta Gentian and Mr. Cave were seated in the study, talking. On the table between them was a pair of candles that burnt with a still flame, glasses, and a half-emptied bottle of wine.

"There's no heat in this liquor, Sparta," Cave was complaining in his grunting accents. "Why can't we have rum, you white doll?—you know well enough I'd rather have rum." His coat was pushed back, his shirt open at the throat—his whole face looked stupid and savage as the mask of a boar. Andrew saw them both very plainly, in spite of the gloom in the room. A taste like

174

the taste of bitter aloes came into his mouth, and he felt his heart turn slowly to a dull, hard, gleaming stone.

"You can't have rum because I choose to talk to you, Charles—not watch you fall asleep with your head in your arms," Sparta's lyric voice had never been more flawed with crystal. "If the wine doesn't suit you—spill it on the floor—I'll wipe it up with my kerchief and wear it for a favor."

"By God, I believe you would," grumbled Mr. Cave, reaching out for her hand. "You're a brave wench, Sparta. Come kiss me for a brave wench."

"Not now," said Sparta steadily. "You smell too much of your wine. You've had enough kisses from me till you master the world and make me proud of you."

"You lie, you golden slut!" said Mr. Cave, and thumped his fist on the table, "I've never had enough of your kisses yet—nor likely—unless you've grown so finicky-fine this last month you'd rather have that sick cat in yellow breeches squeeze you because he sets up for a gentleman—the shopkeeping little snotty-nose! Come kiss me, I say—I want to get the taste of him out of my mind."

"You're a sweet fool, Charles," said Sparta, and went around to him. Then Andrew, glaring down at them from his spy-hole, could have groaned aloud, for he saw divinity incarnate sit down on Mr. Cave's knees like a barmaid, and Mr. Cave's red hand bend back the golden head till his mouth could settle with thirsty violence on the lips that Andrew had kissed in the anguish of a boy's first worship. The sight made him sick and faint, but he could not move away. A bleak fascination held him to the hole in back of the moon, through which he beheld, with incredulous agony, the sky of his self-made universe fall to pieces with a jangle of shattered glass and lie in broken stars in the mud at the bottom of the world.

"There," said Mr. Cave. "And there," in the pauses of his noisy embraces, "that's for every time he's paddled with your hand in the dark—and that's for every pimping New York dolly-name he's ever called you! Oh, kiss me, you jewel!" he squeaked in a sort of ecstasy. "Kiss me and tell me who you love with all your body and bones!"

"Enough, Charles, enough," said Sparta, drowsily, her voice very golden. "You know I love no man but you."

"Well, it's time and more that I heard it," said Cave, releasing her. He seemed to grow quite simple, of a sudden. His voice sank—his mouth drooped like a child's. "Where do you think I've been since you two were betrothed? In hell. In the pit of hell. They lie if they say there's no hell—I know—I've smoked in it. To see him walking with you, with his hand on your arm. You'd best be true with me now, wench." He seemed almost pleading, "You'd best be true."

"I am true, Charles."

"But you betrothed—"

She made a gesture. "Father," she said.

"I know your father," said Cave sullenly. "He's a planny man, your father. He's planned to marry you off to a fool with money ever since you were husband-high."

She laughed sharply. "My father is a lucky gentleman," she said. "He may have planned—but God sent him the perfect fool. How can anyone be so utterly a fool as my Andrew, Charles?"

"He loves you," Cave admitted grudgingly. "A man's blinded, then." He stared at his fist.

"Granted," she said, jeeringly. "But—if you think you have been in hell Charles, these last weeks—to have to take that stammering boy in my arms and give him his lollypop kisses—" Her eyes were bright with hate, "I may have to marry him yet—but if I do—"

"If you do, he'll never bed you," said Cave, in a rigid voice. "I'd have his guts on the floor first."

"No," said Sparta, with an edged and terrible smile. "He may bed me yet, Charles—perhaps—but—he shan't marry me."

"And I tell you," said Cave, starting up, with his eyes little, burning holes.

She stopped him with a gesture. "Hush, Charles," she said. "You don't understand me yet, I'd do anything for you, Charles. Sit down and give me some wine."

He obeyed, muttering. She drank the wine in a gulp and wiped her lips.

"Tell me, Charles, how soon will you be ready?"

"I have my men picked now," said Cave, in a thick voice, "Italians mostly. They're ripe. They hate the Mahonese as the devil hates church-bells."

"And the Mahonese are ready to strike, themselves?"

"If they're not they have no bellies," said Cave, impatiently. "They've been pushed to the wall. You'd think they'd have broken before."

"Very well," said Sparta, calmly. "The Minorcans revolt. My father cannot subdue them—unless you choose. He can't get aid from the governor—the governor's against him. If you choose—"

"There's a price," said Cave, glowering. "I want you. I want the plantation. He wants his life and—I'd give him some place, I suppose. If he doesn't choose it that way—By the way—what about that lover of yours?"

"What you will," said Sparta, and smiled.

"I know what I will. But now, sweetheart, what if your father will not—"

"I would not have you too much concerned about my father," said Sparta, reflectively.

Cave stared at her. "By God, you're a cold piece," he said, huskily.

"Not to you, Charles." She rose to her full height. "I'd see you a king, Charles—not the master of one trifling plantation here."

"And who says I couldn't be a king!" said Cave, with a touch of half-drunken defiance. "Haven't bastards been kings before. What was William Conquer but a common bastard—yet he had all England under his teeth? I'm as good a bastard as he was, any day—I can—"

"Then be a king!" she said in a voice that seemed to shake out a banner with a dragon on it above the quiet yellow spearheads of the candles. She brought her clenched hand down on the table as if she wanted to bruise its softness against something hostile and hard. "My father has money hidden somewhere—he must—you have men—strength—we could take ships—Davis did it —Teach was a fool, but Morgan did it—There are pirate kingdoms, still—I tell you this—I'll be a queen or nothing, Charles— I love you very well, but I must be a queen—I'd starve for it— I'd burn my hand in the flame for it—see—"

Her voice sank to a dry whisper, as she stretched her hand out over the nearest candle. Cave snatched it back, at once, with a terrified wordless sound. Then she was clinging to his shoulders, pleading with him, in that fierce, brittle monotone.

"A queen, Charles—they made Harry Morgan a governor—what

was Spanish Pizarro but a pirate, yet he held Peru like a king—
the time's not over yet—a queen, Charles—and you a king—"

But, "No, lass—no—" he was muttering unsteadily, trying to
seem very bold, yet with shaken eyes, "you're trying me with
talk like that—'tis impossible—I'll raise the colony on your father
right enough—I'll make you a right queen here if that's what
you want, but turn pirate against the world and end in the hemp
and the chains—"

His unsteady hand was fumbling with her hair, trying to quiet
her—she had sunk to the floor now, and was gripping his knees,
still pleading.

"Have done, girl—have done!" he said, in weak repetition but
she would not be quieted, though Mr. Cave was now fairly
sweating with discomfort and surprise. Further protestation was
spared him for the moment, for, on the tail of his last sentence,
the door opened slowly and admitted the tall, stately figure of
Mrs. Gentian to the curious scene. Mr. Cave froze at once, like
a rabbit surprised by an owl, but Sparta rose from the floor with
some dignity and confronted her mother.

"You fool," said the latter, slowly. "You bawdy little fool."

To Andrew, at his stricken post of observation, her voice was
clear and thin as the voice of a corpse speaking from the dust,
and he felt the sweat dry on his hands as he heard it.

She turned to Mr. Cave. "Kennel, dog!" she said, tersely, and
Mr. Cave, after one blustering, ineffective gesture, caught a
glance from Sparta, and passed out of the room with his brow
red and his eyes bent on the floor. Then Mrs. Gentian eyed her
daughter.

"You madam," she said, without rancor. "You madam in gauze.
What do you mean by chambering here with that lackey when
the gentleman you're to marry lies sick in his bed upstairs?"

"Faith, madam," said Sparta, hardly, giving her gaze for gaze.
"It must run in the blood, I think—for my father, too, has a liking
for the servants' hall."

Mrs. Gentian's hand went slowly to her breast, but her face
betrayed no emotion.

"You're indeed his very daughter to say that," she said, quietly,
and now Sparta's eyes wavered and fell before hers. "But let it
be so. I've heard you call the man you're to marry a fool."

"Do you disagree, madam?"

"Not I," said Mrs. Gentian, and laughed. "He's a puff of painted feathers—I'll buy his like for six-pence at a Punch-and-Judy. But, fool or no fool, he's rich, or his father is. Your father needs those riches—and no hot little miss like you is going to lecher him out of them. Do you understand, miss?"

"I had not thought you so greatly attached to my father," said Sparta in a stabbing voice.

"God knows I'm not," said her mother, tiredly. "But I'll not see him humbled."

"And is it your proposal, madam, that I should—"

"I propose this," said Mrs. Gentian. Her hand fell upon Sparta's shoulder and held it. "If this ninny you're to marry once knew what's passed between you and that lawyer's by-blow—he'd throw you aside like an applecore for all his ninnyishness. You must fasten him to you by his ninny's honor or lose him. You'll have him in your room, miss—as soon as he can walk—oh, I'll trust you for that—you have ways that would blind a sailor—but that you'll do. After that—" Her smile was an East wind. "Let him marry you or keep you—it matters little—we have him in a yoke."

Andrew could bear no more. He shut the panel with fumbling fingers and somehow got up the stairs and back to his room. When he reached there, he found the Minorcan girl, just done with tidying his room and about to leave. She gave a soft cry as she saw his face.

"Oh, go away, go away!" he sobbed wildly, as he flung himself into a chair and put his head in his hands. "Go away and pray for me, Caterina—I think I am the unhappiest man in the world!"

6.

Andrew lay on his bed, staring up at the ceiling with tormented eyes. He had thought he had known shock before, when his father's easy voice abolished the Beards of Westmoreland with a sentence. But that half-forgotten wound in the vanity of youth seemed like a wound in silk to this present pain. Again he felt the solid floor of life turn under him dizzily and alter—but this time it did not merely change, it blackened while he looked at it to the color of corrupted silver and soiled thunder walked in iron wherever he could see. The knowledge of good and evil had descended upon him at last, and he lay excruciated beneath it, like a harper crucified upon the strings of his own heart.

That his pain might well have seemed unnecessarily acute to any dispassionate observer would hardly have consoled him, had he known it. He saw the whole world now as a lie, which it was no more than it ever had been. But circumstance had mixed in him the fool and the gentleman—qualities both somewhat in disrepair nowadays—and at present, no doubt, the gentleman was somewhat sunk in the fool. The cold brain of heaven, whose thought is a falling star between illusion and illusion, might properly regard his adolescent strugglings with befitting contempt but that task of scorn may, perhaps, be left to it.

A certain, stale equanimity returned to him at last. He was still dazed and shaken but he began to think. At one moment he was quite confident that what he had seen in Dr. Gentian's study was merely a nightmare of the mind—at another that Sparta, for some inexplicable reason, had been playing a game upon the sullen Mr. Cave. But truth seeped in gradually through his defenses and at last he stood ready to accept the fact.

Seen clearly, the situation was only too plausible. He had often thought humbly enough, that it was strange that Sparta should love him, and strange that she should never have loved before. Well, she had loved before, that was all, and if she chose to garland an ass with roses, such was her prerogative. It seemed curious to Andrew that this wise and reasonable thought brought him so little relief. He began to consider just what there was to be done.

He must get away from New Sparta. But then he shuddered—he and Sparta were still betrothed, as much as they ever had been, he remembered with sudden pain. It hardly lay with decency to call her a slut to her father's face—yet what other reason could he give for so sudden a departure? Then there was Mr. Cave's mad plan of an uprising in the colony—a driving of the Minorcans to revolt. Admitted, he now owed Dr. Gentian little but the hate of a bamboozled sailor for his crimp—the Minorcans were still his friends—Sebastian—he could not go without warning them. Now indeed he felt a net on his body and struggled at the cords in futile disgust. His struggles were interrupted by a light knock at the door. He called. The door opened. Sparta was there.

"Why Andrew, dear," she said, looking at him in affectionate surprise. "I thought to find you still in bed with the fever and bring you your supper. But you are well again—and I am so glad."

Her voice was the same dropping skein of gold-and-crystal that he remembered—the same enchanter slept in her eyes.

He looked at her a long time. No, he could not talk to her now.

"My fever's gone," he said at last. "I think I'll come down to supper, if you'll call the boy to lend me his arm."

7.

He was sitting at table in Dr. Gentian's chair. The room had not changed its aspect—the fruit-piece by Vandermoulen still hung above the sideboard where silver glimmered in the candle-shine. The ladies he supped with took peaches from a bowl and peeled them delicately with silver knives. There was no mark upon their white hands like the mark of a bloody paw—the wine in the decanter at his elbow seemed excellent St. Lucar,—he could savor its bouquet quite naturally. That was odd, thought Andrew dully, as he ate and drank and talked. He felt vaguely that things should have been different—more in keeping with the tiny, persistent sound that tapped like blood flowing from a wound continually inside his head. He had yet to realize that tragedy may occur in a bandbox and that horror needs no set apparatus of skeletons to make the bones feel cold.

It was odd too, that he should be eating and drinking. He watched his knife cut a piece of meat, his fork carry it to his mouth. The hand did not falter at all, nor the throat refuse to swallow. All his muscles obeyed him handily—it was clever of them. He could question and reply in a normal voice—he found himself listening with every appearance of attention to a long, tedious account by Mrs. Gentian of some customs of the Spaniards in St. Augustine.

It appeared there was one called "Shooting the Jews." On the Saturday morning after Good Friday, when the bells rang hallelujah from the Cathedral, the Spanish inhabitants would shoot at straw dummies labelled Judas and Caiaphas, hung up at the corners of certain streets. Really, how interesting, he heard himself saying, while privately he searched Mrs. Gentian's calm face for any signature which might betray that she had been born in hell and was surprised to find none there.

So the servants went and came, and plates were laid and removed, with the passage of innumerable minutes, till the world grew old and white and tottered upon a dry branch like a dying cripple, and a stone hardened in Andrew's breast, and three people sat enchanted around a long table, peeling peaches and putting the flesh of peaches in their mouths. At last it was over, and he was left with his wine.

He arranged nuts on the table, very carefully, in a cross, in a square, in the initials of his brother's name. His mind seemed to have room for nothing but the exactitude of their patterns. He could think consecutively no longer—he was tired of thinking.

A nut rolled away from under his hand, and he cursed it whiningly and replaced it in its design with nice deliberation. Presently he would go up to his room with the India chintz hangings, and, if he had his wish, would die among its printed flowers like an insect crushed between leaves of painted paper. But that would not happen—people did not die as easily as that.

Mrs. Gentian and Sparta had watched each other all through the meal like cat and cat. A detached part of his consciousness told him that now, in the lifeless voice of a boy repeating a dull lesson. And, for once, Mrs. Gentian had seemed the stronger of the two. Did that mean anything—if it did, he was too tired to think what it might mean.

Presently he was pleading fatigue to the ladies and climbing the stairs to his room. The shadows wavered in the corridor before his candle. He wished, vaguely, that he could see that Minorcan girl, now, as he had first seen her, coming toward him like the image of a barbarous saint walking the sea, the light of a single candle ghostly upon the darkness of her brows. But even if she did come, she would turn to something evil as soon as he touched her. All things turned to evil the moment they were touched. There was evil in the very particles of the air, an impalpable dust of black glass, and people took it into their lungs and turned into dolls of spoilt straw and rotten leather that fell to pieces as they moved.

Sebastian's thunder was coming. He could hear it growl in the distance like a dog on a chain. The thought of the bright blade of lightning gave him a little ease—that at least was clean, and could run sick arrogance to the heart.

He was sitting, still dressed, in a chair in his room. Time had passed, but how long a time he did not know. The candle on the table burnt unevenly, with a smoky flame. The house was quiet—the thunder nearer at hand.

He passed his hand over his forehead and tried to collect his thoughts. The heat in his brain like the throb of blood from a spent artery, had eased a little now—he was still in stupor, but the weight of it was not so extreme. He began to realize that, whatever else might have happened to him, the fever was not yet wholly gone from his body. He must sleep—after he had slept, the beat in his head might stop.

He was about to rise when his eyes were drawn to the door. It was opening—a crack—a gap—letting in soft blackness. He stared at it, without fear or surprise. It might be Death—if it were, he would not lift a hand.

A hand, a bare arm, came slowly out of the darkness. The hand held a white flower between its fingers. It was Sparta's hand.

After what seemed a long time, "Andrew," said Sparta's voice, in a low call. He shut his teeth and would not answer. There was silence, while the hand moved a little and the curtains waved in the draft. Then, "Andrew," said the voice again—the fine gold streaking the crystal with threads of radiance. Then hand and flower were slowly withdrawn and the door closed gradually, leaving Andrew staring like a blind man at where they had been.

His pistols lay on the table near him, in their case. He took one of them out and examined it slowly, with minute care. The priming needed to be changed—this damp weather ruined one's priming. But he made no move to change it. He fiddled with the trigger a moment, a childish look on his face, not thinking of anything; then he forgot why he had taken up the pistol, and stuck it in his pocket to get it out of the way. His hands relaxed —the spinning in his mind began to slacken, like a top running down.

After another while, he rose, stiffly, and smiled. The stupor had passed from him—he knew what he would do. If the world were colored like a bat he would take the color of the world. He would take the instant of brisk desire for the image seen in a cloud and know in its entirety the damnation of possession and the wittiness of the flesh. He would despoil as he had been despoiled and lose the rags of gold he had brought from fool's paradise in the quick heat of the blood as a wise man should.

A sudden glare of heat lightning showed his face to him in the mirror. It was haggard and strange, but he smiled at it and went to the door. Down the corridor, packed with bags of darkness, lay another door with a white flower before it, and he was going there to sleep with a ghost.

PART THREE:

THE PIT OF OPPRESSION

All along the corridor, utter night lay reclined like the body of a great, black cat, asleep with its head on its heavy paws. He went softly—to his dizzy mind it seemed as if at any moment his feet might sink into dark, sleek fur and a bristling, gigantic back hump up uneasily beneath them. The corridor seemed much longer than it did in daylight—why had he blown out the candle in his room? He had come some distance and still he could see no door with a white flower before it—he must have passed it, somehow, in this place where darkness was a mask of black satin across the eyes.

He turned about, as he thought, and started to grope his way back, with his hands out before him. They touched against a wall. He grew confused and stopped, trying to fix the points of the compass in his head. He turned again, walked forward and came up against another wall—the corridor was gone—he was trapped in a narrowing box of velvet and ebony whose sides shut in around him like a closing fist. The ludicrous aspect of the situation did not strike him—he had passed beyond humor—his mind was a sharpened point that had given itself entirely to the pull of a dark lodestone and now wished with all its strength to touch that lodestone and cease. He stood perfectly still for a long moment before the unreasonable wall that had so suddenly risen up in front of him, angry, ridiculous, impotent, and more than a little afraid.

Ah, he had it at last. He turned to the left and moved forward —right—the wall was gone. Sparta's chamber must be farther along, on the other side of the cross-corridor—he would find it now. A sound would have helped him greatly—but there was no sound at all in the buried world through which he moved but thunder rattling the iron roof of heaven and the creeping noise of his own shoes. No, wait a moment. There was another sound.

There was another sound, faint and distant, as if it came through mufflings of black wool, but distinct enough when he listened for it, a sound made by some creature in pain. He paused and listened intently. At first he could not fix its direction. It seemed to come at once from everywhere and from nowhere, as if the encompassing and shadowy air of night itself were whispering to itself in quietness a single, monotonous word of obscure anguish. Then at last, after much time, he traced it down. The sound came from above, it was the voice of the Minorcan girl, and she was calling "Water, water, water," very slowly and weakly, as if her throat were small with pain.

He stood irresolute for a few seconds, the blood thudding in his head. Something hot and stinging began to die from his veins. "Water, water, water," said the thread of breath from above, in desolate supplication. He remembered a mole he had seen once, after dogs had worried it—it lay on its side, half-dead, and made much the same feeble, pitiful outcry, thin and incessant as the creak of a locust. He had been ready for desire and hate—for Death playing knucklebones with his joints in a corner—but for this he had not been ready. He could not go to Sparta with that haunted outcry in his ears.

He turned again, and bruised his shin against the bottom step of a stair. He knew where he was, then—he had strayed into the cross-corridor by mistake—the servants' quarters were above. "Water," said the voice, and choked. He started to climb the stair.

The thread of voice led him to a closed door. He tried it—it was locked but the key was on the outside. Then, just at the point of unlocking it, he paused. What was he doing here—he was looking for another door, a door with a flower before it. He had not come all this way with a black hand muffling his face to comfort a serving-wench in the throes of a bad dream. He started to turn back, but as he did so, "Water," said the crucified voice again, and the accents were not those of an imaginary anguish. He cursed himself for a fool, and turned the key.

At first he could see little in the room but the pale square of the window. Then, outside, a jagged thornbush of lightning flowered for an instant and vanished, and in its abrupt glare, brief as the flashing of powder, he saw the Minorcan girl standing upright against the foot of her bed. But now she seemed much taller than he had thought her. She was standing on tiptoe—why was she standing on tiptoe, and why were her arms stretched up stiffly over her head? Then she gave an inarticulate groan and he realized, with a shock, that she was bound, and suspended from the ceiling by a cord tied round her wrists so that the tips of her toes just brushed the floor.

He ran over to her and tried to lift her up in his arms. She gave a moan of relief or pain and her head drooped suddenly on his shoulder. Then he was trying to raise her with one arm and pick at the knots in the cord with his other hand. "Knife," he kept whispering to himself, inanely. "Knife. Knife. Knife. Where's knife?" It seemed hours before the knife was out of his pocket and the cord frayed apart.

He caught her in his arms. Her body was loose and heavy as the body of a rebellious child—she had fainted with exhaustion and pain. Staggeringly, he lifted her on the bed and laid her down as comfortably as he could. She stirred a little and sighed. "*Agua*," she said, in a whisper. He found some water in a ewer, splashed it clumsily on her face, wet her lips with it. Outside the thunder grew fainter and rain began to fall in a black, streaming torrent. He did not notice it. He knew only that he would never breathe easily again, if he did not bring back to life, if but for an instant, this slight, defiant flesh, austere now, coldly wrapped in the husk of a darker flower than Sleep's.

She came back to consciousness, grudgingly, like a child learning to walk, like a visitor long-detained by a gift of pomegranates at a stony threshold and still half-unwilling to return. At last she was strong enough to sit up and make the woman's automatic gesture at arranging her hair.

"Thank Christ," said Andrew, shakily, hardly knowing what he said, "I thought you were dead."

"I was dead," said the Minorcan girl, and smiled a little. "How did you know?"

"I heard you—in the corridor—you were crying—"

She bit her lips. "They hurt my hands," she said, looking at them. "They hurt my hands."

"Who did it?" said Andrew, voice and body cold.

"She said I was her husband's strumpet," said the Minorcan girl, her eyes very black in the darkness. "She said she'd teach me. Then she got Mr. Cave."

"I think I shall kill Mr. Cave," said Andrew. "But your—the other servants—they must have heard—Good God—the key was in the door—"

"They are Greeks," said the Minorcan girl. "Touch a Greek and you touch a rat. Besides—they are hers and Mr. Cave's."

"They are devils," said Andrew, sobbingly. "This is a house of devils—oh, a house of devils—"

"Listen," said the Minorcan girl, with that smile that set her apart from him, in a circle of antique and savage stones. "Even yet, you do not know." And, sitting on the bed, while the rain slashed at the window, and Andrew dabbed at her bloody wrists with a torn handkerchief, she began, quite quietly, her recital of five years' wrong. There was no passion in the sentences—if there had been Andrew felt he could have borne their impact more easily. There was only the calm, insistent pulse of her even voice, throbbing slowly in the darkness like the beating of the wings of a tired bird.

"So they hanged the priest in his robes, on a wooden post, and stuck a piece of bread in his mouth to mock him," her voice tolled gravely. It was the unforgivable sin. "After that—"

"Oh, for God's sake, Caterina—for God's sake—" stammered Andrew, excruciated beyond his strength. "Can't we get away from this house—tonight—in the rain—they can't hear us in the rain—there are horses in the stable—we'll ride to St. Augustine—tell the governor—he'll help us—my father's rich—we'll take Sebastian, too—Oh, come, Caterina, come—" He was pulling at her hands. She clenched her teeth, and he realized that he had hurt her.

"How can I ride, with my hands?" she said, helplessly.

"I'll tie you to the saddle—you can ride pillion behind Sebastian or me—you must, Caterina—you must—we can't stay here any more—" He was pleading with her now, as if for some salvation of spirit that lay hidden between her hands like a coral amulet. Her face was serene as she listened. She made a little gesture.

"Wait," she said, and rose from the bed. When she was on her feet she swayed for an instant. "Ah, Dios," she said, under her breath. Andrew offered her his shoulder, but she put him aside and walked slowly over to the other end of the room. There was a little shrine there—a cheap, plaster image of the Virgin. Her robes had been gaudily colored in staring blues and reds but they were mildewed now and the colors were faint and gentle. A tiny wick burned in a small cup of rancid oil at her feet. Caterina sank to her knees.

"*Madre de Dios*—Mary Virgin—Tower of Ivory—House of Gold—" she began, in Mahonese, in a soft, lulling voice. Andrew watched her perplexedly from the bed. The scene touched him with pity and grief, but it was something he could not understand. He would have been glad enough to kneel beside Caterina himself and pray, if he had thought it would bring her any comfort, but there was something in the absorption of her eyes, as she gazed at the tawdry little doll with a tarnished crown, that made her incomprehensible. It belonged, with the flower of the Spanish bayonet, to an earth that was not his—an earth in which he would always be a stranger. And yet, as the mutter of the prayer went on, he knew that he did not wish to be a stranger to that alien, enchanted ground.

When Caterina had finished, and crossed herself, with head bowed, she came back to him.

"Yes. I will come," she said. Their eyes met—for an instant he seemed to see behind hers, into her heart. There was a message there, clear and pure as if air had written it on a tablet of mountain-snow, but a message he could not read, for it was written in her language, and to him the characters of that language were mysterious as marks carved upon a druid stone. He stared for an instant, vainly—hoping for a Pentecost that did not descend. Then the veil fell between them again.

They crept down the stairs together, hand in hand, like children afraid of the dark. When they got to the long corridor, she turned to go down it but he held her back. "No. Not that way," he said. He felt suddenly as if he could not bear to stumble past the door with the white flower, even to get his other pistol and his father's letters. He was in a torment of impatience to leave the coquina house behind him forever. There must be arms in Dr. Gentian's study—besides, there was less chance of arousing the house if they went through there.

He smiled. The high chamber with the gold stars in its ceiling which had seen his imaginary Eden crumble to ash should be the instrument of their deliverance from this house of pain. He led the way slowly to the hidden stair.

When they had reached the panel behind the moon, an instinct of precaution made him slide it back and look. So, for the second time that day, an odd vision was vouchsafed him.

Dr. Gentian stood in front of the fireplace, warming his hands. He must have been but newly come from the road, for his muddy boots were set in a corner to dry and his riding-coat, stretched out on a chair before the fire, was streaked and spattered. He himself, however, was as neat and trim as ever. He had changed his muddied coat for a loose dressing-gown and his boots for soft Moorish slippers, worked with gold thread and turned up in stiff petals at the toes. On his head was a turban of yellow silk, such as many gentlemen who had served in the Indies affected, and he rubbed his hands over and over each other like a fly cleaning its wings, as he talked to himself in a low, quick voice and smiled at the fire.

Andrew could feel the Minorcan girl's whole body shudder against his for an instant and then grow still. "The gold cap!" she whispered in the voice of a beaten ghost. "He has on the gold cap. We shall never get free of him now."

"Nonsense," said Andrew, though he too was oddly affected by the sight of that spruce, quaint figure crowned with an inverted tulip-flower, smiling dimly and talking under its breath to a burning log. "We'll take the other stairs." He shut the panel and started to go back. But a few steps away from the upper door, he stopped and listened. There were footsteps in the corridor, a light step and a heavy one, going to and fro like the pace of sentries on guard.

"They are looking for me already," said the Minorcan girl, slowly, with a calm despair.

Andrew hesitated, feeling the lips of a velvet trap close slowly upon them both in the narrow darkness. Then he made up his mind. Better face Caesar in his study than chance what might be in the upper corridor. His mind stuck on the thought that the house had orders not to disturb the Doctor when he wished quiet and that there was deadening in the walls of the high-ceiled chamber. His hand slid to the butt of his pistol—he had never killed a man—what was it like when you killed a man? He saw Caesar sprawled in front of the fire with blood on his neck—a little flame stole out shyly from a log and licked at the yellow turban. He shivered. Fool, he was wasting time. "We'll risk it," he said hoarsely, and went sneaking down the stairs again.

At their foot, he paused. The Minorcan girl was on the step behind him—he could hear the flutter of her breath. Beyond, in the study, was another sound—Dr. Gentian's voice, plainer now.

At first Andrew thought some one else must have come into the room—the Doctor's tones were the tones of a man talking intimately to a familiar friend. He put his eyes to a crack in the door. He could see little, but no other form than the Doctor's crossed the range of his vision. Then he realized that though the Doctor's voice questioned and affirmed and at times even pleaded, as if the friend he addressed were a superior in rank, there was never any reply.

The voice went on and on. "I saw Baron Funck in London," it said. "He took me into a room full of silver candlesticks and swore he would show me a secret, but the only secret he showed me was a juggler's trick. Then there was Hauptzehn in Dresden —he had Lully's book but he did not have the key. The Rose-Cross is nothing—they pretend to make diamonds but they do not know the writing on the wall of the tabernacle or the tears of the Golden King. In India I have seen the man climb the rope and the flower rise from the dust and go back again—I have seen the basket thrust through with swords—but I wish more than that. Am I not an Initiate? Have I not heard the goat cry in the dark and scattered the herb in the fire? I cannot seek elsewhere again—I have grown too old." The voice had a note of chant, now. "There is something buried at the roots of the mountains —why can I not put my hand on it? Bacon had the knowledge they say—am I so much less wise? I will not fool myself with crystals and black wafers—these things are folly, but there is something left—something beyond the speculum—behind the glass. I will give my soul for it, I tell you—I will give my soul for it." Now the tones were those of a merchant driving a canny bargain. "I can give you a thousand souls. You are foolish not to bargain with me. Come out of the fire, Baphomet—Baphomet— Baphomet—" the voice reached a shriek of supplication. "Come out of the fire, Baphomet, and buy my souls!"

Through his crack, Andrew saw the yellow turban waver and droop in fatigue like a crocus beaten by the wind. Now. He flung open the door and stepped into the room with his pistol clutched tight in sweating fingers.

The shock of his abrupt appearance, to a gentleman who so obviously expected other visitors, must have been painful in the extreme, but Dr. Gentian bore it with admirable equanimity. He put his hand to his mouth once, slowly, while his face altered. Then he came forward to Andrew, smiling, with hand out-stretched, as if the pistol presented at his heart had no more importance than a sprig of rosemary.

"Ah, Andrew," he said cheerfully, "I had hardly hoped to see you before the morning. Come over by the fire, lad, and warm yourself—the house is chilly with the rain."

"Keep your distance," said Andrew hoarsely, "keep your distance, you miracle of hell, or I'll shoot your heart out."

Dr. Gentian's hand dropped to his side. He looked puzzled and distressed.

"Why lad," he said gently, "are you still so fevered?" He smiled sympathetically, "Or did my playacting just now fright—how much did you hear of it?" he said in a swift breath.

"Enough," said Andrew wretchedly. "Keep your distance, Dr. Gentian—I have no wish to murder you, but I leave your house tonight."

"I forbid it," said Dr. Gentian, promptly, "as your physician, if not as Sparta's father." He came a little nearer. "Let me look at your eyes, lad—yes, they're bright." He shook his head. "Far too bright—and your pulse is beating like a hammer I'll warrant, and your skin—oh, I know the signs! It would be madness for you to ride in this rain—" with each phrase he approached a trifle, delicately, on slippered feet.

"Let me feel your pulse a moment, lad," he said now, stretching out his hand again. Andrew beat it down with a gesture.

"Stop," he said, "I know you. The lot of you. You've plucked me like a pigeon between you—you and your whory daughter and your wife that hangs up servant girls by the thumbs. You torturers. Come out, Caterina," he said, without turning his head.

The door in the wall opened, the Minorcan girl stepped into the room. Dr. Gentian gazed at her for a moment. A tiny drop of blood gathered on one of her wrists and fell. Andrew, looking

191

at the Doctor, thought he seemed more like a Caesar than ever, with the color out of his cheeks, but this time he knew the face. It was no Julian or Augustan coin—it came of a later mintage—the silver was debased—the lids of the eyes grown heavy. Caligula at the Games staring down at a bloody sand, where something moved and cried—Tiberius killing flies like so many black slaves at the window of his villa above the cold, star-amethyst of the sea . . .

The Minorcan girl shut the door slowly behind her. She held out her bloody wrists. She did not speak.

"So," said Dr. Gentian, sucking his breath in. Then, without warning, he sprang for the side of the fireplace and pulled at the bell-cord furiously. The hammer of Andrew's pistol fell. The fire sparked in the flint but that was all. He remembered looking at the pistol, years ago, and thinking it should be reprimed.

"Oh, Christ," said Andrew, with a sob, and leaped forward, throwing the pistol aside. He heard the Minorcan girl cry out. Then a flare like the sudden flare and extinction of a puff of red fire lit the base of his brain for a moment and was succeeded by sparkling darkness.

When he roused, his head felt huge, and as if it would split apart like a cut orange at the slightest movement. He was propped in a corner with his hands bound behind his back and Mr. Cave was standing over him with a gorged, pleased look on his face.

"He has a skull," said Mr. Cave, turning away from him to the Doctor, who seemed engaged in washing his hands in a little basin, "I couldn't use my right hand, even so—by God, all the time you were bandaging him, I thought you were wasting lint." Andrew noticed now that Mr. Cave carried his right arm in a sling. Dully, he wondered why.

"You were admirably prompt, Mr. Cave," said the Doctor, aloofly, drying his hands, "I must thank you. I confess, I have seldom known you so prompt before."

Mr. Cave's face grew sullen. "We were looking for the Minorcan piece," he said, "I thought she might have come down your stair. I heard you pull at the bell as I got to the door."

"A fortunate coincidence," said Dr. Gentian reflectively. "And yet—in future, Mr. Cave—unless by my invitation—"

"I wouldn't have used your damn staircase tonight," said Mr. Cave, flushing, "but I thought—as long as she'd broken away—"

"Quite right," purred the merry Doctor. "You are always right, Mr. Cave."

"What have you done with her?" said Andrew, thickly. His senses were returning, he felt on the point of vomiting from the warm, luke, jellyish taste of blood in his mouth.

The Doctor eyed him with his head cocked on one side, like a bird.

"Do not vex your mind unduly, Andrew," he said. "Your trollop has gone back to her room. She will doubtless undergo a little discipline in the morning, but that is all. I shall not even put her back in the fields."

"May God damn your soul in hell," said Andrew, retching. "If I could only get loose—"

"You would merely do yourself an injury," said Dr. Gentian briskly. He turned. "You sent for the soldiers, Mr. Cave?"

"Yes, sir," Mr. Cave grinned. "They'll have work to do for once."

"Ah, yes," said the Doctor. "By the way—" He picked up an object from the table, daintily and came over to Andrew, holding it at fingers' length. "Do you recognize this, my boy?"

Andrew stared at the object. It was the knife he had given Sebastian, but now there were rusty stains along the blade.

"Yes. It's my knife," he said. He was about to add that it had not been his for three months, but did not because each word he uttered was a stab in his head.

"Thank you," said the Doctor, "that is very satisfactory. You see, Andrew, your Minorcan friend, Zafortezas, happened to stab poor Mr. Cave in the arm with that knife a few hours ago. A flesh-wound only, fortunately. Your knife. Curious. And the same evening, you, for some inexplicable reason, attempt to murder me with a pistol. It begins to look like a plot, Andrew—it begins to look like a plot"—and he shook his head sorrowfully, while his eyes danced with little points of light.

"You—" said Andrew, raging impotently.

"Yes, Andrew. A plot to take my plantation from me. Ah, Andrew, Andrew, I wouldn't have believed it of you," he said.

Andrew was silent, feeling unmanly tears of weak fury prick at his eyes. Then he thought of something.

"I appeal to the governor," he said.

"Inadvisable," said Dr. Gentian. "The governor may not be

my friend—but I doubt if he would give much weight to any appeal from a Northern rebel."

"Rebel?" said Andrew, dizzily.

"Rebel. Oh, I forgot—you have not had your mail. Well, you may take it to jail with you, and read it there. Yes, Andrew—the Northern Colonies are in revolt. There's been blood spilt—" He tossed a packet of letters into Andrew's lap. "Most interesting —especially the one from your brother. He seems to be deeply involved in the rebellion. Your father is greatly concerned."

Andrew was struck dumb. So it had come at last. He saw his brother Lucius firing at a man in a red coat—his father sitting at his desk in the home on Wall Street with a newspaper crumpled before him and his eyes looking into a darkness—and felt, for a bitter moment, that he himself was the most futile person alive.

"When did it happen?" he said.

"In April," Dr. Gentian smiled, "at a place called Lexington —and Concord—near Boston, aren't they? They say the colonials ran like hares."

"You lie," said Andrew, with an intensity that surprised him. "They wouldn't run before a parcel of lobsterbacks."

"No?" said Dr. Gentian. He smiled again. "You will note, Mr. Cave, that our friend has just insulted the entire British army *in toto*."

"I'll note it," said Mr. Cave, greedily, "I'll remember it."

A knock came at the door.

"There, sir," said Mr. Cave, "there are our lobsterbacks now."

He opened the door. Three soldiers headed by a corporal marched into the room and grounded arms. Andrew thought tiredly that they looked like disgruntled footmen in their draggled uniforms. The corporal's face was still puffy with sleep. By some trick of mind he remembered his first tour of inspection when they had passed the tiny guardhouse near the wharves and Dr. Gentian had jested about his military forces. There were only eight men at the post—where were the other five? It seemed inappropriate that they should not join in this nightmare joke of arresting him as a murderer and a rebel.

The corporal was a decent fellow—he had often given him tobacco. But tonight his face was as stiff and wooden as a face carved on the bowl of a pipe. It betrayed not the slightest sign that he had ever seen Andrew before. All soldiers were like that—

they came out of a giant toy-box and turned into flat pieces of painted wood whenever someone spoke to them with a frog in his throat. He looked at the corporal's feet accusingly—they should be glued into a little green stand. Also, it was thoughtless of Dr. Gentian to leave his soldiers out in the rain. They would have to be repainted, tomorrow, clumsily, with sticky stuff that came off on your tongue when you licked the brush. Presently he would get up and push the corporal in the chest—then the corporal would totter on his stand and fall in one piece against the nearest private, and all three of them would clatter to the floor with a woodeny sound, because they were only toys, and this was a dream. Dr. Gentian was saying something.

"Put him in the cell with the Minorcan," he was saying. "They are both concerned in the attempt to assassinate Mr. Cave and myself and capture the colony. In addition, this young man is strongly suspected of being in league with the rebellion in the Northern Colonies. Seditious newspapers have been found in his room and his brother is a prime-mover in the revolt. He will be transferred to St. Augustine later, for trial. The charge is treason and attempted murder. Very well, corporal. Take charge of the prisoner."

"Get him up on his feet," said the corporal in a voice of board. "Can he walk? All right—bring him along between you."

They passed by the great main staircase on their way to the door, and Andrew, turning his head caught a glimpse of Sparta Gentian. She was standing half up the stairway, leaning on the rail, the shawl with the vivid flowers on it wrapped around her. Their eyes met for an instant. As she looked at him a slow smile widened on her mouth and her eyes began to burn. Then she leaned forward deliberately and spat at him from the stair.

"Damn the woman—she's spit on my coat," grumbled the private on Andrew's right as they went out of the door.

"Less talk there, you," said the corporal ahead. "Shut your mouth and pretend you're a duck—it's raining like bloody hell."

2.

There was darkness and the smell of damp stone and rotten mold—things ran about in the darkness on light, innumerable feet. The air was the air of a cellar that has been built underneath a well. For a moment Andrew was oddly reminded of the dairy-house on the country place that bordered the Boston road—cool even in lion-colored August with the coolness of slabs of stone buried deep in the ground. He was a tanned little boy in knee-breeches with flushed cheeks and damp hair, standing before a gleaming pan on a table and stretching out a stealthy finger through the pleasant gloom to dabble its tip in the risen cream, thick and yellow as daffodil-petals clotted together. Through the deep, barred window Summer came and the smell of it, the smell of heat and harvest and grain bursting out of the ear. Then he remembered. The little boy and the cool dairy belonged to another life which some stranger had lived in a void. This was the pit of oppression and he would lie in it like a truss of dis-carded hay till they took him out to hang him to an orange-tree in the bright morning, while Spanish ladies looked out from be-hind black fans from the jutting balconies of old houses in St. Augustine, and a curly-haired drummer-boy rattled out a dead march and then, for an instant, silenced his drum.

He moved forward unsteadily, in the darkness. "Sebastian?" he called querulously, "Sebastian?"

There was a stir in a corner.

"I am here, my friend," said a disembodied voice.

"Have they hurt you much, Sebastian?"

"The knife slipped," said the voice in answer. "He was too quick. The knife slipped in my hand." Then it was silent and the running things resumed their activities.

Andrew felt his way over to the corner. His outstretched hand touched a shoulder that winced beneath the touch.

"Have they hurt you much?" he said again.

"No," said Sebastian very bitterly. Andrew's eyes were grow-ing accustomed to the blackness—now he saw the blur of a face. "I am well enough. But the knife was dedicated—it should not have slipped when I struck."

"I fired at him point-blank," said Andrew sitting down in a puddle. "But the priming was wet. Then they hit me over the head."

"You should have had a silver bullet," said Sebastian. "People like that are not killed with steel or lead."

"I will have a silver bullet next time," said Andrew, and fell silent. The two friends sat together in the dark for some time without saying anything more. Both were gazing into the shadow that encompassed them and Andrew's hand lay lightly on Sebastian's shoulder. There seemed little need of speech between them at the moment—each knew well enough what the other felt and thought. When Andrew had first entered this mildewed night, he had been curious to hear Sebastian's story and eager to tell his own. Now he felt as if both had been told and judged and found unimportant. There were only three things left of any importance, an ache in the skull, a darkness before the eyes, and the quick sound of scuttling feet in the other corners of the room.

After a while, however, Andrew spoke.

"Do you think there'll be a next time, Sebastian?" he said, heavily.

"Who knows?" said Sebastian. "We are always between God's fingers—now no less than ever."

At any other time the words would have struck Andrew as insufferably bigoted and submissive. Now they seemed to him what they were, a calm statement of fact. To Sebastian God was a visible and tangible presence—therefore He was here, in this pit, no more so and no less than He was everywhere. He was with the soldiers in the guardroom, also, as they drank out of empty cups and cut at toy food that stuck to its plate. He was with Dr. Gentian in his study when devils hatched in the fire. No sin could avert that scrutiny, no blasphemy or righteousness deter its penetration by the width of a hair. When the time came for judgment, they should all be judged—meanwhile it behooved them to act according to their lights, for, within their limits of flesh, they were free to do good or evil. God had bound them all with a light, indivisible cord—when He wished, He could gather them up and count them like the buttons on Peggy's button string. In the meantime, He might never lift a finger to avert a present anguish—for so are martyrs left without justification.

Andrew wished that he could think of God like that, but he could not. To him God was something vague to pray to, for happiness or against the approach of pain—something which might be there. God was a cushioned pew and a prayer-book and a clergyman in robes as opposed to a hard pew and a long hymn and a preacher in a black Geneva gown. He had never thought much about God except as a superior kind of Archbishop of Canterbury who sat on a cloud and looked at Papists sternly. But

Stephen Vincent Benét

Sebastian was a Papist—and Sebastian had taken God in his mouth
—and God was with him now. It was very strange and just a little
unfair.

"They say I'm a traitor," he said idly. "They say the Northern
colonies have revolted and there was a fight between our men and
the soldiers—and my brother was in it, so I must be a traitor, too."

"When the ass is spurred too hard it tries to kick off its rider,"
said Sebastian, who had proverbs in his blood. "Are you for
the rider or the ass?"

"I don't know," said Andrew, puzzled. "My house is divided.
I should have thought more about it before. I know my father
must be for the King."

"Then you must be for the King," said Sebastian, with Latin
respect for paternal authority. "It is ugly when a cause divides
son and father—even a good cause."

"I don't know," said Andrew again. "It doesn't seem real yet."
Again he saw the dim picture of his brother aiming a musket at
a toy-soldier corporal—the picture was fantastic—it could not
have occurred. "I can't believe they're really fighting," he added,
"I can't. The ministry has passed some bad laws, of course—but
Hancock and Adams—who'd ever fight for them?"

"Once men have started to fight, they forget what set them
on," Sebastian said. "It is like a game of ball—the ball is nothing
—the thing is to throw the ball so it counts for your side. Those
who watch the game see better than the players. Only, in war,
you cannot stand off and watch the game."

"I don't want to fight the King's soldiers, though," said
Andrew. "Why should I? And I certainly can't imagine fighting
Lucius."

"You will have to do one or the other," said Sebastian, placidly.
"But the winning side is always hard to tell."

"Not this time," said Andrew, feeling his tongue grow curiously bitter. "If there really is a revolt, they'll put it down as they
put down the Pretender at Culloden. Butcher Cumberland. They
have a trained army. We have nothing. I mean the Colonials have
nothing," he added hastily.

"God sometimes gets tired of the man on the ass," said Sebastian. "If I didn't think that, I would strangle myself here with my
own hands."

198

"Perhaps," said Andrew, considering. "But if I were betting, I should bet on the man."

"You have already bet on the ass, my friend," said Sebastian, with a chuckle. "If you had not, you would not be here."

His shoulder was withdrawn from beneath Andrew's hand. He turned over on his side. "I have some letters from home," muttered Andrew, "I can tell better when I read them—is there ever any light in this place, Sebastian?"

"A little, in the morning. I remember when we first made this cellar, I wondered why it was dug so deep." He was silent. Andrew heard him begin to breathe deeply and quietly.

"What's the matter, Sebastian—are you going to sleep?"

"Why not?" said a drowsy voice, "I may dream my knife did not slip after all."

"I wonder if my head will come off, if I try to sleep," said Andrew to himself. "I suppose it won't, though it feels like it." He stretched himself out on the straw and shut his eyes. "But listen, Sebastian," he said, after a long pause, "do you really believe God is here in prison with us, in this room?" He waited, but there was no answer. Then he sighed and arranged himself a little more comfortably, hoping the things that ran would not scamper over him much, once he was quiet. In the morning, they could plan, perhaps—not now—the thick stupor of fatigue rocked him in a cradle of lead. It seemed odd that the dawn which would wash the tiny window above him with pale waters of light tomorrow was the very same colored dawn that should have found him dozing in Sparta Gentian's bed, with her hair spread over their pillow like a scarf of drawn gold.

3.

As Sebastian had said, light came to their habitation in the morning—a slanting, shallow column, but enough to enable Andrew to read his letters. Also they had been given fresh water and a dish of boiled rice. The corporal had brought them these, but had refused to answer any questions. Andrew had asked for a razor, which was, of course, denied.

"I never saw them hang a fellow with a beard," the corporal

remarked judicially after the request. "But then I haven't seen much hanging." His mouth was sad. "When they hung the great pirates at Execution Dock I was as near to it as could be, but somebody had to stay with Gramfer. Crippled all up he was, and twice he'd fallen in the fire with nobody by. Well, I was the youngest and the least account, so I didn't see it. They say Kidd made a fine show. My father saw him," he added, with some pride. "Twirled he did and kicked for a while. Well, 'tis all in the drop, they say—a proper drop and 'tis over as soon as bite your nails," he concluded cheerfully and disappeared.

Andrew could not hate the man for his graveyard remarks— his face was as honest and foolish as the face of a giant pumpkin. But he felt his neck tenderly for a moment after the fellow had gone.

Now Sebastian was finishing the boiled rice, and he was reading the last of his letters. From them he got anxiety and excitement but little solace. Lexington—Concord—he tried to remember Lexington—he had passed through it once on a memorable trip to Boston with his father and Lucius. He remembered the leathery smell of the coach and how his father had gone to sleep with a red silk handkerchief over his face distinctly enough, but Lexington itself eluded him. A blur of trees—a village green where a goose waddled and stretched out its neck to hiss as a pinafored little girl—a white church with a steeple—the open door of a blacksmith shop where a man in a leather apron spat upon a fiery horseshoe—these scraps were all he could dredge up from the ragbag of memory. He stitched them into a town, in no way different from a dozen other little Massachusetts towns through which their coach had rolled, and yet now, somehow, very different. A month ago, when morning was only half-awake and the shadows lay the wrong way, men had died on that dim grass, awkwardly, unexpectedly—the brimstone smell of burnt powder had drifted in through the windows of the white church and the open door of the smithy—where the goose had waddled the green, bullets had journeyed as casually, with much the same hissing sound. He saw a plump woman with a queer white face stand at the foot of a stairway, listening, and his brother, the macaroni with two watches, dandy no longer but dirty and smooched, with a cut on his cheek, hiding behind a wall to fire at broken red dots running over a bridge. And still he could not comprehend.

"Disperse ye Rebels says He but we were Not for Dispersing . . . So, as I say, We Chast them till they met with their Other Force . . . Lord Percy's it is Said . . . I have a Fine Blister on Both my Feet because of it and a better prospect of Hanging than Ever I had but oh Andrew you should have Seen the Sweet Way they Ran . . ."

That was Lucius' letter. So no more at Present from Yr. Bro. It was odd to think of Lucius, the correct, the mannered, helping Massachusetts bumpkins to hunt a lord like a fox.

One thing, however, stood out plainly. His father was a broken man. Suspected by both sides, the invisible swordsman had forced him to the wall at last. The handwriting in his last epistle was shaky and old—the ends of the letters trailed off feebly as if it had been too great a care to finish them aright. "I have had a Stroke, my dear Sonn, and though they say 'Twas not the True Apoplexy, yr. Mother is greatly Concerned." Andrew felt pain tear at his heart, ragged and sharp. Pain and satire, for the words were followed by a formal blessing "Upon your Projected Marriage." For an instant Andrew wished, humanly enough, that he had never found Sparta out. His father seemed to set such store by the fact that his younger son, at least, was safe from the worries that beset himself. The mood was succeeded by one quite as youthful though more practical. He started up. He must get back to New York at once—see his father—find out the truth of the quarrel between colonies and King. His head was better now and his fever, queerly enough, quite gone. He was almost at the door before he remembered. Then he put his head in his hands and groaned aloud.

He felt Sebastian touch him on the arm. "Come my friend," said a voice, "sorrow eases the heart, but we have no time for it now. There must be a way out of this hole—the rats come in and go out, and between us we have at least as much sagacity as a rat."

It was later. The slanting column of light through the window had almost disappeared. They had searched the boundaries of their prison, floors and walls, as far as their hands could reach, like misers looking for a penny, and still they had found nothing to aid their escape. Two crannies through which rats could pass, a litter of soiled straw tossed over and over—that was all. Andrew thought of the tools hanging from the bench of the carpenter's shop by the wharf with a hopeless longing. He would have given any dubious immortality for the little file down by the end.

"We must think of some way to get the soldier in here and knock him on the head," said Sebastian, rising from his knees after a last picking over of the straw. "We cannot take the wall apart with our fingernails."

"Even if we did, though . . ." said Andrew.

"Yes," said Sebastian, "there's only one way out and that's through the guardroom. But it is our only chance."

"Wait a minute," said Andrew. He took up the dish and the pitcher that had held their breakfast and stared at them with greedy searching eyes.

"I thought of that," said Sebastian. He tapped the dish, "Wood," the pitcher, "Clay." "Even if we broke the pitcher, the pieces would crumble on the stone."

"There must be something, somewhere," said Andrew, against reason. Again his eyes slowly traversed the familiar walls of the room from ceiling to floor. Then he stiffened all over like a dog coming to point. High up in the wall and hardly visible in the gloom, beyond the reach of their hands, was a large, projecting nail.

"Get up on my shoulders, Sebastian—there is our tool," he said, his voice shaken as if he had just risen from deep water with a sea-pearl in his hand.

It took an hour or so to work the nail loose from the wall. When they had it down at last, it proved bent and rusty but they gloated over it with a solemn joy.

"Now," said Sebastian, practically, "where?" and he looked around him.

"We could never tunnel through from below in time," said Andrew. "That stone beneath the window—can you reach it, if you stand on my shoulders again?"

"I can just reach up to the middle of the bar," said Sebastian, after he had tried.

"Sentry outside?"

Sebastian peered cautiously, "I don't see one. But there may be one. There's a ditch, and a little rise beyond it."

Spanish Bayonet

"Thank God the light's gone away. He'd hardly see us, any-how, in the darkness—and we'll just have to chance being heard. Is the window too small?"

"Yes. Even if we could cut the bar."

"Well then," said Andrew, gritting his teeth and wishing Sebastian weighed less. "We'll have to take out the stone."

They spelled each other, all afternoon, at short intervals, the one who was below listening for the footsteps of the guard. The nail grew dull—then sharp again as it filed itself against the stone —then dull once more. Once it almost broke in two and once they were nearly caught by the unexpected return of the cor-poral soon after he had brought them a scant and nasty dinner. It was hard, exhausting work—the mortar at which they picked was only a little less indurate than the stones it cemented and the man who worked had to support himself with one hand against the wall while his human stepladder suffered rigid agonies in back and loins. When they were too beaten with fatigue to work any more it seemed to them as if they had accomplished as little as a pair of caterpillars gnawing blindly at the sides of an iron box, but at least a beginning had been made. They dis-guised their work with a paste of mud and spittle and rested achingly.

The next day was the same, and the next—a fever of labor in the dark to the accompaniment of the slight rasp of the worn nail against the stone—a driving of cramped, rebellious muscles to the same monotonous, tiny task. Pick, pick, pick, went the sound of the nail—pick, pick, pick. The sound wore a shallow groove in Andrew's mind. He could hear it continue interminably through the uneasy veil of sleep and his fingers twitched me-chanically as if they still held the nail.

Pride and hope alike were gone, the body was gone, of the body only the hands remained, picking, picking unendingly like clumsy thieves at the lock of a closed door. He had long ago ceased to be Andrew Beard. He was a smoke, a shadow, that crawled up upon another shadow's shoulders in obliterated gloom, to pick, pick, pick with a shadowy fang at a deepening crack between two blocks of darkness. Sometimes it was the black, dully-gleaming heart of Night itself at which he dug, and he half-expected his nail at any moment to slip through some crack in heaven and shatter itself to bits against the points of a star.

Why he did what he was doing, he no longer remembered. The thought of any actual escape was buried deep under tiny crumbs of mortar and flakes of iron-rust. He felt at times that if some one had opened the door and told him he was free, he would merely have stared and grunted and returned to the corner beneath the window to bend his back again like a burdened ass while Sebastian stood upon it and nibbled at a coffin of coquina somewhere above him, for ages, with that slight, rasping sound till his fingers refused their office and it was time for Andrew to crawl up and nibble in his turn.

Toward mid-evening of the third day, the stone could be loosened a little. If both had been able to get any purchase on it, at the same time, they might have been able to wrench it away from the bar which was cemented into it from above. As it was the stone would only give one useless and exasperating fraction of an inch, and the problem of the bar remained. The bar, too, was harder to get at, and they could hardly file it with what was left of the nail.

"Is it deep sunk, do you think, Sebastian?" said Andrew, lying dead on the floor after a straining and unsuccessful attempt to tear the stone out of the wall by main force.

"I think so," said Sebastian wearily. "We shall have to pick the mortar out of its socket and bend it up somehow. Then, perhaps, the stone will loosen."

"I wish I had your patience," said Andrew. "Myself, I think we shall die before we pick out that mortar."

He rose. "Make me a back, Sebastian. I'll see if I can reach it."

He clung with one hand to the sill and reached the other up awkwardly to pick at the mortar that held the bar. His hand was unsteady with fatigue and the stroke went wild. The nail slipped, his knuckles rapped on the stone. His fingers jerked apart mechanically at the pain, the nail flew out, hopped between the bars and dropped over the outer edge of the window sill. He heard it clink on a stone and felt sick and old. He tried to reach over through the bars, but the window opening was deep and narrow—from his cramped position he could just put his hand out over the outer edge. There was a ditch beyond, a couple of feet in depth, where the nail had fallen. Try as he might he could not reach to the bottom of that ditch.

His muscles gave way. He slid down.

"Kill me, Sebastian," he gasped, "I have lost the nail," and fell in a heap on the floor.

"We must find another nail," said Sebastian, after a long silence, but even as he spoke both knew that there was no other nail.

"Perhaps, if we rest for a while, we will be able to move the stone without it," said Andrew, but his voice was entirely without hope. The stone had come to have a personality to them both in the hours they had labored upon it. At times they cursed it in hushed voices as one curses an ungrateful woman—at other times they pled with it for a sulky god. Now it had turned into a god forever, a dumb god with a broad, flat, roughened, eyeless face, that sat across the door of life like a plummet of lead, and blocked it, and would not move away.

"We will have to kill the guard after all," said Sebastian, tonelessly. "Kill him somehow and chance the rest." His voice showed the utter desperation of the expedient.

"Stone walls do no-ot a pri-son make. Nor i-ron BARS a c-a-g-e-" giggled Andrew suddenly. "That's funny, isn't it, Sebastian? I remember my mother used to sing that—she had a good voice. But the man who wrote the song was a liar all the same. Oh, wasn't he a liar, Sebastian—" he continued, half-hysterically.

"Put me on your shoulders, Andrew," said the other, quietly. "My arm is a little longer than yours—perhaps I can reach it."

Andrew gulped, recovered his wits, and started to obey. But just as he bent his back, something rattled on the floor.

They looked at each other incredulously, holding their breath —two hunched images of shadow staring at each other intently like apes in a cage. There was another tiny rattle on the floor. Then Andrew felt a pebble strike on his cheek.

"Window, Sebastian," he said fiercely, while hope grew up in his mind like a winter-rose.

It seemed to him that he stood for hours with Sebastian's feet digging into his shoulders while Sebastian whispered hurriedly in Mahonese to another whisper, swift and gentle as the rustle of a green leaf on a budded tree. Then at last Sebastian was down and talking in fierce, little, jerky phrases.

"Caterina," he said. "She managed to get away. There's a sentry but he's a fool. Sleeps. Oh, you English—you think you can watch a rathole with a lazy cat. Boat, by the old wharf. To-morrow night. They'll think we've gone by land. She'll be at the boat. Your boy helped. Carlos. He says you gave him a dollar. He's very grateful."

"What about the nail?" said Andrew, still tormented by its loss.

"We have better than nails now," said Sebastian, luxuriously. He opened his hand and showed Andrew a thin glass bottle full of yellow liquid. He shook it lovingly. It rattled. "Files," he said huskily. "Two files. And oil to quiet them."

Andrew began to laugh soundlessly—a painful laughter that racked the pit of his stomach. Then he thought of something else, and his laughter stopped.

"What did they do to her?" he said, trembling.

"Caterina? They whipped her, that next morning. That's why she couldn't come before. Even now—" He stretched out his arms. The slow roll of his voice filled the chamber like the beat-ing of an iron heart. "Oh, Christ on the Cross—" he prayed. "Oh, Christ on the Cross—You have given us a way to the air—Give us vengeance too—if only a little—a little—" He broke off. "We must rest for a while," he said more naturally. "Even with the bar cut through we will need all our strength for the stone."

4.

The bar was all but cut through—the cut plastered over and concealed. Then they had to wait. They had rested longer than they had intended before starting the work, sinking down into a black, murmuring bog of sleep as soon as their heads touched the floor, and when the task was nearly done, the air beyond the win-dow had changed, and, behind dark gauzes, yellow dawn began to stir faintly, like a bird still hidden in the egg. After that, they could sleep again for a while, but not as they had slept before. They were too tense, the bog refused to receive them, they napped in uneasy snatches like dogs before a hunt. Andrew, waking a dozen times, each time glowered up at the window and was angry to see how slowly the first pale stiletto of light broad-ened into a yellow sword.

When the corporal brought their breakfast they were both

broad awake and very restless. They tried to hold him in talk to make the minutes pass but he was surly and would only mutter in general terms against sergeants who cheated honest men out of their pay with dice that had a spell on them.

"By God," he growled, "if both of you weren't such traitors, I'd change you a bottle of Augustine rum for the promise of a couple of knucklebones after you were hanged. They say a hanged man's knucklebones make wizardy dice, if he's strung up in the natural course of crime—but being traitors, yours wouldn't serve most likely—'tis just my luck—I never played jailer before except on a black fellow that stole the Governor's wig for a heathen idol in Jamaica and he was a poor pagan that didn't leave me as much as a copper ear-ring. I was born with a caul, too, but I've never had any luck from it. When I was christened parson opened the book at the wrong place and started blazing away at the Burial Service most savagely before a' could be halted and it's shadowed me ever since. I can feel the Resurrection and the Life stuck in my throat at night like a slice of apple—You're lucky to be decently hanged, you are, there's some more grievous and judgmatical death in store for me, and it rises my dinner in me to have to think of it—" So he mourned himself away, leaving them alone with a vast desert of time.

The light grew, the hours dragged, they could not keep their eyes from the bar and the stone. They would talk to each other feverishly for a while and then, without intention, fall suddenly into a staring silence. Andrew found at last that he was talking to himself under breath. "Night," he was murmuring. "Night. Oh *lente, lente, currite, noctes equi—*" no, that was the wrong quotation, that asked night's coursers to slacken their pace.

"What time do you suppose it is, Sebastian?" he said for the twentieth time.

"We must have hours yet," said Sebastian. Andrew had expected the answer, but he sighed all the same. He looked at the bar again. To the eyes of both the crack in it had grown, all through the morning. Now it yawned—a blunt, metal mouth, insecurely stuffed with mud and straw. It seemed impossible that the stupidest of jailers should not detect it at a glance.

"Sebastian, do you think if—" began Andrew, and stopped himself. He must keep his eyes from the bar—if he did not something would make him leap up and swing from it chattering like a monkey. For a moment he half-wished the corporal had seen the crack and suspected. Anything was better than this waiting. Then he made a sort of formless prayer to anything which might be listening not to pay the slightest attention to his wish.

There were footsteps in the corridor—coming nearer. Andrew felt his body grow taut—glancing over at Sebastian he saw that he too was rigid. His wish had been granted. They were found out. They were coming to take them to some other cell, deep down, where even a file would be of no use. They were coming to hang them, now, while the light still held and the air was sweet.

The door opened. The corporal was there with two other men.

"You're wanted," he said, jerking his thumb at Andrew. "No—not you—him," as Sebastian started to rise.

Andrew got up slowly, feeling sweat on his palms. Sebastian and he were to be separated—ironed perhaps. Either step would be fatal to both, now. Why hadn't they chanced it last night?

"Who wants me?" he said, licking his mouth.

"You're wanted," said the corporal, grinning. "Come on now—shake a leg."

"*Adios, amigo,*" murmured Andrew stiffly as he passed Sebastian. They touched hands.

"Come on now," said the corporal impatiently, "last Wills and Testaments not executed at this shop without longer notice."

5.

"Well, Andrew," said Dr. Gentian, pleasantly, "I am sorry to see you so unkempt. I wish I could lend you a razor. When I was in prison at Poona," he continued reflectively, rubbing his chin, "I managed to shave with a broken cowrie-shell. But it was a painful expedient, at best. I should not advise its imitation, though it passes the time as well as trying to tame a rat. I wonder at the patience of those men who find prison-rats so easy to tame. Mine were savage little beasts—Orpheus himself could not have made them affable." He broke off, tracing a little pattern with his right thumb in the silver scrollwork on the butt of Andrew's pistol.

Spanish Bayonet

The two were alone—the soldiers had retired outside the door. Andrew, through lowered lids calculated the distance between them and the possibility of springing across the table and getting that firm throat between his hands before the balanced fore-finger could pull the trigger.

"I wouldn't," said the doctor, smiling. "This priming happens to be dry and—let me compliment you on your taste in small-arms, Andrew. You may not have observed it, but this particular pistol is a weapon of delightful precision. I experimented with it this morning upon a humming-bird—the poor thing was blown into feathers at twenty paces."

"What do you want with me?" said Andrew, heavily. His eyes were still blinking with the unaccustomed plenty of day-light in this windowed room. He had almost forgotten there were such rooms, he realized, now—and realized too, distastefully, the scarecrow figure he must cut before the immaculate Doctor. His clothes were ragged and foul—dirty stubble covered his face—he had not been clean for days. His eyes were furtive—his body had a prison smell to it—when he walked, he walked like a prisoner, with a heavy, shuffling step. In a tale, such tiny things would not matter to the heroic captive—it was monstrously un-fair that they should matter now.

"I wanted to see you, Andrew," said the Doctor, softly, "and now that I have, I confess myself satisfied."

Andrew hardly heard him—his mind was busy with a different problem. "For God's sake tell them to give me a clean shirt, you devil!" he burst out suddenly, and instantly felt ashamed.

The Doctor laughed. "Your request is quaintly put," he said, with enjoyment, "but I'll grant it. You shall have a clean shirt —yes, Andrew—and soap and a razor—and go wherever you wish. For a price, of course," he added, tracing his pattern.

Andrew had straightened up at the first of his words. Now his shoulders sagged again.

"There would be," he said, flatly. "No."

"You haven't heard my terms yet," said the Doctor. "I ask very little. Only a lapse of memory." He looked at Andrew but Andrew did not reply.

"I do not even ask you to go on with your projected mar-riage." He continued, "A son-in-law," his thumb crept along a

209

tiny silver scroll, "whose brother is—disaffected—whose father—will be bankrupt—would hardly fit with my plans. All I ask is—seven days forgotten. Completely. Your word on it. Then you're free."

"Why?" said Andrew, bluntly. "Why not hang me out of hand at once?"

"Oh—call it a whim—a vagary," said the Doctor with masked eyes, "I've always rather loved fools—after my own fashion. And then—I'll be frank enough—trying you in Augustine would be such a tedious business—I could carry it through—don't mistake me—but there might be embarrassing questions. I'd rather have your word."

"Suppose I broke my word?"

"To be frank," said the Doctor, "I do not care very greatly what you do—out of the Floridas. Till then—you would sign a—confession—I have drawn up. You could have it back—in time."

"Confession of what?" said Andrew.

"Oh—not too much," said the Doctor, pursing his lips. "Disloyalty, chiefly—an attempt on my daughter's honor, perhaps—just enough to discredit you. I assure you I should use it with the greatest reluctance," and, strangely enough, Andrew thought that he spoke the truth.

"Sebastian and Caterina?" he said.

The Doctor pondered. "You can have the girl," he said finally. "I should regret it, but after all—Mrs. Gentian deserves consideration. The man, no. I must keep discipline. But I might merely send him to St. Augustine prison, then."

"What happens to him otherwise?" said Andrew, breathing.

"The currycomb," said the Doctor in a wisp of voice. "A distressing end."

Andrew looked at him.

"I should really advise against it," said the Doctor very softly, with his forefinger alert. "You could not possibly reach me in time. Besides, there are always the soldiers."

Andrew drew a long breath.

"And—I—?" he said.

"Oh, you would merely hang," said the Doctor, recovering his cheerfulness. "Merely hang. You're young to hang, Andrew."

Andrew passed his hand over his eyes, trying to think. He

Spanish Bayonet

could save Sebastian's life, Caterina's, his own. Sebastian was patient and clever—even in the dungeons of St. Augustine he might find some way of escape. Then they would all be saved. The other way was death. He could refuse for himself, and die, but he would not have to die in torment as Sebastian must.

For an instant he saw himself free, at the rail of a ship, with Caterina at his side. Her hand was lightly on his, she was telling him he had done well, her eyes were gentle. Cool as the fronds of lilies floating on a hushed and evening pool, her fingers touched his, and met, and somewhere, Sebastian was smiling at them both from his dungeon . . .

His mind revolted from the mirage, smarting with shame and self-disgust. Dr. Gentian was very adroit. He had put this thing so subtly that he, Andrew, could not only save himself but Caterina for himself and fool his mind into thinking he had acted nobly. No one could accuse him if he did this—Sebastian would not—his own spirit might for a while but it would grow sleepy— a year from now, this present would be forgotten, buried under a drifting red-and-yellow heap of leaf-brittle days like the skeleton of a rat, to crumble into earth and water and sun. And Sebastian would be still in his dungeon—but perhaps Caterina and he could buy him out somehow if he had not died . . .

The stone. The bar. The escape.

But it seemed impossible that they should really escape. Dr. Gentian was too strong. He had been in prison himself—he would not have left them there, together, unchained, without providing against any escape. All the time that they had been gnawing in the dark he had been outside the window, listening, smiling, till he could no longer contain the mirth in his belly and went slowly back to laugh at them aloud with the devils that lived in the chimney of his study. Yes, he must have been doing that.

There was no use trying to bargain with him over Mr. Cave's projected plan of revolt. He knew of that, too, undoubtedly— and if, by some miracle, he did not, it offered the one slim chance that, in the confusion of such an event, they might escape indeed.

Was he overrating Dr. Gentian's powers? Perhaps. But as he stared at him now, with heavy eyes, he saw him as a man no longer, not even a Caesar, but something inhuman, with the transient powers of the inhuman over human stuff. An undying figure that walked from the East, with a cloud of flies above it, and a gilt pomander in its hand.

"Aren't you ever afraid of hell?" he found himself saying, queerly, with a catch in his voice. "I should think you'd be afraid of hell."

The smile on Dr. Gentian's face became a rictus cut in ivory, the muscles of the jaw stood out.

"Why this is hell, nor am I out of it," he quoted in a slow, dry voice. " 'Think'st thou that I'—did you ever read Marlowe, Andrew? The style is very impure—bombastic, even—he cannot compare with Pope—but there are things in his Faustus which—"

He stopped. His mouth relaxed. But while he spoke, there had been something in his face that Andrew had never expected to see there—a turn of the mouth—a shape behind the eyes—something ruined and very lonely—a statue defaced—a barren bough in the gale.

It passed. "Well?" said the easy voice.

Andrew looked at the floor. He was twenty-two. When you were twenty-two, Death was something far-off that happened to other people. It needn't happen to him for a long time.

What if the Minorcans were oppressed? They weren't actually slaves. They got along. Some people, maybe, had to be oppressed. It wasn't his quarrel.

Then he saw them, young and old, women and children, the dead on the voyage, the dead in the first months of fever, the priest swinging in his robes, the sallow boy, screaming, under the currycomb. But it wasn't his quarrel.

There were two doors open. One meant life, and a clean shirt, and Caterina's hand on his hand, by the rail of a ship, at night, while the moon climbed up in heaven like a silver woman. The other was death for all of them. He shut his eyes and chose death.

"No, I won't," he said, in a voice he was surprised to find so even.

Dr. Gentian sighed. "I'm sorry," he said. "Dying is so wasteful. You can have twenty-four hours to think it over, Andrew. I will see you again tomorrow, when they are up. Think it over. Sergeant," he called and struck on a bell. "I hate to hang you, Andrew—it will be a great nuisance. I had a parrot once that amused me. I had to wring its neck. It is much the same. You may take the prisoner back now, Sergeant, if you will."

Spanish Bayonet

6.

"He gave me twenty-four hours," Andrew ended. He looked at his friend.

"It is more than enough," said Sebastian. "We shall escape in twelve."

Before the certitude of his tone the image of Dr. Gentian that towered in Andrew's mind like a genie rising from a bottle in a blue, magic fume, diminished gradually. He became what he was, a man of great parts, whose knowledge of his own abilities had swollen with power till it festered, and so spoiled a tyrant instead of making a king. Seen so, he was no longer terrific or even hateful, only beggared, as all men are beggared in one way or another who seek from life a passion more intense than the body can bear. He was a king in check—a torch inverted—a fire that wasted itself against a column of salt—and as Andrew began to perceive this, slowly and delicately as the slow lifting of a slab of bronze from his breast, the fear of death passed from him and left him composed. It would return, undoubtedly, but for this moment, brief as the flight of a bird between tree and tree, it had gone. He could smell the mignonette in his mother's garden. Dr. Gentian could kill them both, but that was all he could do.

"What are you going to do, Sebastian, when we are free?" he said casually, out of a strange peace.

"Tell the governor to free my people," said Sebastian. The cool stone of peace had touched at his lips as well, he spoke with the simplicity of a ghost. "When they are free—" he shrugged. "Who knows? Life is long—there are many things to do before the priest comes with his oil. If I had money I should like to buy a fishing-boat—my father was a fisherman. I should like to marry, too, and have a son. It is good to have a son to help you draw in the nets. And you, my friend?"

"I shall go North," said Andrew. "Perhaps to help the ass you spoke of kick off his rider—yes." It was the first time he had definitely put the thought at the back of his mind into words. He was astonished to find how rational it sounded. "After all— as long as they've called me a traitor—" he said, musingly. He wondered if that were really what he would do. It was difficult to see himself with a ragamuffin musket, presenting it at Lion and Unicorn.

Sebastian nodded. "I thought so," he said. "There are three things one cannot run away from—war, love and death." His voice held that indolent fatalism that has so often deceived the North by its languid pride. "Sometime I should like to go back to Minorca," he confessed. His eyes glittered. "This is a good country, here, but it is not Fererias."

"Tell me about your island," said Andrew, childishly. He settled himself in a corner to listen.

"You'd laugh at it, if you went there," said Sebastian. "It is small and harsh and poor. But the people are friendly there. My uncle lives in Mahon, if he has not died—he is a very friendly and hospitable person. My aunt has copper pans in her kitchen," he continued, with some pride. "They tease her about being rich —she is not—they came from her father who was a copper-smith —but few of us have copper vessels, even in the town—" His voice droned on, lulling Andrew into the content of a sleepy child. It was now almost entirely dark in their cell, though outside the sun had not yet set. There would be hours still before they would be safe in cutting through the rest of the bar, but now Andrew did not care how many there were. The fear of death no longer ran about with the rats in the darkness and he was quite happy listening to the slow story of certain doings in the family of a foreign copper-smith which could not possibly interest any person of gentility.

7.

Dr. Gentian laid his book down with a sigh, and glanced at his watch. He rose, and stood for a moment, observing how surely and skilfully the petal of a flower grew in rose-colored silk upon gauze, under the deft, shining strokes of his wife's embroidery needle.

"That must tire your eyes, my dear—especially at night," he said, with solicitude.

"I am never tired." She did not turn her head to answer. "Are you going now?"

"Yes, my dear. I am going now. You need not wait up for me. I shall not be back till late."

She made a knot in the silk. "You never believe me," she said.

"Even if I told you, you were walking into a pitfall—you wouldn't believe me."

He smiled. "I should merely think your natural concern for my safety had overbalanced your excellent reason," he said.

"No doubt," she said wearily, her face still averted. "Well—you can go, then. I shan't wait up."

"It matters to you still," he said, consideringly. "That seems strange."

"Strange enough." Her eyes were fixed on her work. "You'd be a clever man, Hilary, if you left well enough alone."

"A clever man never leaves well enough alone," he said and smiled.

The silk thread broke in her fingers. "You're blind," she said. "Blind and deaf. There's a shadow on your back tonight. But you're deaf and blind. You only think of playing cat and mouse with that boy."

"One must have games." The Doctor's tone was amused. "And cat and mouse is an excellent game, for the cat."

"You'd better watch your daughter." She turned her face now and looked at him.

"My dear!"

"I've told you. She and her lackey. They've been too quiet these last days. Oh, well—go your road. But my Greeks talk to me. There's a rat in the wall of this house, Hilary—a rat in the wall—"

Her voice ceased. Her fingers busied themselves re-threading the needle.

"I think you have the gift, tonight," he said quietly, regarding her. "See for me, my dear."

His hand fell on her shoulder, light as a butterfly. She put it off. "No," she said in a dry, thin voice. "You're wrong. I haven't had the sight for years. If I had it tonight, would I use it? No."

"Not for me?" His mouth had honey in it.

"No." Her fingers were moving again, she seemed to have no mind for anything but her silk. "Not for you."

He sighed. "Be consoled," he said. "I shan't live for ever. Indeed, sometimes I wonder that I have been able to live this long."

"It would be like you to die first," she agreed, remorselessly. A flash passed over her face. "I'd save you from that," she said, with a prick of her needle.

He chuckled a little. "I believe you. I believe you, indeed. But if something should—cripple me, for instance—just enough —eh?"

She drew in a deep breath. "Some time," she said, huskily. "Soon or late. The candle's not burnt to the wick yet. I can wait for it."

"Really, sometimes, one would think you believed in the fates, my dear. If one didn't know you."

"I believe in waiting," she said, nodding her head. "Yes, I believe in waiting."

His fingers twitched, momentarily. "I wish you'd see for me," he said.

She made no reply. He hesitated for a moment, oddly indecisive. Then he looked at his watch again and turned toward the door.

"Good night, my dear."

The second petal of the flower was half-completed, the needle stitched on, the face was averted anew. "Good night," said the dry, colorless voice. Dr. Gentian passed out of the room. With his hand on the latch of the front door he hesitated for a second time and threw a glance back up the stairs. Then he shook his head impatiently, opened the door and went out.

As soon as his footsteps had died away, Mrs. Gentian rose. Very softly indeed, she climbed the stairs to the upper corridor and paused, listening, outside the door of her daughter's room. She scratched on the panel twice, gently—no sound replied. "Sparta," she called in a low, sharp voice, waited, repeated the call. The name fell into darkness and was absorbed, no echo mocked it even. Mrs. Gentian laughed under her breath and opened the door of the room. The light of her candle showed it empty, the bed undisturbed. She nodded, as if in assent to an unspoken query and stood in the doorway for a moment, erect as an effigy, not seeming to notice that when her candle guttered it shook flecks of hot wax on her dress. Then she shut the door and went softly down the stairs again, returning to her chair and her needlework. Her face seemed at once resolved and satisfied, and, for a time, the pattern of her embroidery had never grown more swiftly. Then, after a while, the pace of her fingers slackened and stopped. The embroidery still lay in her lap, but she worked at it no longer, though she remained sitting in the chair, with folded hands and that curious expression on her face, her head bent a little forward, as if she were listening for the wind to bring her a piece of long-expected news.

Meanwhile, Dr. Gentian was walking briskly down the road to the guardhouse. He carried a light cane in one hand and was humming to himself and now and then cutting little flourishes in the air with his cane. The moon was up enough for him to pick his way along the well known path without hesitation, while his mind turned over one thing and another in its usual active fashion. His wife's words had stirred him more than he cared to admit and, not for the first time, he felt, with some annoyance, that there was some quality in her which even he could only master by snatches, unless she willed to have it so.

She was the only person he had ever met who did not sooner or later betray himself or herself by talking too much. He had taught her that trick of reticence, likely enough—but now it seemed to him, uneasily, that the pupil was beginning to outstrip her master. It must not be so—yet what could he do to change it? He could not deal with her as he dealt with others— from their first meeting he had thought of her as the living symbol of his luck and the broadening of that vein of superstition which was his weakness, during these later years, had only increased the feeling. The fierce passion that had first united them was long extinguished, but her words still carried a certain weight of omen for him, and at times he came closer being afraid of her than he ever had been of any merely human being.

He smiled a little, recalling certain events. What a sharp, wild, dazzling creature she had been in her first youth—not fair in Sparta's fashion, not fair at all in the way he consciously admired, but with a fire in her like the fire at the heart of his emerald. Wooing her had been like wooing a tiger-cub—his mind still bore the scars of it, for all its balance, as his body bore the thin, seamed scar of the knife she had struck him with, long ago, when she thought he looked too often at that dark little Cypriote. For an instant his body felt young, and he saw, from a tossing boat, a torch flaring at the mouth of a cave and a girl's intense and eager face in the red gush of light.

She would not strike him with a knife again. That had been in the days of their passion, and they and his youth were over. Her love had taken a deal of killing, certainly. He felt that to be unfortunate, honestly enough, for unnecessary ugliness always offended him. But it would have been the same with any other man—she was not the sort that lived easily. In any event, she hated him now, but it did not matter, for, in spite of her hate, he had a unique sort of confidence in her. The struggle between them would only end with life, but in the pauses of it they understood each other.

He smiled—it would seem a queer way of living to that boy in the guardhouse. One had to give up youth to taste the full flavor of hazard—youth lacked the steadiness of hand. For himself, the constant experiment of sharing meat and drink, year-in, year-out, with a creature whose heart still held the savage so barely kept in check by mere adroitness of eye and hand, was life and a good one. Some day, no doubt, the eye would fail or the hand lose cunning, and he would be torn. Well, let it be so, he had had his game.

Meanwhile, there were other diversions, such as that he purposed for this evening. He would think of that now, and taste it in expectation. But when he tried to do so, his wife's words beat in his ears, and he came to a halt for a moment, leaning a little on his cane. After all, it was possible to alter his plans. He had given too much time to young Beard these last months—too little to the plantation. Cave, too, he had been careless recently with Cave—he suspected Cave and the lesser animals in general of getting a little out of hand. Perhaps it might be well to—then he shook his head. His project for tonight was too well matured—tomorrow would be time enough for Cave and the others. He cut a weed down with his cane and went on, but, though a stranger would have thought his bearing composed enough, he was not entirely at ease.

Now it seemed to him that he could hear movement far off in the woods at his left. He stopped again and listened. Something was abroad in the woods, undoubtedly, but the sound was too indistinct for him to make it out clearly. A shadow darted between two trees near the road—a man with a bag on his back —he opened his mouth to call at it—no, it was only a trick of the eye. As for the distant sound, now quieted, it might be a couple of strayed deer or a band of half-tame Indians on a rice-stealing expedition—the latter most probably. The Indians had been growing bold, lately—he must see to that, too. Again, he was almost on the point of turning back to the coquina-house.

Then he looked at his watch once more—it was later than he had supposed—the tiny fact decided him. He marched on, swinging his cane—the moon had a bright face tonight—the features of the man in it were distinct. He thought of the old story and smiled. The moon, as a post of observation, would have its advantages.

He turned a corner—there were guardhouse and storehouses below him, their roofs wintry with moonlight. The quiet familiarity of the scene blew the last of his uneasiness away— he had never felt more sure of himself or his luck. A few paces away from the guardhouse door he was challenged in a low voice by a sentry, held a conversation in whispers for a minute, and then went in.

The minutes passed, the still, glittering face rose higher in the sky till the night was perfect. It cast a long straggling shadow over the barred window of Andrew's cell and a bright pool on the floor of Sparta Gentian's empty chamber. In the deep woods that gave upon the St. Augustine road it barely pierced enough to touch with occasional silver the faces and bodies of men and women who came slipping silently between the trees, one by one, like deer trooping together, till the road was full of them. They came from the direction of the colony, burdened with packs or children—there seemed no end to their number—they greeted each other in hushed voices—soon the first of them were filtering away down the road.

In the colony itself the silver dagger fell upon a different sort of surreptitious stir, and a clotting together of shadowy shapes on the skirts of the Italian quarter. Dr. Gentian had wished better than he knew when he had wished for a post of observation upon the cold peaks of the moon, and it was unfortunate for him that his wish could not have been granted. As it was he sat in the guardhouse, tapping his snuffbox and recapitulating the heads of a certain discourse he intended to deliver shortly, ignorant that events already in train were to render that discourse quite unnecessary.

Mrs. Gentian, however, was soon to be better informed. Her rigid attitude of the listener had not altered for the last half hour, she sat in her chair like a sculpture, her hands were marble. Only her eyes discovered life in them, deep in the pupils, contained, patient and somehow dreadful in its certitude, like the life in the eyes of a spirit caught in a cleft stone. She was waiting for a sound, and already the last moments of her vigil were upon her. A mile away, even as one shape among the clotted shapes at the edge of the Italian huts began to issue orders to the others, a Greek boy watched from a shadow and then crawled off, to break into a run for the coquina-house as soon as he was well away from the huts.

PART FOUR:

THE FIRE ON THE BEACH

The file grated for an instant and then bit air. Andrew gave a tug at the bar and nearly fell over backward as it came out in his hand. He stared at it incredulously. The end of their work had come.

"We're through, Sebastian," he whispered, "Sebastian, Sebastian, give me a hand with the stone!"

The stone was stubborn, but at last they managed to pry it free. Then they stood and gazed at the gap for a second of triumph.

It only lasted a second. Even while they gazed at it they knew, dreadfully, that they had miscalculated. The hole was just too small. Both tried it, hopefully, defiantly, hopelessly.

"Cut through another bar," said Andrew, finally, when they knew they were beaten. "Cut through another bar." The thought of starting in at the beginning again appalled him so that he could not trust himself to say any more. This last stroke, at the very edge of deliverance, was the worst of all. He had thought himself free of Fear—he had been a child shaking a rattle. Fear had only crept away for a moment to make its return more deadly—now it settled into his back like a huge, soft animal whose claws were iron needles. He could feel the cold, salt sweat of it on his forehead and hands.

"Anyhow, it will give us two weapons instead of one," muttered Sebastian with bitter philosophy as he worked in a contained fury of haste. Andrew could have hated him for saying that, if there had been time. But there was no time for either hate or thought or self-pity—there was only time for fear and the continuous, muffled grate of the file.

After a while they discovered that, with the stone gone, they could cramp themselves against each other perilously in such a way that both could file. Even so, it took an eternity till the second bar was cut through. But at last that too was accomplished.

"Now," said Sebastian, shivering. "Now, my friend."

Half the window was blocked by his shoulders—then he was worming out on his side. Andrew's last view of him was of a pair of shoe-soles that waggled absurdly for a moment and disappeared. He waited ten breaths. No sound. Sebastian must be safe in the ditch. He transferred the iron thing he was clutching to his left hand. It was cold in his hand. He gulped and started to follow Sebastian.

He slid into the ditch head-first, and lay there on his belly, flat as a lizard. After his days of confinement the outside world seemed formidably large and open. He was glad for the walls of the ditch—even with their protection, he felt as lonely and conspicuous as a shelled oyster. He listened. All that he could hear was the distant bubble of water in an irrigation canal and the mutter of wind in the palms. Now the wind rattled a dry leaf somewhere, like a boy shaking a fan, and he started. Where was Sebastian? He stretched out his hand, by inches, and was enormously relieved when at last it touched a shod heel.

"Sebas—" he started to whisper.

"Ssh," a whisper answered, "sentry." The heel started to writhe away from him. He followed it, doing his best to make no noise. That had been the plan, to worm along the ditch till they were on the side of the prison farthest from the guardroom, opposite the smaller storehouse. Then they would have to take to the open.

This crawling was a slow, ludicrous business, especially when you had to carry a bar of iron in one hand. For a moment he was reminded of a sack-race, and almost giggled aloud. How the devil did Sebastian get ahead so fast? He could get along faster if he dropped this silly bar. No, better not.

They were around the corner now. He raised his head, gingerly, and caught a glimpse of the black bulk of the storehouse.

Sebastian had stopped. A hand came back through the darkness and dug into his shoulder. Keep quiet, that meant. He lay frozen to the ground.

Suddenly, and without the slightest warning, a grumbling voice spoke out of invisibility—a voice that seemed not a dozen feet away from his head.

"Devil fly away with this musket—my arm's gone asleep again!" it said, in tones of cockney irritation. Something stamped on the ground.

"Shut your mouth, you misbegotten son of a sweep," said another voice, low and irate. "Are you a soldier or a nursemaid?"

"I'm a nursemaid," grumbled the first voice—Andrew knew it now—it belonged to one of the privates who had marched him to prison—the other voice was the sergeant's. "A bloody private nursemaid to a couple of stinkin' prisoners what's going to escape and what never escapes. Why in 'ell can't 'Is Majesty let 'em escape in daylight when a man can see to shoot?"

"You let them get through and you'll find out what, soon enough," said the other voice, grimly. "Orders are, take alive or dead. Remember that."

"Just button 'em up in my pocket *I* suppose," said the first voice in an unimpressed whine. The other voice seemed to choke for a while. When it recovered it discussed a question of ancestry with some vividness.

"Oh, all right, sergeant, all right," commented the first voice, resignedly. "But a man can't 'elp 'is feelin's. If it was an eskylade now, I'd be breathin' as easy as a babby. But this 'ole and corner work ain't work for a soldier. W'y can't 'Is Majesty shoot the pore buggers 'imself if 'e wants 'em shot? Tell me that, now," it concluded triumphantly, "an' I'll stand you a pot o' beer."

"Go ask him," said the sergeant's voice, very bitterly. "Go ask him, Bowbells. He's in the guard-room now, just waiting for some son of a whore to ask him a question like that. By God, he'd crucify you."

"Like enough," grunted the other. "Doctor 'e calls 'imself." He spat. "*I* wouldn't trust him to poison a sergeant."

"You're a drunk disgrace to the British Army," said the sergeant's voice with sour finality, "and I'd have you in the calabooze this minute if—"

"Aye," said the other, thoughtfully, "*if* I wasn't a pearl o' marksmen—and if you could draw a cordon round 'ere without me—and *hif* I didn't know 'oo buggered the last payroll—Most likely. Run along, sergeant, and wipe the other boys' noses for 'em. You can rest easy about this side—there'll be two beautiful corpses to show 'Is Majesty if they tries to run *my* post."

"You're drunk, you fool," said the sergeant acridly, and departed. "Wish I was," said the other voice, a trifle plaintively, as Andrew heard the heavy boots crunch away.

He raised his head cautiously, inch by inch. There was a little bush at the lip of the ditch—it would hide him as he reconnoitered.

The sentry was just too far away, in the shadowed door of the storehouse. For all his sleepy arm, he seemed terribly alert and there were at least thirty yards of open moonlit ground between him and them. If they rushed him, one of them would be killed or disabled in the rush and the other would have to kill at once, in his turn, before the shot brought up the rest of the guard.

It was like Dr. Gentian, this. Very like him. He could see Dr. Gentian in a cane-chair in the guard-room, waiting composedly for his birds to fly into the snare.

He sank back into the ditch again. He felt stiff and cramped. Dying couldn't be much worse. Sebastian had turned around somehow, he could see his face. He put his own face close. "When you say, Sebastian," his lips formed, without sound. He saw Sebastian's body grow taut and his own muscles tightened. Then Sebastian's expression changed. "Not yet," he whispered. He hunched down and began to crawl still farther along the ditch.

Andrew followed him without hope. As he crawled, he thought of a rat he had seen once in a stable. It was an old, sick-looking rat with gray streaks in its fur and it had been hitching slowly along the wall, looking for its hole. When it had heard his step it had shown yellow teeth in a weak snarl and crouched to the floor and he had realized that its eyes were white and blind. He felt a certain kinship now for that rat.

They had reached the end of the ditch on that side of the guardhouse. Sebastian had stopped and was raising himself up a little. Madness. No, not entirely. The ground fell away sharply beyond this part of the ditch. If they could take five steps across a swathe of moonlight they could roll into a shadow. But even as Andrew saw this, the sentry at the storehouse turned his head slowly toward them. He ducked his head down again with a little gulp. If a cloud would only cross the moon! But there seemed to be no real clouds in all the expanse of heaven—only a few little wisps of silver wool that would hardly veil the bright face for more than an instant.

Sebastian was fumbling in the bottom of the ditch for something—a stone. He crouched with the stone in his hand, looking up at the sky. One of the little wisps was blowing toward the moon like a drifted feather. Sebastian drew his arm back, waiting. Now the feather touched the disk, and, for an instant, as Sebastian's stone, cleanly flung, crashed into the bushes at the sentry's left, the heart went out of the moonlight.

The next moment they were out of the ditch and huddled together in the shadow. Andrew, out of the tail of his eye, had somehow caught a glimpse of the sentry whirling away from them to face the bushes where the stone had fallen. Now every moment he waited for a cry or a musket shot, but moment after moment passed, and there was neither shot nor cry. Luck was with them—so far, they had not been seen. He wondered where the other sentries were posted.

They crawled along to the edge of their shadow, hugging it fondly. The slight fall in ground deepened to a little gully that hid them better—now the storehouse was between them and the first sentry and they could breathe a trifle easier. They were going in the opposite direction from the wharves, but that they could not help till they were sure of having passed beyond the cordon. When it seemed that they must have done so, they began to circle back, Sebastian leading the way. He slipped along like an Indian, Andrew tried despairingly to copy his lightness of foot. At last they were down below the storehouse and the way ahead seemed clear. Andrew snatched a look at the sentry through a screen of brush. The man was yawning, eyes squinted, head thrown back. He had a ridiculous impulse to flip a pebble at the gaping mouth, and between that and dreading the sound of his own feet was so absorbed that when Sebastian, creeping ahead of him, suddenly darted into the door of a deserted and roofless hut by the side of the woodpath, his nerves jerked like plucked fiddlestrings.

Once inside the hut, he soon knew the reason for their taking cover. There were footsteps and a mumble of talk coming up toward the hut from the lower road. "Tricked," said a leaden accent. "Tricked, by God. A pack of lousy indigo-diggers to trick us so." Andrew recognized the dull, detested voice with a pang of hate. A lucid whisper—serene pulse of gold trembling in hollow of crystal shell—answered the voice and soothed it. "It does not matter, Charles. We can do without the Mahonese."

"Aye," said Cave. "Aye. We'll have to do without them, now. But—tricked, by God. I can't get over it, sweetheart. Who'd have thought they had the guts in them to run away?"

"Charles, Charles, don't think of that now. We are wasting time."

There was a mutter, then the voices sank. Andrew glared cautiously through a chink in the rotten wall of the hut. It was folly he knew, but he could not lie there and listen without trying to see. Not ten steps away, in a patch of moonlight, stood Sparta and Mr. Cave. They were talking together in soft, tense voices—she had her hand on his wrist, she was wheedling him as if he were an unruly child.

She was dressed entirely in dark stuffs, a dark handkerchief hid her hair, the cold chastity of the light gave her features a new beauty, severe, untainted by color, the sharp beauty of the cutting edge. Andrew thought of a silver axe in a scabbard of black glass—she had put away gold for the time and with it the burning gleam of dayspring and planet—the dark handkerchief capped her head as smoothly and reticently as a helmet—she looked like the merciless genius of combat itself, neither man nor woman nor spirit, but something arisen out of the ground with an arrow in its hand. He could see her standing in a chariot, Hippolyta, the amazon queen with the maimed and iron breast, wrapped in the glittering fleece of a golden ram and urging her cloud-born horses like harnessed gods across the tarnished bodies of the dead. For an instant, as her face sank into his mind, it seemed just that it should be so, and he forgot alike that he had loved her and that she had betrayed him.

She had too much of her father in her to live securely, with an even heart. Only violence and the brittle loadstone of danger could release from its cage of sleep, the immortal enemy which lay enchained in that flesh like an archangel in bonds. Now he saw it released, a pillar of darkness, and trembled, but not wholly with fear or hate. The beauty it had was the beauty of the tiger and the killing frost, but it was beauty, and somewhere at a point beyond the system of the stars, the unappeasable ecstasy of its pain lay down on a glittering field and slept between a dove and a hooded eagle. Cave was a different matter—his darkness was the muddy darkness of a fire of wet straw—and Andrew felt he could have killed him without the slightest compunction. But in Sparta, as she was tonight, there was something that would have turned his hand aside.

Now the two separated, having come to some decision between them that Andrew was unable to catch, and Sparta glided away toward the rear of the storehouse. Andrew could only follow her progress vaguely, but it seemed to him that she left a stir in the darkness behind her as she passed. Cave remained where he was for some moments, biting his nails. Andrew gestured to Sebastian, inquiringly—attack him? Sebastian shook his head violently, jerked a thumb toward the way that Sparta had gone and made motions of counting a troop of men. Andrew nodded, his heart thumping. There were others, then—they had blundered into the hut just in time.

He regarded Mr. Cave's back with sullen distaste—would he never move away and set them free? Now he turned, his eye fell casually on the hut, he made as if to come closer but thought better of it. Andrew felt the muscles of his belly contract, and his fingers clench on the bar. A mocking-bird whistled from somewhere, and Mr. Cave grew still. It whistled again and he put his shoulders back and started to walk toward the sentry, crackling the twigs underfoot deliberately as he went as if he wanted the sentry to hear.

The sentry heard and stiffened, musket to his shoulder. "Who goes there?" he challenged softly.

Mr. Cave stopped just on the edge of the open ground. "Overseer Cave," he said in a flat voice, his bearish shoulders stooped.

"Come out where I can look at you, overseer," said the sentry briskly, his eye along the barrel.

Mr. Cave approached slowly. "It's all right, Jenkin," he said in a confidential voice, "I know your orders. They don't apply to me. I've a message for the Doctor."

"Sorry, overseer," said the sentry, lowering his musket. "Have to wait till the sergeant makes rounds again. Strict orders—nobody to pass."

"You can read, I suppose," said Mr. Cave with heavy sarcasm, coming nearer, "I have a pass. Dr. Gentian's signature."

The sentry shook his head.

"Don't know anything about passes," he said. "Show it to the sergeant," but he brought his musket down and leaned forward as if to inspect a paper.

"But I'm in a hurry, I tell you," said Mr. Cave, very near him. Then, to Andrew's astonishment, the sentry continued to lean forward till he had passed his center of balance and, with a gasp, was falling as if he intended to embrace Mr. Cave in his outstretched arms. Mr. Cave caught him deftly and lowered him to the ground.

"Well done, lass," he said in a whisper to the skirted shadow that had crept around the other corner of the storehouse and struck the sentry down from behind. He raised his voice a little. "Come on, boys," he called softly, and the night was suddenly populous with catlike shapes. One stooped over the fallen sentry —his hand glittered with something thin and bright—there was the *chuck* of a flat stone striking water on its edge, and a horrible, muffled coughing.

"Sergeant of the Guard!" came a doleful howl from another quarter of the compass, "Sergeant of the Guard!" A musket shot clanged on the moonlight. Then events began to succeed each other far too rapidly for Andrew to keep track of them.

He was out of the hut, with Sebastian, and running. A man with big white teeth which glittered like dominoes, rose out of a bush like an evil fairy and struck at him violently with a long, curved hook. He felt the iron bar in his hand whirl down and hit something that smashed like a loaded egg and jarred his wrist. He stumbled and fell. There was shouting in his ears and a pop-pop-pop of musketry abruptly silenced. He caught a glimpse of their lugubrious jailer-corporal jabbing furiously at something behind a tree. Mr. Cave bellowed a command—an even voice that Andrew knew called orders in reply. Something that hummed like a wasp snipped a twig from a bough in front of his face— he jerked and went into an irrigation ditch with a smacking splash —behind him somebody was screaming "Oh, Jesus, oh, Jesus, oh,

Jesus!" in a high, affronted whine—now Sebastian was pulling him out of the ditch and they were running again. Then, abruptly, he was dragged into a dark pocket between two buildings while a dozen men whose leader carried a truss of blazing straw on a pole went by at a trot.

"Where are we?" he wheezed, lungs laboring. He discovered, with surprise, that the iron bar was still in his hand. The other end of it dripped.

"They've missed us," said Sebastian. "Too busy—up there—" He too was panting, but furiously busy, ramming home a charge in a musket he had somehow acquired.

"Where did"—began Andrew, staring at it, dazedly.

"Fool with a cap," panted Sebastian. It seemed sufficient explanation. "Look," he said, "Fire."

Andrew peeped around the corner of the building. They were still much nearer the guardhouse than he had supposed. On one hand the moon lit the scene with precise, bleak radiance, on the other, a little hut, to the right of the guardhouse, was burning like a spill of paper with fierce, brief flame.

Mr. Cave and his men had taken such cover as storehouse and trees afforded. He could see them swarming in the shadows like uneasy flies. On the lit and open ground between them and the guardhouse lay a number of broken dolls in attitudes of discomfort. One had on a red coat and lifted up an arm now, to let it drop again as if it were too heavy. There were various cries.

Andrew caught his breath. Dr. Gentian could not have more than a couple of men with him in the guardhouse now. Mr. Cave must have fifty at least. Yet Mr. Cave and his men had not been able to cross that little stretch of open, moonlit ground. True, the besieged were poorly armed and the besiegers had every advantage of shelter, but even so. . . .

Even as he watched, a dozen men dashed out from cover, their heads down as if they were running into a rain, and made for the guardhouse door. They carried a log among them—the intent was evident. A loophole coughed at them and the leading man stumbled and fell as if something invisible had struck him across the shins. The charge wavered—a second man sank slowly to his knees, like a tired horse—the others broke, dropping the log—one of them was wringing his hand and putting it to his mouth, like a boy with burnt fingers. Mr. Cave was cursing.

Something tugged at Andrew's sleeve. "Give me one of your buttons," said Sebastian's voice in his ear, fierce and hurried. "They are silver, aren't they—I must have silver, too—no, a little one—"

Andrew wrenched one of the tarnished buttons loose from his coat and saw, uncomprehendingly, Sebastian take it, drop it into the narrow, black well of the musket-barrel, ram it down. Then Sebastian was crouching on one knee, muttering to himself, musket poised.

Mr. Cave was roaring in the trees like a bull, trying to lift his men across that patch of open ground. But they would not be lifted, they stuck where they were. There was a weight on their limbs, the invisible weight of a name, it pressed them to the earth. The beasts had turned on the beast-tamer, but they were still afraid of his whip.

Andrew caught a second's glimpse of Mr. Cave, as he darted from one shadow to another, raging. Sebastian cursed softly— the glimpse had been too short for him to fire. Now they heard a shrill, frightened squealing, and the thud of boots kicking flesh. Mr. Cave encouraging his followers. Then again, for an instant, he was in clear view, recklessly exposed against the glare of the burning hut. His hands were cupped to his mouth, he was calling aloud.

"Come out, you damned old wizard!" he roared, in a furious, weeping voice. "Come out and surrender—your life if you'll surrender!—if you don't, by God, we'll roast you there in your shell!"

A flash answered from a window and Mr. Cave's broad hat spun from his head as if a gust of wind had tweaked it. Dr. Gentian's clear, sharp voice called back something in Italian, threat or promise, and Andrew could see the besiegers stir uneasily in the darkness. Then four things happened, almost in the same instant.

A man with a bloody face and a naked scythe in his hand burst out of a clump of darkness, followed by a score of others, and fell upon the flank of Mr. Cave's forces. The clear, sharp voice cried out to them like a joyous cock. Mr. Cave, his body convulsed, leapt to rally his men—and the musket in Sebastian's hands exploded.

It was a long shot, and at first Andrew thought that it had missed. Then he saw Mr. Cave hitch, queerly, in his stride, get on again, and then collapse slowly into the ground, as if quicksand had taken him. A form that must have been Sparta's, for it had streaming hair, ran out of an eddy of conflict and fell upon the body like a dog on a grave.

"The wharves!" called the clear, sharp voice, weaker now, but still very joyous. "Head them off from the wharves, you Greeks— they're making for the wharves!"

They were running again. There was clamor and a flare behind them, where men hunted other men in the moon-splashed darkness like terriers chasing rats in a moonlit barn. Sebastian was ahead of him—behind there were many, but the beaten Italians were throwing their weapons away and calling "Surrender— Surrender—" in high, shrill voices. Andrew threw a glance over his shoulder, and saw, in a nightmare flicker, a fellow twenty yards behind him stare stupidly at a point of steel that stuck abruptly out of his breast and fall, tripping the man who had run him through the back. Then the ground under Andrew's feet rang hollow suddenly—the wharf. He slipped on greasy wood—was down on his knees—up again. "Here," called Caterina's voice—he caught at a hand—leapt—sprawled into the bottom of a rocking boat.

There was an oar somewhere—he grabbed at it and began to splash with it furiously. They were moving away from the wharf now, but the damn sail wouldn't catch the wind. *Row!* The boat seemed to stick in the water like a bug in a stream of molasses but the gap between it and the wharf was widening— just in time, for there was shouting behind them now. He stole a glance back. There was the man with the bloody face. His left arm dangled at his side like a broken stick. He was yelling something and pointing. There was a ragged spatter of sound —something jumped under Andrew's oar like a frog taking water —he heard a gasp from the bow of the boat. "Hit, Caterina?" he called, but "No, no," said a voice.

Then the sail filled at last, and the wind and the current took them. The man with the bloody face was shouting and dancing up and down, but his voice was fainter. They swept around a curve, he was blotted out. There was nothing left of New Sparta but a confused, diminishing uproar and a dying redness in the sky.

He stopped splashing with his oar and put it down. The boat must be the little pleasure-boat which he and Sparta had used in their expeditions for turtle, Andrew noticed now. He wondered how seaworthy it would be when they got outside the bay.

Another thought struck him. Carlos, the boy, who was to have been with them.

"What happened to Carlos?" he said.

"At the last moment, he was afraid," said Caterina, calmly. "So he went with them."

"With who?"

"With the other Minorcans. They heard they were to be killed tonight, so they went away."

"Went away! In God's name, how could they go away?"

"The soldiers were busy. Mr. Cave had been to them and told them to revolt, but they did not trust him. So the old people met and decided. They told Mr. Cave they would be ready tonight, but as soon as it was night, they tied up their overseers and began to go away, one by one. A few were left, to deceive. The Italians did not stop them, they thought it was part of the plan. When they found out, it was too late. Mr. Cave had to choose between running after them and fighting Dr. Gentian."

Andrew gasped. So that explained Mr. Cave's grumbling. "Tricked, by God!"

If Dr. Gentian had been watchful or Mr. Cave loyal, so appallingly obvious a plan could never have succeeded—but the Doctor's watchfulness had been employed solely upon Andrew and Sebastian and Mr. Cave's treachery had wrecked his own scheme. Add to this the firm belief in the animal stupidity of the Minorcans which both Cave and his master held as a tenet of faith, and the thing was done. After years of rule, men grew careless, forgetting the ruled can have any craft. If Mr. Cave had won, he would doubtless have blamed the slaughter of Dr. Gentian on the departed Minorcans and, with Sparta's word to back him, could have looted the plantation as he pleased. Andrew pondered these circumstances in his mind.

"Did you know of this, Sebastian?" he said.

"When you told me what that dead man planned, I thought

there must be some way out for my people. I told Caterina to tell them to do what seemed best and not think of us—that we would rescue ourselves."

The fact of Mr. Cave's death struck Andrew now with a queer force—he had hardly taken it in before. Mr. Cave would never dabble his fingers in Sparta Gentian's hair again or rave impotently at the legitimate world. It seemed odd to think of that strong, bulky body empty of violence—those heavy hands no longer able to afflict or destroy. There must be something left —a soul?—where was it? He saw it fluttering in the wind like a burnt rag, maimed, stupid, defiant and alone. "Poor devil," he thought for a moment—the rag fluttered at him angrily—it did not want pity—it still wanted to hurt but it no longer had the power—the thought made him a little sick. . . .

"Think they'll chase us?" he said, after a while.

"Have their hands full," said Sebastian. "Caterina says the Italians were going to pay off old scores and fire the Greek huts. If they did, they'll be fighting fire all the rest of the night."

They were far down the river now, the breeze had freshened, the current ran smooth and fast. All sound but the sound of water and wind and trees had died away. Andrew trailed his hand over the side and drew it up, dripping. His mind was quieting gradually. Already the furious scene in which, such a short time ago, he had taken such active part seemed unreal as a stage-play. Yet it had been real. He had passed through just such a painted and bedizened adventure as he had always envied and wished against hope might be his own, when he was a little boy playing under a table, listening to the ship-captains and soldiers tell their sparse, enthralling tales. He had broken a prison—he had killed a man—even now he was running away from death in a leaky pleasure-boat, perhaps to be wrecked on an island like Robinson Crusoe's, perhaps merely to drown. Yet it did not seem to him that this adventure was his, as the adventure in the tales had been his while he listened to them.

Now he knew why those tales had been so sparse and crudely-fashioned. When you were living a tale you did not have time to color it as it should be colored—your mind stuck on odd useless trifles—the teeth of a man you struck—the feel of an iron bar—the shape of a sail against the stars. Besides, in life, you were hungry and thirsty and had to make water—things which did not happen in a tale, or if they did, assumed heroic proportions. He felt betrayed, somehow, as he thought of this. Even he should have a trace at least of attractive venturesomeness upon him now, but if it were there, he could not see or feel it. The thought of the long, baking voyage still ahead of them brought no flavor of romance with it, no smell of strange flowers. It would be hot and irksome and dangerous, and he would be very glad when it was done.

Something splashed overside—Caterina was bailing the boat. He sighed and started to help her. After a while she stopped, but he went on.

"Tired, Caterina?" he said, in a pause.

"No—yes—but it does not matter," she said, with face half turned. She shut her eyes for an instant—the moon laid a silver penny on each closed lid. He stared at her face. Then she started to bail again, and the slight charm was broken.

She gave a little sigh after a moment. "I think they hit me, after all," she said in a commonplace voice.

He crawled over to her, anguished suddenly. "Where is it?" he said.

"There—ah"—his fingers touched something sticky and warm. On her left side her dress was soaked—blood or water?—he could not tell.

"Do you hear, Sebastian? She's hurt," he said, in a sharp, angry voice. The dark figure at the tiller moved uneasily, the boat shifted, spray blew in Andrew's face.

"Is it deep, Caterina?"

"No, no—only a flesh wound—nothing—" But her voice seemed changed. "See, when I put my hand on it—it stops the blood."

Andrew put her hand aside, gently. He started to tear a strip from his shirt to bandage the wound. But the shirt was dirty and hard to tear. "Have you a handkerchief—anything—Caterina?" he asked anxiously. He felt in the darkness—she was wearing a scarf at her waist. He held her up and undid it.

"My poor scarf," she said, smiling. Her eyelids fluttered and closed again—her face looked more content.

He bandaged the wound as best he could with the scarf. "There, is that better?"

"Much," she said, and sighed lazily. "Thank you, *señor* Beard."

"Don't call me *señor*," said Andrew.

Stephen Vincent Benét

"I won't call you anything," she said, with a faint laugh. "I shall go to sleep. I am tired. Wake me when it is time to bail again."

He helped her to stretch out as comfortably as possible in the bottom of the boat, pillowing her head on the coat from which Sebastian had taken the button. Then he crawled back aft and crouched there, his head by Sebastian's knees. They were out in the little bay, now, the moonlight was ghostly on its white shelves of sand, the line of foam on the beach was a pale thread spun by a ghost on a shuttle of pearl. Presently they would run past the headland and the broad sea would take them.

Sebastian tested the wind. "Good," he muttered. "Can you handle her, *amigo*, after we get out of this bay?"

"Uh," said Andrew, nearly asleep. Sebastian laughed. "I'll wake you when you have to take her," he said.

Andrew threw back his head and looked up at the sky, breathing deep. The moon was a sailor's lamp now, a lamp of silver salt, sea-crusted, at the masthead of heaven. The stars were lights in a rigging. As he lay back he felt not only the movement of the boat, but a larger, vaguer roll, the roll of earth itself, a dark, huge ark plunging forward slowly through a black-and-silver waste. The slow way of that tremendous passage shook in his heart. He felt suddenly very happy and no longer dismayed by what might be in store for them. They had escaped, they were free. Caterina lay sleeping there in the bow: he could make out the huddle of her shoulder. In the morning he would see her as he had never seen her, familiar, friendly, with no mark of fear or oppression between her brows. They would live together always, somehow, Sebastian, Caterina and he—and gradually the stigmata of the stranger would depart from him and he would be able to read the runes enciphered in the ivory box of her heart.

His eyes, however, were closing. They could not really have closed, for it did not seem a moment before Sebastian nudged him to take the tiller and the sheet. Yet they stuck when he tried to open them, and when he had the tiller in his hand at last, the bay was gone and the boat was climbing endless hummocks of black-and-silver glass. It was rougher than it had been in the bay and the boat seemed diminished and apologetic in the wide face of ocean, but it settled to its work like a tired and patient pony, and after a few moments Andrew felt less afraid of drowning them all. The breeze was steady, he had little to do but follow the coastline and keep from going to sleep. Twice he shipped unnecessary water and once just averted jibing disastrously in a sudden puff, then he settled back into the way of it as a man who has not ridden for some time settles back into the way of a horse. The heavy drowsiness of exhaustion no longer pawed at his throat—the black-and-silver monotony, the rushing of the near water, lulled him, but not toward sleep, rather into a shining, half-bodiless wakefulness. He felt that he could steer forever, through an endless, fluid universe of wet shadow streaked with radiance while the boat answered his hand.

2.

The sky was a flight of gray doves touched with faint, pink markings like the markings inside a seashell, the sea was a heap of rose-quartz and gray stones, the light that came seemed to struggle through dew and roughened glass. It was the illusory hour, the hour just before dawn, when the tide of the blood sets back toward life again, and birds ruffle their feathers, and a light wind rises from nowhere to run across the tops of grass-blades, shaking a crystal bauble, whose tiny clapperless bells utter only the ghost of sound.

Andrew, heavy-eyed, saw the boat and his companions solidify and emerge from a world where all was mist and water of light. Sebastian changed from a heap of sacks to a man asleep—there was a little fur of dew on his garments. Andrew looked down at his own shirt—yes, it too was damp and the tiller beyond his hand was beaded at the edges. Of a sudden he felt very cold and shivered. Well, he would be hot enough when the sun was up.

He stared at the shore-line, wondering how far they had come. He had no idea. Wet rocks and white beach—a palm-tree like a green feather duster on end—a hedge of wild Spanish bayonet on the brow of a cliff—it might be anywhere on the Florida coast. He felt lost and alone in a world, except for him and the sleepers in the boat, so completely deserted of humanity that he had the odd feeling he should breathe very slowly and gently or the whole misty picture of land and sea and sky would rise from around them in a sudden thunder of wings, like a flight of scared partridge, and leave boat and cargo swinging in a sparkling, measureless void. Now a gull rose squawking from between two humps of water and he took odd comfort in that harsh and living sound. The universe altered slowly from gray and rose as he watched the gull, the colors of morning deepened, the east caught fire from a burning bush.

The day would be hot and calm. Already the wind was changing and dying as it changed. All day they would crawl over flawed sapphire under the point of a brazen arrow. He must wake the others. He wondered how much fresh water they had on board. He had crept in too near the coast—they were on the edge of rocky waters. Wake Sebastian, yes.

He leaned over and shook Sebastian by the shoulder. "Wake up!" he said. Sebastian stirred and groaned. Should he wake Caterina? He looked over at her where she lay in the bow.

Her head had slipped off his coat in the night; it was pillowed on her arm now, uncomfortably. Her other arm lay lax—the hand trailed in a puddle of water. He rubbed his eyes—she must be very tired to sleep in so cramped a posture. Then he saw that the red color in the puddle was not the reflection of the sun, and that, if she were sleeping, she slept with open eyes.

He was stumbling over to her, wildly, across Sebastian's body. The boat yawed violently and nearly flung him overboard. He heard Sebastian give a startled shout. Then he had her in his arms and the world was steady again.

"You're not dead," he kept saying to her. "You can't be dead." His hand passed over her forehead a dozen times, smoothing it. He felt at her wrist, at her heart, there was nothing to feel but flesh. Her fingers were cool, but it was the insensate coolness of wax and stone. The blood on her dress was drying already—she must have bled a great deal for all the water around her was stained.

Still holding her, he stared anxiously down at her face, trying to realize. This at least—death could not have come in horror but only as a slow dissolving tincture, for, though there was no smile upon them, her features were composed. She looked very tired and a little stern, but not dead as he thought of death. There was a stain on her mouth where she had bitten her lip: he wiped it off with his sleeve.

No, to her death could not have been as horrible as it might have been, but to him it was most horrible that she should have died so quietly, without a word. Perhaps she had meant to call out and had been too weak—he tried to remember dizzily if he had heard a sound in the night—she must have made some sort of sound. He could remember nothing.

He looked back. Sebastian was staring at them fixedly from the helm. His hand lay on the tiller as if he had forgotten it—a little muscle twitched in his cheek—his eyes were fey. Andrew thought, oddly, that he looked much as a man looks who has just got a sharp, excruciating blow in the groin—his mouth had the same sick stiffness.

He laid Caterina down. Then, bending over her, he looked ahead and felt a hoarse, startled cry tear out of his throat. "Rocks!" he yelled. "Sebastian! We're going on the rocks!" and fell in the stained water in the bottom of the boat as the boat jerked and the sail slatted over. There was a firm little jar beneath him like a sharp push from a heavy hand—a ripping sound —then catastrophe had passed, and they were going on again.

"Get out farther—from coast—" he said weakly, scrambling up. He looked back. Another moment and they would have struck that jagged line of black stumps full on. As it was they had just scraped across the edge where the water simmered uneasily like a bubbling pot. They had just escaped.

His feet were wetter than they had been. He stared down. A little spring of water was pumping up in the bottom, diluting the bloody puddles with fresh clear green. That slight firm push had been enough to ruin them. The boat was filling.

"Have to beach her, Sebas'," he said in a lifeless voice. "We're sinking."

Sebastian did not seem to hear: he was still staring ahead, with those blind, busy eyes, as if he were intent on counting every wave in the sea.

"Christ," said Andrew, flatly, and went back to shake him alive.

They beached the boat just in time. Twenty yards more to go or a rougher sea and they could not have done it. As it was, when a slow, huge roller took her at last and sludged her nose in the sand, she hesitated in its grip like a flogged, unwieldy mare, and the sea nearly took her and Caterina back again before they could haul up into safety. When they had done so, they lifted out Caterina's body between them and carried it up on the beach.

They had landed in a little cove. The sand was very clean and white—their footsteps dinted it sharply. It was morning now—the dew had vanished—the world was a glittering toy of silver and blue enamel.

"We must bury her," said Sebastian dully. "We cannot take her with us to consecrated ground." The muscle throbbed in his cheek. It was the first time he had spoken.

"I wish there were a priest," he said, looking about. "We must put up a cross." His mouth jerked.

Andrew followed his glance. There were other marks on the sand beside the marks of their footsteps and those of the gulls. A long slouching track crossed the beach and broke off at the edge of the rocks, the pawprints indented freshly like the marks of a devil's signet-ring.

"We can't just bury her and leave her," he said, with a shudder. He stared at the tracks. In the darkness something came down from the woods and pawed at a new mound.

He turned to his friend.

"Help me get some wood, Sebastian," he said, with a sob. "They can't hurt her if we burn her."

They toiled all morning, making the pyre. There was driftwood scattered on the beach and, up a little gully, they came upon the dry, tindery carcass of a dead tree. At last, toward afternoon, they had enough and sat down to rest for a while and to try to eat. The hard bread and boucanned meat with which the boat had been provisioned was soaked and dirty, the water in the keg brackish and warm, but neither of them noted these things. Andrew heard the tinkle of running water, somewhere up in the woods. "Stream, Sebastian," he said, but he was too tired to go and look for it. He brushed the crumbs from his knees and rose. "Come along," he said.

The pyre was a tangled heap of wood—broken jackstraws cluttered together. They covered it with the sail, smoothing it out clumsily. Then they laid Caterina upon it. Sebastian had closed her eyes and her dress was as much in order as they could manage. Now Sebastian crossed her hands on her breast and, taking a little brass medal from a string about his neck, put it between them. "I should not have prayed for vengeance," he muttered, his mouth shaking. Then he got down.

They both stood for a moment, gazing. She lay reclined on the sail in a posture of stiff ease—she looked smaller than he remembered her, but neither pitiful nor strange. Andrew thought of the first time he had seen her, a barbarous saint, walking through the deep coils of night with a candle in her hand. She had seemed removed enough then, now she was forever removed. The fingers had been cool, the alien heart had carried a treasure secretly, wrapped in a gleaming cloth. Now the secret and she were air, he could follow them no longer, the treasure was lost, the runner in chains had shaken off the burden. What had been the mystery in the blood, so jealously guarded—the writing behind the eyes? Had she loved him, had she loved Sebastian, had she loved any man on earth? It did not matter now, she had taken her knowledge with her, clutched between stiff fingers, like a relic returned to its saint, secure alike from worshippers and blasphemers. It was gone, now, and with it had gone the youthful part of his heart.

He wished, idly, that he had not torn her scarf, the night before, to bandage her wound. She had not liked his tearing her scarf.

"Wait," he said, as Sebastian bent to strike the flint on the steel. He looked about desperately—there must be something else —something he could give. His glance fell on a bush of green spikes near the foot of the cliff. The Spanish bayonet was just coming into flower again, as he had seen it in flower, in Judge Willo's garden. He ran ploddingly over to the bush and thrust his hand among the thorns. His arm was bleeding from a dozen scratches when he pulled it out, but he had the flower. It had not yet come to full bloom, but it was enough.

He laid the white stalk on her breast—it rested there like an order bestowed by the Moon. He touched her fingers an instant. Then he crouched down at Sebastian's feet to blow the tinder into sparks.

The sparks hung for a moment and caught, the tinder started to burn. They fed the flame carefully, with small pieces, till it grew strong, then they stood aside. The bottom logs began to crackle, a little at first, then more. The driftwood burned eerily with ghosts of blues and greens, strange as the colors of an enchanter's rose; as it mounted, the flame grew purer.

Soon the whole pyre was well alight. The tiny cracklings blended into a fiercer, deeper utterance, strangely petulant in that quietude where the only other sound was the slow crash of a single, heavy breaker on the sand, repeated at even intervals like the firing of minute-guns for the burial of a mermaid queen in a tomb of coral and weed. Above the pyre the heat began to tremble in the still air like threads of isinglass. They could not have quenched the fire now if they had wished—it had become a furnace—the petulant mutter settled to a harsh, husky roar. Now the overlapping edge of the sail felt the pure aspiration of the flame—a wisp of smoke blew across Caterina's face—a running creeper of fire sprang up and crouched at her feet.

Andrew turned away. Sebastian was lying face down in the sand, his arms out, his body in the shape of a cross. He was silent, but now and then a convulsive shudder rippled the muscles of his back and broke.

Andrew looked blindly at the palm of his own hand, surprised to find it unscorched, undefaced by fire. He would not look at the pyre again, to see that body altered and the last revenge of flesh on spirit. So he looked once, hastily, but saw nothing but flame and smoke. Through the rest of his life, he thought, in stupor of mind, he would go his ways like a man caught up alive out of hell, with the rustle of fire always in his ears and the thin, acrid reek of it clung to his flesh.

They had to feed the fire once, when it slackened, but by then they were numb and went about the task like sleepers.

It was over at last. The pyre had sunk to a bed of ashes and sparks. There were charred things lying there, but they did not gather them up. What little wind there was had scattered some of the ashes, they could not tell which were hers. They heaped stones in a rough sort of cairn over the place and covered the stones with sand. Soon the mound looked as if it had always been there. At the top of the finished mound, Sebastian put a badly-fashioned cross—two pieces of wood lashed together with rope. Andrew looked at it, thinking the next gale would blow it down.

He had intended to cut a name on the cross, but the only knife they had was dull, and now there was no time.

He tried to recollect what he could of the burial service they read in Trinity Church, in the brown gloom, under the puffy busts of gilded angels. "I am the resurrection and the life," he muttered, but the remembered syrup of the minister's voice spoiled the words. Besides, any words seemed an affront to the bleak impermanence of that heap of sand and stones.

Spanish Bayonet

The sun was low in the sky—his shadow on the sand was long and black. They could not have mended the boat without tools and they had no tools but a musket and a dull knife. They would have to go on. They would have to try and find the road.

"We'd better get on," he murmured, lifting from the ground the little pack of bread and dried meat he had tied up in his coat.

3.

They had known before what it was to go on when they stood at the end of resource, now they were to know what it was to go on beyond that end. There were two courses open to them—to plunge into the woods at a venture, hoping to strike the road and the Minorcans—or to attempt to reach St. Augustine by the beaches, alone. They would make better time at first, along the beach, but at the end of the cove a headland jutted out into rocks and they would have to swim for it. They chose the woods, staking what was left them on finding the road in the few hours of daylight that remained.

At first, it was easy. At the top of the gully they climbed was a long open glade, full of lush, deep grass. But at the end of the glade the underbrush began. They tried to keep a straight course by picking one tree out of the many to guide them, but, as they had to fight their way through the underbrush, their guidepost-tree would mix with other trees, and though they would imagine they had found the right one again, they could not be sure. Their tree had had a lightning-blaze on its left side —this one was blazed there too, but the blaze seemed a different shape.

Twilight came and with it the fear of the woods, the fear of going around and around the circle of a tethered horse till at last something cracked in the mind as they stumbled again upon the deep-trodden track they had made before, and they began to strike at the trees with their hands. The light faded inexorably, night crept between the trees, soft-footed, dark-eyed. "Mustn't run," said Andrew to himself, plodding ahead through a confusion of shadows.

There was a dry stirring in the bushes at his right—a sound half-yawn, half-hiss, like the hiss of an angry cat. He froze. In his mind he could feel the blunt, cool, deadly head of a moccasin

241

against his thigh. Indians, too,—he remembered the Indian he had seen peer out of a bush and vanish. "Mustn't run," he repeated to himself with a gulp. It was very dark now. When he got back in a house, he would never let it be dark. He would sleep with a dozen candles flaring in his room and buy a slave to keep them tended all through the night. A bough stung his cheek. "Mustn't run," but, insensibly, he knew his pace had increased.

He plunged through a little thicket that seemed full of fish-hooks and came out upon an open space. Where was Sebastian? He couldn't hear Sebastian behind him any more. He stood trembling on the edge of the clearing like a beaten hound. He did not dare call to Sebastian—there might be no answer. If there were no answer, he would go quite mad.

"Mustn't run," he advised himself for the last time, and then, tearing the pack from his shoulders with a jerk, began to run blindly across the clearing on drunken feet, moaning to himself as he ran. Things struck at him with springy clubs, but he kept on, thrashing his arms against them like a drowning man. Then at last the ground itself betrayed him and gave way beneath him, and he was rolling into a hidden pit where Fear and Night lay crouched like twin spiders, ready to swathe him in suffocating, innumerable folds of glutinous, dark silk the moment he touched bottom.

His next conscious memory was of a dark, concerned face, grinning down at him through a red shadow. "*Amigo*," said the face. "*Amigo. Que tal, señor?*" He grinned back at the face. It was Carlos, the boy he had given a Spanish dollar, years ago. He sat up, feeling his head spin. "Where's Sebastian?" he said.

"Sebastian!" called the boy, joyously, "Sebastian!" and now Sebastian came running out of the red shadow with a wooden bowl in his hand. He set the bowl down, and dropping beside Andrew, kissed him solemnly and smackingly on both cheeks, while Carlos clucked his approval. For a nervous moment Andrew thought Carlos was going to kiss him, too, but he did not. He trotted back toward the campfire that made the red shadow, calling something as he went. Then Sebastian had picked up the wooden bowl and was feeding Andrew hot, tasty bits of pepper-stew with his fingers.

Their luck had turned at last. The Minorcans had heard him shouting in the woods, and thinking one of their stragglers had lost his way, had sent out a party which came upon him as he rolled into the road like a shot rabbit. He had missed Sebastian because Sebastian, a little behind him, had seen firelight through the trees and had stopped to make sure. Then Sebastian had called to him, but his ears had been too full of his own terror to hear the call.

Revived by the stew, he listened eagerly to the news from New Sparta. A house-boy who had been unable to get away with the main body of the Minorcans had caught them up toward evening on a stolen horse. Of the post of eight soldiers, only the lugubrious corporal and a badly-wounded private remained. Dr. Gentian had been hurt in the fight but was alive, and Mrs. Gentian and the sub-overseers now ruled the wreck of the plantation. It was she who had checkmated Cave with a handful of her favorite Greeks—at the last moment there had been jealousy between the Greek and Italian sides of Cave's forces and the Greeks had finally decided to betray the revolt, just in time to save Dr. Gentian's life.

The Italians—what was left of them—were cowed. Some of them had managed to get hold of the sloop and take it half-way down the inlet, but there, having no sailors among them, they had stranded and decided to throw themselves on Mrs. Gentian's mercy. The colony was still unsettled and apprehensive, but Mrs. Gentian was definitely in the saddle and she rode with a tight rein. The man did not know what policy she intended to adopt towards the Minorcans—three messengers at least had ridden for St. Augustine, but two of them had already fallen into the Minorcans' hands, not unwillingly—and she could not afford to send many more.

Andrew asked for the other news, hesitatingly. About Miss Gentian he did not know—she was nursing her father, he thought. The words offered Andrew an incredible picture. He saw Dr. Gentian nightcapped, in a curtained bed, taking a cup from Sparta with a weak hand. They were looking at each other with blank, acquiescent eyes. That the cup contained more than beverage seemed improbable. Both understood, both hated, but both were under the whip, for the tall woman with the proud nose and the secret mouth had come to her kingdom at last and bound them equally, without compunction or passion. While she lived, they would live as she willed, now. They had the strength of beauty and violence and wit, but she had the strength of silence, and her strength engulfed theirs, as the well of darkness under the world engulfs its fallen stars.

He could see them living together for years—a devoted family—a pair of serpents under an iron bar, not daring to strike each other because the bar was mute and cold, and they could not tell what it would do if they struck. Some day Sparta, no doubt, would marry—her mother's man, this time. To the world they would present a united front. They would carry it off—oh, yes, —he trusted them for that.

He shuddered a little, seeing them all at table together, a year, five years from now. A curly-haired young man, dressed in the extreme of frippery, with a face as bland and foolish as a face painted on an egg, sat at Sparta's left, making tabletalk to his new relations. Poor rabbit, thought Andrew, and smiled. The last shreds of youth's dearest delusion, the delusion that life will come to a climax of thunder and cease, fell from him silently. Only by accident was life as neat a workman as that. The climax might come a dozen times, but after each climax the workman would go on, like an idiot building a castle, adding story upon story to what was already complete.

His own life, by all canons of art and taste, should have finished when the last sand fell upon the mound on the beach they had left behind. Instead, here he was, eating pepper-stew, and relishing it, on the whole. If there were any moral inherent in the course of events which had happened to him, he had yet to descry it. But for accident he would be lying in the prison ditch with lead in his lungs, and Mr. Cave would be alive and roaring. Was he any better off as it was and Mr. Cave any worse?—he did not know. He felt that he was fast becoming a pagan and it hurt his sense of the fitness of things. Then the Scotch strain in him, that drop which with the Jewish drop and the Irish, can survive a dozen admixtures of blood to dominate a mind, reasserted itself and told him grimly that it was not his business to question the schemes of God, but to hold on dourly to a predestined path between damnation and damnation, and distrust the vain speculations of the Egyptians. He could not quite believe its voice—would it call Caterina a vain Egyptian, he wondered—but it sufficed to send him off to sleep as soundly as if he were hearing John Knox preach.

Spanish Bayonet

4.

The camp broke up before dawn. The women gathered up their babies and their cooking pots—the head of the column straggled out in the road—the dust began to rise—the day's march was on. Andrew watched perhaps a quarter of the column pass, spectral in the early light, with a sense of dream, before he fell in the ranks at Sebastian's side. He had always liked the Minorcans, but his ruling impression of them had been one of gravity; he was amazed to see how lightly they seemed to take this wild expedition. They had left the promised land they had labored on for five years behind them and with it the greater part of their few possessions. They were marching to an unknown future, perhaps to prison or death, but the general mood seemed that of children on a holiday, and ahead some boy was strumming a cracked guitar.

A child ran out of the ranks to pick a flower, was brought back howling, and given a slap and a sweetmeat. A mysterious Spanish joke on a plump young man was passed from rank to rank with an accompaniment of laughter and pointing fingers. Andrew could see the back of the neck of the young man in question, redden under its tan—then he turned to fling back a snorting expletive over his shoulder and the laughter grew ecstatic. One waddling matron frankly sat down in the middle of the road to laugh her fill and was promptly surrounded by a circle of arguing, encouraging relations. A girl and a boy had their hands locked together as they marched, and the ranks around them turned into one vast admiring family that tickled them with solemn or ribald advice, to which they paid not the slightest attention. A grave, white-bearded elder carried a trussed live chicken under his arm—it squawked incessantly and pecked at his sleeve.

They had few arms and scant provender—most of the men had no better weapons than clubs or rude wooden pikes. Sebastian was a person of great importance since he carried a musket. An Indian attack in force would mean massacre, a journey too long drawn out the hunger pinch, but they seemed to have considered these things and put them aside. Now Andrew began to understand the quality in them that had taken them across an ocean to live in a strange land for five years under a rod without losing heart. There was a hardness hidden somewhere under their grace that called up all the Scot in him to answer it and he found himself whistling "The Bonny House of Airlie" as he trudged along in the dust.

5.

Grief, autumnal color of the stained and fugitive wood, sad vesture of red and gold, severe counsellor, true companion—your hands touch at the heart as lightly and idly as a child's and leave it shaken, then like a child you depart, on light feet, idly. Honest playfellow, candid guest, your company is strict, but for young men, brief; no matter how straitly the spirit would detain you, mind and body and time are too strong to endure for longer than a terse and appointed term so reticent a visitant. The earth stirs in its mail of frost, the geese begin to fly North again, the fire dies in the chimney, it is time for you to go. The wind will blow over the field but your voice will be in it no longer, the rain fall from the sky in showers, no longer austere with the echo of your sober bells. Now only the old, discarded traveller in the hearth-corner keeps your shadow alive in his breast, stretching out cold, knotted fingers before a diminishing flame.

That even the deepest sorrow can be transient was, however, a fact which Andrew, like most people, had to learn for himself. At first Caterina haunted the march for him, sleeping or waking, but even twenty-four hours made a little difference, not in the honesty of his grief but in its power to obliterate the rest of the universe. Certain things must be done, certain motions gone through. The constant activity of body, the uncertain imminence of danger, left no time for that luxurious melancholy which feeds upon a full stomach and an empty mind. Enforcedly, he began to live in the world again—the resurrection was painful and gradual enough but, once begun, it continued implacably.

6.

Four days later, the picture on the highway had changed somewhat in details but not in the whole. The same slow stream of humanity clotted the road, taking it easy to all appearances, yet stirring the dust relentlessly with passing feet. A child had died,

Spanish Bayonet

another child had been born. The dead lay buried by the road-side, four men carried the new mother and her charge on an improvised litter toward the rear of the column. Tomorrow, or the next day, she would be back in the ranks again. The talk was less continual, faces showed fatigue, feet went limping. But what talk there was seemed cheerful, and those who fell behind for a while straggled back into line eventually, some stronger impulse than fear urging them on.

Andrew and Sebastian were at the head of the column when they sighted the cavalry-patrol.

It was a small force, some twenty men in all, commanded by a tall, leathery captain with a London drawl, who kept blowing his nose on a lace handkerchief because of the dust and then looking around savagely at his men to try and catch a smile on their faces. He commenced to shout at the Minorcans in abominable Spanish when they were yet some distance away, and though both Sebastian and Andrew called back in English, it seemed to make no impression on his mind for a long time.

"Damn my boots, what a precious lot of ragamuffins!" Andrew could hear him saying to himself as they approached. "You can't talk their lingo, can you, sergeant? I thought not—a pretty affair, damn my boots, to send a gentleman with his Majesty's commission to shepherd a pack of mutinous blackguards into town. If the Governor were of my mind, he'd shoot down every last man jack of them in the ditch of the fort, by pox and thunder —don't you think so, sergeant? Hey, you there, the man with the dirty shirt—" he called suddenly as Andrew came nearer, "can you talk English? Damn my boots he's staring at me like a codfish—why don't you salute an officer, man? Stap me, the creature stinks in the wind like Billingsgate fish-market! Talk English, fellow! Parlay English, Anglish—yes—no?" he howled abruptly at Andrew from a distance of five paces, as if Andrew, being a foreigner, must be stone-deaf.

It did not surprise Andrew to be taken for one of the Minorcans. With a ten days' beard on his face and his skin burned by the sun, he could have passed for a scavenger. He was only surprised when the captain, after a few interchanges, grew fairly civil on the whole. He was like other English officers Andrew had known, apparently in a continual sweat of puzzled exasperation whenever he had a task to accomplish, and yet somehow getting the

247

task done with a certain slack efficiency that seemed to surprise himself. His bloodthirstiness was entirely a matter of conversation. Andrew saw him later in the day with a fat Minorcan two-year-old on the saddle before him and an expression of weary fury on his face, muttering savagely, "Damn my boots, you think you're a fine whelp, don't you—a fine little piece of mutiny to boil for officers' soup—how he claws at me, damme sergeant! I think I'd better drop him in the road and break his head." But his arm was tightly clutched around the child, and the child was squeaking delightedly as it pulled at the horse's mane.

Andrew made himself as inconspicuous as possible during the rest of the march and did not attempt to interview the captain till it was ended. A year ago he would have done so at once, without thinking how strange his important talk of the house of Alexander Beard and Son would sound on the lips of a dirty, unshaven boy. Now he knew his cue was self-effacement till he could get to the Governor. From the talk of the patrol he gathered that His Excellency was at least not ill-disposed toward the Minorcans and intended to give them a chance to state their case. But he and Sebastian stood in a different position from the rest of the host.

The other Minorcans could come into court with hands clean of anything but a bloodless rebellion against an unjust employer. Sebastian and he had been charged with murder and treason— Sebastian had killed Mr. Cave—both had broken prison—to mix their grievance with the general one would only impair the latter's chance of redress. On the other hand, if the Governor were really Dr. Gentian's foe, Andrew's testimony, being that of an Englishman, might clinch the matter definitely in the Minorcans' favor. He had plenty of time to think the matter through from every angle, and decided finally, that his best course was to keep his identity hidden till the end of the march came.

7.

They were camped on the outskirts of St. Augustine at last. The captain had held a long interview with the prominent men of the colony. In the afternoon, the Governor would ride out to see them. Meanwhile, they must be patient. A small ration-party might go into town, but the main body was to remain in camp and fraternize as little as possible with the townspeople. He gave his word for the safe-conduct of the ration-party and his assurance that if these conditions were fulfilled, the Governor would grant them a fair and open hearing.

Then he solemnly posted sentries between the camp and the town. It was purely for effect—both he and the Minorcans knew that if the five hundred wished they could brush aside the sentries and descend on the town like locusts. But, being for effect, it served. Hemmed in by a larger force, the Minorcans would have begun to mill like frightened cattle. As it was they settled down quietly enough, the women to tending their children, the men to listen to the boy with the cracked guitar or to try and repair gear damaged on the road.

Now, thought Andrew, the time had come for him to make his stroke. He asked to speak with the captain in private and in a few words stated his name and his wish for an interview with the Governor.

"Damn my boots and breeches," said the captain, staring at him keenly, while his hand drummed on the pommel of his saddle, "I thought you spoke odd English for a Spaniard—but, body of hell, what a tale! I wouldn't have believed—to be frank, sir, even for a gentleman in straits, you make a damned queer appearance, if you'll excuse the remark."

"My grandfather carried a pack," said Andrew, deliberately, smiling. The dream of the Beards of Westmoreland departed forever as he said it, leaving no scar behind. He might play the exquisite again, when he had money and clean clothes, but never without a certain feeling of masquerade. In theory, one could always tell a gentleman, no matter how dirty he was—in practice, the matter seemed a trifle more complicated.

"Oh, well—" said the captain, apparently somewhat relieved. He stared at Andrew again. "It sounds so damnable odd," he confessed frankly. "Of course you'll have some acquaintance in the city to—." He waved his hand.

Andrew thought. He could hardly call on any of the gentlemen he had met at Judge Willo's to bear out his story—they were all Dr. Gentian's intimates.

"The Governor might remember me, if I were shaved," he

249

said slowly, "and then—is the Pride of the Colonies still in port? Captain Stout would recognize me, I know."

"Oh, if that's your man!" said the captain, "Captain Stout's with the Governor now, I imagine—he's had the devil of a time getting cargo—and then the Governor's been holding him back to question him about this insurrection in the North. He sails this afternoon—you may catch him at the Governor's if you make haste. Sergeant—Sergeant—" he called peevishly, "where's one of those damned horses? I want to mount this man and send him to the Governor."

He turned sharply to Andrew. "You watch yourself in the town," he said. "They're going to burn some of your rebels in effigy in the square today—silly nuisance burning fellows in effigy, but looks damned well as an expression of loyalty in a report"—and he laughed like a fox barking.

"Sergeant—take this man into town with you and see he gets to His Excellency."

"Shall I tie him, sir?" said the sergeant, stolidly, saluting.

"Damn your boots, no. Why are you such a damned old fool? You can knock him on the head if he tries any tricks," he added thoughtfully, "but don't tie him now."

8.

So Andrew, for the second time, presented to the streets of St. Augustine a queer and disreputable figure, under the hot sun. But this time, though he was ragamuffin indeed, he cared not at all where at first he had cared so greatly. He scuffed his broken shoes in his stirrups, comfortably, and was only interested to note that a little tail of pointing, giggling children followed himself and the sergeant to the Governor's door.

"He see the Governor!" said a dewlapped Paunch with an amber-topped cane, regarding Andrew with evident disgust. "He can't see the Governor! Ridiculous, sergeant! The Governor's closeted—even if he were not—the fellow's far too foul."

"Captain Strahan's orders. To see His Excellency at once," repeated the sergeant metallically. Andrew gathered that he did not like the Paunch.

"Captain Strahan's orders?" yammered the Paunch, nervously.

"Well, why didn't you say it was Captain Strahan's orders—if you'd said it was Captain Strahan's—"

The Paunch's importance had shrunk—he was bustling away through a door.

"Silly old capon," said the sergeant, devastatingly, with the air of one who spits to relieve his mind.

The Paunch was back again, ushering Andrew along with fat, fluttering hands. The sergeant clanked after them.

"No tricks," he was muttering. "Captain's orders. No tricks at all."

Then a door was flung open and Andrew stumbled into a big, cool room where two men were facing each other across a desk. Both looked up as he entered. The next moment a chair went to the floor with a crash—and the hard paws of Captain Stout were gripping both his hands.

It was later. Andrew and the Governor were alone. He had told his story in detail, with certain suppressions, chiefly involving Sparta and the killing of Mr. Cave. The Governor had put a number of questions, most of them in regard to things that seemed to Andrew of little importance. Now at last he seemed satisfied.

Andrew had tried to gage him during the interview. He was a narrow man and a touchy one, but he seemed honest. Of his long-banked hate of Dr. Gentian there could be no doubt whatever—it showed in every line of his face when the name came up. Andrew's description of the conditions at New Sparta had seemed to shock him genuinely, though not quite in the way that Andrew had expected. He seemed much more shocked, for instance, at Dr. Gentian's failure to inform him fully that he had arrested Andrew as a traitor.

"It won't do," he kept saying. "Won't do; man must be mad. Political prisoners should be brought before me at once."

"Well, sir!" said Andrew finally, when there seemed to be no more questions the Governor wished to ask.

The Governor fiddled with his inkstand a moment. Then he looked at Andrew.

"You've put me in a queer position, Mr. Beard," he said at length. "Oh, I don't doubt your story. It only confirms what I've suspected, ever since the colony started—but my predecessor was a firm friend of Dr. Gentian's and—" He frowned. "Damn it, if I could only put you in the witness-box," he burst out. "As it is, I half-wish you'd never come to see me at all."

"I'm sorry," said Andrew. It seemed the only possible remark. "Oh, don't apologize," said the Governor, worriedly. "After all you've done me a service. My mind's made up now. Oh, I've no doubt the Minorcans would have proved their point in any case, but your tale clinches it for me. They shall have their rights, Mr. Beard. I'll settle them here—God knows a couple of hundred good workers will be a godsend to the town. But now, Mr. Beard." He rapped on the desk. "What are we going to do with you?"

"I am quite at your disposal sir," said Andrew, drawing a vast breath of relief.

"No, no," said the Governor, querulously, "that's just what you can't be. If you stay here, some of Gentian's friends are sure to stir up trouble about that absurd charge of treason he's brought against you." He smiled. "Officially, Mr. Beard, I have not as yet, as I say, been informed of that charge through the proper channels. But if someone here should take it into his head to lodge a direct accusation—I should have to notice it—yes —I should have to notice it—I should have to hold you for examination, Mr. Beard—and then, damn it, the moment I do" —he exploded again, "the fat's in the fire and the whole Minorcan case is muddled with yours."

"Of course, sir, if you wish to"—began Andrew, slowly.

"Examine you? In God's name, why?" said the Governor, brusquely. "I know your father's name—Captain Stout's told me of the sacrifices he's already made for the Crown." Captain Stout had obviously omitted any mention of Lucius, and Andrew was very grateful. "If you were a traitor, why the devil would you be sitting here talking to me?" the Governor ended. The question seemed unanswerable, and Andrew himself began to wonder why.

"No, Mr. Beard," the Governor went on. "The charge against you is absurd, but it must not be pressed. I've no doubt Captain Stout will trust your father's son for a passage to New York. When you reach there, you will, naturally, join the army. They say De Lancey's raising a troop of loyalist horse—well, Mr. Beard, there's my advice, unofficially. Do you find it reasonable?"

"Most reasonable, your Excellency," said Andrew, with a slight smile. "I shall, as you say, return to New York at once—and join the army."

"Good," said the Governor, rising. "I shan't ask you for a deposition, Mr. Beard—it will be best if your name is not brought in at all. You'll find Captain Stout in the anteroom—and I should advise you going aboard at once, if I may suggest it."

"I have to say good-by to a friend," said Andrew. "After that I shall go aboard as soon as possible."

"A friend?" said the Governor. "Oh, yes—the Minorcan boy who was in prison with you. I wish we could get him away too. He'll only serve to confuse things—and I want a clear case." He looked at Andrew.

"Perhaps it can be managed," said Andrew, thanking his gods for the narrow strength of the Governor's hate of Dr. Gentian, that now blinded him to everything but the prospect of the latter's ruin. "Good day, your Excellency—and thank you."

"Good day, Mr. Beard, and a safe voyage," said the Governor, turning back to his papers, and Andrew bowed and retreated from the lion's jaws.

9.

He had arranged to meet Sebastian in the Plaza, near noon, if Sebastian could get leave from the ration party—and it was there he now proceeded with Captain Stout. The matter of his passage was settled—Captain Stout had offered it, before he had had time to speak. He mentioned Sebastian. "Body servant, too, I'm sure," said Captain Stout, amicably, and Andrew thought it best not to explain further at present. He looked at Captain Stout as they walked along, trying to read his political opinions in his face, but he could make nothing out of those weathered features.

Fooling the Governor or letting him fool himself was one thing; he did not like the idea of fooling Captain Stout. But then, even yet—was he quite sure of his own intent? He had been quite sure; but in the Governor's room, with its air of power and order long established, the old colors of things had crept back to them insensibly, making a world where rebels were rebels and no gentleman in his wits thought of fighting for anything but a king. He sighed, cursing himself for a vacillation he could not help—habit and custom are strong chains. But he was a shop-keeper's son, not a gentleman in his wits . . . oh, well, look at the people in the streets and put off thinking for a while. The narrow streets were crowded with people going to the Plaza; when they came to the Plaza, it was crowded too.

"Is this a fiesta day?" he asked of his companion.

"Not exactly," said the captain, slowly. "They were talking about burning some Guy Fawkses or something—I'm as glad my boys are on board except for the boat's crew—"

Then Andrew remembered. The demonstration of loyalty. He saw a pile of wood in the center of the square and was horribly reminded of another such pile of wood he had helped to build. His heart began to pound. He wanted to get away. But Sebastian must be found first—ah, there he was, standing in the mouth of an alleyway. Andrew threw up his hand and called out over the sea of heads. Sebastian heard him, turned, waved back, and started to worm his way toward them, as a ragged shout went up from the other side of the square.

A drum was beating, a voice was calling, "Make way! Make way!" The crowd chattered and jostled. From the cramped mouth of the street on the other side of the square a procession debouched, the crowd fell away before it. Andrew felt Captain Stout's grip tighten on his arm. Now the head of the procession was out in the square itself—a rout of men dressed in sorry rags of carnival. Some had faces blacked with soot, like boys on Guy Fawkes' Day, others wore painted ludicrous masks. They were singing and shouting—the crowd roared its approval—the front ranks pressed back on the toes of those behind to leave a clear path to the woodpile in the center.

Then Andrew heard himself saying, "Damn you! Damn you all!" in a hurried whisper, as the effigies came into sight. There were two of them, great lolling dummies of straw, absurdly garbed, borne high on the shoulders of the crowd. They had halters around their necks, before them marched a man with a butcherlike face, dressed in hangman's black. A rope was slung over his arm and he carried a placard on a pole—"Death to all traitors!" in Spanish and English. There were other placards in the crowd, and two signs flapped at the bellies of the dum-mies. Andrew could make them out now, "Jackie Hancock"—· "Sammy Adams"—

Spanish Bayonet

A gratified whoop went up from the crowd at the sight of the dummies. A big, sweating woman with a large pink chamber-pot in her hand skipped nimbly out of the crowd and flung the contents of the vessel in the face of the dummy marked "Adams," with a shrill, joyous scream, splattering its bearers.

Andrew wrenched himself loose from Captain Stout's hand. "Stop it—stop it—you Spanish bastards—" he was crying, with tears of rage in his eyes. He saw a thousand grinning faces turned toward him, and struck at the nearest wildly, fighting and going down.

10.

A young man with a newly-broken head lay in a tossing bunk in the cabin of a ship at sea, and began to feel the first qualms of seasickness taint his relative content. He stirred, and said as much.

"Means you've come out of it nicely," said Captain Stout, bending over him. "You'll be pleased to know, Mr. Beard— the man that hit you with the stick'll carry a thick ear some time yet," he added.

"I acted like a fool," said Andrew. "I don't see how you got away. But I couldn't stand the woman."

"There," said the Captain, soothingly. "It's natteral. Young blood's hot. *I* wasn't too pleased," he went on. "No, we wasn't any of us too pleased with the goings on. Told 'em you were one of my crew with a touch of sun. They swallowed it. I wanted to tell them something else. But you'll thank your Spanish friend—I couldn't have got you off alone—let alone talk their jabber fast enough—"

"What happened to him?" said Andrew feebly.

"He's here." The Captain chuckled. "Ain't you, Spanish?"

"*Si señor*," came a voice from the upper bunk. "But sick as a soldier. How are you, my friend?"

"Much as you are," said Andrew, and laughed. "I'm glad you're here, Sebastian."

"*Gracias*," said the voice from above. "We changed knives— I follow my knife. Besides," he added, after a moment, "I, too, have a certain desire to help the donkey we spoke of kick off his rider. The rider wears too red a coat to suit me."

255

"What about you, Captain?" said Andrew, after a pause.

"Oh, we're all liberty-boys, now," said the Captain, with a casual chuckle. "Didn't say so before, you being your father's son; but we're all liberty-boys on the Pride now—if I didn't tell the Governor. Lord, I thought he'd have me a dozen times, but I never saw a soldier that wasn't a turniphead."

"Does my father know you're a liberty-boy, sir?" said Andrew, smiling.

"Not yet," said the Captain. "That'll go hard, it will. Well, I thought I'd do my duty by him, this last time. And then, if it's going to be as long a war as I reckon it, what's the harm in doing a bit of trading first?" He spat out the porthole. "Seem queer at the start, going counter to old King George," he added thoughtfully. "Not that I've ever seen the man, but I've always had a sort of picture of him. Well, life's unexpected and that's a fact." He seemed to take comfort in the truism.

"They've got a flag with a rattlesnake on it," he continued. "Liberty or Death. It'll be queer to raise it. The Pride's had British colors up ever since she was launched. She's used to them. Well, she'll have to learn new ways. I hope she'll like them, but I'm doubtful." He shook his head.

"We'll all have to get used to new ways," said Andrew. He stared into the future, trying to pierce it, but he could see nothing. It did not matter, his own course was plain.

"How long will it take us, Captain?" he said.

"Couldn't say, Mr. Beard, but the rumpus'll still be going when we get back. The lobsters think it won't, but it will. You see, King George Third's gone too far—and we mean to break loose now. That makes the difference."

"I suppose so," said Andrew, lying back and thinking of all that had passed since he last lay in a ship's bunk. What had he got from all of it—what had he done? The Minorcans had rescued themselves—he had not even killed Mr. Cave. Caterina—he had not thought much of that mound in the little cove since they had left it, he had not had time or strength. He thought of it now. She had saved him, her he had been unable to save. He had only been able to leave a part of his youth where she lay, for the wind to blow off like ash. Even now he was not sure that he had loved her, as he understood love—nor could he see her his, in life, by any fantasy of mind. There had been a spell between them—an incantation—it had worked itself out and passed—gone back beyond the moon. For the last time, as the ship tossed and the sea grew rougher, the shape of the Spanish bayonet arose in his mind, with its thorns and its white flower, incongruous, enchanted, pure.

Out of all the confused and brilliant turmoil of the past year that visionary semblance alone remained steadfast—that semblance and his friend Sebastian—perhaps they were enough.

Yet he trembled, hurt and aching, uncomforted by the knowledge that hurt and ache would pass, as in time they would, and become only a colored memory, a ghost of perfume. Now he only knew that he wanted to hear Caterina's voice, and that she was dead. But even at the worst of this bitterness, other thoughts came—New York—Lucius—a musket—a rebel army—a lion and a unicorn hunted through green Massachusetts woods. In a short while, unconsciously, he found himself seeing Sebastian and a boy with his own face cooking hominy on a griddle over a soldier's campfire. His inexperience of war lent the picture a plausibility, a charm almost. The risen sun cast a broad path of illusion at the feet of the two figures, the blue smoke of the fire fluttered, there was a smell of burning leaves in the air. Soon enough the drum would assert its sharp, monotonous scorn.

"Well, sir," said the Captain, "you'll be feeling better tomorrow." He was going now. "No objection to your Spanish friend bunking in with you?"

"No. He's my friend," said Andrew, as if in explanation of more than the question had asked. "Good night, Captain."

"Good night, Mr. Beard. You'll find dirty weather when you get up tomorrow—it's coming on to blow."

TALES OF OUR TIME

Tales of Our Time

TOO EARLY SPRING

I'M writing this down because I don't ever want to forget the way it was. It doesn't seem as if I could, now, but they all tell you things change. And I guess they're right. Older people must have forgotten or they couldn't be the way they are. And that goes for even the best ones, like Dad and Mr. Grant. They try to understand but they don't seem to know how. And the others make you feel dirty or else they make you feel like a goof. Till, pretty soon, you begin to forget yourself—you begin to think, "Well, maybe they're right and it was that way." And that's the end of everything. So I've got to write this down. Because they smashed it forever—but it wasn't the way they said.

Mr. Grant always says in comp. class: "Begin at the beginning." Only I don't know quite where the beginning was. We had a good summer at Big Lake but it was just the same summer. I worked pretty hard at the practice basket I rigged up in the barn, and I learned how to do the back jackknife. I'll never dive like Kerry but you want to be as all-around as you can. And, when I took my measurements, at the end of the summer, I was 5 ft. 9¾ and I'd gained 12 lbs. 6 oz. That isn't bad for going on sixteen and the old chest expansion was O. K. You don't want to get too heavy, because basketball's a fast game, but the year before was the year when I got my height, and I was so skinny, I got tired. But this year, Kerry helped me practice, a couple of times, and he seemed to think I had a good chance for the team. So I felt pretty set up—they'd never had a Sophomore on it before. And Kerry's a natural athlete, so that means a lot from him. He's a pretty good brother too. Most Juniors at State wouldn't bother with a fellow in High.

It sounds as if I were trying to run away from what I have to write down, but I'm not. I want to remember that summer,

Stephen Vincent Benét

too, because it's the last happy one I'll ever have. Oh, when I'm an old man—thirty or forty—things may be all right again. But that's a long time to wait and it won't be the same.

And yet, that summer was different, too, in a way. So it must have started then, though I didn't know it. I went around with the gang as usual and we had a good time. But, every now and then, it would strike me we were acting like awful kids. They thought I was getting the big head, but I wasn't. It just wasn't much fun—even going to the cave. It was like going on shooting marbles when you're in High.

I had sense enough not to try to tag after Kerry and his crowd. You can't do that. But when they all got out on the lake in canoes, warm evenings, and somebody brought a phonograph along, I used to go down to the Point, all by myself, and listen and listen. Maybe they'd be talking or maybe they'd be singing, but it all sounded mysterious across the water. I wasn't trying to hear what they said, you know. That's the kind of thing Tot Pickens does. I'd just listen, with my arms around my knees—and somehow it would hurt me to listen—and yet I'd rather do that than be with the gang.

I was sitting under the four pines, one night, right down by the edge of the water. There was a big moon and they were singing. It's funny how you can be unhappy and nobody know it but yourself.

I was thinking about Sheila Coe. She's Kerry's girl. They fight but they get along. She's awfully pretty and she can swim like a fool. Once Kerry sent me over with her tennis racket and we had quite a conversation. She was fine. And she didn't pull any of this big sister stuff, either, the way some girls will with a fellow's kid brother.

And when the canoe came along, by the edge of the lake, I thought for a moment it was her. I thought maybe she was looking for Kerry and maybe she'd stop and maybe she'd feel like talking to me again. I don't know why I thought that—I didn't have any reason. Then I saw it was just the Sharon kid, with a new kind of bob that made her look grown-up, and I felt sore. She didn't have any business out on the lake at her age. She was just a Sophomore in High, the same as me.

I chunked a stone in the water and it splashed right by the

262

canoe, but she didn't squeal. She just said, "Fish," and chuckled. It struck me it was a kid's trick, trying to scare a kid.

"Hello, Helen," I said. "Where did you swipe the gunboat?"

"They don't know I've got it," she said. "Oh, hello, Chuck Peters. How's Big Lake?"

"All right," I said. "How was camp?"

"It was peachy," she said. "We had a peachy counselor, Miss Morgan. She was on the Wellesley field-hockey team."

"Well," I said, "we missed your society." Of course we hadn't, because they're across the lake and don't swim at our raft. But you ought to be polite.

"Thanks," she said. "Did you do the special reading for English? I thought it was dumb."

"It's always dumb," I said. "What canoe is that?"

"It's the old one," she said. "I'm not supposed to have it out at night. But you won't tell anybody, will you?"

"Be your age," I said. I felt generous. "I'll paddle a while, if you want," I said.

"All right," she said, so she brought it in and I got aboard. She went back in the bow and I took the paddle. I'm not strong on carting kids around, as a rule. But it was better than sitting there by myself.

"Where do you want to go?" I said.

"Oh, back towards the house," she said in a shy kind of voice. "I ought to, really. I just wanted to hear the singing."

"K. O.," I said. I didn't paddle fast, just let her slip. There was a lot of moon on the water. We kept around the edge so they wouldn't notice us. The singing sounded as if it came from a different country, a long way off.

She was a sensible kid, she didn't ask fool questions or giggle about nothing at all. Even when we went by Petters' Cove. That's where the lads from the bungalow colony go and it's pretty well populated on a warm night. You can hear them talking in low voices and now and then a laugh. Once Tot Pickens and a gang went over there with a flashlight, and a big Bohunk chased them for half a mile.

I felt funny, going by there with her. But I said, "Well, it's certainly Old Home Week"—in an offhand tone, because, after all, you've got to be sophisticated. And she said, "People are funny," in just the right sort of way. I took quite a shine to her after that and we talked. The Sharons have only been in town three years and somehow I'd never really noticed her before. Mrs. Sharon's awfully good-looking but she and Mr. Sharon fight. That's hard on a kid. And she was a quiet kid. She had a small kind of face and her eyes were sort of like a kitten's. You could see she got a great kick out of pretending to be grown-up —and yet it wasn't all pretending. A couple of times, I felt just as if I were talking to Sheila Coe. Only more comfortable, because, after all, we were the same age.

Do you know, after we put the canoe up, I walked all the way back home, around the lake? And most of the way, I ran. I felt swell too. I felt as if I could run forever and not stop. It was like finding something. I hadn't imagined anybody could ever feel the way I did about some things. And here was another person, even if it was a girl.

Kerry's door was open when I went by and he stuck his head out, and grinned.

"Well, kid," he said. "Stepping out?"

"Sure. With Greta Garbo," I said, and grinned back to show I didn't mean it. I felt sort of lightheaded, with the run and everything.

"Look here, kid—" he said, as if he was going to say something. Then he stopped. But there was a funny look on his face.

And yet I didn't see her again till we were both back in High. Mr. Sharon's uncle died, back East, and they closed the cottage suddenly. But all the rest of the time at Big Lake, I kept remembering that night and her little face. If I'd seen her in daylight, first, it might have been different. No, it wouldn't have been.

All the same, I wasn't even thinking of her when we bumped into each other, the first day of school. It was raining and she had on a green slicker and her hair was curly under her hat. We grinned and said hello and had to run. But something happened to us, I guess.

I'll say this now—it wasn't like Tot Pickens and Mabel Palmer. It wasn't like Junior David and Betty Page—though they've been going together ever since kindergarten. It wasn't like any of those things. We didn't get sticky and sloppy. It wasn't like going with a girl.

Gosh, there'd be days and days when we'd hardly see each

Too Early Spring

other, except in class. I had basketball practice almost every after-noon and sometimes evenings and she was taking music lessons four times a week. But you don't have to be always twos-ing with a person, if you feel that way about them. You seem to know the way they're thinking and feeling, the way you know yourself.

Now let me describe her. She had that little face and the eyes like a kitten's. When it rained, her hair curled all over the back of her neck. Her hair was yellow. She wasn't a tall girl but she wasn't chunky—just light and well made and quick. She was awfully alive without being nervous—she never bit her finger-nails or chewed the end of her pencil, but she'd answer quicker than anyone in the class. Nearly everybody liked her, but she wasn't best friends with any particular girl, the mushy way they get. The teachers all thought a lot of her, even Miss Eagles. Well, I had to spoil that.

If we'd been like Tot and Mabel, we could have had a lot more time together, I guess. But Helen isn't a liar and I'm not a snake. It wasn't easy, going over to her house, because Mr. and Mrs. Sharon would be polite to each other in front of you and yet there'd be something wrong. And she'd have to be fair to both of them and they were always pulling at her. But we'd look at each other across the table and then it would be all right.

I don't know when it was that we knew we'd get married to each other, some time. We just started talking about it, one day, as if we always had. We were sensible, we knew it couldn't happen right off. We thought maybe when we were eighteen. That was two years but we knew we had to be educated. You don't get as good a job, if you aren't. Or that's what people say.

We weren't mushy either, like some people. We got to kissing each other good-by, sometimes, because that's what you do when you're in love. It was cool, the way she kissed you, it was like leaves. But lots of the time we wouldn't even talk about getting married, we'd just play checkers or go over the old Latin, or once in a while go to the movies with the gang. It was really a won-derful winter. I played every game after the first one and she'd sit in the gallery and watch and I'd know she was there. You could see her little green hat or her yellow hair. Those are the class colors, green and gold.

And it's a queer thing, but everybody seemed to be pleased.

That's what I can't get over. They liked to see us together. The grown people, I mean. Oh, of course, we got kidded too. And old Mrs. Withers would ask me about "my little sweetheart," in that awful damp voice of hers. But, mostly, they were all right. Even Mother was all right, though she didn't like Mrs. Sharon. I did hear her say to Father, once, "Really, George, how long is this going to last? Sometimes I feel as if I just couldn't stand it."

Then Father chuckled and said to her, "Now, Mary, last year you were worried about him because he didn't take any interest in girls at all."

"Well," she said, "he still doesn't. Oh, Helen's a nice child—no credit to Eva Sharon—and thank heaven she doesn't giggle. Well, Charles is mature for *his* age too. But he acts so solemn about her. It isn't natural."

"Oh, let Charlie alone," said Father. "The boy's all right. He's just got a one-track mind."

But it wasn't so nice for us after the spring came.

In our part of the state, it comes pretty late, as a rule. But it was early this year. The little kids were out with scooters when usually they'd still be having snowfights and, all of a sudden, the radiators in the classrooms smelt dry. You'd got used to that smell for months—and then, there was a day when you hated it again and everybody kept asking to open the windows. The monitors had a tough time, that first week—they always do when spring starts—but this year it was worse than ever because it came when you didn't expect it.

Usually, basketball's over by the time spring really breaks, but this year it hit us while we still had three games to play. And it certainly played hell with us as a team. After Bladesburg nearly licked us, Mr. Grant called off all practice till the day before the St. Matthew's game. He knew we were stale—and they've been state champions two years. They'd have walked all over us, the way we were going.

The first thing I did was telephone Helen. Because that meant there were six extra afternoons we could have, if she could get rid of her music lessons any way. Well, she said, wasn't it wonderful, her music teacher had a cold? And that seemed just like Fate.

Well, that was a great week and we were so happy. We went

Too Early Spring

to the movies five times and once Mrs. Sharon let us take her little car. She knew I didn't have a driving license but of course I've driven ever since I was thirteen and she said it was all right. She was funny—sometimes she'd be awfully kind and friendly to you and sometimes she'd be like a piece of dry ice. She was that way with Mr. Sharon too. But it was a wonderful ride. We got stuff out of the kitchen—the cook's awfully sold on Helen—and drove way out in the country. And we found an old house, with the windows gone, on top of a hill, and parked the car and took the stuff up to the house and ate it there. There weren't any chairs or tables but we pretended there were.

We pretended it was our house, after we were married. I'll never forget that. She'd even brought paper napkins and paper plates and she set two places on the floor.

"Well, Charles," she said, sitting opposite me, with her feet tucked under, "I don't suppose you remember the days we were both in school."

"Sure," I said—she was always much quicker pretending things than I was—"I remember them all right. That was before Tot Pickens got to be President." And we both laughed.

"It seems very distant in the past to me—we've been married so long," she said, as if she really believed it. She looked at me.

"Would you mind turning off the radio, dear?" she said. "This modern music always gets on my nerves."

"Have we got a radio?" I said.

"Of course, Chuck."

"With television?"

"Of course, Chuck."

"Gee, I'm glad," I said. I went and turned it off.

"Of course, if you *want* to listen to the late market reports—" she said just like Mrs. Sharon.

"Nope," I said. "The market—uh—closed firm today. Up twenty-six points."

"That's quite a long way up, isn't it?"

"Well, the country's perfectly sound at heart, in spite of this damnfool Congress," I said, like Father.

She lowered her eyes a minute, just like her mother, and pushed away her plate.

"I'm not very hungry tonight," she said. "You won't mind if I go upstairs?"

"Aw, don't be like that," I said. It was too much like her mother.

"I was just seeing if I could," she said. "But I never will, Chuck."

"I'll never tell you you're nervous, either," I said. "I—oh, gosh!" She grinned and it was all right. "Mr. Ashland and I have never had a serious dispute in our wedded lives," she said—and everybody knows who runs *that* family. "We just talk things over calmly and reach a satisfactory conclusion, usually mine."

"Say, what kind of house have we got?"

"It's a lovely house," she said. "We've got radios in every room and lots of servants. We've got a regular movie projector and a library full of good classics and there's always something in the icebox. I've got a shoe closet."

"A what?"

"A shoe closet. All my shoes are on tipped shelves, like Mother's. And all my dresses are on those padded hangers. And I say to the maid, 'Elsie, Madam will wear the new French model today.'"

"What are my clothes on?" I said. "Christmas trees?"

"Well," she said. "You've got lots of clothes and dogs. You smell of pipes and the open and something called Harrisburg tweed."

"I do not," I said. "I wish I had a dog. It's a long time since Jack."

"Oh, Chuck, I'm sorry," she said.

"Oh, that's all right," I said. "He was getting old and his ear was always bothering him. But he was a good pooch. Go ahead."

"Well," she said, "of course we give parties—"

"Cut the parties," I said.

"Chuck! They're grand ones!"

"I'm a homebody," I said. "Give me—er—my wife and my little family and—say, how many kids have we got, anyway?"

She counted on her fingers. "Seven."

"Good Lord," I said.

"Well, I always wanted seven. You can make it three, if you like."

"Oh, seven's all right, I suppose," I said. "But don't they get awfully in the way?"

"No," she said. "We have governesses and tutors and send them to boarding school."

"O. K.," I said. "But it's a strain on the old man's pocketbook, just the same."

"Chuck, will you ever talk like that? Chuck, this is when we're rich." Then suddenly, she looked sad. "Oh, Chuck, do you suppose we ever will?" she said.

"Why, sure," I said.

"I wouldn't mind if it was only a dump," she said. "I could cook for you. I keep asking Hilda how she makes things."

I felt awfully funny. I felt as if I were going to cry.

"We'll do it," I said. "Don't you worry."

"Oh, Chuck, you're a comfort," she said.

I held her for a while. It was like holding something awfully precious. It wasn't mushy or that way. I know what that's like too.

"It takes so long to get old," she said. "I wish I could grow up tomorrow. I wish we both could."

"Don't you worry," I said. "It's going to be all right."

We didn't say much, going back in the car, but we were happy enough. I thought we passed Miss Eagles at the turn. That worried me a little because of the driving license. But, after all, Mrs. Sharon had said we could take the car.

We wanted to go back again, after that, but it was too far to walk and that was the only time we had the car. Mrs. Sharon was awfully nice about it but she said, thinking it over, maybe we'd better wait till I got a license. Well, Father didn't want me to get one till I was seventeen but I thought he might come around. I didn't want to do anything that would get Helen in a jam with her family. That shows how careful I was of her. Or thought I was.

All the same, we decided we'd do something to celebrate if the team won the St. Matthew's game. We thought it would be fun if we could get a steak and cook supper out somewhere—something like that. Of course we could have done it easily enough with a gang, but we didn't want a gang. We wanted to be alone together, the way we'd been at the house. That was all we wanted. I don't see what's wrong about that. We even took home the paper plates, so as not to litter things up.

Boy, that was a game! We beat them 36-34 and it took an extra period and I thought it would never end. That two-goal lead they had looked as big as the Rocky Mountains all the first half. And they gave me the full school cheer with nine Peters when we tied them up. You don't forget things like that.

Afterwards, Mr. Grant had a kind of spread for the team at his house and a lot of people came in. Kerry had driven down from State to see the game and that made me feel pretty swell. And what made me feel better yet was his taking me aside and saying, "Listen, kid, I don't want you to get the swelled head, but you did a good job. Well, just remember this. Don't let anybody kid you out of going to State. You'll like it up there." And Mr. Grant heard him and laughed and said, "Well, Peters, I'm not proselytizing. But your brother might think about some of the Eastern colleges." It was all like the kind of dream you have when you can do anything. It was wonderful.

Only Helen wasn't there because the only girls were older girls. I'd seen her for a minute, right after the game, and she was fine, but it was only a minute. I wanted to tell her about that big St. Matthew's forward and—oh, everything. Well, you like to talk things over with your girl.

Father and Mother were swell but they had to go on to some big shindy at the country club. And Kerry was going there with Sheila Coe. But Mr. Grant said he'd run me back to the house in his car and he did. He's a great guy. He made jokes about my being the infant phenomenon of basketball, and they were good jokes too. I didn't mind them. But, all the same, when I'd said good night to him and gone into the house, I felt sort of let down.

I knew I'd be tired the next day but I didn't feel sleepy yet. I was too excited. I wanted to talk to somebody. I wandered around downstairs and wondered if Ida was still up. Well, she wasn't, but she'd left half a chocolate cake, covered over, on the kitchen table, and a note on top of it, "Congratulations to Mister Charles Peters." Well, that was awfully nice of her and I ate some. Then I turned the radio on and got the time signal—eleven—and some snappy music. But still I didn't feel like hitting the hay.

So I thought I'd call up Helen and then I thought—probably she's asleep and Hilda or Mrs. Sharon will answer the phone and be sore. And then I thought—well, anyhow, I could go over and

Too Early Spring

walk around the block and look at her house. I'd get some fresh air out of it, anyway, and it would be a little like seeing her.

So I did—and it was a swell night—cool and a lot of stars—and I felt like a king, walking over. All the lower part of the Sharon house was dark but a window upstairs was lit. I knew it was her window. I went around back of the driveway and whistled once—the whistle we made up. I never expected her to hear.

But she did, and there she was at the window, smiling. She made motions that she'd come down to the side door.

Honestly, it took my breath away when I saw her. She had on a kind of yellow thing over her night clothes and she looked so pretty. Her feet were so pretty in those slippers. You almost expected her to be carrying one of those animals that kids like—she looked young enough. I know I oughtn't to have gone into the house. But we didn't think anything about it—we were just glad to see each other. We hadn't had any sort of chance to talk over the game.

We sat in front of the fire in the living room and she went out to the kitchen and got us cookies and milk. I wasn't really hungry, but it was like that time at the house, eating with her. Mr. and Mrs. Sharon were at the country club, too, so we weren't disturbing them or anything. We turned off the lights because there was plenty of light from the fire and Mr. Sharon's one of those people who can't stand having extra lights burning. Dad's that way about saving string.

It was quiet and lovely and the firelight made shadows on the ceiling. We talked a lot and then we just sat, each of us knowing the other was there. And the room got quieter and quieter and I'd told her about the game and I didn't feel excited or jumpy any more—just rested and happy. And then I knew by her breathing that she was asleep and I put my arm around her for just a minute. Because it was wonderful to hear that quiet breathing and know it was hers. I was going to wake her in a minute. I didn't realize how tired I was myself.

And then we were back in that house in the country and it was our home and we ought to have been happy. But something was wrong because there still wasn't any glass in the windows and a wind kept blowing through them and we tried to shut the doors but they wouldn't shut. It drove Helen distracted and we were both running through the house, trying to shut the doors, and we were cold and afraid. Then the sun rose outside the windows, burning and yellow and so big it covered the sky. And with the sun was a horrible, weeping voice. It was Mrs. Sharon's saying, "Oh, my God, oh my God."

I didn't know what had happened, for a minute, when I woke. And then I did and it was awful. Mrs. Sharon was saying "Oh, Helen—I trusted you . . ." and looking as if she were going to faint. And Mr. Sharon looked at her for a minute and his face was horrible and he said, "Bred in the bone," and she looked as if he'd hit her. Then he said to Helen—

I don't want to think of what they said. I don't want to think of any of the things they said. Mr. Sharon is a bad man. And she is a bad woman, even if she is Helen's mother. All the same, I could stand the things he said better than hers.

I don't want to think of any of it. And it is all spoiled now. Everything is spoiled. Miss Eagles saw us going to that house in the country and she said horrible things. They made Helen sick and she hasn't been back at school. There isn't any way I can see her. And if I could, it would be spoiled. We'd be thinking about the things they said.

I don't know how many of the people know, at school. But Tot Pickens passed me a note. And, that afternoon, I caught him behind his house. I'd have broken his nose if they hadn't pulled me off. I meant to. Mother cried when she heard about it and Dad took me into his room and talked to me. He said you can't lick the whole town. But I will anybody like Tot Pickens. Dad and Mother have been all right. But they say things about Helen and that's almost worse. They're for me because I'm their son. But they don't understand.

I thought I could talk to Kerry but I can't. He was nice but he looked at me such a funny way. I don't know—sort of impressed. It wasn't the way I wanted him to look. But he's been decent. He comes down almost every weekend and we play catch in the yard.

You see, I just go to school and back now. They want me to go with the gang, the way I did, but I can't do that. Not after Tot. Of course my marks are a lot better because I've got more time to study now. But it's lucky I haven't got Miss Eagles though Dad made her apologize. I couldn't recite to her.

I think Mr. Grant knows because he asked me to his house

Too Early Spring

once and we had a conversation. Not about that, though I was terribly afraid he would. He showed me a lot of his old college things and the gold football he wears on his watch chain. He's got a lot of interesting things.

Then we got talking, somehow, about history and things like that and how times had changed. Why, there were kings and queens who got married younger than Helen and me. Only now we lived longer and had a lot more to learn. So it couldn't happen now. "It's civilization," he said. "And all civilization's against nature. But I suppose we've got to have it. Only sometimes it isn't easy." Well somehow or other, that made me feel less lonely. Before that I'd been feeling that I was the only person on earth who'd ever felt that way.

I'm going to Colorado, this summer, to a ranch, and next year, I'll go East to school. Mr. Grant says he thinks I can make the basketball team, if I work hard enough, though it isn't as big a game in the East as it is with us. Well, I'd like to show them something. It would be some satisfaction. He says not to be too fresh at first, but I won't be that.

It's a boys' school and there aren't even women teachers. And, maybe, afterwards, I could be a professional basketball player or something, where you don't have to see women at all. Kerry says I'll get over that; but I won't. They all sound like Mrs. Sharon to me now, when they laugh.

They're going to send Helen to a convent—I found out that. Maybe they'll let me see her before she goes. But, if we do, it will be all wrong and in front of people and everybody pretending. I sort of wish they don't—though I want to, terribly. When her mother took her upstairs that night—she wasn't the same Helen. She looked at me as if she was afraid of me. And no matter what they do for us now, they can't fix that.

THE STORY ABOUT THE ANTEATER

The younger child sat bolt upright, her bedclothes wrapped around her.

"If you're going down to look at them," she whispered accusingly, "I'm coming, too! And Alice'll catch you."

273

"She won't catch me." Her elder sister's voice was scornful. "She's out in the pantry, helping. With the man from Gray's."

"All the same, I'm coming. I want to see if it's ice cream in little molds or just the smashed kind with strawberries. And, if Alice won't catch you, she won't catch me."

"It'll be molds," said the other, from the depths of experience, "Mother always has molds for the Whitehouses. And Mr. Whitehouse sort of clicks in his throat and talks about sweets to the sweet. You'd think he'd know that's dopey but he doesn't. And, anyhow, it isn't your turn."

"It never is my turn," mourned her junior, tugging at the bedclothes.

"All right," said the elder. "If you *want* to go! And make a noise. And then they hear us and somebody comes up—"

"Sometimes they bring you things, when they come up," said the younger dreamily. "The man with the pink face did. And he said I was a little angel."

"Was he dopey!" said her elder, blightingly, "and anyhow, you were sick afterwards and you know what Mother said about it."

The younger child sighed, a long sigh of defeat and resignation.

"All right," she said. "But next time it *is* my turn. And you tell me if it's in molds." Her elder nodded as she stole out of the door.

At the first turn of the stairs, a small landing offered an excellent observation post, provided one could get there unperceived. Jennifer Sharp reached it soundlessly and, curling herself up into the smallest possible space, stared eagerly down and across into the dining room.

She couldn't see the whole table. But she saw at once that Mrs. Whitehouse had a thing like a silver beetle in her hair, that Colonel Crandall looked more like a police dog than ever, and that there were little silver baskets of pink and white mints. That meant that it was really a grand dinner. She made a special note of the ice cream for Joan.

Talk and laughter drifted up to her—strange phrases and incomprehensible jests from another world, to be remembered, puzzled over, and analyzed for meaning or the lack of it, when she and Joan were alone. She hugged her knees, she was having

The Story About the Anteater

a good time. Pretty soon, Father would light the little blue flame under the mysterious glass machine that made the coffee. She liked to see him do that.

She looked at him now, appraisingly. Colonel Crandall had fought Germans in trenches and Mr. Whitehouse had a bank to keep his money in. But Father, on the whole, was nicer than either of them. She remembered, as if looking back across a vast plain, when Father and Mother had merely been Father and Mother—huge, natural phenomena, beloved but inexplicable as the weather—unique of their kind. Now she was older—she knew that other people's fathers and mothers were different. Even Joan knew that, though Joan was still a great deal of a baby. Jennifer felt very old and rather benevolent as she considered herself and her parents and the babyishness of Joan.

Mr. Whitehouse was talking, but Father wanted to talk, too —she knew that from the quick little gesture he made with his left hand. Now they all laughed and Father leaned forward. "That reminds me," he was saying, "of one of our favorite stories—" How young and amused his face looked, suddenly!

His eldest daughter settled back in the shadow, a bored but tolerant smile on her lips. She knew what was coming.

When Terry Farrell and Roger Sharp fell in love, the war to end war was just over, bobbed hair was still an issue, the movies did not talk and women's clothes couldn't be crazier. It was also generally admitted that the younger generation was wild but probably sound at heart and that, as soon as we got a businessman in the White House, things were going to be all right.

As for Terry and Roger, they were both wild and sophisticated. They would have told you so. Terry had been kissed by several men at several dances and Roger could remember the curious, grimy incident of the girl at Fort Worth. So that showed you. They were entirely emancipated and free. But they fell in love very simply and unexpectedly—and their marriage was going to be like no other marriage, because they knew all the right answers to all the questions, and had no intention of submitting to the commonplaces of life. At first, in fact, they were going to form a free union—they had read of that, in popular books of the period. But, somehow or other, as soon as Roger started to call, both families began to get interested. They had no idea of paying the slightest attention to their families. But, when your family happens to comment favorably on the man or girl that you are in love with, that is a hard thing to fight. Before they knew it, they were formally engaged, and liking it on the whole, though both of them agreed that a formal engagement was an outworn and ridiculous social custom.

They quarreled often enough, for they were young, and a trifle ferocious in the vehemence with which they expressed the views they knew to be right. These views had to do, in general, with freedom and personality, and were often supported by quotations from *The Golden Bough*. Neither of them had read *The Golden Bough* all the way through, but both agreed that it was a great book. But the quarrels were about generalities and had no sting. And always, before and after, was the sense of discovering in each other previously unsuspected but delightful potentialities and likenesses and beliefs.

As a matter of fact, they were quite a well-suited couple—"made for each other," as the saying used to go; though they would have hooted at the idea. They had read the minor works of Havelock Ellis and knew the name of Freud. They didn't believe in people being "made for each other"—they were too advanced.

It was ten days before the date set for their marriage that their first real quarrel occurred. And then, unfortunately, it didn't stop at generalities.

They had got away for the day from the presents and their families, to take a long walk in the country, with a picnic lunch. Both, in spite of themselves, were a little solemn, a little nervous. The atmosphere of Approaching Wedding weighed on them both—when their hands touched, the current ran, but, when they looked at each other, they felt strange. Terry had been shopping the day before—she was tired, she began to wish that Roger would not walk so fast. Roger was wondering if the sixth usher—the one who had been in the marines—would really turn up. His mind also held dark suspicions as to the probable behavior of the best man, when it came to such outworn customs as rice and shoes. They were sure that they were in love, sure now, that they wanted to be married. But their conversation was curiously polite.

The lunch did something for them, so did the peace of being

The Story About the Anteater

alone. But they had forgotten the salt and Terry had rubbed her heel. When Roger got out his pipe, there was only tobacco left for half a smoke. Still, the wind was cool and the earth pleasant and, as they sat with their backs against a gray boulder in the middle of a green field, they began to think more naturally. The current between their linked hands ran stronger—in a moment or two, they would be the selves they had always known.

It was, perhaps, unfortunate that Roger should have selected that particular moment in which to tell the anteater story.

He knocked out his pipe and smiled, suddenly, at something in his mind. Terry felt a knock at her heart, a sudden sweetness on her tongue—how young and amused he always looked when he smiled! She smiled back at him, her whole face changing.

"What is it, darling?" she said.

He laughed. "Oh nothing," he said. "I just happened to remember. Did you ever hear the story about the anteater?"

She shook her head.

"Well," he began. "Oh, you must have heard it—sure you haven't? Well, anyway, there was a little town down South . . .

"And the coon said, 'Why, lady, that ain't no anteater—that's Edward!'" he finished, triumphantly, a few moments later. He couldn't help laughing when he had finished—the silly tale always amused him, old as it was. Then he looked at Terry and saw that she was not laughing.

"Why, what's the matter?" he said, mechanically. "Are you cold, dear, or—"

Her hand, which had been slowly stiffening in his clasp, now withdrew itself entirely from his.

"No," she said, staring ahead of her, "I'm all right. Thanks."

He looked at her. There was somebody there he had never seen before.

"Well," he said, confusedly, "well." Then his mouth set, his jaw stuck out, he also regarded the landscape.

Terry stole a glance at him. It was terrible and appalling to see him sitting there, looking bleak and estranged. She wanted to speak, to throw herself at him, to say: "Oh, it's all my fault—it's all my fault!" and know the luxury of saying it. Then she remembered the anteater and her heart hardened.

It was not even, she told herself sternly, as if it were a dirty story. It wasn't—and, if it had been, weren't they always going

277

to be frank and emancipated with each other about things like that? But it was just the kind of story she'd always hated—cruel and—yes—vulgar. Not even healthily vulgar—vulgar with no redeeming adjective. He ought to have known she hated that kind of story. He ought to have known!

If love meant anything, according to the books, it meant understanding the other person, didn't it? And, if you didn't understand them, in such a little thing, why, what was life going to be afterwards? Love was like a new silver dollar—bright, untarnished and whole. There could be no possible compromises with love.

All these confused but vehement thoughts flashed through her mind. She also knew that she was tired and wind-blown and jumpy and that the rub on her heel was a little red spot of pain. And then Roger was speaking.

"So sorry you found my story so unamusing," he said in stiff tones of injury and accusation. "If I'd known about the way you felt, I'd have tried to tell a funnier one—even if we did say—"

He stopped, his frozen face turned toward her. She could feel the muscles of her own face tighten and freeze in answer.

"I wasn't in the *least* shocked, I assure you," she said in the same, stilted voice. "I just didn't think it was very funny. That's all."

"I get you. Well, pardon my glove," he said, and turned to the landscape.

A little pulse of anger began to beat in her wrist. Something was being hurt, something was being broken. If he'd only been Roger and kissed her instead of saying—well, it was his fault, now.

"No, I didn't think it was funny at all," she said, in a voice whose sharpness surprised her, "if you want to know. Just sort of cruel and common and—well, the poor Negro—"

"That's right!" he said, in a voice of bitter irritation, "pity the coon! Pity everybody but the person who's trying to amuse you! I think it's a damn funny story—always have—and—"

They were both on their feet and stabbing at each other, now.

"And it's vulgar," she was saying, hotly, "plain vulgar—not even dirty enough to be funny. Anteater indeed! Why, Roger Sharp, it's—"

"Where's that sense of humor you were always talking about?"

he was shouting. "My God, what's happened to you, Terry? I always thought you were—and here you—"

"Well, we both of us certainly seem to have been mistaken about each other," she could hear her strange voice, saying. Then, even more dreadfully, came his unfamiliar accents, "Well, if that's the way you feel about it, we certainly have."

They looked at each other, aghast. "Here!" she was saying, "here! Oh, Lord, why won't it come off my finger?"

"You keep that on—do you hear, you damn little fool?" he roared at her, so unexpectedly that she started, tripped, caught her shoe in a cleft of rock, fell awkwardly, and, in spite of all her resolves, burst undignifiedly and conventionally into a passion of tears.

Then there was the reconciliation. It took place, no doubt, on entirely conventional lines, and was studded with "No, it was my fault! Say it was!" but, to them it was an event unique in history.

Terry thought it over remorsefully, that evening, waiting for Roger. Roger was right. She had been a little fool. She knew the inexplicable solace of feeling that she had been a little fool.

And yet, they had said those things to each other, and meant them. He had hurt her, she had actually meant to hurt him. She stared at these facts, solemnly. Love, the bright silver dollar. Not like the commonplace coins in other people's pockets. But something special, different—already a little, ever-so-faintly tarnished, as a pane is tarnished by breath?

She had been a little fool. But she couldn't quite forget the anteater.

Then she was in Roger's arms—and knew, with utter confidence, that she and Roger were different. They were always going to be different. Their marriage wouldn't ever be like any other marriage in the world.

The Sharps had been married for exactly six years and five hours and Terry, looking across the table at the clever, intelligent face of her affectionate and satisfactory husband, suddenly found herself most desolately alone.

It had been a mistake in the first place—going to the Lattimores for dinner on their own anniversary. Mr. Lattimore was the head of Roger's company—Mrs. Lattimore's invitation had almost the force of a royal command. They had talked it over, Roger and she, and decided, sensibly, that they couldn't get out of it. But, all the same, it had been a mistake.

They were rational, modern human beings, she assured herself ferociously. They weren't like the horrible married couples in the cartoons—the little woman asking her baffled mate if he remembered what date it was, and the rest of it. They thought better of life and love than to tie either of them to an artificial scheme of days. They were different. Nevertheless, there had been a time when they had said to each other, with foolish smiles, "We've been married a week—or a month—or a year! Just think of it!" This time now seemed to her, as she looked back on it coldly, a geologic age away.

She considered Roger with odd dispassionateness. Yes, there he was—an intelligent, rising young man in his first thirties. Not particularly handsome but indubitably attractive—charming, when he chose—a loyal friend, a good father, a husband one could take pride in. And it seemed to her that if he made that nervous little gesture with his left hand again—or told the anteater story—she would scream.

It was funny that the knowledge that you had lost everything that you had most counted upon should come to you at a formal dinner party, while you talked over the war days with a dark-haired officer whose voice had the honey of the South in it. Then she remembered that she and Roger had first discovered their love for each other, not upon a moon-swept lawn, but in the fly-specked waiting room of a minor railroad station—and the present event began to seem less funny. Life was like that. It gave, unexpectedly, abruptly, with no regard for stage setting or the properties of romance. And, as unexpectedly and abruptly, it took away.

While her mouth went on talking, a part of her mind searched numbly and painfully for the reasons which had brought this calamity about. They had loved each other in the beginning—even now, she was sure of that. They had tried to be wise, they had not broken faith, they had been frank and gay. No deep division of nature sundered them—no innate fault in either, spreading under pressure, to break the walls of their house apart. She looked for a guilty party but she could find none. There was only a progression of days; a succession of tiny events that followed in each other's footsteps without haste or rest. That was all, but that seemed to have been enough. And Roger was looking over at her—with that same odd, exploring glance she had used a moment ago.

What remained? A house with a little boy asleep in it, a custom of life, certain habits, certain memories, certain hardships lived through together. Enough for most people, perhaps? They had wanted more than that.

Something said to her, "Well and if—after all—the real thing hasn't even come?" She turned to her dinner partner, for the first time really seeing him. When you did see him, he was quite a charming person. His voice was delightful. There was nothing in him in the least like Roger Sharp.

She laughed and saw, at the laugh, something wake in his eyes. He, too, had not been really conscious of her, before. But he was, now. She was not thirty, yet—she had kept her looks. She felt old powers, old states of mind flow back to her; things she had thought forgotten, the glamor of first youth. Somewhere, on the curve of a dark lake, a boat was drifting—a man was talking to her—she could not see his face but she knew it was not Roger's—

She was roused from her waking dream by Mrs. Lattimore's voice.

"Why, I'd never have dreamt!" Mrs. Lattimore was saying, "I had no idea!" She called down the table, "George! Do you know it's these people's anniversary—so sweet of them to come—and I positively had to worm it out of Mr. Sharp!"

Terry went hot and cold all over. She was sensible, she was brokenhearted, love was a myth, but she had particularly depended on Roger not to tell anybody that this was their anniversary. And Roger had told.

She lived through the congratulations and the customary jokes about "Well, this is your seventh year beginning—and you know what they say about the seventh year!" She even lived through Mrs. Lattimore's pensive "Six years! Why, my dear, I never would have believed it! You're children—positive children!"

She could have bitten Mrs. Lattimore. "Children!" she thought, indignantly, "When I—when we—when everything's in ruins!" She tried to freeze Roger, at long distance, but he was not looking her way. And then she caught her breath, for a worse fate was in store for her.

Stephen Vincent Benét

Someone, most unhappily, had brought up the subject of pet animals. She saw a light break slowly on Roger's face—she saw him lean forward. She prayed for the roof to fall, for time to stop, for Mrs. Lattimore to explode like a Roman candle into green and purple stars. But, even as she prayed, she knew that it was no use. Roger was going to tell the anteater story.

The story no longer seemed shocking to her, or even cruel. But it epitomized all the years of her life with Roger. In the course of those years, she calculated desperately, she had heard that story at least a hundred times.

Somehow—she never knew how—she managed to survive the hundred-and-first recital, from the hideously familiar, "Well, there was a little town down South . . .," to the jubilant "That's Edward!" at the end. She even summoned up a fixed smile to meet the tempest of laughter that followed. And then, mercifully, Mrs. Lattimore was giving the signal to rise.

The men hung behind—the anteater story had been capped by another. Terry found herself, unexpectedly, tête-à-tête with Mrs. Lattimore.

"My dear," the great lady was saying, "I'd rather have asked you another night, of course, if I'd known. But I am very glad you could come tonight. George particularly wished Mr. Colden to meet your brilliant husband. They are going into that Western project together, you know, and Tom Colden leaves tomorrow. So we both appreciate your kindness in coming."

Terry found a sudden queer pulse of warmth through the cold fog that seemed to envelop her. "Oh," she stammered, "but Roger and I have been married for years—and we were delighted to come—" She looked at the older woman. "Tell me, though," she said, with an irrepressible burst of confidence, "doesn't it ever seem to you as if you couldn't bear to hear a certain story again —not if you *died?*"

A gleam of mirth appeared in Mrs. Lattimore's eyes.

"My dear," she said, "has George ever told you about his trip to Peru?"

"No."

"Well, don't let him." She reflected. "Or, no—do let him," she said. "Poor George—he does get such fun out of it. And you would be a new audience. But it happened fifteen years ago, my dear, and I think I could repeat every word after him verbatim,

282

once he's started. Even so—I often feel as if he'd never stop."

"And then what do you do?" said Terry, breathlessly—far too interested now to remember tact.

The older woman smiled. "I think of the story I am going to tell about the guide in the Uffizi gallery," she said. "George must have heard that story ten thousand times. But he's still alive."

She put her hand on the younger woman's arm.

"We're all of us alike, my dear," she said. "When I'm an old lady in a wheel chair, George will still be telling me about Peru. But then, if he didn't, I wouldn't know he was George."

She turned away, leaving Terry to ponder over the words. Her anger was not appeased—her life still lay about her in ruins. But, when the dark young officer came into the room, she noticed that his face seemed rather commonplace and his voice was merely a pleasant voice.

Mr. Colden's car dropped the Sharps at their house. The two men stayed at the gate for a moment, talking—Terry ran in to see after the boy. He was sleeping peacefully with his fists tight shut; he looked like Roger in his sleep. Suddenly, all around her were the familiar sights and sounds of home. She felt tired and as if she had come back from a long journey.

She went downstairs. Roger was just coming in. He looked tired, too, she noticed, but exultant as well.

"Colden had to run," he said at once. "Left good-by for you—hoped you wouldn't mind—said awfully nice things. He's really a great old boy, Terry. And, as for this new Western business—"

He noticed the grave look on her face and his own grew grave.

"I *am* sorry, darling," he said. "Did you mind it a lot? Well, I did—but it couldn't be helped. You bet your life that next time—"

"Oh, next time—" she said, and kissed him. "Of course I didn't mind. We're different, aren't we?"

That intelligent matron, Mrs. Roger Sharp, now seated at the foot of her own dinner table, from time to time made the appropriate interjections—the "Really?"s and "Yes indeed"s and "That's what I always tell Roger"s—which comprised the whole duty of a hostess in Colonel Crandall's case. Colonel Crandall was singularly restful—give him these few crumbs and he could be depended upon to talk indefinitely and yet without creating a conversational desert around him. Mrs. Sharp was very grateful to him at the moment. She wanted to retire to a secret place in her mind and observe her own dinner party, for an instant, as a spectator—and Colonel Crandall was giving her the chance.

It was going very well indeed. She had hoped for it from the first, but now she was sure of it and she gave a tiny, inaudible sigh of relief. Roger was at his best—the young Durwards had recovered from their initial shyness—Mr. Whitehouse had not yet started talking politics—the soufflé had been a success. She relaxed a little and let her mind drift off upon other things.

Tomorrow, Roger must remember about the light gray suit, she must make a dental appointment for Jennifer, Mrs. Quaritch must be dealt with tactfully in the matter of the committee. It was too early to decide about camp for the girls but Roger Junior must know they were proud of his marks, and if Mother intended to give up her trip just because of poor old Miss Tompkins—well, something would have to be done. There were also the questions of the new oil furnace, the School board and the Brewster wedding. But none of these really bothered her—her life was always busy—and, at the moment, she felt an unwonted desire to look back into Time.

Over twenty years since the Armistice. Twenty years. And Roger Junior was seventeen—and she and Roger had been married since nineteen-twenty. Pretty soon they would be celebrating their twentieth anniversary. It seemed incredible but it was true.

She looked back through those years, seeing an ever-younger creature with her own face, a creature that laughed or wept for forgotten reasons, ran wildly here, sat solemn as a young judge there. She felt a pang of sympathy for that young heedlessness, a pang of humor as well. She was not old but she had been so very young.

Roger and she—the beginning—the first years—Roger Junior's birth. The house on Edgehill Road, the one with the plate rail in the dining room, and crying when they left because they'd never be so happy again, but they had, and it was an inconvenient house. Being jealous of Milly Baldwin—and how foolish!—and the awful country-club dance where Roger got drunk; and it wasn't awful any more. The queer, piled years of the boom—the crash—the bad time—Roger coming home after Tom Colden's suicide and the look on his face. Jennifer. Joan. Houses. People.

The Story About the Anteater

Events. And always the headlines in the papers, the voices on the radio, dinning, dinning "No security—trouble—disaster—no security." And yet, out of insecurity, they had loved and made children. Out of insecurity, for the space of breath, for an hour, they had built, and now and then found peace.

No, there's no guarantee, she thought. There's no guarantee. When you're young, you think there is, but there isn't. And yet I'd do it over. Pretty soon we'll have been married twenty years.

"Yes, that's what I always tell Roger," she said, automatically. Colonel Crandall smiled and proceeded. He was still quite handsome, she thought, in his dark way, but he was getting very bald. Roger's hair had a few gray threads in it but it was still thick and unruly. She liked men to keep their hair. She remembered, a long while ago, thinking something or other about Colonel Crandall's voice, but she could not remember what she had thought.

She noticed a small white speck on the curve of the stairway but said nothing. The wrapper was warm and, if Jennifer wasn't noticed, she would creep back to bed soon enough. It was different with Joan.

Suddenly, she was alert. Mrs. Durward, at Roger's end of the table, had mentioned the Zoo. She knew what that meant—Zoo—the new buildings—the new Housing Commissioner—and Mr. Whitehouse let loose on his favorite political grievance all through the end of dinner. She caught Roger's eye for a miraculous instant. Mr. Whitehouse was already clearing his throat. But Roger had the signal. Roger would save them. She saw his left hand tapping in its little gesture—felt him suddenly draw the party together. How young and amused his face looked, under the candlelight!

"That reminds me of one of our favorite stories," he was saying. She sank back in her chair. A deep content pervaded her. He was going to tell the anteater story—and, even if some of the people had heard it, they would have to laugh, he always told it so well. She smiled in anticipation of the triumphant "That's Edward!" And, after that, if Mr. Whitehouse still threatened, she herself would tell the story about Joan and the watering pot.

Jennifer crept back into the darkened room.
"Well?" said an eager whisper from the other bed.

285

Jennifer drew a long breath. The memory of the lighted dinner table rose before her, varicolored, glittering, portentous—a stately omen—a thing of splendor and mystery, to be pondered upon for days. How could she ever make Joan see it as she had seen it? And Joan was such a baby, anyway.

"Oh—nobody saw me," she said, in a bored voice. "But it was in molds, that's all—oh yes—and Father told the anteater story again."

SCHOONER FAIRCHILD'S CLASS

When he said good night to his son and Tom Drury and the rest of them, Lane Parrington walked down the steps of the Leaf Club and stood, for a moment, breathing in the night air. He had made the speech they'd asked him to make, and taken pains with it, too—but now he was wondering whether it wasn't the same old graduate's speech after all. He hadn't meant it to be so, but you ran into a lingo, once you started putting thoughts on paper—you began to view with alarm and talk about imperiled bulwarks and the American way of life.

And yet he'd been genuinely pleased when the invitation came —and they'd asked him three months ahead. That meant something, even to the Lane Parrington of United Investments—it was curious how old bonds held. He had been decorated by two foreign governments and had declined a ministry—there was the place in Virginia, the place on Long Island, the farm in Vermont and the big apartment on the river. There were the statements issued when sailing for Europe and the photographs and articles in news-weeklies and magazines. And yet he had been pleased when they asked him to speak at the annual dinner of an undergraduate club in his own college. Of course, the Leaf was a little different, as all Leaf members knew. When he had been a new member, as his son was now, the speech had been made by a Secretary of State.

Well, he'd done well enough, he supposed—at least Ted had come up, afterward, a little shyly, and said, "Well, Dad, you're quite an orator." But, once or twice, in the course of the speech, he had caught Ted fiddling with his coffee spoon. They were almost always too long—those speeches by graduates—he had tried to remember that. But he couldn't help running a little overtime —not after he'd got up and seen them waiting there. They were only boys, of course, but boys who would soon be men with men's responsibilities—he had even made a point of that.

One of the things about the Leaf—you got a chance of hearing what—well, what really important men thought of the state of the world and the state of the nation. They could get a lot from professors but hardly that. So, when a sensible fellow got up to explain what sensible men really thought about this business at Washington—why, damn it, nobody was going to ring a gong on him! And they'd clapped him well, at the end, and Ted's face had looked relieved. They always clapped well, at the end.

Afterward, he had rather hoped to meet Ted's friends and get in a little closer touch with them than he did at the place in Virginia or the place on Long Island or the apartment in New York. He saw them there, of course—they got in cars and out of cars, they dressed and went to dances, they played on the tennis courts and swam in the pool. They were a good crowd—a typical Leaf crowd, well-exercised and well-mannered. They were polite to Cora and polite to him. He offered them cigars now and then; during the last two years he offered them whisky and soda. They listened to what he had to say and, if he told a good story, they usually laughed at it. They played tennis with him, occasionally, and said, "Good shot, sir!"—afterward, they played harder tennis. One of them was Ted, his son, well-mannered, well-exercised, a member of the Leaf. He could talk to Ted about college athletics, the college curriculum, his allowance, the weather, the virtues of capitalism and whether to get a new beach wagon this summer. Now, to these subjects was added the Leaf and the virtues of the Leaf. He could talk to Ted about any number of things.

Nevertheless, sometimes when the annual dinner was over, there would be a little group at the Leaf around this graduate or that. He remembered one such group his senior year, around a sharp-tongued old man with hooded eyes. The ex-senator was old and broken, but they'd stayed up till two while his caustic voice made hay of accepted catchwords. Well, he had met Ted's friends and remembered most of their names. They had congratulated him on his speech and he had drunk a highball with them. It had all been in accord with the best traditions of the Leaf but it hadn't lasted very long.

For a moment, indeed, he had almost gotten into an argument with one of them—the pink-faced, incredibly youthful one with the glasses who was head of the Student Union—they hadn't had student unions in his time. He had been answering a couple of questions quite informally, using slang, and the pink-faced youth had broken in with, "But, look here, sir—I mean, that was a good speech you made from the conservative point of view and all that—but when you talk about labor's being made responsible, just what do you mean and how far do you go? Do you mean you want to scrap the Wagner Act or amend it or what?"

But then the rest of them had said, "Oh, don't mind Stu—he's our communist. Skip it, Stu—how's dialectic materialism today?" and it had passed off in kidding. Lane Parrington felt a little sorry about that—he would have enjoyed a good argument with an intelligent youngster—he was certainly broad-minded enough for that. But, instead, he'd declined another highball and said, well, he supposed he ought to be getting back to the inn. It had all been very well-mannered and in accord with the best traditions of the Leaf. He wondered how the old ex-senator had got them to talk.

Ted had offered to walk along with him, of course, and, equally, of course, he had declined. Now he stood for a moment on the sidewalk, wondering whether he ought to look in at class headquarters before going back to the inn. He ought to, he supposed—after all, it was his thirtieth reunion. It would be full of cigar smoke and voices and there would be a drunk from another class—there was always, somehow or other, a drunk from another class who insisted on leading cheers. And Schooner Fairchild, the class funny man, would be telling stories—the one about the Kickapoo chief, the one about President Dodge and the telephone. As it was in the beginning, is now and ever shall be. He didn't dislike Schooner Fairchild any more—you couldn't dislike a man who had wasted his life. But Schooner, somehow, had never seemed conscious of that.

Yes, he'd go to class headquarters—he'd go, if for no other reason than to prove that he did not dislike Schooner Fairchild. He started walking down Club Row. There were twelve of the clubhouses now—there had been only eight in his time. They all looked very much alike, even the new ones—it took an initiated eye to detect the slight enormous differences—to know that Wampum, in spite of its pretentious lanterns, was second-rate and would always be second-rate, while Abbey, small and dingy, ranked with Momus and the Leaf. Parrington stood still, reliving the moment of more than thirty years ago when he'd gotten the bid from Wampum and thought he would have to accept it. It hadn't been necessary—the Leaf messenger had knocked on his door at just three minutes to nine. But whenever he passed the Wampum house he remembered. For almost an hour, it had seemed as if the destined career of Lane Parrington wasn't going to turn out right after all.

The small agonies of youth—they were unimportant, of course, but they left a mark. And he'd had to succeed—he'd had to have the Leaf, just as later on, he'd had to have money—he wasn't a Schooner Fairchild, to take things as they came. You were geared like that or you weren't—if you weren't, you might as well stay in Emmetsburg and end up as a harried high school principal with sick headaches and a fine Spencerian handwriting, as his father had. But he had wanted to get out of Emmetsburg the moment he had realized there were other places to go.

He remembered a look through a microscope and a lashing, tailed thing that swam. There were only two classes of people, the wigglers and the ones who stood still—he should have made his speech on that—it would have been a better speech. And the ones who stood still didn't like the wigglers—that, too, he knew, from experience. If they saw a wiggler coming, they closed ranks and opposed their large, well-mannered inertia to the brusque, ill-mannered life. Later on, of course, they gave in gracefully, but without real liking. He had made the Leaf on his record—and a very good record it had had to be. He had even spent three painful seasons with the track squad, just to demonstrate that desirable all-aroundness that was one of the talking points. And even so, they had smelled it—they had known, instinctively, that he wasn't quite their kind. Tom Drury, for instance, had always been pleasant enough—but Tom Drury had always made him feel that he was talking a little too much and a little too loud. Tom Drury, who, even then, had looked like a magnificent sheep. But he had also been class president, and the heir to Drury and Son. And yet, they all liked Schooner Fairchild—they liked him still.

And here was the end of Club Row, and the Momus House. He stopped and took out a cigar. It was silly to fight old battles, especially when they were won. If they asked the Drurys to dinner now, the Drurys came—he'd been offered and declined a partnership in Drury and Son. But he had helped Tom out with some of their affiliates and Tom had needed help—Tom would always be impressive, of course, but it took more than impressiveness to handle certain things. And now Ted was coming along —and Ted was sound as a bell. So sound he might marry one of the Drury daughters, if he wanted—though that was Ted's business. He wondered if he wanted Ted to marry young. He had done so himself—on the whole, it had been a mistake.

Funny, how things mixed in your mind. As always, when he remembered Dorothy, there was the sharp, sweet smell of her perfume; then the stubborn, competent look of her hands on the wheel of a car. They had been too much alike to have married —lucky they'd found it out in time. She had let him keep the child—of course he would have fought for it anyway—but it was considered very modern in those days. Then the war had washed over and obliterated a great deal—afterward, he had married Cora. And that had worked out as it should—Ted was fond of her and she treated him with just the right shade of companionableness. Most things worked out in the end. He wondered if Dorothy had gotten what she wanted at last—he supposed she had, with her Texan. But she'd died in a hospital at Galveston, ten years ago, trying to have the Texan's child, so he couldn't ask her now. They had warned her about having more children—but, as soon as you warned Dorothy about anything, that was what she wanted to do. He could have told them. But the Texan was one of those handsome, chivalrous men.

Strange, that out of their two warring ambitions should have come the sound, reliable, healthy Ted. But, no, it wasn't strange —he had planned it as carefully as one could, and Cora had helped a great deal. Cora never got out of her depth and she had a fine social sense. And the very best nurses and schools from the very first—and there you were! You did it as you ran a business—picked the right people and gave them authority. He had hardly ever had to interfere himself.

There would be a great deal of money—but that could be taken care of—there were ways. There were trust funds and foundations and clever secretaries. And Ted need never realize it. There was no reason he should—no reason in the least. Ted could think he was doing it all.

He pulled hard on his cigar and started to walk away. For the door of the Momus Club had suddenly swung open, emitting a gush of light and a small, chubby, gray-haired figure with a turned-up nose and a jack-o'-lantern grin. It stood on the steps for a moment, saying good night a dozen times and laughing. Lane Parrington walked fast—but it was no use. He heard pattering footsteps behind him—a voice cried, "Ought-Eight!" with conviction, then, "Lane Parrington, b'gosh!" He stopped and turned.

"Oh, hello, Schooner," he said, unenthusiastically. "Your dinner over, too?"

"Oh, the boys'll keep it up till three," said Schooner Fairchild, mopping his pink brow. "But, after an hour and a half, I told them it was time they got some other poor devil at the piano. I'm not as young as I was." He panted, comically, and linked arms with Lane Parrington. "Class headquarters?" he said. "I shouldn't go—Minnie will scalp me. But I will."

"Well," said Lane Parrington uncomfortably—he hated having his arm held, "I suppose we ought to look in."

"Duty, Mr. Easy, always duty," said Schooner Fairchild and chuckled. "Hey, don't walk so fast—an old man can't keep up with you." He stopped and mopped his brow again. "By the way," he said, "that's a fine boy of yours, Lane."

"Oh," said Lane Parrington awkwardly. "Thanks. But I didn't know—"

"Saw something of him last summer," said Schooner Fairchild cheerfully. "Sylvia brought him around to the house. He could have a rather nice baritone, if he wanted."

"Baritone?" said Lane Parrington. "Sylvia?"

"Eldest daughter and pride of the Fairchild château," said Schooner Fairchild, slurring his words by a tiny fraction. "She collects 'em—not always—always with Father's approval. But your boy's a nice boy. Serious, of course." He chuckled again, it seemed to Lane Parrington maddeningly. "Oh, the sailor said to the admiral, and the admiral said he—" he chanted. "Remember that one, Lane?"

"No," said Lane Parrington.

"That's right," said Schooner Fairchild, amiably. "Stupid of me. I thought for a minute, you'd been in the quartet. But that was dear old Pozzy Banks. Poor Pozzy—he never could sing 'The Last Rose of Summer' properly till he was as drunk as an owl. A man of great talents. I hoped he'd be here this time but he couldn't make it. He wanted to come," he hummed, "but he didn't have the fare . . ."

"That's too bad," said Lane Parrington, seriously. "And yet, with business picking up . . ."

Schooner Fairchild looked at him queerly, for an instant. "Oh, bless you!" he said. "Pozzy never had a nickel. But he was fun." He tugged at Lane Parrington's arm, as they turned a corner and saw an electric sign—1908—above the door. "Well, here we go!" he said.

An hour later, Lane Parrington decided that it was just as he had expected. True, the drunk from the unidentified class had gone home. But others, from other classes, had arrived. And Schooner Fairchild was sitting at the piano.

He himself was wedged uncomfortably at the back of the room between Ed Runner and a man whose name, he thought, was either Ferguson or Whitelaw, but who, in any case, addressed him as "Lane, old boy." This made conversation difficult, for it was hard to call his neighbor either "Fergy" or "Whitey" without being sure of his name. On the other hand, conversation with Ed Runner was equally difficult, for that gentleman had embarked upon an interminable reminiscence whose point turned upon the exact location of Bill Webley's room Sophomore year. As Lane Parrington had never been in any of Bill Webley's rooms, he had very little to add to the discussion. He was also drinking beer, which never agreed with him, and the cigar smoke stung his eyes. And around the singer and the piano boiled and seethed a motley crew of graduates of all classes— the Roman togas of 1913, the convict stripes of 1935, the shorts and explorers' helmets of 1928. For the news had somehow gone around, through the various class headquarters, that Schooner Fairchild was doing his stuff—and, here and there, among the crowd, were undergraduates, who had heard from brothers and uncles about Schooner Fairchild, but had never seen him before in the flesh.

He had told the story of the Kickapoo chief, he had given

the imitation of President Dodge and the telephone. Both these and other efforts, Lane Parrington noted wonderingly, had been received with tumultuous cheers. Now he played a few chords and swung around on the piano stool.

"I shall now," he said, with his cherubic face very solemn, "emit my positively last and final number—an imitation of dear old Pozzy Banks, attempting to sing 'The Last Rose of Summer' while under the influence of wine. Not all of you have been privileged to know dear old Pozzy—a man of the most varied and diverse talents—it is our great regret that he is not with us tonight. But for those of you who were not privileged to know Pozzy, may I state as an introduction that dear old Pozzy is built something on the lines of a truck, and that, when under the influence of wine, it was his custom to sing directly into his hat, which he held out before him like a card tray. We will now begin." He whirled round, struck a few lugubrious notes and began to sing.

It was, as even Lane Parrington had to admit, extremely funny. He heard himself joining in the wild, deep roar of laughter that greeted the end of the first verse—he was annoyed at himself but he could not help it. By some magic, by some trick of gesture and voice, the chubby, bald-headed figure had suddenly become a large and lugubrious young man—a young man slightly under the influence of wine but still with the very best intentions, singing sentimentally and lugubriously into his hat. It was a trick and an act and a sleight of hand not worth learning—but it did not fail in its effect. Lane Parrington found himself laughing till he ached—beside him, the man named either Ferguson or Whitelaw was whooping and gasping for breath.

"And now," said Schooner Fairchild, while they were still laughing, "let somebody play who *can* play!" And, magically crooking his finger, he summoned a dark-haired undergraduate from the crowd, pushed him down on the piano stool, and, somehow or other, slipped through the press and vanished, while they were still calling his name.

Lane Parrington, a little later, found himself strolling up and down the dejected back yard of class headquarters. They had put up a tent, some iron tables and a number of paper lanterns, but, at this hour, the effect was not particularly gay. It must be very late and he ought to go to bed. But he did not look at his watch. He was trying to think about certain things in his life and get them into a proportion. It should be a simple thing to do, as simple as making money, but it was not.

Ted—Dorothy—the Leaf—Emmetsburg—Schooner Fairchild—Tom Drury—the place in Virginia and the mean house at Emmetsburg—United Investments and a sleight-of-hand trick at a tiny piano. He shuffled the factors of the equation about; they should add up to a whole. And, if they did, he would be willing to admit it; he told himself that. Yes, even if the final sum proved him wrong for years—that had always been one of the factors of his own success, his knowing just when to cut a loss.

A shaky voice hummed behind him:
"Oh, the ship's cat said to the cabin boy,
To the cabin boy said she . . ."

He turned—it was Schooner Fairchild and, he thought at first, Schooner Fairchild was very drunk. Then he saw the man's lips were gray, caught him and helped him into one of the iron chairs.

"Sorry," wheezed Schooner Fairchild. "Must have run too fast, getting away from the gang. Damn' silly—left my medicine at the inn."

"Here—wait—" said Lane Parrington, remembering the flask of brandy in his pocket. He uncorked it and held it to the other man's lips. "Can you swallow?" he said solicitously.

An elfish, undefeated smile lit Schooner Fairchild's face. "Always could, from a child," he gasped. "Never ask a Fairchild twice." He drank and said, incredibly, it seemed to Lane Parrington, "Napoleon . . . isn't it? Sir, you spoil me." His color began to come back. "Better," he said.

"Just stay there," said Lane Parrington. He dashed back into club headquarters—deserted now, he noticed, except for the gloomy caretaker and the man called Ferguson or Whitelaw, who was ungracefully asleep on a leather couch. Efficiently, he found glasses, ice, soda, plain water and ginger ale, and returned, his hands full of these trophies, to find Schooner Fairchild sitting up in his chair and attempting to get a cigarette from the pocket of his coat.

His eyes twinkled as he saw Lane Parrington's collection of glassware. "My!" he said. "We *are* going to make a night of it. Great shock to me—never thought it of you, Lane."

"Hadn't I better get a doctor?" said Lane Parrington. "There's a telephone—"

"Not a chance," said Schooner Fairchild. "It would worry Minnie sick. She made me promise before I came up to take care. It's just the old pump—misses a little sometimes. But I'll be all right, now—right as a trivet, whatever a trivet is. Just give me another shot of Napoleon."

"Of course," said Lane Parrington, "but—"

"Brandy on beer, never fear," said Schooner Fairchild. "Fairchild's Medical Maxims, Number One. And a cigarette . . . thanks." He breathed deeply. "And there we are," he said, with a smile. "Just catches you in the short ribs, now and then. But, when it's over, it's over. You ought to try a little yourself, Lane —damn' silly performance of mine and you look tired."

"Thanks," said Lane Parrington, "I will." He made himself, neatly, an efficient brandy and soda and raised the glass to his lips. "Well—er—here's luck," he said, a little stiffly.

"Luck!" nodded Schooner Fairchild. They both drank. Lane Parrington looked at the pleasant, undefeated face.

"Listen, Schooner," said Lane Parrington, suddenly and harshly, "if you had the whole works to shoot over again—" He stopped.

"That's the hell of a question to ask a man at three o'clock in the morning," said Schooner equably. "Why?"

"Oh, I don't know," said Lane Parrington. "But that stuff at the piano you did—well, how did you do it?" His voice was oddly ingenious, for Lane Parrington.

"Genius, my boy, sheer, untrammeled genius," said Schooner Fairchild. He chuckled and sobered. "Well, somebody has to," he said reasonably. "And you wouldn't expect Tom Drury to do it, would you?—poor old Tom!"

"No," said Lane Parrington, breathing. "I wouldn't expect Tom Drury to do it."

"Oh, Tom's all right," said Schooner Fairchild. "He was just born with an ingrowing Drury and never had it operated on. But he's a fine guy, all the same. Lord," he said, "it must be a curse —to have to be a Drury, whether you like it or not. I never could have stood it—I never could have played the game. Of course," he added hastily, "I suppose it's different, if you do it all yourself, the way you have. That must be a lot of fun."

Stephen Vincent Benét

"I wouldn't exactly call it fun," said Lane Parrington earnestly. "You see, after all, Schooner, there are quite a good many things that enter into . . ." He paused, and laughed hopelessly. "Was I always a stuffed shirt?" he said. "I suppose I was."

"Oh, I wouldn't call you a stuffed shirt," said Schooner, a little quickly. "You just had to succeed—and you've done it. Gosh, we all knew you were going to, right from the first—there couldn't be any mistake about that. It must be a swell feeling." He looked at Lane Parrington and his voice trailed off. He began again. "You see, it was different with me," he said. "I couldn't help it. Why, just take a look at me—I've even got a comedy face. Well, I never wanted anything very much except—oh, to have a good time and know other people were having a good time. Oh, I tried taking the other things seriously—I tried when I was a broker, but I couldn't, it was just no go. I made money enough —everybody was making money—but every now and then, in the middle of a million-share day, I'd just think how damn silly it was for everybody to be watching the board and getting all excited over things called ATT and UGI. And that's no way for a broker to act—you've got to believe those silly initials mean something, if you want to be a broker.

"Well, I've tried a good many things since. And now and then I've been lucky, and we've gotten along. And I've spent most of Minnie's money, but she says it was worth it—and we've got the five girls and they're wonders—and I'll probably die playing the piano at some fool party, for you can't keep it up forever, but I only hope it happens before somebody says, 'There goes poor old Schooner. He used to be pretty amusing, in his time!' But, you see, I couldn't help it," he ended diffidently. "And, you know, I've tried. I've tried hard. But then I'd start laughing, and it always got in the way."

Lane Parrington looked at the man who had spent his wife's money and his own for a sleight-of-hand trick, five daughters, and the sound of friendly laughter. He looked at him without understanding, and yet with a curious longing.

"But, Schooner—" he said, "with all you can do—you ought to—"

"Oh," said Schooner, a trifle wearily, "one has one's dreams. Sure, I'd like to be Victor Boucher—he's a beautiful comedian.

296

Schooner Fairchild's Class

Or Bill Fields, for instance. Who wouldn't? But I don't kid my-self. It's a parlor talent—it doesn't go over the footlights. But, Lord, what fun I've had with it! And the funny things people keep doing, forever and ever, amen. And the decent—the very decent things they keep doing, too. Well, I always thought it would be a good life, while you had it." He paused, and Lane Parrington saw the fatigue on his face. "Well, it's been a good party," he said. "I wish old Pozzy could have been here. But I guess we ought to go to bed."

"I'll phone for a cab," said Lane Parrington. "Nope—you're riding."

Lane Parrington shut the door of Schooner Fairchild's room behind him and stood, for a moment, with his hand on the knob. He had seen Schooner safely to bed—he had even insisted on the latter's taking his medicine, though Schooner had been a little petulant about it. Now, however, he still wondered about calling a doctor—if Schooner should be worse in the morning, he would have Anstey come up by plane. It was nothing to do, though not everybody could do it, and Anstey was much the best man. In any case, he would insist on Schooner's seeing Anstey this week. Then he wondered just how he was going to insist.

The old elevator just across the corridor came to a wheezing stop. Its door opened and a dark-haired girl in evening dress came out. Lane Parrington dropped his hand from the doorknob and turned away. But the girl took three quick steps after him.

"I'm sorry," she said, a little breathlessly, "but I'm Sylvia Fairchild. Is Father ill? The elevator boy said something—and I saw you coming out of his room."

"He's all right," said Lane Parrington. "It was just the slight-est sort of—"

"Oh!" said the girl, "do you mind coming back for a minute? You're Ted's father, aren't you? My room's next door, but I've got a key for his, too—Mother told me to be sure—" She seemed very self-possessed. Lane Parrington waited uncomfortably in the corridor for what seemed to him a long time, while she went into her father's room. When she came out again, she seemed relieved.

"It's all right," she said, in a low voice. "He's asleep, and his color's good. And he's . . ." She paused. "Oh, damn!" she said.

"We can't talk out here. Come into my room for a minute—we can leave the door open—after all, you *are* Ted's father. I'll have to tell Mother, you see—and Father will just say it wasn't anything."

She opened the door and led the way into the room. "Here," she said. "Just throw those stockings off the chair—I'll sit on the bed. Well?"

"Well, I asked him if he wanted a doctor . . ." said Lane Parrington humbly.

When he had finished a concise, efficient report, the girl nodded, and he saw for the first time that she was pretty, with her dark, neat head and her clever, stubborn chin.

"Thank you," she said. "I mean, really. Father's a perfect lamb —but he doesn't like to worry Mother, and it worries her a lot more not to know. And sometimes it's rather difficult, getting the truth out of Father's friends. Not you," she was pleased to add. "You've been perfectly truthful. And the brandy was quite all right."

"I'm glad," said Lane Parrington. "I wish your father would see Anstey," he added, a trifle awkwardly. "I could—er—make arrangements."

"He has," said the girl. Her mouth twitched. "Oh," she said. "I shouldn't have gone to the dance. I couldn't help the Momus Club, but he might have come back afterward, if I'd been here. Only, I don't know."

"I wouldn't reproach myself," said Lane Parrington. "After all—"

"Oh, I know," said the girl. "After all! If you don't all manage to kill him, between you! Friends!" she sniffed. Then, suddenly, her face broke into lines of amusement. "I sound just like Aunt Emma," she said. "And that's pretty silly of me. Aunt Emma's almost pure poison. Of course it isn't your fault and I really do thank you. Very much. Do you know, I never expected you'd be a friend of Father's."

"After all," said Lane Parrington stiffly, "we were in the same class."

"Oh, I know," said the girl. "Father's talked about you, of course." Her mouth twitched again, but this time, it seemed to Lane Parrington, with a secret merriment. "And so has Ted, naturally," she added politely.

298

"I'm glad he happened to mention me," said Lane Parrington, and she grinned, frankly.

"I deserved that," she said, while Lane Parrington averted his eyes from what seemed to be a remarkably flimsy garment hung over the bottom of the bed. "But Ted has, really. He admires you quite a lot, you know, though, of course, you're different generations."

"Tell me—" said Lane Parrington. "No, I won't ask you."

"Oh, you know Ted," said the girl, rather impatiently. "It's awfully hard to get him to say things—and he will spend such a lot of time thinking he ought to be noble, poor lamb. But he's losing just a little of that, thank goodness—when he first came to Widgeon Point, he was trying so hard to be exactly like that terrible Drury boy. You see—" she said, suddenly and gravely, "he could lose quite a lot of it and still have more than most people."

Lane Parrington cleared his throat. There seemed nothing for him to say. Then he thought of something.

"His mother was—er—a remarkable person," he said. "We were not at all happy together. But she had remarkable qualities."

"Yes," said the girl. "Ted's told me. He remembers her." They looked at each other for a moment—he noted the stubborn chin, the swift and admirable hands. Then a clock on the mantel struck and the girl jumped.

"Good heavens!" she said. "It's four o'clock! Well—good night. And I do thank you, Mr. Parrington."

"It wasn't anything," said Lane Parrington. "But remember me to your father. But I'll see you in the morning, of course."

The following afternoon, Lane Parrington found himself waiting for his car in the lobby of the inn. There had been a little trouble with the garage and it was late. But he did not care, particularly, though he felt glad to be going back to New York. He had said good-by to Ted an hour before—Ted was going on to a house party at the Chiltons'—they'd eventually meet on Long Island, he supposed. Meanwhile, he had had a pleasant morning, attended the commencement exercises, and had lunch with Ted and the Fairchilds at the inn. Schooner had been a little subdued and both Ted and the girl frankly sleepy, but he had enjoyed the occasion nevertheless. And somehow the fact that the president's baccalaureate address had also viewed with alarm and talked about imperiled bulwarks and the American way of life—

299

had, in fact, repeated with solemn precision a good many of the points in his own speech—did not irk Lane Parrington as it might have the day before. After all, the boys were young and could stand it. They had stood a good deal of nonsense, even in his own time.

Now he thought once more of the equation he had tried too earnestly to solve, in the back yard of commencement headquarters—and, for a moment, almost grinned. It was, of course, insoluble—life was not as neat as that. You did what you could, as it was given you to do—very often you did the wrong things. And if you did the wrong things, you could hardly remedy them by a sudden repentance—or, at least, he could not. There were still the wigglers and the ones who stood still—and each had his own virtues. And because he was a wiggler, he had thoughtfully and zealously done his best to make his son into the image of one of the magnificent sheep—the image of Tom Drury, who was neither hungry nor gay. He could not remedy that, but he thought he knew somebody who could remedy it, remembering the Fairchild girl's stubborn chin. And, in that case at least, the grandchildren ought to be worth watching.

"Your car, Mr. Parrington," said a bellboy. He moved toward the door. It was hard to keep from being a stuffed shirt, if you had the instinct in you, but one could try. A good deal might be done, with trying.

As he stepped out upon the steps of the inn, he noticed a figure, saluting—old Negro Mose, the campus character who remembered everybody's name.

"Hello, Mose!" said Lane Parrington. "Remember me?"

"Remember you—sho', Mr. Parrington," said Mose. He regarded Lane Parrington with beady eyes. "Let's see—you was 1906."

"Nineteen hundred and eight," said Lane Parrington, but without rancor.

Mose gave a professional chuckle. "Sho'!" he said. "I was forgettin'! Let's see—you hasn't been back fo' years, Mister Parrington—but you was in Tom Drury's class—an' Schooner Fairchild's class—"

"No," said Lane Parrington and gave the expected dollar, "not Tom Drury's class. Schooner Fairchild's class."

EVERYBODY WAS VERY NICE

Yes, I guess I have put on weight since you last saw me—not that you're any piker yourself, Spike. But I suppose you medicos have to keep in shape—probably do better than we downtown. I try to play golf in the week-ends, and I do a bit of sailing. But four innings of the baseball game at reunion was enough for me. I dropped out, after that, and let Art Corliss pitch.

You really should have been up there. After all, the Twentieth is quite a milestone—and the class is pretty proud of its famous man. What was it that magazine article said: "most brilliant young psychiatrist in the country"? I may not know psychiatry from marbles, but I showed it to Lisa, remarking that it was old Spike Garrett, and for once she was impressed. She thinks brokers are pretty dumb eggs. I wish you could stay for dinner—I'd like to show you the apartment and the twins. No, they're Lisa's and mine. Boys, if you'll believe it. Yes, the others are with Sally—young Barbara's pretty grown up, now.

Well, I can't complain. I may not be famous like you, Spike, but I manage to get along, in spite of the brain trusters, and having to keep up the place on Long Island. I wish you got East oftener—there's a pretty view from the guest house, right across the Sound—and if you wanted to write a book or anything, we'd know enough to leave you alone. Well, they started calling me a partner two years ago, so I guess that's what I am. Still fooling them, you know. But, seriously, we've got a pretty fine organization. We run a conservative business, but we're not all stuffed shirts, in spite of what the radicals say. As a matter of fact, you ought to see what the boys ran about us in the last Bawl Street Journal. Remind me to show it to you.

But it's your work I want to hear about—remember those bull-sessions we used to have in Old Main? Old Spike Garrett, the Medical Marvel! Why, I've even read a couple of your books, you old horse thief, believe it or not! You got me pretty tangled up on all that business about the id and the ego, too. But what I say is, there must be something in it if a fellow like Spike Garrett believes it. And there is, isn't there? Oh, I know you couldn't give me an answer in five minutes. But as long as there's a system—and the medicos know what they're doing.

Stephen Vincent Benét

I'm not asking for myself, of course—remember how you used to call me the 99 per-cent normal man? Well, I guess I haven't changed. It's just that I've gotten to thinking recently, and Lisa says I go around like a bear with a sore head. Well, it isn't that. I'm just thinking. A man has to think once in a while. And then, going back to reunion brought it all up again.

What I mean is this—the thing seemed pretty clear when we were in college. Of course, that was back in '15, but I can remember the way most of us thought. You fell in love with a girl and married her and settled down and had children and that was that. I'm not being simple-minded about it—you knew people get divorced, just as you knew people died, but it didn't seem something that was likely to happen to you. Especially if you came from a small Western city, as I did. Great Scott, I can remember when I was just a kid and the Prentisses got divorced. They were pretty prominent people and it shook the whole town.

That's why I want to figure things out for my own satisfaction. Because I never expected to be any Lothario—I'm not the type. And yet Sally and I got divorced and we're both remarried, and even so, to tell you the truth, things aren't going too well. I'm not saying a word against Lisa. But that's the way things are. And it isn't as if I were the only one. You can look around anywhere and see it, and it starts you wondering.

I'm not going to bore you about myself and Sally. Good Lord, you ushered at the wedding, and she always liked you. Remember when you used to come out to the house? Well, she hasn't changed—she's still got that little smile—though, of course, we're all older. Her husband's a doctor, too—that's funny, isn't it?—and they live out in Montclair. They've got a nice place there and he's very well thought of. We used to live in Meadowfield, remember?

I remember the first time I saw her after she married Mc-Conaghey—oh, we're perfectly friendly, you know. She had on red nail polish and her hair was different, a different bob. And she had one of those handbags with her new initials on it. It's funny, the first time, seeing your wife in clothes you don't know. Though Lisa and I have been married eight years, for that matter, and Sally and I were divorced in '28.

Of course, we have the children for part of the summer. We'll have Barbara this summer—Bud'll be in camp. It's a little difficult

302

Everybody Was Very Nice

sometimes, but we all co-operate. You have to. And there's plenty to do on Long Island in the summer, that's one thing. But they and Lisa get along very well—Sally's brought them up nicely that way. For that matter, Doctor McConaghey's very nice when I see him. He gave me a darn good prescription for a cold and I get it filled every winter. And Jim Blake—he's Lisa's first husband—is really pretty interesting, now we've got to seeing him again. In fact, we're all awfully nice—just as nice and polite as we can be. And sometimes I get to wondering if it mightn't be a good idea if somebody started throwing fits and shooting rockets, instead. Of course I don't really mean that.

You were out for a week end with us in Meadowfield—maybe you don't remember it—but Bud was about six months old then and Barbara was just running around. It wasn't a bad house, if you remember the house. Dutch Colonial, and the faucet in the pantry leaked. The landlord was always fixing it, but he never quite fixed it right. And you had to cut hard to the left to back into the garage. But Sally liked the Japanese cherry tree and it wasn't a bad house. We were going to build on Rose Hill Road eventually. We had the lot picked out, if we didn't have the money, and we made plans about it. Sally never could remember to put in the doors in the plan, and we laughed about that.

It wasn't anything extraordinary, just an evening. After supper, we sat around the lawn in deck chairs and drank Sally's beer —it was long before Repeal. We'd repainted the deck chairs ourselves the Sunday before and we felt pretty proud of them. The light stayed late, but there was a breeze after dark, and once Bud started yipping and Sally went up to him. She had on a white dress, I think—she used to wear white a lot in the summers—it went with her blue eyes and her yellow hair. Well, it wasn't anything extraordinary—we didn't even stay up late. But we were all there. And if you'd told me that within three years we'd both be married to other people, I'd have thought you were raving.

Then you went West, remember, and we saw you off on the train. So you didn't see what happened, and, as a matter of fact, it's hard to remember when we first started meeting the Blakes. They'd moved to Meadowfield then, but we hadn't met them.

Jim Blake was one of those pleasant, ugly-faced people with steel glasses who get right ahead in the law and never look young

303

or old. And Lisa was Lisa. She's dark, you know, and she takes a beautiful burn. She was the first girl there to wear real beach things or drink a special kind of tomato juice when everybody else was drinking cocktails. She was very pretty and very good fun to be with—she's got lots of ideas. They entertained a good deal because Lisa likes that—she had her own income, of course. and she and Jim used to bicker a good deal in public in an amusing way—it was sort of an act or seemed like it. They had one little girl, Sylvia, that Jim was crazy about. I mean it sounds normal, doesn't it, even to their having the kind of Airedale you had then? Well, it all seemed normal enough to us, and they soon got to be part of the crowd. You know, the young married crowd in every suburb.

Of course, that was '28 and the boom was booming and everybody was feeling pretty high. I suppose that was part of it—the money—and the feeling you had that everything was going faster and faster and wouldn't stop. Why, it was Sally herself who said that we owed ourselves a whirl and mustn't get stodgy and settled while we were still young. Well, we had stuck pretty close to the grindstone for the past few years, with the children and everything. And it was fun to feel young and sprightly again and buy a new car and take in the club gala without having to worry about how you'd pay your house account. But I don't see any harm in that.

And then, of course, we talked and kidded a lot about freedom and what have you. Oh, you know the kind of talk—everybody was talking it then. About not being Victorians and living your own life. And there was the older generation and the younger generation. I've forgotten a lot of it now, but I remember there was one piece about love not being just a form of words mumbled by a minister, but something pretty special. As a matter of fact, the minister who married us was old Doctor Snell and he had the kind of voice you could hear in the next county. But I used to talk about that mumbling minister myself. I mean, we were enlightened, for a suburb, if you get my point. Yes, and pretty proud of it, too. When they banned a book in Boston, the lending library ordered six extra copies. And I still remember the big discussion we had about perfect freedom in marriage when even the straight Republicans voted the radical ticket. All except

Everybody Was Very Nice

Chick Bewleigh, and he was a queer sort of bird, who didn't even believe that stocks had reached a permanently high plateau.

But, meanwhile, most of us were getting the 8:15 and our wives were going down to the chain store and asking if that was a really nice head of lettuce. At least that's the way we seemed. And, if the crowd started kidding me about Mary Sennett, or Mac Church kissed Sally on the ear at a club revel, why, we were young, we were modern, and we could handle that. I wasn't going to take a shotgun to Mac, and Sally wasn't going to put on the jealous act. Oh, we had it all down to a science. We certainly did.

Good Lord, we had the Blakes to dinner, and they had us. They'd drop over for drinks or we'd drop over there. It was all perfectly normal and part of the crowd. For that matter, Sally played with Jim Blake in the mixed handicap and they got to the semifinals. No, I didn't play with Lisa—she doesn't like golf. I mean that's the way it was.

And I can remember the minute it started, and it wasn't anything, just a party at the Bewleighs'. They've got a big, rambling house and people drift around. Lisa and I had wandered out to the kitchen to get some drinks for the people on the porch. She had on a black dress, that night, with a big sort of orange flower on it. It wouldn't have suited everybody, but it suited her.

We were talking along like anybody and suddenly we stopped talking and looked at each other. And I felt, for a minute, well, just the way I felt when I was first in love with Sally. Only this time, it wasn't Sally. It happened so suddenly that all I could think of was, "Watch your step!" Just as if you'd gone into a room in the dark and hit your elbow. I guess that makes it genuine, doesn't it?

We picked it up right away and went back to the party. All she said was, "Did anybody ever tell you that you're really quite a menace, Dan?" and she said that in the way we all said those things. But, all the same, it had happened. I could hear her voice all the way back in the car. And yet, I was as fond of Sally as ever. I don't suppose you'll believe that, but it's true.

And next morning, I tried to kid myself that it didn't have any importance. Because Sally wasn't jealous, and we were all modern and advanced and knew about life. But the next time I saw Lisa, I knew it had.

305

Stephen Vincent Benét

I want to say this. If you think it was all romance and rose-buds, you're wrong. A lot of it was merry hell. And yet, every-body whooped us on. That's what I don't understand. They didn't really want the Painters and the Blakes to get divorced, and yet they were pretty interested. Now, why do people do that? Some of them would carefully put Lisa and me next to each other at table and some of them would just as carefully not. But it all added up to the same thing in the end—a circus was going on and we were part of the circus. It's interesting to watch the people on the high wires at the circus and you hope they don't fall. But, if they did, that would be interesting too. Of course, there were a couple of people who tried, as they say, to warn us. But they were older people and just made us mad.

Everybody was so nice and considerate and understanding. Everybody was so nice and intelligent and fine. Don't misunder-stand me. It was wonderful, being with Lisa. It was new and exciting. And it seemed to be wonderful for her, and she'd been unhappy with Jim. So, anyway, that made me feel less of a heel, though I felt enough of a heel, from time to time. And then, when we were together, it would seem so fine.

A couple of times we really tried to break it, too—at least twice. But we all belonged to the same crowd, and what could you do but run away? And, somehow, that meant more than running away—it meant giving in to the Victorians and that mumbling preacher and all the things we'd said we didn't be-lieve in. Or I suppose Sally might have done like old Mrs. Pierce, back home. She horsewhipped the dressmaker on the station plat-form and then threw herself crying into Major Pierce's arms and he took her to Atlantic City instead. It's one of the town's great stories and I always wondered what they talked about on the train. Of course, they moved to Des Moines after that—I remember reading about their golden wedding anniversary when I was in college. Only nobody could do that nowadays, and, besides, Lisa wasn't a dressmaker.

So, finally, one day, I came home, and there was Sally, per-fectly cold, and, we talked pretty nearly all night. We'd been awfully polite to each other for quite a while before—the way you are. And we kept polite, we kept a good grip on ourselves. After all, we'd said to each other before we were married that if either of us ever—and there it was. And it was Sally who brought that up, not me. I think we'd have felt better if we'd fought. But we didn't fight.

Of course, she was bound to say some things about Lisa, and I was bound to answer. But that didn't last long and we got our grip right back again. It was funny, being strangers and talking so politely, but we did it. I think it gave us a queer kind of pride to do it. I think it gave us a queer kind of pride for her to ask me politely for a drink at the end, as if she were in somebody else's house, and for me to mix it for her, as if she were a guest.

Everything was talked out by then and the house felt very dry and empty, as if nobody lived in it at all. We'd never been up quite so late in the house, except after a New Year's party or when Buddy was sick, that time. I mixed her drink very carefully, the way she liked it, with plain water, and she took it and said "Thanks." Then she sat for a while without saying anything. It was so quiet you could hear the little drip of the leaky faucet in the pantry, in spite of the door being closed. She heard it and said, "It's dripping again. You better call up Mr. Vye in the morning—I forgot. And I think Barbara's getting a cold—I meant to tell you." Then her face twisted and I thought she was going to cry, but she didn't.

She put the glass down—she'd only drunk half her drink—and said, quite quietly, "Oh, damn you, and damn Lisa Blake, and damn everything in the world!" Then she ran upstairs before I could stop her and she still wasn't crying.

I could have run upstairs after her, but I didn't. I stood looking at the glass on the table and I couldn't think. Then, after a while, I heard a key turn in a lock. So I picked up my hat and went out for a walk—I hadn't been out walking that early in a long time. Finally, I found an all-night diner and got some coffee. Then I came back and read a book till the maid got down—it wasn't a very interesting book. When she came down, I pretended I'd gotten up early and had to go into town by the first train, but I guess she knew.

I'm not going to talk about the details. If you've been through them, you've been through them; and if you haven't, you don't know. My family was fond of Sally, and Sally's had always liked me. Well, that made it tough. And the children. They don't say the things you expect them to. I'm not going to talk about that.

Oh, we put on a good act, we put on a great show! There

weren't any fists flying or accusations. Everybody said how well we did it, everybody in town. And Lisa and Sally saw each other, and Jim Blake and I talked to each other perfectly calmly. We said all the usual things. He talked just as if it were a case. I admired him for it. Lisa did her best to make it emotional, but we wouldn't let her. And I finally made her see that, court or no court, he'd simply have to have Sylvia. He was crazy about her, and while Lisa's a very good mother, there wasn't any question as to which of them the kid liked best. It happens that way, sometimes.

For that matter, I saw Sally off on the train to Reno. She wanted it that way. Lisa was going to get a Mexican divorce— they'd just come in, you know. And nobody could have told, from the way we talked in the station. It's funny, you get a queer bond, through a time like that. After I'd seen her off—and she looked small in the train—the first person I wanted to see wasn't Lisa, but Jim Blake. You see, other people are fine, but unless you've been through things yourself, you don't quite understand them. But Jim Blake was still in Meadowfield, so I went back to the club.

I hadn't ever really lived in the club before, except for three days one summer. They treat you very well, but, of course, being a college club, it's more for the youngsters and the few old boys who hang around the bar. I got awfully tired of the summer chintz in the dining room and the Greek waiter I had who breathed on my neck. And you can't work all the time, though I used to stay late at the office. I guess it was then I first thought of getting out of Spencer Wilde and making a new connection. You think about a lot of things at a time like that.

Of course, there were lots of people I could have seen, but I didn't much want to—somehow, you don't. Though I did strike up quite a friendship with one of the old boys. He was about fifty-five and he'd been divorced four times and was living permanently at the club. We used to sit up in his little room—he'd had his own furniture moved in and the walls were covered with pictures—drinking Tom Collinses and talking about life. He had lots of ideas about life, and about matrimony, too, and I got quite interested, listening to him. But then he'd go into the dinners he used to give at Delmonico's, and while that was interesting, too, it wasn't much help, except to take your mind off the summer chintz.

He had some sort of small job, downtown, but I guess he had an income from his family too. He must have. But when I'd ask him what he did, he'd always say, "I'm retired, my boy, very much retired, and how about a touch more beverage to keep out the sun?" He always called it beverage, but they knew what he meant at the bar. He turned up at the wedding, when Lisa and I were married, all dressed up in a cutaway, and insisted on making us a little speech—very nice it was too. Then we had him to dinner a couple of times, after we'd got back, and somehow or other, I haven't seen him since. I suppose he's still at the club—I've got out of the habit of going there, since I joined the other ones, though I still keep my membership.

Of course, all that time, I was crazy about Lisa and writing her letters and waiting till we could be married. Of course I was. But, now and then, even that would get shoved into the background. Because there was so much to do and arrangements to make and people like lawyers to see. I don't like lawyers very much, even yet, though the people we had were very good. But there was all the telephoning and the conferences. Somehow, it was like a machine—a big machine—and you had to learn a sort of new etiquette for everything you did. Till, finally, it got so that about all you wanted was to have the fuss over and not talk about it any more.

I remember running into Chick Bewleigh in the club, three days before Sally got her decree. You'd like Chick—he's the intellectual type, but a darn good fellow too. And Nan, his wife, is a peach—one of those big, rangy girls with a crazy sense of humor. It was nice to talk to him because he was natural and didn't make any cracks about grass-bachelors or get that look in his eye. You know the look they get. We talked about Meadowfield—just the usual news—the Bakers were splitting up and Don Sikes had a new job and the Wilsons were having a baby. But it seemed good to hear it.

"For that matter," he said, drawing on his pipe, "we're adding to the population again ourselves. In the fall. How we'll ever manage four of them! I keep telling Nan she's cockeyed, but she says they're more fun than a swimming pool and cost less to keep up, so what can you do!"

He shook his head and I remembered that Sally always used to say she wanted six. Only now it would be Lisa, so I mustn't think about that.

"So that's your recipe for a happy marriage," I said. "Well, I always wondered."

I was kidding, of course, but he looked quite serious.

"*Kinder, Küche und Kirche?*" he said. "Nope, that doesn't work any more, what with pre-schools, automats and the movies. Four children or no four children, Nan could still raise hell if she felt like raising hell. And so could I, for that matter. Add blessings of civilization," and his eyes twinkled.

"Well then," I said, "what is it?" I really wanted to know.

"Oh, just bull luck, I suppose. And happening to like what you've got," he answered, in a sort of embarrassed way.

"You can do that," I said. "And yet——"

He looked away from me.

"Oh, it was a lot simpler in the old days," he said. "Everything was for marriage—church, laws, society. And when people got married, they expected to stay that way. And it made a lot of people as unhappy as hell. Now the expectation's rather the other way, at least in this great and beautiful nation and among people like us. If you get a divorce, it's rather like going to the dentist—unpleasant sometimes, but lots of people have been there before. Well, that's a handsome system, too, but it's got its own casualty list. So there you are. You takes your money and you makes your choice. And some of us like freedom better than the institution and some of us like the institution better, but what most of us would like is to be Don Juan on Thursdays and Benedick, the married man, on Fridays, Saturdays and the rest of the week. Only that's a bit hard to work out, somehow," and he grinned.

"All the same," I said, "you and Nan——"

"Well," he said, "I suppose we're exceptions. You see, my parents weren't married till I was seven. So I'm a conservative. It might have worked out the other way."

"Oh," I said.

"Yes," he said. "My mother was English, and you may have heard of English divorce laws. She ran away with my father and she was perfectly right—her husband was a very extensive brute. All the same, I was brought up on the other side of the fence, and I know something about what it's like. And Nan was a minister's daughter who thought she ought to be free. Well, we argued about things a good deal. And, finally, I told her that I'd be very highly complimented to live with her on any terms at all, but if she wanted to get married, she'd have to expect a marriage, not a trip to Coney Island. And I made my point rather clear by blacking her eye, in a taxi, when she told me she was thinking seriously of spending a week end with my deadly rival, just to see which one of us she really loved. You can't spend a romantic week end with somebody when you've got a black eye. But you can get married with one and we did. She had raw beefsteak on it till two hours before the wedding, and it was the prettiest sight I ever saw. Well, that's our simple story."

"Not all of it," I said.

"No," he said, "not all of it. But at least we didn't start in with any of this bunk about if you meet a handsomer fellow it's all off. We knew we were getting into something. Bewleigh's Easy Guide to Marriage in three installments—you are now listening to the Voice of Experience, and who cares? Of course, if we hadn't—ahem—liked each other, I could have blacked her eye till doomsday and got nothing out of it but a suit for assault and battery. But nothing's much good unless it's worth fighting for. And she doesn't look exactly like a downtrodden wife."

"Nope," I said, "but all the same——"

He stared at me very hard—almost the way he used to when people were explaining that stocks had reached a permanently high plateau.

"Exactly," he said. "And there comes a time, no matter what the intention, when a new face heaves into view and a spark lights. I'm no Adonis, God knows, but it's happened to me once or twice. And I know what I do then. I run. I run like a rabbit. It isn't courageous or adventurous or fine. It isn't even particularly moral, as I think about morals. But I run. Because, when all's said and done, it takes two people to make a love affair and you can't have it when one of them's not there. And, dammit, Nan knows it, that's the trouble. She'd ask Helen of Troy to dinner just to see me run. Well, good-by, old man, and our best to Lisa, of course——"

After he was gone, I went and had dinner in the grill. I did

Stephen Vincent Benét

a lot of thinking at dinner, but it didn't get me anywhere. When I was back in the room, I took the receiver off the telephone. I was going to call long distance. But your voice sounds different on the phone, and, anyway, the decree would be granted in three days. So when the girl answered, I told her it was a mistake.

Next week Lisa came back and she and I were married. We went to Bermuda on our wedding trip. It's a very pretty place. Do you know, they won't allow an automobile on the island?

The queer thing was that at first I didn't feel married to Lisa at all. I mean, on the boat, and even at the hotel. She said, "But how exciting, darling!" and I suppose it was.

Now, of course, we've been married eight years, and that's always different. The twins will be seven in May—two years older than Sally's Jerry. I had an idea for a while that Sally might marry Jim Blake—he always admired her. But I'm glad she didn't—it would have made things a little too complicated. And I like McConaghey—I like him fine. We gave them an old Chinese jar for a wedding present. Lisa picked it out. She has very good taste and Sally wrote us a fine letter.

I'd like to have you meet Lisa sometime—she's interested in intelligent people. They're always coming to the apartment—artists and writers and people like that.

Of course, they don't always turn out the way she expects. But she's quite a hostess and she knows how to handle things. There was one youngster that used to rather get in my hair. He'd call me the Man of Wall Street and ask me what I thought about Picabia or one of those birds, in a way that sort of said, "Now watch this guy stumble!" But as soon as Lisa noticed it, she got rid of him. That shows she's considerate.

Of course, it's different, being married to a person. And I'm pretty busy these days and so is she. Sometimes, if I get home and there's going to be a party, I'll just say good night to the twins and fade out after dinner. But Lisa understands about that, and I've got my own quarters. She had one of her decorator friends do the private study and it really looks very nice.

I had Jim Blake in there one night. Well, I had to take him somewhere. He was getting pretty noisy and Lisa gave me the high sign. He's doing very well, but he looks pretty hard these days and I'm afraid he's drinking a good deal, though he doesn't often show it. I don't think he ever quite got over Sylvia's dying.

Four years ago. They had scarlet fever at the school. It was a great shock to Lisa, too, of course, but she had the twins and Jim never married again. But he comes to see us, every once in a while. Once, when he was tight, he said it was to convince himself about remaining a bachelor, but I don't think he meant that.

Now, when I brought him into the study, he looked around and said, "Shades of Buck Rogers! What one of Lisa's little dears produced this imitation Wellsian nightmare?"

"Oh, I don't remember," I said. "I think his name was Slivovitz."

"It looks as if it had been designed by a man named Slivovitz," he said. "All dental steel and black glass. I recognize the Lisa touch. You're lucky she didn't put murals of cogwheels on the walls."

"Well, there was a question of that," I said.

"I bet there was," he said. "Well, here's how, old man! Here's to two great big wonderful institutions, marriage and divorce!"

I didn't like that very much and told him so. But he just wagged his head at me.

"I like you, Painter," he said. "I always did. Sometimes I think you're goofy, but I like you. You can't insult me—I won't let you. And it isn't your fault."

"What isn't my fault?" I said.

"The setup," he said. "Because, in your simple little heart, you're an honest monogamous man, Painter—monogamous as most. And if you'd stayed married to Sally, you'd have led an honest monogamous life. But they loaded the dice against you, out at Meadowfield, and now Lord knows where you'll end up. After all, I was married to Lisa myself for six years or so. Tell me, isn't it hell?"

"You're drunk," I said.

"*In vino veritas,*" said he. "No, it isn't hell—I take that back. Lisa's got her damn-fool side, but she's an attractive and interesting woman—or could be, if she'd work at it. But she was brought up on the idea of Romance with a big R, and she's too bone-lazy and bone-selfish to work at it very long. There's always something else, just over the horizon. Well, I got tired of fighting that, after a while. And so will you. She doesn't want husbands —she wants clients and followers. Or maybe you're tired already."

"I think you'd better go home, Jim," I said. "I don't want to have to ask you."

"Sorry," he said. "*In vino veritas.* But it's a funny setup, isn't it? What Lisa wanted was a romantic escapade—and she got twins. And what you wanted was marriage—and you got Lisa. As for me," and for a minute his face didn't look drunk any more, "what I principally wanted was Sylvia and I've lost that. I could have married again, but I didn't think that'd be good for her. Now, I'll probably marry some client I've helped with her decree—we don't touch divorce, as a rule, just a very, very special line of business for a few important patrons. I know those—I've had them in the office. And won't that be fun for us all! What a setup it is!" and he slumped down in his chair and went to sleep. I let him sleep for a while and then had Briggs take him down in the other elevator. He called up next day and apologized—said he knew he must have been noisy, though he couldn't remember anything he said.

The other time I had somebody in the study was when Sally came back there once, two years ago. We'd met to talk about college for Barbara and I'd forgotten some papers I wanted to show her. We generally meet downtown. But she didn't mind coming back—Lisa was out, as it happened. It made me feel queer, taking her up in the elevator and letting her in at the door. She wasn't like Jim—she thought the study was nice.

Well, we talked over our business and I kept looking at her. You can see she's older, but her eyes are still that very bright blue, and she bites her thumb when she's interested. It's a queer feeling. Of course, I was used to seeing her, but we usually met downtown. You know, I wouldn't have been a bit surprised if she'd pushed the bell and said, "Tea, Briggs, I'm home." She didn't, naturally.

I asked her, once, if she wouldn't take off her hat and she looked at me in a queer way and said, "So you can show me your etchings? Dan, Dan, you're a dangerous man!" and for a moment we both laughed like fools.

"Oh, dear," she said, drying her eyes, "that's very funny. And now I must be going home."

"Look here, Sally," I said, "I've always told you—but, honestly, if you need anything—if there's anything——"

"Of course, Dan," she said. "And we're awfully good friends, aren't we?" But she was still smiling.

I didn't care. "Friends!" I said. "You know how I think about you. I always have. And I don't want you to think——"

She patted my shoulder—I'd forgotten the way she used to do that.

"There," she said. "Mother knows all about it. And we really are friends, Dan. So——"

"I was a fool."

She looked at me very steadily out of those eyes.

"We were all fools," she said. "Even Lisa. I used to hate her for a while. I used to hope things would happen to her. Oh, not very bad things. Just her finding out that you never see a crooked picture without straightening it, and hearing you say: 'A bird can't fly on one wing,' for the dozenth time. The little things everybody has to find out and put up with. But I don't even do that any more."

"If you'd ever learned to put a cork back in a bottle," I said. "I mean the right cork in the right bottle. But——"

"I do so! No, I suppose I never will." And she laughed. She took my hands. "Funny, funny, funny," she said. "And funny to have it all gone and be friends."

"Is it all gone?" I said.

"Why, no, of course not," she said. "I don't suppose it ever is, quite. Like the boys who took you to dances. And there's the children, and you can't help remembering. But it's gone. We had it and lost it. I should have fought for it more, I suppose, but I didn't. And then I was terribly hurt and terribly mad. But I got over that. And now I'm married to Jerry. And I wouldn't give him up, or Jerry Junior, for anything in the world. The only thing that worries me is sometimes when I think it isn't quite a fair deal for him. After all, he could have married—well, somebody else. And yet he knows I love him."

"He ought to," I said rather stiffly. "He's a darn lucky guy, if you ask me."

"No, Dan, I'm the lucky girl. I'm hoping this minute that Mrs. Potter's X-rays turn out all right. He did a beautiful job on her. But he always worries."

I dropped her hands.

"Well, give him my best," I said.

"I will, Dan. He likes you, you know. Really he does. By the way, have you had any more of that bursitis? There's a new treatment—he wanted me to ask you——"

"Thanks," I said, "but that all cleared up."

"I'm glad. And now I must fly. There's always shopping when you come in from the suburbs. Give my best to Lisa and tell her I was sorry not to see her. She's out, I suppose."

"Yes," I said. "She'll be sorry to miss you—you wouldn't stay for a cocktail? She's usually in around then."

"It sounds very dashing, but I mustn't. Jerry Junior lost one of his turtles and I've got to get him another. Do you know a good pet shop? Well, Bloomingdale's, I suppose—after all, I've got other things to get."

"There's a good one two blocks down on Lexington," I said. "But if you're going to Bloomingdale's—— Well, good-by, Sally, and good luck."

"Good-by, Dan. And good luck to you. And no regrets."

"No regrets," I said, and we shook hands.

There wasn't any point in going down to the street with her, and besides I had to phone the office. But before I did, I looked out, and she was just getting into a cab. A person looks different, somehow, when they don't know you're seeing them. I could see the way she looked to other people—not young any more, not the Sally I'd married, not even the Sally I'd talked with, all night in that cold house. She was a nice married woman who lived in Montclair and whose husband was a doctor; a nice woman, in shopping for the day, with a new spring hat and a fifty-trip ticket in her handbag. She'd had trouble in her life, but she'd worked it out. And, before she got on the train, she'd have a black-and-white soda, sitting on a stool at the station, or maybe she didn't do that any more. There'd be lots of things in her handbag, but I wouldn't know about any of them nor what locks the keys fitted. And, if she were dying, they'd send for me, because that would be etiquette. And the same if I were dying. But we'd had something and lost it—the way she said—and that was all that was left.

Now she was that nice Mrs. McConaghey. But she'd never be quite that to me. And yet, there was no way to go back. You couldn't even go back to the house in Meadowfield—they'd torn it down and put up an apartment instead.

So that's why I wanted to talk to you. I'm not complaining and I'm not the kind of fellow that gets nerves. But I just want to know—I just want to figure it out. And sometimes it keeps going round and round in your head. You'd like to be able to tell your children something, especially when they're growing up. Well, I know what we'll tell them. But I wonder if it's enough.

Not that we don't get along well when Bud and Barbara come to see us. Especially Barbara—she's very tactful and she's crazy about the twins. And now they're growing up, it's easier. Only, once in a while, something happens that makes you think. I took Barbara out sailing last summer. She's sixteen and a very sweet kid, if I say it myself. A lot of kids that age seem pretty hard, but she isn't.

Well, we were just talking along, and, naturally, you like to know what your children's plans are. Bud thinks he wants to be a doctor like McConaghey and I've no objection. I asked Barbara if she wanted a career, but she said she didn't think so.

"Oh, I'd like to go to college," she said, "and maybe work for a while, afterwards, the way mother did, you know. But I haven't any particular talents, dad. I could kid myself, but I haven't. I guess it's just woman's function and home and babies for me."

"Well, that sounds all right to me," I said, feeling very paternal.

"Yes," she said, "I like babies. In fact, I think I'll get married pretty young, just for the experience. The first time probably won't work, but it ought to teach you some things. And then, eventually, you might find somebody to tie to."

"So that's the way it is with the modern young woman?" I said.

"Why, of course," she said. "That's what practically all the girls say—we've talked it all over at school. Of course, sometimes it takes you quite a while. Like Helen Hastings' mother. She just got married for the fourth time last year, but he really is a sweet! He took us all to the matinee when I was visiting Helen and we nearly died. He's a count, of course, and he's got the darlingest accent. I don't know whether I'd like a count, though it must be fun to have little crowns on your handkerchiefs like Helen's mother. What's the matter, daddy? Are you shocked?"

317

"Don't flatter yourself, young lady—I've been shocked by experts," I said. "No, I was just thinking. Suppose we—well, suppose your mother and I had stayed together? How would you have felt about it then?"

"But you didn't, did you?" she said, and her voice wasn't hurt or anything, just natural. "I mean, almost nobody does any more. Don't worry, daddy. Bud and I understand all about it—good gracious, we're grown up! Of course, if you and mother had," she said, rather dutifully, "I suppose it would have been very nice. But then we'd have missed Mac, and he really is a sweet, and you'd have missed Lisa and the twins. Anyhow, it's all worked out now. Oh, of course, I'd rather hope it would turn out all right the first time, if it wasn't too stodgy or sinister. But you've got to face facts, you know."

"Face facts!" I said. "Dammit, Barbara!"

Then I stopped, because what did I have to say?

Well, that's the works, and if you've got any dope on it, I wish you'd tell me. There are so few people you can talk to—that's the trouble. I mean everybody's very nice, but that's not the same thing. And, if you start thinking too much, the highballs catch up on you. And you can't afford that—I've never been much of a drinking man.

The only thing is, where does it stop, if it does? That's the thing I'm really afraid of.

It may sound silly to you. But I've seen other people—well, take this Mrs. Hastings, Barbara talked about. Or my old friend at the club. I wonder if he started in, wanting to get married four times. I know I didn't—I'm not the type and you know it.

And yet, suppose, well, you do meet somebody who treats you like a human being. I mean somebody who doesn't think you're a little goofy because you know more about American Can than who painted what. Supposing, even, they're quite a lot younger. That shouldn't make all the difference. After all, I'm no Lothario. And Lisa and I aren't thinking of divorce or anything like that. But, naturally, we lead our own lives, and you ought to be able to talk to somebody. Of course, if it could have been Sally. That was my fault. But it isn't as if Maureen were just in the floor show. She's got her own specialty number. And, really, when you get to know her, she's a darned intelligent kid.

ALL AROUND THE TOWN

I like it, winter or summer. But I guess I like it the best when it gets really hot and they turn on the fire hydrants for a while and the little kids splash in the water. That's when the noise lasts till after twelve and, if you look out of the window, you can see a man in his shirt sleeves and his fat wife beside him, sitting out in front of the store in a couple of kitchen chairs. I know nobody's supposed to. But that's the way I like New York.

No, I was born in Brooklyn, but I don't remember much about that. We moved to the East Side afterwards, before I could remember. The old man was a watch repairer—I guess that's where I get my liking for tinkering at things. He worked at Logan's, up on Fourteenth, and I remember how disappointed I was when I found he didn't own the whole store. He was Swiss and Ma was Irish, so I've got the two sides to me. They get along well enough, usually, but sometimes they fight.

I know now he had disappointments, but I didn't know it as a kid. He was always talking about a nice place in the country, with chickens, but he never got there. Once or twice, before I was born,—I came along kind of later,—he tried to set up in a small town. But something always happened, and he had to come back to the city. He didn't really object to it, but he felt it wasn't right to raise his kids there. But Ma always said it was up to her to take care of that. She did a good job by us, too, and she kissed me on both sides of my face when I got the silver medal for penmanship at St. Aloysius's. I didn't tell her it was because I'd promised Jerry Toole I'd beat the mush off him if he came in ahead of me. He was always the one to get the prizes, and I thought it was time I had one of my own to take home and show. My old man made a little wooden box for it and carved my initials on top. It took him quite a little while to do it,—he was a slow worker, but very careful,—but it pleased him a lot. And me, too.

I guess I don't know how to tell a story, because, when I think about it, it gets all mixed up. They ask you what was the city like, in those days, and what are you going to tell them? I remember the horsecars, to be sure, and the gaslights in the streets, and the tangle of overhead wires, like a crazy spiderweb, and the big white stages. But, when you begin thinking back, you don't know if you're right or not. My old man had big gray moustaches that went out like a pair of wings, and he always wore a derby hat to his work. It was rounder, somehow, than they make derbies now—I'd recognize it among a million, but they don't have them any more. And, when Ma was baking, you could smell the clean, fresh bread all over the house. The first policeman I ever saw was standing under a gaslight, twirling his stick in front of his belly. We called him Mister Ryan and I thought him the greatest and largest man in the world. Well, that's the thing you remember. That, and the sprinkling carts, and the brown afternoon in the street, and the old woman who sold hot chestnuts, with her cheeks as red as red apples, a winter evening, under the El, when the horses were slipping on the ice.

All the same, it wasn't so big, then. I remember when the Flat-iron was the biggest one and the out-of-town people bought postcards, just the way they do, this moment, with the Empire State. It got built without our knowing it, almost—it went up into the sky. Nobody decided about it—it stretched like a boy growing up, and now, there it is. The city, I mean—yes, the city. I remember my tall, laughing Irish uncles stamping into the house and swinging Ma from one to another of them and kissing her till she'd slap their faces. She was always little Katy, the bird, to them, though she'd had a great hand in bringing most of them up. I remember when Uncle Ally got in the Fire Department and his coming around, proud as Punch, to show us his new uniform. A well-set-up man he was, and his helmet very impressive. He was killed in a big loft fire in the garment district, the year that I was sixteen. The whole wall fell like a stone and they couldn't get the bodies for two days.

All the same, they gave the three of them a Department funeral and there were pieces in all the papers about it. I think it helped break Ma's heart—he was her favorite brother. But I rode in the carriage with her and she sat up straight as a ramrod, in her new black clothes. Afterwards she had me cut the pieces out of the papers, and it wasn't till night that I heard her crying. I can hear the cry in my ears, though it's many years gone.

My old man and my uncles were polite enough to each other, but they didn't really get along. He liked to sit out on the stoop, after dinner, smoking his big pipe with the silver lid on it and reading the evening paper. But he was a quiet man, and when my uncles came in, full of life and gayety, he'd have less to say than ever, though he always sent to the corner for the beer. He'd never have a drop of whiskey in the house, except for medical purposes—but he liked the steam beer at Schaeffer's, though I never saw him take too much. The day he came home with the chill, Ma made him a toddy, but even then he wouldn't take it. It scared me to see him in bed in the daytime, with his red-bordered nightshirt on. When you're young, you never think your parents can get sick or die. I remember that. But he got over it; and it wasn't till after I was married that he died.

He liked Eileen and she was very good to him—I'll always remember that. She used to call him Father Weiss,—she was dainty in her conversation,—but he'd always say, "Joost Poppa, *mein liebliches Kind*." Then he'd stroke her hand, very gently, with the tips of his big, clever fingers. That was after Ma had gone, and we had the responsibility. The girls did what they could, but, of course, they had their own families by then, except Nellie, and she wouldn't come to see him if any of the others were coming.

It wouldn't be held a disgrace, now—certainly not. The kids pray to go into the movies—and isn't that the same? But we held it a disgrace to us. I guess Nellie was my favorite sister—she took more after the uncles than the rest of us. She wasn't pretty, exactly, but she had a black-haired imp in her, and she was the first to marry of all the girls. I can see her face under the bridal veil, looking frightened. That's funny for Nellie O'Mara, the Wild Irish Rose. O'Mara was my grandda's name—she took it when she ran off with her piano pounder and started showing her legs on the public stage. The old man, queer enough, didn't mind so much—he had European ideas about the theatre. But Ma was horrified and so were the other girls.

I was horrified myself—I had to fight three boys on account of it. And Nellie's husband, Ed Meany, would come around and sit on the stoop, looking as if he'd just had a tooth pulled and telling all he'd done for Nellie, and how, even now, he'd been willing to take her back. He was a good man, no doubt, but he talked till you'd feel like shooting him. It wasn't till I had my own trouble that I knew how he felt.

The other girls married all right and respectable,—Grace and

Kathleen,—though I never did think much of Carl Schuhmacher. He always looked too much like one of his own sirloin steaks, but that was Grace's affair, not mine, and the meat market's a good business. We thought she could have done better for herself, but I don't know, as things turned out. He had some trouble, during the war, till young Carl was killed at Cantigny. I guess he's forgotten the trouble—I don't mean forgotten young Carl. They've still got the picture in the parlor, and the uniform looks queer, now. But he and John Pollard—that's Kathy's husband—get on a lot better than they did. There was feeling between the two families for a long time, over the meat-carving set and the Irish lace doilies. Well, Grace was always a grabber, and she did her best to make John Pollard feel small. But he got to be principal of Van Twiller for six months before they retired him—and I've seen his office. He was the steady sort that works up, and they couldn't keep him out of the position, though they tried. Now he's got the testimonial framed and it means something to him. I know that by the way he looks at it, now and then. Their youngest's teaching at Hunter, and they make a lot of that.

II

I can't say I've had a bad life, though it hasn't been quite what I expected. If I'd gone in with Uncle Martin—he was always the clever one! And I was his favorite, in a manner of speaking. But I couldn't stand the bother of politics—not even when he got to be district leader. He might have gone far, I think, but he picked the wrong side, in the Hall. That's the unforgivable mistake. Then, later on, he had his trouble—well, the jury disagreed at both trials. But it was all over the papers, and that sticks to a man. My clever, low-spoken uncle! I remember him always, a little disdainful of the rest of them, and you felt he took a drink to be friendly, and yet not to be really friendly. And then, at the trial, he was an old man, with jowls and white hair, answering just as clever and low-spoken as he always had, and yet not making a good impression. Because times had changed—that was all—and yet, how would he have done different? It was in his blood to rise by any means he could lay hands on, and pull up his family, too. But I'm glad that it didn't interest me—though he helped me get my first position.

Well, now, I was young and strong, though you might not think it. I wanted to go on the Force—but then the job came along. My old man wanted me to follow in his own line of business. But I didn't feel like messing around all day with little wheels and springs and an eyeglass stuck in one eye. They were building the Subway in those days—well, that's how I started. It was good pay, for the time, and I wanted to marry Eileen.

It's queer what a man's work in life will turn out to be. You go around the top of the city—well, I know that, too. But it's underneath where I've worked, the strong part of my life. You don't often get to thinking of it—a man's work is his work, wherever it lies. But, if it wasn't for thousands of men whose names you've never heard of, all living their lives underground, it wouldn't be a city, or the same city. I'd think of it, now and again, on the night shift, when things got quiet above. They'd have gone to sleep by then,—yes, even the rich and proud,—but we'd be working. It's hard to put to you so you'll understand it. You see the place in the street where it's planked over, and the taxi has to slow up, and you start to swear. But, underneath, there's the work gangs, and the lights.

It gives you a pride, in a way, to be part of it—at least, at times. You feel as if the people just walking the streets were different people and didn't know. It's hard for me to explain that—I don't know the way to say it. But I'm glad I did what I did—if it did mean ending up in a change booth, and then the pension. It does for Martha and me.

Eileen always expected more of me, and maybe she was right to do so. But a young man, in his strength, that's bossing a gang —well, that's all a young man might like. He could well be wrong about it, but he'd have to be shown where he was wrong. But, when I found out what was happening, I broke every stick of furniture in the flat. I did so. She wasn't afraid of me, either— I'd have killed her if she had been. But she stood there, cold and proud, with the look she'd had when I first saw her, the look of a woman untouched. He'd come as a boarder because we had the extra room that wasn't needed for the baby after all—a whey-faced, shrewd little man. I wasn't as angry at him, for some queer reason—I think he did his best to be decent, through it all. But she was ambitious, always, and we had no children.

Well, he made the money—he made a great deal before he died. Mrs. Loring Masters and the big house on Long Island and the children sent to fine colleges, except for the one that killed himself. When the daughter was married, I saw the picture in the paper, and she had just the look of Eileen. I wished her no ill—I wished her great good fortune. I wished her mother no ill —yet I wondered if the man had really touched her, after all. There were times when we lay beside each other, in our youth, and asked no better. I know that, for that is not something a man forgets. And it was the same with her. But she wanted other than that.

I don't know how to tell it all—I wish I knew. How am I to tell what it's like to come home, to the quiet street, after the night shift, with nothing but the milkman's horse clopping his way along—and be tired to bone and marrow and yet satisfied? How am I to tell what it's like, day after day? The city stretches and you don't notice it, till one day you go to the Park, and the buildings have grown up like a fence around it. I remember talking to my Uncle Matthew. He'd had thirty-five years on the Force and retired as inspector, and he should know if anyone did. Well, he talked about many changes, in an old man's voice, and how there was still as much law in the end of a night stick as in many law books. But he didn't really touch it.

It reminds me of the one time I went to Proctor's when Nellie was on the bill. She did well, and I was shamed to the bone, but I couldn't help applauding. The audience liked her, too—they knew she came from Third Avenue and was one of their own. I've given her change at the window, since, and she didn't know me. Nobody ever looks at the man in the change booth—nobody knows if he has a face. Why should I be worried about that? Well, I'm not, to tell you the truth. But it's given me a chuckle, now and then, when somebody's come along and said, "Why, Ed!"

Have I given you any idea? Most likely not. I've seen Teddy Roosevelt, the young dude back from the war, and his teeth were just the way they are in the pictures. I've shook hands with John McGraw—and seen the sudden, white, Irish rage on his face when somebody yelled "Muggsy" at him out of the crowd. I've

seen the Mayor, by the Zoo, showing his boy the polar bears—
and him in his queer black hat and people leaving him alone.
But where do you begin and end? I remember John Pollard,
that's educated, telling me once about some city in Europe
where you dug down and under the city was the ruins of
another city and under that ruin another till you could not
come to the end of them. Now that's something any New
Yorker could understand. It's Jimmy Walker's town and Rabbi
Wise's, it's LaGuardia's and J. P. Morgan's and Cardinal Spell-
man's, and the new strong hitter on the Yankees' and Katharine
Cornell's. It belongs to the telephone repairmen and the Park
Avenue dolls, to the fellow that peddles the racing sheets and
the choirboys in the Cathedral and all the hackers in their cabs.
Now how would I say whose town it was, precisely? Yet I'd
like to know.

Well, now, there was my friend Louis Jordan, went into domestic service. It didn't seem work for a man to me, at first,
and yet I liked him well. I ran into him first at Joe's place, the
summer that Eileen had left me—a very dignified creature, though
drink was his weakness. But you could neither smell it nor see
it on him—at least at that time. The rich man he worked for
had closed his house for the summer and left Louis and his
wife the caretaking of it. A dignified creature, I say, with soft,
puffy hands and a face not far off a priest's. His wife was a
little thin woman, most respectable, in black. But, when he got to
know me well, he'd ask me back for a nip, now and then, at the
house. Man, dear, you never saw a kitchen stove to equal that one
—it could have roasted an ox. Then we'd have our nip and his
wife would run the cards for me, very considerate and respectable, for she knew I'd had troubles. And all around us and over
us was the big, grand, stately house with its pictures and its fine
furniture, and yet we the only things alive in it, like mice in a
cheese.

He took me through the whole of it, one warm Sunday afternoon. There was a bathtub of marble, though it looked like dusty
stone, and the man of the house had twenty suits left in his closet,
and yet he had others, for he'd not appear naked where he was.
It gave me a queer feeling to see all those suits, hanging up on
their hangers. Then, when we got back to the kitchen, we
found that Mrs. Jordan had got hold of the gin bottle and was

stretched out, highly respectable but stiff as a corpse, on the floor. So, after that, I knew his sorrow, as he had known mine. Yet, the next winter, I happened to pass by the house. There was a red carpet down and all the fine carriages drawing up at the door. And, just as the door opened, I saw Louis Jordan, like a sentinel on post in his dress suit, receiving them all, with the young men to help him. Very fine he looked, and not like the man with his collar off that I'd drunk with, in the kitchen. And she, no doubt, was helping equally, with the ladies. Well, that's a long time ago, and the house is gone.

III

I've seen some queer sights, I have. I've stuck my head up from a manhole and seen six elephants, marching down Eighth Avenue, holding on to each other's tails. It was only for the circus in Madison Square Garden, but it gave you a turn. Then there was the bar the midgets used to frequent. I don't remember the name of it, but I stumbled in there one night and thought I'd gone mad when all the little faces turned at me. I've seen other things as well. I've seen them shower the ticker tape and the torn paper from the high buildings and got a glimpse of the face of the man they were welcoming. It might be one face or another, but it looked white and dazzled. And next week you'd have forgotten his name.

I used to go to the ball games often, with Martha, and that's a sight, too, when the game goes into extra innings and the crowd sits tight and the shadow begins to grow on the infield. Her brother was with the Giants, for a year—Swede Nansen, they called him—a tall, blond, slow-spoken boy. He could pitch with the best, on his day, but he liked farming better, which is a queer thing in a man. I remember the time he struck out nine Cubs in five innings, and the yelling of the crowd. But the next year his arm went bad on him and nothing could be done for it. He played for Atlanta a while,—the South being recommended for him,—then he gave up the game and settled down to his farming, and now, every Christmas, he sends us a box of pecans. But his record's still in the books, and the game where he beat Alexander. I should like to see him again, for he was a man I respected, but I doubt now that I will.

All Around the Town

She's been a good wife to me, Martha, and never ashamed of a man that worked with his hands—though I do not do so any more. At one time we had the money, and that was a contrary experience. She was left five hundred dollars, and that sharp little fellow, Abe Leavis, told us what to buy. At first I felt queer, going into the grand office, but soon I saw my money was as good as another's. Yet, though I will not criticize any other man's work, it does not seem to me a man's occupation to do nothing but watch the figures change on a blackboard. They thought, for a while, that I was lucky, for those days had no sense to them at all. And indeed, I thought so myself. I've had men in their handmade suits ask me for advice, and take it, too. They'd have taken advice, at that time, from a horse, if the horse was winning on the market. Well, it was forty thousand dollars before it was nothing—so you can say that I've had the experience of riches. It takes a man's mind off his work—that's all I can say. But we had the sealskin coat for Martha—and the washing machine.

If I told you about Abe Leavis, that would be part of it, too. That was a rubber ball of a man, a rubber ball bounced up and down the pavements. I have seen him so thin and pitiful it would break your heart; I have seen him round and plump, with his pockets full of cigars. You could kill that man, but you could not put him down. But how he loved the smell and taste of the city! I'll forgive a man much for that. No, it wasn't my city he loved—it was Fifth and Park and the riches—the big shining toy-store where everything's for sale. It was like a tonic to him to pay maybe twenty dollars for a pair of theatre tickets and get there late for the play. But that's part of it, too.

Now there's whole sections and locations I've never seen. It wasn't so long ago that I visited my grandnephew, Francis. He married a Jewish girl when he'd finished his interneship— a pretty, bright young thing—and they've got an apartment on the Grand Concourse. I walked twenty blocks after I'd left them and it was like another city. And yet it couldn't have been any other city. It couldn't have been.

I don't know if it's the two rivers make it—though I knew the captain of the *Michael T. McQuillan*, and a good man he was and told me the work there is to get the big, proud liners into dock. I don't know if it's the climate that makes it—the fine fall and the dirty winter, the hot summer and the spring that comes with the flower carts and touches your heart. It's a healthy climate, I've always thought, though others may differ. Now when Martha and I were first married we'd go as far as Far Rockaway for a bite of the summer. And that was a change and healthy—but I noticed we were glad to get back where you knew the look of the streets. I don't know—I couldn't say—it's hard for me to tell.

Well, now, there's the being old. But we got along very comfortable. There's a lot of them move away—to Florida, let's say —and then they send you the postcards, saying what a fine time they're having. No doubt they are, if they like it, but I never could see it made them look any younger. There was my friend, the Dutchman, that retired from his delicatessen and went to live with his granddaughter at White Plains. It was a nice house, to be sure, and he kept the lawn very well cut. I congratulated him on that. Then he looked at me and there was a grief in his eyes. "Vy, Ed," he said, "it's all right. But you can't cut the lawn all day. I tell you, some nights, I vake up and listen for the noise of the El. And, ven it ain't there, I feel old. Ed, I'd give ten dollars if Mrs. Burke was to come in—the fussy one—just to tell me she vouldn't put up with this kind of service no more." Then his granddaughter came to tell him it was time for his nap, and, though she was very polite, I knew I should go away. Thank God, I've been spared that—though we've neither chick nor child.

It's cool enough in the flat, and if there's a breeze we get it. And there's always something to look at—the boys playing ball in the streets, shouting under the light, summer evenings, and the taxis drawing up to the apartment house opposite, and a young woman coming out, with bare arms. Phil Kelly, the doorman there, is a friend of mine, though he comes from Ulster. They'd be surprised, in that house, if they knew the things that I know about them. I don't mean any ugly things—just the odd little circumstances. It's my hope that the pretty dark girl will marry the young man with glasses. He's steadier than the one that's better-dressed. I'd like to tell her that, only how would I tell her?

There isn't a trace or a place of my childhood's house. There isn't a trace or a place of the house where I lived with Eileen. Now last year, when I went to the cemetery, it took me an hour to find Uncle Martin's grave, though they'd kept it decent, and he was a well-known man.

You'd think such a thing might make you sad, but again, it does not. It's comfortable, in a way, to be like the dust in the air. It's hard for me to tell it, and yet, what I mean is this. Last summer I went to the Fair, and that's a great sight, no doubt of it. Oh, the crowds and the proud buildings of the nations of the earth and the horns tooting "All around the town"!

It was some State Day when we went there, and there was the Governor of the State, with the sirens blowing in front of him to clear the way. Well, I wouldn't remember which State it was, but that makes little difference. There were all the top hats there to receive him, and that's only courtesy. And yet he was swallowed up in the Fair itself, and, except for the people from his own State, there was no one knew he was there, or cared at all. So it came upon me, that day—sitting on a bench, with my feet tired—it all came upon me. For they all seemed to pass by me, the rich and the great and the proud, with the sirens blowing in front of them. And yet, that wasn't the city, and when the Fair itself was finished, there'd be many still in the city that hadn't even seen it. It was a fine sight to see, but they hadn't missed it, in their lives.

And so it was with the most of us—and with the city itself. For it wasn't the mayors and the millionaires and the Presidents—though I've walked by the President's house and seen him go in. It was my Uncle Ally and my Uncle Matthew, my friend Louis Jordan and my sister, Nellie O'Mara, the boys that were on the gang with me and the boys that died underground. It's the small, new honeymoon couples, buying a coffee ring at the corner bakery, and the guards who walk the museums, clean and pudgy; the thieves in the morning round-up and the good men, like my old man, who live and die without notice. It's all that, and the moon at the end of the street where you never expected a moon.

I said, "Martha, I'm tired, I think," and she took me home. So next day, when I was no better, she called my grandnephew, Francis. He's been very kind, and, where some might be afraid of the hospital, I am not. It's a good, sunny room, the ward, and the nurses very attentive to an old man. From where I lie on my back, I can see the river.

329

So, since it's to be that way, I'm glad it's to be that way. Wouldn't I have been the fool to go to a place like White Plains and die there? A man could hardly die easy in those foreign places—a man who's seen what I've seen. I'm aware there are other cities. The day orderly comes from London, and we've talked about that one.

I was born in Brooklyn, but we moved to the East Side, afterwards. I remember my mother's baking bread, and the Empire State, when it was new. You won't remember Swede Nansen, though his record's in the book, but I remember him. You won't remember Martin O'Mara, but he was part of it. You won't remember Logan's on Fourteenth Street, but it was a fine, large store.

When they bomb the town to pieces, with their planes from the sky, there'll be a big ghost left. When it's gone, they'd better let the sea come in and cover it, for there never will be one like it in the ages of man again.

GLAMOUR

I used to read quite a lot of books when I was younger, but now they just make me sore. Marian keeps on bringing them back from the lending library and, occasionally, I'll pick one up and read a few chapters, but sooner or later you're bound to strike something that makes you sick. I don't mean dirt or anything—just foolishness, and people acting the way they never act. Of course, the books she reads are mostly love stories. I suppose they're the worst kind.

But what I understand least is the money angle. It takes money to get drunk and it takes money to go around with a girl—at least that's been my experience. But the people in those books seem to have invented a special kind of money—it only gets spent on a party or a trip. The rest of the time they might as well be paying their bills with wampum, as far as you can figure it out.

Of course, often enough, the people in books are poor. But then they're so darn poor, it's crazy. And, often enough, just when everything's at its worst, some handy little legacy comes along and the new life opens out before them right away, like a great big tulip. Well, I only had one legacy in my life and I know what I did with that. It darn near ruined me.

Uncle Bannard died up in Vermont in 1924, and when his estate was settled, it came to $1237.62 apiece for Lou and me. Lou's husband put her share in Greater Los Angeles real estate —they live out on the Coast—and I guess they've done pretty well. But I took mine and quit the firm I was with, Rosenberg and Jenkins, mechanical toys and novelties, and went to Brooklyn to write a novel.

It sounds crazy, looking back on it. But I was a bug about reading and writing in those days, and I'd done some advertising copy for the firm that pulled. And that was the time when everybody was getting steamed up about "the new American writers," and it looked like a game without much overhead. I'd just missed the war—I was seventeen when it finished—and I'd missed college because of father's death. In fact, I hadn't done much of anything I really wanted since I had to quit high school —though the novelty business was all right as businesses go. So when I got a chance to cut loose, I cut.

I figured I could easily live a year on the twelve hundred, and, at first, I thought of France. But there'd be the nuisance of learning frog-talk and the passage there and back. Besides, I wanted to be near a big library. My novel was going to be about the American Revolution, if you can picture it. I'd read "Henry Esmond" over and over and I wanted to write a book like that.

I guess it must have been a bunch of my New England ancestors that picked Brooklyn for me. They were pioneers, all right —but, gosh, how they hated to take any chance but a big one! And I'm like that myself. I like to feel tidy in my mind when I'm taking a chance.

I figured I could be as solitary in Brooklyn as I could in Pisa, and a lot more comfortable. I knew how many words it took to make a novel—I'd counted some of them—so I bought enough paper and a second-hand typewriter and pencils and erasers. That about cleaned out my ready cash. I swore I wouldn't touch the legacy till I was really at work. But I felt like a million dollars —I swear I felt as if I were looking for treasure—when I got into the subway that shiny autumn day, and started across the river to look for a room.

It may have been my ancestors that sent me to Brooklyn, but

Stephen Vincent Benét

I don't know what landed me at Mrs. Forge's. Old Wrestling Southgate, the one who was bothered with witches, would probably have called it a flowered snare of the fiend. And I'm not so sure, looking back, that he'd have been wrong.

Mrs. Forge opened the door herself—Serena was out. They'd talked about putting an ad in the paper but they'd just never got around to it; and, naturally, they wouldn't have put up a card. If it hadn't looked like the sort of house I'd wanted, I'd never have rung the bell. As it was, when she came to the door, I thought that I had made a mistake. So the first thing I did was beg her pardon.

She had on her black silk dress—the one with the white ruffles —just as if she were going out calling in the barouche. The minute she started to speak, I knew she was Southern. They all had that voice. I won't try to describe it. There's nothing worse than a whiny one—it beats the New England twang. But theirs didn't whine. They made you think of the sun and long afternoons and slow rivers—and time, time, time, just sliding along like a current, not going anywhere particular, but gay.

I think she liked my begging her pardon, for she took me in and gave me a slice of fruit cake and some lemonade. And I listened to her talk and felt, somehow, as if I'd been frozen for a long time and was just beginning to get warm. There was always a pitcher of lemonade in the ice-box, though the girls drank "coke," mostly. I've seen them come in from the snow, in the dead of winter, and drink it. They didn't think much of the cold, anyway, so they more or less pretended it didn't exist. They were that way.

The room was exactly what I wanted—big and sunny, with an outlook over a little backyard where there was the wreck of a forsythia bush and some spindly grass. I've forgotten to say the house was in one of those old-fashioned side-streets, not far from Prospect Park. But it doesn't matter where it was. It must be gone, now.

You know, it took all my nerve to ask Mrs. Forge the price. She was very polite, but she made me feel like a guest. I don't know if you can understand that. And then she couldn't tell me.

"Well, now, Mr. Southgate," she said, in that soft, gentle, helpless voice that ran on as inexorably as water, "I wish my daughter Eva had been here to receive you. My daughter Eva has accepted a business position since we came here for my daughter Melissa's art training. And I said, only this morning, 'Eva, honey, suppose Serena's away and some young person comes here, askin' for that room. I'll be bound to say somethin' to them, sugar, and I'll feel right embarrassed.' But just then some little boys started shoutin' down the street and I never did rightly hear what she answered. So if you're in a hurry, Mr. Southgate, I don't just know what we can do."

"I could leave a deposit," I said. I'd noticed, by this time, that the black silk had a tear in it and that she was wearing a pair of run-down ball-slippers—incredibly small they were. But, all the same, she looked like a duchess.

"Why, I suppose you could, Mr. Southgate," she said, with an obvious lack of interest. "I suppose that would be businesslike. You gentlemen in the North are always so interested in business. I recollect Mr. Forge sayin' before he died, 'Call them d—— Yankees if you like, Milly, but we've all got to live in the same country and I've met some without horns.' Mr. Forge was always so humorous. So, you see, we're quite accustomed to Northerners. You don't happen to be kin to the Mobile Southgates, do you, Mr. Southgate? You'll excuse an old lady's askin'—but you seem to favor them a little, now your face is in the light."

I'm not trying to put down just the way she talked—she didn't say "ah" and "nah"—it was something lighter and suaver. But her talk went on like that. They all did it. It wasn't nervousness or trying to impress you. They found it as easy and restful to talk as most of us do to keep still; and, if the talk never got anywhere, they'd never expected it would. It was like a drug—it made life into a dream. And, of course, it isn't that.

Finally, I simply went for my stuff and moved in. I didn't know how much I was paying or what meals would be included in it, but I somehow felt that these things would be shown unto me when the time was ripe. That's what an hour and a half with Mrs. Forge did to me. But I did resolve to have a clear understanding with "my daughter, Eva," who seemed to be the business head of the family.

Serena let me in when I came back. I gave her fifty cents to get in her good graces and she took an instant dislike to me which never wavered. She was small and black and withered, with bright little sparks of eyes. I don't know how long she'd been with them, but I thought of her growing on the family, like mistletoe, from immemorial time.

Whenever I heard her singing in the kitchen, I felt as if she were putting a private curse on me. "Honey-bird—" she'd croon —"honey-bird, no one gwine tuh fly away wid mah honey-bird. Ole buzzard, he try his wings—he flap and he flap—man wid a gun he see him—hi, hi, hi—shoot ole buzzard wid a buckshot and never tetch mah honey-bird."

I knew who the old buzzard was, all right. And it may sound funny—but it wasn't. It was spooky. Eva wouldn't see it; they'd all treat Serena like a combination of unavoidable nuisance and troublesome child. I don't understand how they can treat servants that way. I mean friendly and grand at the same time. It isn't natural.

It sounds as if I were trying to keep from telling about Eva. I don't know why I'm doing that.

I got unpacked and pretty well settled. My room was on the third floor, back, but I could hear the girls coming home. There'd be the door and steps and a voice saying, "Honey, I'm so tired —I'm just plumb dragged out," and Mrs. Forge saying, "Now, honey, you rest yourself." There were three of those. I kind of wondered why they were all so tired. Later on, I found that was just something they said.

But then Mrs. Forge would begin to talk and they wouldn't be tired any more. They'd be quite excited and there'd be a good deal of laughter. I began to feel very uncomfortable. And then I got stubborn. After all, I'd rented the room.

So, when Eva finally knocked at the door, I just grunted, "Come in!" the way you would to a chamber-maid. She opened the door and stood in the doorway, hesitant. I imagine Melissa had bet her she wouldn't have the nerve.

"Mr. Southgate, I believe?" she said, quite vaguely, as if I might be anything from a cloud to a chest of drawers.

"Dr. Livingstone, I presume?" I said. There was an old picture on the wall—the two Englishmen meeting formally in the middle of a paper jungle. But I'll hand her something—she saw I wasn't trying to be fresh.

"I reckon we have been making a lot of racket," she said. "But that's mostly Melissa. She never was rightly raised. Won't you

Glamour

give us the favor of your company downstairs, Mr. Southgate?
We-all don't act crazy. We just sound like it."

She was dark, you know, and yet she had that white skin.
There's a kind of flower called freesia—when the petals are very
white, they have the color of her skin. And there's a strong sweetness to it—strong and ghostly at the same time. It smells like
spring with the ghosts in it, between afternoon and dusk. And
there's a word they call glamour. It was there.

She had small white teeth and red lips. There was one little
freckle in the hollow of her throat—I don't know how she happened to have only one. Louisa was the beauty and Melissa the
artist. They'd settled it that way. I couldn't have fallen in love
with Louisa or Melissa. And yet, I liked to see them all together—
the three sisters—I'd liked to have lived in a big, cool house by a
river and spent my life seeing them all together. What fool
thoughts you get, when you're young! I'd be the Northern cousin
who managed the place. I used to send myself to sleep with it,
every night, for months.

Mrs. Forge wasn't in it, or Serena. It was a big place—it went
on for miles and miles. Most of the land wasn't good for much
and the Negroes were bone-lazy, but I made them work. I'd get
up in the first mist of morning and be in the saddle all day, overseeing and planning. But, always, I'd be coming back, on a tired
horse, up that flowery avenue and they'd be waiting for me on
the porch, the three white dresses bunched like a bouquet.

They'd be nice to me, because I was weary, and I'd go upstairs
to the room looking over the river and change out of my hot
clothes and wash. Then Eva would send me up a long drink with
mint in it and I'd take it slowly. After supper, when I wasn't doing accounts, they'd sing or we'd all play some foolish sort of
round game with ivory counters. I guess I got most of it out of
books, but it was very real to me. That's one trouble with books
—you get things out of them.

Often we got old, but it never seemed to change us much.
Once in a while the other girls were married and, sometimes, I
married Eva. But we never had any children and none of us ever
moved away. I kept on working like a dog and they accepted it
and I was content. We had quite a few neighbors, at first, but I
got tired of that. So I made it a river island you could only reach
by boat, and that was more satisfactory.

335

It wasn't a dream, you know, or anything sappy like that. I just made it up in my head. Toward the end of the year, I'd lie awake for hours, making it up, but it never seemed to tire me. I never really told Eva about it at all, not even when we were engaged. Maybe it would have made a difference, but I don't think so.

She wasn't the kind of person you'd tell any dreams to. She was in the dream. I don't mean she was noble or fatal or like a ghost. I've had her in my arms and she was warm and alive and you could have had children by her, because things are that way. But that wasn't the point—that wasn't the point at all.

She didn't even have much imagination. None of them had. They just lived, like trees. They didn't plan or foresee. I've spent hours trying to explain to Mrs. Forge that, if you had ten dollars, it wasn't just ten dollars, it was something you could put in a savings bank. She'd listen, very politely. But ten dollars, to her, was just something that went away. They thought it was fine if you had money, but they thought it was equally fine if you had a good-looking nose. Money was rather like rain to them—it fell or it didn't—and, they knew that there wasn't any way to make it rain.

I'm sure they'd never have come North at all, if it hadn't been for some obscure family dispute. They often seemed to wonder about it themselves. And I heard the dispute talked about dozens of times but I never really got the gist of it, except that it was connected with two things, the new spur-track to the turpentine plant, and Cousin Belle. "Cousin Belle, she just acted so mean— she gave up her manners," Mrs. Forge would say, placidly. "She left us no reco'se, Bannard—no reco'se at all." And then the girls would chime in. I suppose they got the money to come North from selling land to the turpentine plant, but even of that I am not sure.

Anyhow, they had golden visions, as they would have. Louisa was going to be a great actress and Melissa a great artist—and Eva —I don't know exactly what Eva expected, even now. But it was something. And it was all going to happen without any real work, it was going to fall from a cloud. Oh, yes, Melissa and Louisa went to classes and Eva had a job, but those, you felt, were stopgaps. They were passing the time till the cloud opened and the manna fell.

Glamour

I'll say this for them—it didn't seem to hurt them to have their visions fail. The only person it really hurt was me.

Because I believed them, at first. How could I help it? The dream I had wasn't so wrong. They were living on an island—an island in the middle of Brooklyn—a piece of where they came from. People came to the house—art students and such—there were always plenty of young men. But, once inside the house, they submitted to the house. Serena would pass the cold ham, at supper, and you'd look out of the window and be surprised to find it snowing, for the window should have been open and the warm night coming through. I don't know what roomers they'd ever had before, but in my time there was only myself and Mr. Budd. He was a fat little clerk of fifty, very respectable, and he stayed because of the food, for Serena was a magnificent, wasteful cook.

Yes, I believed it, I believed in it all. It was like an enchantment. It was glamour. I believed in all they said and I saw them all going back to Chantry—the three famous sisters with their three distinguished husbands—like people in a fairy-tale.

We'd all have breakfast together, but the only person who talked much then was Mr. Budd. The Forges never were properly alive till later in the day. At breakfast, you saw them through a veil. Sometimes I'd feel my heart beat, staring at Eva, because she looked like one of those shut flowers in greenhouses—something shut and mysterious so you fairly held your breath, waiting for it to open. I suppose it was just because she took a long time to wake up.

Then Mr. Budd and the girls would go away, and, when my bed was made, I'd go up and work. I'm not saying much about the novel, but I worked hard on it. I'd made a little chart on cardboard with 365 squares and each day I'd ink one in.

I'd go out for lunch and take a walk afterwards. A man has to have regular exercise, and that's free. Then I'd work some more, until they started to come home. I couldn't work after that—not after the first months. But I'd make myself not listen for Eva's step.

The first time I kissed Eva was the New Year's party. One of Louisa's beaus had brought some red wine and we were singing and fooling around. Serena was off for the evening and Eva and I were out in the kitchen, looking for clean glasses. We were both feeling gay and it just seemed natural. I didn't even think of it again till the next afternoon, when we'd all gone to the movies. And then I suddenly began to shake all over, as if I had a chill, remembering, and she said, "What is it, honey?" and her hand slipped into my hand.

That was how it began. And that night I started inventing the river plantation. And I'm not a fool and I've been around. But I held hands with that girl through January, February, and most of March before I really kissed her again. I can't explain it at all. She wasn't being coy or mean or trying to fight me. It was as if we were floating downstream in a boat together, and it was so pleasant to look at her and be near her, you didn't need any more. The pain hadn't started, then.

And yet, all through that time, something in me was fighting, fighting, to get out of the boat, to get away from the river. It wasn't my river at all, you know. It never was. And part of me knew it. But, when you're in love, you haven't got common sense.

By the end of March, the novel was more than half finished. I'd allowed two months for revision and making contacts, which seemed sensible. And, one evening, it was cold, and Eva and I took a walk in the park. And when we came in, Mrs. Forge made us some hot cocoa—the other girls had gone to bed early, for once—and, while we were drinking it, Mrs. Forge fell asleep in her chair. And we put down our cups, as if it were a signal, and kissed—and the house was very quiet and we could hear her breathing, like sleep itself, through the long kiss.

Next morning, I woke up and the air felt warm and, when I looked out in the yard, there were leaves on the forsythia bush. Eva was just the same at breakfast, shut and mysterious, and I was just the same. But, when I went up to work, I shook my fist at old Wrestling Southgate, the fellow that was bothered with witches. Because I was going to marry Eva, and he could go to grass.

I tell you, they didn't plan or foresee. I told Mrs. Forge very straight just how I stood—finances and everything—and they treated it like a party. They were all as kind and excited as they could be, except Serena. She just refused to believe it and sang a lot more about buzzards. And, somehow or other, that made me feel queerer than ever. Because I knew Serena hated me but I knew she was a real person. I could understand her, she was close

Glamour

to the ground. And I loved the others but I didn't understand them, and sometimes I wouldn't be sure they were quite real. It was that way with Eva, even though we were in love.

I could kiss her but I couldn't be sure that she was always there when I kissed her. It wasn't coldness, it was merely another climate. I could talk for hours about what we were going to do when we were married and every time I stopped she'd say, "Go on, honey, it makes me feel so nice to hear you talk." But she'd have been as pleased if I'd sung it instead. God knows I didn't expect her to understand the novelty business, or even writing. But, sometimes, I'd honestly feel as if we didn't speak the same language. Which was foolish, because she wasn't foreign.

I remember getting angry with her one evening because I found out she was still writing to this boy friend, down South, and hadn't even told him about us. She opened her eyes very wide.

"Why, honey," she said, in the most reasonable of voices, "I couldn't stop writing Furfew right off like that. I've just always been sort of engaged to Furfew."

"Well, now you're engaged to me," I said.

"I know," she said. "That's why I can't stop writing him, honey. It would hurt Furfew something dreadful if he knew I had to stop writing him because I was engaged to you."

"Look here," I said, wondering which of us was crazy, "are we going to be married?"

"Of co'se, honey."

"Then what," I said, "has this Furfew got to do with it? Are you engaged to him or me?"

"Of co'se I'm engaged to you, honey, and we're going to get married. But Furfew, he's kind of like kin, and we been engaged a long time. It seems right mean and uncivil to break off with him short like that."

"I don't believe it," I said, "I don't believe there are any Furfews. It sounds like something you grow under glass. What's he like?"

She thought for a long time.

"He's right cute," she said finally. "But he's got a little doin's of a black moustache."

I managed to find out, however, that he owned the turpentine plant and was considered quite the John D. Rockefeller of Chantry. I was so used to no one in Chantry ever having any money that was worth anything, that this came as an unpleasing surprise. After that, Furfew used to try to come to the river plantation in a very shiny motor-launch with a red-and-white awning and I would warn him off with a shotgun.

But then the money business began. You like to give a girl presents when you're in love—you like to do things right. Well, Lord knows, Eva was no gold-digger—she was as likely to be pleased with a soda as a pair of imported gloves. On the other hand, she was as likely to be pleased with the gloves.

I kept on schedule with the work, but I couldn't with the money. Each week, I'd be just a little over the line. I tell you, the people in books don't know about money. The people who write them can tell what it's like to be broke. But they don't tell what it's like to go around with clothes enough to cover you and food enough to satisfy you, and still have your heart's desire depend on money you haven't got.

Sure, I could have gone back in the novelty business and Eva could have kept on working. That would have been right for nine people out of ten. But it wouldn't have been right for the way I felt about Eva. It can be like that.

I wanted to come to her—oh, like a rescuer, I suppose. Like a prince, like the Northern cousin that saved the plantation. I didn't want to make the best of things—I wanted it all. You can't compromise with glamour. Or that's the way I feel.

Besides, I'd put in eight months' work on that novel and it didn't seem sensible to throw it all away. It might be a ladder to climb out on. It might have been.

Eva never complained, but she never understood. She'd just say we could all go back and live in Chantry. Well, I'm not that kind of man. If it had only been the river plantation! But, by now, I knew Chantry as well as if I'd been born there, and there wasn't a thing for me to do. Except maybe a job in Furfew's turpentine plant. And wouldn't that have been pretty?

Then, gradually, I got to know that the Forges, too, were almost at the end of their string. I had to get it casually—they never talked about those things directly. But when you keep on spending what you've got, there comes a time when you don't have it any more. Only, it always surprised them. I wish I was built that way.

Glamour

It was the middle of July by this time, and one Saturday afternoon Eva came home and said she'd been let off at her office. They were cutting down the staff. I'd just been going over my accounts, and when she told me that, I started laughing as if I couldn't stop.

She looked rather surprised at first, but then she laughed, too.

"Why, honey," she said, "you're the killin'est. You always take things so serious. And then, sometimes, you don't take them serious a bit."

"It's an old Northern custom," I said. "They call it 'Laugh, clown, laugh.' For God's sake, Eva, what are we going to do?"

"Why, honey," she said, "I suppose I could get me another position." She never told me it was up to me. She never would have. "But I just sort of despise those mean old offices. Do you think I ought to get me another position, honey?"

"Oh, darling, it doesn't matter," I said, still laughing. "Nothing matters but us."

"That's mighty sweet of you, honey," she said and she looked relieved. "That's just the way I feel. And, when we get married, we'll fix things up right nice for Melissa and Louisa, won't we? And mother, of co'se, because she just can't stand Cousin Belle."

"Sure," I said. "Sure. When we're married, we'll fix up everything." And we went out in the back yard to look at the forsythia bush. But that night, Furfew brought his launch inshore and landed on the lower end of the island. He pitched camp there, and I could see his fire at night, through a glass.

I can't describe the next two months very well. They were all mixed up, the reality and the dream. Melissa and Louisa had to give up their classes, so we were all home, and lots of people came to the house. Some of them were callers and some of them were bill-collectors but, whoever they were, they generally stayed to a meal. Serena never minded that, she liked company. I remember paying a grocery bill, with almost the last of my legacy, toward the end. There were eight hams on the bill and ten cases of "coke." It hadn't been paid for a long time.

Often, we'd all pile into an old Ford that belonged to one of the art students and go down to a public beach for the day. Eva didn't care so much about swimming but she loved to lie in the sand. And I'd lie beside her, painfully happy, and we'd hardly say anything at all. My God, but she was beautiful against those beach colors—the clear greens of the water and the hot white and tan of the sand. But then, she was just as beautiful, sitting in the plush rocker in the front parlor, under that green lamp.

They say the time between the Ordinance of Secession and the firing on Sumter was one of the gayest seasons Charleston ever had. I can understand that. They'd come to the brink of something, and fate was out of their hands. I got to feel that way.

Everything mixed, I tell you, everything mixed. I'd be sitting on the beach with Eva and, at the same time, I'd be riding around the river plantation, getting reports from my foreman and planning years ahead. I got to love that place. Even toward the end, it was safe, it didn't change. Of course, we kept having more and more trouble with Furfew; he kept extending his lines from the lower end of the island, but it never came to actual warfare—just fights between our men.

Meanwhile, I finished the novel and started revising it. And sometimes Eva would say why didn't we get married, anyway, and I knew we couldn't. You can't get married without some future ahead of you. So we started having arguments, and that was bad.

Why didn't I just seduce her like the big, brave heroes in books? Well, there were times when I thought it might be the answer for both of us. But it never happened. It wasn't shame or good principles. It just isn't so awfully easy to seduce a dream.

I knew they were writing letters but I didn't want to know any more. I knew the legacy was gone and my savings account was going, but I didn't care. I just wanted things to go on.

Finally, I heard that Furfew was coming North. I was going around like a sleepwalker most of the time, then, so it didn't hit me, at first. And then it did hit me.

Eva and I were out in the back yard. We'd fixed up an old swing seat there and it was dusky. Serena was humming in the kitchen. "Ole buzzard he fly away now—buzzard he fly away." I can't sing, but I can remember the way she sang it. It's funny how things stick in your head.

Eva had her head on my shoulder and my arms were around her. But we were as far away as Brooklyn and New York with the bridges down. Somebody was making love, but it wasn't us.

"When's he coming?" I said, finally.

Glamour

"He's drivin' up in his car," she said. "He started yesterday."
"Young Lochinvar complete with windshield," I said. "He ought to be careful of those roads. Has he got a good car?"
"Yes," she said. "He's got a right pretty car."
"Oh, Eva, Eva," I said. "Doesn't it break your heart?"
"Why, honey," she said. "Come here to me."
We held each other a long time. She was very gentle. I'll remember that.

I stayed up most of that night, finishing revision on the novel. And, before I went to sleep, Furfew came to the house on the river plantation and walked in. I was standing in the hall and I couldn't lift a hand to him. So then I knew how it was going to be.

He came in the flesh, next afternoon. Yes, it was a good car. But he didn't look like Benedict Arnold. He was tall and black-haired and soft-voiced and he had on the sort of clothes they wear. He wasn't so old, either, not much older than I was. But the minute I saw him beside Eva, I knew it was all up. You only had to look at them. They were the same kind.

Oh, sure, he was a good business man. I got that in a minute. But, underneath all the externals, they were the same kind. It hadn't anything to do with the faithfulness or meanness. They were just the same breed of cats. If you're a dog and you fall in love with a cat, that's just your hard luck.

He'd brought up some corn with him and he and I sat up late, drinking it. We were awfully polite and noble in our conversation but we got things settled just the same. The funny thing is, I liked him. He was Young Lochinvar, he was little Mr. Fix-it, he was death and destruction to me, but I couldn't help liking him. He could have come to the island when Eva and I were married. He'd have been a great help. I'd have built him a house by the cove. And that's queer.

Next day, they all went out in the car for a picnic, and I stayed home, reading my novel. I read it all through—and there was nothing there. I'd tried to make the heroine like Eva, but even that hadn't worked. Sometimes you get a novelty like that—it looks like a world-beater till you get it into production. And then, you know you've just got to cut your losses. Well, this was the same proposition.

So I took it down to the furnace and watched it burn. It takes quite a while to burn four hundred sheets of paper in a cold furnace. You'd be surprised.

On my way back, I passed through the kitchen where Serena was. We looked at each other and she put her hand on the bread-knife.

"I'll like to see you burning in hell, Serena," I said. I'd always wanted to say that. Then I went upstairs, feeling her eyes on my back like the point of the bread-knife.

When I lay down on the bed, I knew that something was finished. It wasn't only Eva or the novel. I guess it was what you call youth. Well, we've all got to lose it, but generally it just fades out.

I lay there a long time, not sleeping, not thinking. And I heard them coming back and, after a while, the door opened gently and I knew it was Eva. But my eyes were shut and I didn't make a move. So, after another while, she went away.

There isn't much else to tell. Furfew settled everything up—don't tell me Southerners can't move fast when they want to—and the packers came and four days later they all started back for Chantry in the car. I guess he wasn't taking any chances, but he needn't have worried. I knew it was up. Even hearing Cousin Belle had "come around" didn't excite me. I was past that.

Eva kissed me good-by—they all did, for that matter—the mother and the three sisters. They were sort of gay and excited, thinking of the motor-trip and getting back. To look at them, you wouldn't have said they'd ever seen a bill-collector. Well, that was the way they were.

"Don't write," I said to Eva. "Don't write, Mrs. Lochinvar."

She puckered her brows as she did when she was really puzzled.

"Why, honey, of co'se I'll write," she said. "Why wouldn't I write you, honey?"

I am sure she did, too. I can see the shape of the letters. But I never got them because I never left an address.

The person who was utterly dumbfounded was Mr. Budd. We camped in the house for a week, getting our own meals and sleeping under overcoats—the lease wasn't up till the first and Furfew had made an arrangement with the owner. And Mr. Budd couldn't get over it.

"I always knew they were crazy," he said. "But I'll never get such cooking again." I could see him looking into a future of boarding-houses. "You're young," he said. "You can eat anything. But when a man gets my age——"

He was wrong, though. I wasn't young. If I had been, I wouldn't have spent that week figuring out three novelties. Two of them were duds, but the third was Jiggety Jane. You've seen her—the little dancing doll that went all over the country when people were doing the Charleston. I made the face like Serena's at first, but it looked too lifelike, so we changed the face. The other people made most of the money, but I didn't care. I never liked the darn thing anyway. And it gave me a chance to start on my own.

They couldn't stop me after that. You're harder to stop, once you get rid of your youth. No, I don't think it was ironic or any of those things. You don't, outside of a book. There wasn't any connection between the two matters.

That fall I met Marian and we got married a year later. She's got a lot of sense, that girl, and it's worked out fine. Maybe we did have the children a little quick, but she'd always wanted children. When you've got children and a home, you've got something to keep you steady. And, if she gets a kick out of reading love stories, let her. So I don't have to.

In a book, I'd have run across Eva, or seen Furfew's name in a paper. But that's never happened and I suppose it never will. I imagine they're all still in Chantry, and Chantry's one of those places that never gets in the news. The only thing I can't imagine is any of them being dead.

I wouldn't mind seeing Furfew again, for that matter. As I say, I liked the man. The only thing I hold against him is his moving them back, that way, before the lease was up. It was all right and he had his reasons. But they had two weeks left—two weeks till the first. And that would just have finished the year.

And when I get to sleep nowadays, Marian's there in the next bed, so that's all right, too. I've only tried to go back to the river plantation once, after a convention in Chicago when I was pretty well lit. And then, I couldn't do it. I was standing on the other side of the river and I could see the house across the water. Just the way it always was, but it didn't look lived in. At least nobody came to the window—nobody came out.

NO VISITORS

When the man in the bed woke up, it was early in the after-noon. He had learned, some weeks before, that it was a good thing, when you woke up, to hold yourself perfectly still for a moment, until you were wide awake. In that way you wouldn't make an unexpected movement and the pain, if any, wouldn't jump at you. It was the jumping at you that mattered—if you merely lay still and let it seep into you, you could stand it quite nobly and heroically, even if no one else were around. But this afternoon there was nothing—just a little whisper, a little rem-iniscence—nothing real. Just enough to make you conscious that there had been a great deal of it, once. It was wonderful.

"Boy!" said John Blagden to himself. "You're going to get well. Do you know it? You're going to be O.K."

He sat up a little higher in bed and listened to the sounds of Floor 7. The radio was on as usual, next door, at "No Visitors," muted and throbbing—the old guy across the hall was getting a different program. "Now, Lucy Lee, don't you worry—we'll get them cows back for you." It was a little loud, but John Blagden didn't mind. The old guy was just a mild heart case—let him amuse himself. When you'd had a McWhirter, with adhesions, you could afford to be generous to people like that.

As he often did, when he waked up, he had a sense of the whole big mechanism of the hospital, cut off from the rest of the world, yet self-sufficient, like a boat or a train. That was a hang-over from the dreams after the operation. But it made an amount of sense. There was a routine, with fixed stops, and you saw a great deal of people you would probably never see again. Sometimes you didn't even see them—just knew them as you knew his neighbor, No Visitors, from a card stuck in a door and a radio heard through the wall. Nevertheless, he had been able to build up a pretty good picture of his neighbor. She was small and faded and whiny, and she put on a bright pink bed jacket before the doctor came. She didn't like Orson Welles, but she just loved Nelson Eddy and, though she complained about the food, she didn't want to die. He wondered if she had any children —there was probably a toothy, successful son somewhere. The grandchildren weren't brought to see her, because she'd cry at them. But the son sent flowers on Monday, and she talked to the nurses about him. Yes, that would be it. Afterwards, when it was over, the marcelled daughter-in-law would talk about mother's illness to her friends, with a proprietary pride. "Ed had everything possible done—you know how generous Ed is!" No, he couldn't really like No Visitors. But it must be tough, being No Visitors, day after day.

He could do with a cigarette. When he stretched his arm for it, the shadow of pain increased by a fraction, but that had no significance. He lit the cigarette cautiously and inhaled. For the first time, it tasted right, not like hay and ether. He drew the smoke all the way inside him—inside his body that had been sick and was getting well.

"Have a nice nap?" said the nurse, coming in. "That's a good boy."

She smiled, professionally, and put cold fingers on his wrist, glancing at her watch. Some of their hands were warm and some were cold, but they were all nice girls, except for the one night nurse who had said she had no orders to give him the hypo, that time. He didn't even know what she looked like, but he had hated her for a long while. Now, it seemed silly to have hated her —indeed, silly to have hated anybody. *I'm Tiny Tim, himself and in person,* he thought. *But I don't mind.*

"How is it outside?" he said.

"It's cold," said the nurse, "but I like it cold. I'm from Vermont. A lot of the girls don't like it, but I do. Don't you want the bed up—you'll want to read your book, I guess."

She went to work, smoothly and efficiently, fixing the pillows, cranking the bed with the little crank, while he thought about her being from Vermont. As she bent to lift him, her black hair was neat under her cap and her body touched him, impersonally. It was funny, being taken care of by somebody you knew as well and yet as little as you knew a nurse. Must be funny for them too.

"All righty?" she said, smiling.

"All righty," he said. "Oh, look, would you just get me that board? I might do a little work."

"Did doctor say ——" said the nurse.

"Oh, it's O.K. with Doctor Dennis." said John Blagden. "I've talked to him. Anyhow, I've got to start making some money or you'll throw me out for nonpayment of dues."

"I guess we're not worrying," said the nurse. "A famous author and everything." She shook her head. "You men," she said. "Always wanting to get back to your business. There's a very nice gall bladder in 735 and he keeps in touch with his office three times a day. But it's not so good for him—he's the fussy kind. Always fussing. I'd pull out his phone if I were Doctor De Lacey. Lucky I'm not, I guess."

"Am I the fussy kind?" said John Blagden, unable to help himself.

"No, you're a model patient. Only I'm not saying what model," said the nurse. It was, obviously, a routine jest.

John Blagden laughed obediently.

"That's what I always tell them," said the nurse, with satisfaction. "They're all model patients—only I'm not saying what model. It makes them see the humorous side of it."

"I can see it would," said John Blagden. He drew a breath. "Doctor Dennis didn't come in, did he?" he said, in a slightly altered voice. "I mean, while I was taking my nap."

The nurse shook her head. "No, doctor hasn't been on the floor since I came on," she said. "But he'll be in."

"He was going to look at my pictures," said John Blagden. "He and Doctor Seaver. So I was just wondering."

"Now, don't you worry about your pictures," said the nurse. "Any time Doctor Seaver operates, things are going to be all right." She spoke almost reprovingly. "Of course, they have to take the pictures afterwards," she said. "Just to check."

"All the same, he must lose some patients," said John Blagden, drawing on his cigarette. "I mean anyone must."

"Well, there was that poor old man—such a sweet old man," said the nurse. "But that was before you came in. Gee, that was a shame, though—I felt awfully sorry for his family. Such nice people. They were so appreciative, too—they knew Doctor Seaver had done everything he could."

"What was the matter?" said John Blagden.

"Complications," said the nurse, with a veil on her face. "But you don't have to worry. It wasn't a bit like yours." She looked at her watch. "Gee, I've got to hurry," she said. "I'm late now with my pulses. But if you want anything you know what to do."

348

No Visitors

"You bet," said John Blagden. He stubbed out the cigarette and lay back. It was fine to lie back, to carry on a normal conversation. It was fine to be able to talk about a nice old man who'd had complications and not have it worry you. In fact, everything was fine. He'd better call Rosalie and tell her so.

He lifted the phone, gave the number.

"Is Mrs. Blagden there? . . . Oh, hello, Edna. . . . Yes, this is Mr. Blagden. . . . Yes, I'm much better, thanks. . . . All right, I'll hold on."

He waited, tasting the moment, while little footsteps went away inside the phone and something crackled. Then there was the warm, known voice.

"Hello, honey. . . . Oh, perfectly fine. I had a nap. Pete's coming in later to tell me about the pictures. And look, honey, don't try to come up this evening. It looks darn cold. . . . No, honestly, don't. Charlie may come in, and if he doesn't I'll just lie around and work. I think I've got a new slant on the chapter. How are the kids?"

He listened, talked and laughed. The warm, known voice told him the small familiar things—about Susan's being in the play and Bill's arithmetic. They were good to hear. He could see them all, living in the apartment without him, as if he were looking into a doll's house. They looked pleasant, a pleasant family. They had a dog and goldfish, a servant and food on plates and lamps that turned off and on. The doll called Father wasn't there, right now, but that would get fixed, in time.

He'd never much thought of their being a family before—never stood off from them to look. It seemed, in a sense, ridiculous that he, John Blagden, should have a family. As if he were pretending. And yet, they were there. They'd made something, he and Rosalie, something that wasn't just getting married and renting an apartment. They had done so, almost without thinking, and yet it was going to go on.

" 'By, honey," he said. "Take care of yourself." He heard the warm voice, " 'By, darling." *Yes, we've done it pretty well,* he thought. *Poor kid—this has been tough on her. She was scared, that night. I could see her being scared and not showing it. Well, we'll make it up, somehow. You're a lucky stiff, Blagden. You don't know how lucky you are. You might have had a wife like Jo Pritchett and children with web feet.*

349

He put back the phone and stared at the sheets of yellow paper on the board. It seemed a geologic age since he had last written words on yellow paper, but that, too, was going to be all right. He could see, now, that the last two chapters of the novel were bad—he must have been sick when he wrote them. But he had a new slant now, and could push ahead. He drew a few squiggles, a house with smoke coming out of the chimney and a bird with spotted wings. That was necessary, for some reason. Then he crumpled that piece of paper, threw it on the floor and began to write.

An hour later he put the pencil down. About five hundred words, maybe. Not much, but a start. And it came all right—it had left him tired, but it came. It was going to be a good book—maybe better than that. At forty-three, you ought to be able to write a good book, if you were ever going to. The old boys had. He saw deliciously and for a large, childish instant the long reviews, all saying the same thing. It didn't matter, it meant nothing; you wrote for a different reason—but, when it came, it was like honey on the tongue. He had had it just once before, for *The Years Are Bold*, eight years ago, and he was still known as the author of *The Years Are Bold*. But the new one was going to change that. He had the stuff to change it, now.

There was nothing like a blank sheet of yellow paper and a pencil in the hand—neither love nor health nor youth. There was nothing comparable. He supposed Pete Dennis got an equal kick out of medicine, but he did not see how Pete could.

Now the shadow of pain had strengthened, but you could expect that, still, in the afternoon. You didn't get over a serious operation in a day or a week. Only now the docs knew what to do. *I suppose, fifty years ago I'd be dead*, he thought solemnly. It was good to be able to think of that quickly and without fear. He took out the thing in the secret part of his mind and looked at it. Yes, he had been afraid to die. Even talking offhandedly with Pete and in spite of the pain, it had come for a moment like a wave, the blind primal terror. He'd held on to Rosalie's hand. And then they'd given him the shot and you had to be a gentleman. But the terror had been there.

There was a knock at the door. "Mr. Fentriss to see you, Mr. Blagden." Then Charlie, a trifle hushed, as all visitors were, and not knowing quite what to do with the flowers. He was glad to see old Charlie, with his crisp, waxed moustache and his good suit.

"Well," he said. "You horse thief. Thanks a lot. They look swell."

"You look swell yourself," said Charlie. "I think you're faking." He sat down on the edge of a chair, as visitors did.

"Oh, I'm fine," said John Blagden. "It was just a little McWhirter."

"A little what?" said Charlie.

"It's what they call it," said John Blagden, "when they cut a lot of you out and sew it together again. They found some adhesions, too," he said, with pride.

"And you were three hours on the table and the doctors said it was a miracle," said Charlie. He grinned. "I know," he said. "What I do for ten per cent! I bet I've had more long-distance operations than any man in New York. Well, I'm glad it's over. We were kind of worried." His eyes brightened. "Done any work?"

"No, Simon Legree. But I'm going to."

"That's good," said Charlie. His waxed moustache bristled like a friendly cat's. "A couple of things came up," he said. "I haven't bothered you about them, but I just thought we'd run through them. TDS wants to do a version of *The Flowers That Bloom* on their workshop hour. They'll only pay a hundred—it's sustaining—but the hour's been getting attention, so I said all right." He paused. "Hank Lieber wants another Ma Hudgins story."

"I won't," said John Blagden. "I'm sick of Ma. And I want to get ahead with the novel."

"All right," said Charlie. "But they'll go up two hundred and fifty, and I had to ask you." His voice was sad.

"Tell them I'll think about it," said John Blagden. "In other words, tell them to hell with it, in a nice way."

"All right," said Charlie. "But I just thought, coming up here —well, suppose Ma Hudgins had an operation. You ought to have the background cold by now."

"Body snatcher!" said John Blagden, with affection. "Tell them I'll think about it."

"All right," said Charlie, "but just remember, if you do, it establishes the new price. Now ——"

He went on; John Blagden listened and answered. It was good

to talk about work, to hear that this was a hit and that wasn't doing so well—to get back into the familiar, smoky world of shop-
talk and publishers' gossip and contracts and prices. At the end,
Charlie rapidly told three funny stories, picked up his neat hat
and neat overcoat and left, with an unexpected "When you're
over this, you'll feel a lot better, fella. I did, after my bust."

"I never knew you had a bust," said John Blagden.

"That was when you were in England," said Charlie. "They
had to give me two transfusions. But I've taken a lot better care
of myself ever since. Well, I'll call Rosalie and tell her you're
just a big bluff."

He left, and John Blagden thought about Ma Hudgins. Charlie
was right, as Charlie generally was. *Ma Hudgins Goes to the
Hospital* was a definite story, worth a definite price. He was
sick of writing Ma Hudgins stories, but he could begin to feel
the plot form in his mind. Well, plenty of time.

The orderly came in.

"Afternoon, Mr. Blagden."

"Afternoon, Jim." He rolled over, gingerly. He didn't ask
what his temperature was—only new patients did that and he was
an old inhabitant. When the orderly had gone, however, he wondered. There might be a little temperature—just a little. The bed
felt scratchier and less comfortable than it had an hour ago. But,
even if there were a little temperature, it didn't matter. He closed
his eyes.

When he opened them again, the room was dark and there
was a presence at the door. "Hello," he said, with a thick tongue.

"Hello, Jack," said Pete Dennis. "Did I wake you up?"

"Nope," said John Blagden. "I wasn't really sleeping. Come in,
Pete, and switch on the light."

Pete came in, as always, diffidently. He had dull red hair and
a pleasant, ugly face. His white coat was a little rumpled, but it
suited him. He sat down in a chair, looking big for it.

"Well," he said, "what kind of day has it been?"

"Oh, fine," said John Blagden. "I even did a little work."

"On the novel?"

"Yes."

"That's fine. Lord!" said Pete Dennis, "I don't see how you
do it. When I even have to write a report, I sweat."

"It's a gift," said John Blagden, smiling. "Just naked genius."

He leered at his friend. "I'm going to do a Ma Hudgins about a hospital. The hero will be a man in white."

"Oh, for God's sake!" said Pete Dennis, with patient despair.

"Charlie suggested it," said John Blagden. "It won't be very bad. You'll be a clean-eyed young idealist, but you won't have to discover the secret of cancer or anything."

"Thanks," said Pete Dennis. His voice sounded friendly but absent, and a small cold wave went over John Blagden's skin.

"Well," he said, very casually, "did you look at the pictures?"

"Yes," said Pete Dennis, "I went over them with Seaver." He paused. "We went over the last tests, too," he said. "It's nothing to worry about, Jack. But, talking it over, we decided we might have to go in again."

"You decided what?" said John Blagden, in a voice of complete incredulity. He could feel the pain jump at him now.

"I told you I was keeping my fingers crossed," said Pete Dennis. "Sure, I'd rather it had happened the other way. But, every now and then you get a different situation—well, I told you about that."

There was a small silence in the room.

"A doctor!" said John Blagden, breathing deeply. "A doctor! I wouldn't trust you to poison a dog!"

"Go ahead, if it helps," said Pete Dennis. His head was heavy and averted—the dull red hair shone under the bright light. The big body looked tired and worn. *It's what he always does*, thought John Blagden—*my God, it's my having to cheer him up when he was an intern! It's what makes him a good doctor, I guess.*

"Sorry, Pete," he said. "I didn't mean that at all."

"That's all right," said Pete Dennis, hurting himself. "You've got every sort of right. And I told Seaver I'm not going into it bullheaded. I want to have Abbott take a look at you."

"I—don't—need—a—consultation," said John Blagden slowly. "If you and Seaver ——"

"I want to have Abbott look at you," said Pete Dennis inexorably. "He's about the best man in the country. He'll be in tonight—it just happens he's down here for a meeting and I got him on the phone. You needn't worry about the bills," he said quickly. "Abbott's very decent. It's just that we'd feel a little surer."

353

"Oh, I won't worry," said John Blagden. "I won't worry at all." He laughed sharply.

"Listen, Jack!" said Pete Dennis firmly. "In the first place, if Abbott doesn't think so, we won't do it. In the second place, even if he does, we're not shooting in the dark. It's a perfectly well-known operation. If you want to know about it technically ——"

His slow, reassuring voice continued. John Blagden listened, not listening.

"All right," he said, at the end. "You're the doctor."

"You'll like Abbott," said Pete Dennis earnestly. "Don't get put off if he talks to you about eighteenth-century chamber music. He knows his stuff."

"Okay," said John Blagden. "And, by the way, when will you cut?"

"Depends on Abbott," said Pete Dennis, his face still heavy and averted. "But don't worry. We won't rush you."

"That's a good idea," said John Blagden. He began to talk quickly. "Look here, Pete," he said, "you know I believe everything you've said. But you've got to give me a little time, that's all. I mean, it's only sensible to take precautions. Well, for instance, I haven't made a will since Bill was born. And that throws things out in New York State. I can get Jimmy Williams up tomorrow and fix it."

"We-el," said Pete Dennis, "if it makes you feel any better ——"

"Of course it does," said John Blagden. "I mean it's a sensible precaution. I'd do it if I were having my appendix out. I ought to have done it before." He breathed deeply. "How much chance is there, Pete?" he said. "I've known you long enough—you ought to be honest."

Pete Dennis made a sharp gesture. "Listen, Jack," he said, "there's a chance in every operation. There's a chance in having a tooth out. But ——"

"Thanks," said John Blagden. "That's what I wanted to know."

"Don't be a fool," said Pete Dennis.

"I'm not," said John Blagden. "After all, I've been through it before. When's Abbott coming?"

"Oh, ten—ten-thirty—as soon as he's through with his meeting," said Pete Dennis in a relieved voice. He smiled his pleasant, ugly smile. "I'll be with him," he said. "He may show up in a tuck, but he'll know his business. And then, when he's through, we can really talk over the whole works." He rose. "Frances sent her best," he said. "She'd have been in to see you before, but she's had a cold. And, Jack, this is just a little setback. You've got to think of it that way. I won't have you thinking anything else."

"Check," said John Blagden. He watched the big shoulders swing out of the door. Old Pete. He'd first run into Pete twenty years ago. They'd drunk beer at Jerry's place, with a man who was dead and a man who had come to nothing and "Hooks" Wilson, the prof, who had had the scandal, later. And now Pete was a first-class doctor, and he was a well-known writer. But a doctor had it over a writer—he got nearer to the bone. If Pete said the operation was going to be all right, it was going to be all right.

His tray came in and he ate, keeping something at bay. When the tray was gone and he had joked with the nurse, it came back, not to be denied, the trained, automatic knowledge. A writer's business was seeing and hearing—to note the tone and the inflection and mark them down on the wax record of the brain. And, that being so, he had seen and he had heard. Pete was awfully good at his stuff, but he knew when Pete was worried about a case. He lay still, taking it, while two radios played.

It was not the fault of the doctors that the hospital had thin walls—they would have liked it otherwise, but an architect had designed the hospital. It was not the fault of the doctors that his body had to have another operation. It was nobody's fault. It just happened, and there it was, like a splinter of ice.

It had happened to Mr. Sherwood, down the line; it was happening, slowly, next door, at No Visitors. Mr. Sherwood had taken two days to die, quite noisily. There were times when everybody could hear him, even with the door shut. He had called for his mother, like somebody dying in a second-rate novel; he had carefully and loudly explained the interminable details of a business transaction in which he seemed to have been cheated by two brothers named Purvis. You could write a better death scene in your sleep—it was badly constructed and banal—but, at the end, Mr. Sherwood had died; at the end, No Visitors would die. So that was that.

It would be a good idea to read, at this point, but he didn't feel like reading. If he hadn't been lazy this summer, he'd be two-thirds through his novel. If he hadn't had to do Ma Hudgins, it might be finished and in proof. Just as well. You couldn't die with a really good book unfinished, in spite of the people who had.

He switched on his radio—the station didn't matter. Out of humming and crackles, there came suddenly and authoritatively the bright, loving voice that was peace and solace to all mankind: "And next week, at the very same hour, we hope you all will be guests again at another of Aunt Mandy's Supper Parties, bringing you the glint and the glamour of old plantation days. Until then—and with thanks to you, Kay Kibbey and your Jugtown Jugblowers—and special thanks to you, Doris Delavan, for the haunting freshness you lend to the great songs of Stephen Foster—Aunt Mandy and Plantation Pork Products say to you-all, 'Good night! Keep a-smilin'!' "

The voice dwelt upon the last words, tenderly, richly, sorry to go. A gong struck. "It is now 8:30 P.M. by Hawkeye—*H-A-W-K-E-Y-E* —— The timepiece of a nation," said another voice, with omen. John Blagden switched off the radio.

Yes, he thought. *It's eight-thirty p.m. The kids will be going to bed*. He discovered that his hands were damp. That had better stop. But it wouldn't help to turn on the radio again.

He saw, with the sharp eyes of fever, the bright, pleasant, lighted doll house—the life he and Rosalie had made. It wasn't so much to ask—just to keep that. But it wasn't a question of asking or denying.

He found himself thinking back, trying to find some logic in the pattern. There were all the priceless, worthless memories, from the look of the little silver cologne bottle on mother's bureau to kissing a yellow-haired girl named Rosalie Marsh in a taxi on 56th Street, without premeditation and for keeps. The memories included landscapes and furniture and people, they included poverty and Charlie Fentriss and the faces of two children and your name on the cover of a book. Together, they made up a life, and nobody else could ever know them all. There must be a logic and a pattern. But, instead, there were only gaps and flashes, like country seen at night from the window of a train.

A comfortable train enough, and you went along with it, with your pasteboard slip in your hatband. Until suddenly there was the destination—the stop called No Visitors. He could see it—a bare, wintry platform. Beyond it there was night and snow and the elemental cold. He could see a small John Blagden, getting down from the train to the platform and standing there, minute, lonely and afraid.

There was a knock at the door and John Blagden sweated. But it was only the black-haired intern who liked to be sociable. "Well, Mr. Blagden," he said, "getting along all right?"

"Oh, fine," said John Blagden. He braced himself. "How did you like the show?" he said.

"I laughed my fool head off. He certainly knows his stuff, doesn't he?"

"George Crandall?" said John Blagden. "Yes, he's about as skillful as they come. And, of course, Jimmy Trevor gives a beautiful performance."

"Do you know him?" said the intern, interestedly. "What's he like?"

"Oh, I've seen him around. Nice fellow—very pleasant and modest. He married Betty Dunn—she's a peach. We've had them at the house."

It sounded gay and exciting, saying it. The intern looked impressed, which was as it should be. Go into your dance, John Blagden—tell some fascinating anecdotes about the world of letters. It's a nice youngster and it still thinks writers and artists are something special. If you asked it what dying was like, it would be very professional and no help at all.

"I remember when Betty was playing in 'Thar She Blows,' " said John Blagden. His hands were wet, under the bedclothes, but he told the anecdote with crispness and point. The intern laughed appreciatively. John Blagden wished that the intern would die or be called on the phone or anything that would get him out of the room, so a man could have peace. But none of these things ever happened and he knew they would not.

When the intern had left, John Blagden looked at his watch. About nine—almost nine. And Abbott might come at ten. Just about an hour. The train was going faster—he could feel it sway on the grades. Pretty soon, too soon, John Blagden would have to get down and stand on that bare, wintry platform. So what was there to do about it? . . . Call Rosalie? . . . No.

A phrase, unbidden, flashed into his mind: "To prepare the soul for the great day." But if you didn't believe in things like that you didn't; no use faking. They didn't, most of the people he knew, though they went to church now and then, and were open-minded.

It's time for it, boy—for the consolations of philosophy, if any. You've been an artist and a modern and a free spirit. Well, you get what you pay for. Let's see what you've got. There's a novel and a half, five short stories, and a one-act play. "Among minor figures of the period"—yes. And I could have tried harder to get Tom Whitter into Chi Sigma, but I didn't. But that's washed up— I can't change it. I can't change being mean to Rosalie, that time. And a man should be judged by his work. We'll call it three short stories—we'll compromise for that. Dear God, if there is a God, save my soul, if I have a soul. Dear God, if there is a God, let somebody be reading my three short stories, sometime—some- body who isn't a Ph.D. with a thesis. And don't let poor Nelly starve. But that was Charles II and he didn't carry insurance. The insurance would take care of that end of it. At least, for a while, and better not think after that.

So it was all modern and scientific and well-arranged. You could die very nearly as privately in a modern hospital as you could in the Grand Central Station, and with much better care. And there would be the nice, kind drugs at the end—Pete Dennis would see to that. It all became part of a ceremony and, though you were the central figure, your lines didn't matter. No matter how badly you played the part, the notices would be favorable, on the whole.

His grandfather, the revivalist, had died shouting and praying in the black-walnut room at Englemere. He'd seen that and hated every minute of it, even as a child. It was phony, from first to last, with the family arranged in rows and Aunt Ellen leading the hymn. It was completely phony—it had had a fierce strength, which was gone. You could not summon back that strength, and yet there was nothing to replace it.

He was thinking very logically and clearly about the whole question. Yet, he must have dozed, for, suddenly, Pete Dennis was there in the room and there was a good deal more pain. The white-moustached, pink-faced little man with Pete Dennis had on a white coat as well, but you could see his stiff collar and black tie.

"Doctor Abbott?" said John Blagden. "It's awfully good of you to do this."

After the examination, John Blagden lay flat on his back. In the wall, the muted radio that belonged to No Visitors throbbed meaninglessly. He felt a sudden kinship with the sound. They'd be talking him over, outside, but he didn't much care what they said. You didn't, when it was decided. The porter was getting his bag now, and taking it to the end of the car.

"Save my soul, if I have a soul"—but it wasn't as simple as that. There remained the problem, and the question. For an instant, it seemed to him that he saw through the wall—saw into the next room, with its photographs on the dresser, and the small, faded woman in the bed jacket, playing her radio against the encompassing dark. It was a small soul, but so was his; so were all souls, faced with the fact. There was a community, somehow; it didn't really matter who you were.

Why, it's easy to do, thought John Blagden, with sudden surprise. *They make a great fuss about it, but it's easy to do. It doesn't take a religion, or even a technique. All it takes is being mortal.*

He let go and had the pain come in. It was very considerable, but something remained untouched. That also would go, no doubt, with the drugs and the rest, but, while one had it, one had it. Having lived, it did not matter if you fumbled the last lines of the part.

"I am the resurrection and the life," said John Blagden, quoting. It did not matter now, if the words were true or not. They had been greatly said, though they were said for the living.

"Glad to meet you, No Visitors," said John Blagden. "Both members of the same club."

Then Pete came in, with his fine, poised smile, and the verdict written all over him.

A DEATH IN THE COUNTRY

After the years, Tom Carroll was going back to Waynesville —to stand by a kinswoman's grave, in the country of his youth. The names of the small, familiar stations were knots on a thread that led back into the darkness of childhood. He was glad Claire had not come. She hated death and memories. She hated cramped, local trains that smelled of green plush and cinders. Most of all she would hate Waynesville, even in mid-September and the grave light of afternoon.

Well, he wasn't looking forward to a pleasant time. He felt fagged and on edge already. There was work for the active partner of Norman, Buckstone, and Carroll in his brief-case, but he could not get down to the work. Instead he remembered, from childhood, the smell of dyed cloth and poignant, oppressive flowers, the black wisp tied on the knocker, the people coming to the door. The house was full of a menace—full of a secret— there were incomprehensible phrases, said in a murmur, and a man in black gloves who came, and a strangeness behind a shut door. Run out and play, run out and play; but there was no right way to play any more—even out in the yard you could smell the sweet, overpowering flowers—even out in the street you could see the people coming and coming, making that little pause as they saw the black wisp. Beautiful, they said, she looks beautiful; but the glimpse of the face was not mother, only somebody coldly asleep. Our sister has gone to dear Jesus . . . we shall meet on that beautiful shore . . . but the man spoke words, and the harsh box sank into the hole, and from it nothing arose, not even a white thing, not even silver vapor; the clay at the sides of the hole was too yellow and thick and cold. He's too young to realize, said a great many voices—but for months nothing was right. The world had stopped being solid, and people's smiles were different, and mother was Jesus's sister, and they gave her clothes away. Then, after a long time, the place was green again and looked just like the other graves, and the knife in your pocket was a comfort, going out there Sundays in the street car.

Barbarous. And tomorrow would be barbarous, as well. The family met only at funerals and weddings, now; and there had been more funerals than weddings for the past ten years. The big Christmas tree was gone from the house on Hessian Street— the majestic tree whose five-pointed, sparkling star had scratched against the ceiling of heaven in the back parlor, spreading wide its green boughs to shelter all generations and tribes of the Pyes and Merritts and Chipmans, their wives and their children, their menservants and their maidservants, their Noah's arks and cigar-cases and bottles of *eau-de-cologne*. The huge tablecloth of Thanksgiving lay folded away at the bottom of a chest—the tables now were too small. There would never be another turkey, with a breast like a mountainside, to fall into endless slices under the shining magic of Uncle Melrose's knife. Aunt Louise and Aunt Emmy had been the last of Hessian Street and, after tomorrow, there would only be Aunt Emmy and the ghosts.

The faces around the table had been masterful and full of life. They had been grown-up and permanent—one could not imagine them young or growing old. Together, they made a nation; they were the earth. If one took the trains of the morning, even as far as Bradensburg, lo, Uncle Melrose was there, at his desk with the little brass postage-scale on top of it, as it had been from the first. If one walked out to Mount Pleasant through the buckeye fall, at the end there was the white gate of Cousin Edna and the iron nigger boy with the rainstreaked face, holding out his black hand stiffly for the buckboards that drove no more. There were princes and dominations and thrones and powers; but what were these beside Aunt Emmy and Cousin Millie, beside the everlasting forms of Mrs. Bache and Mr. Beaver, of the ladies at the Women's Exchange and the man who lighted the gas street-lamps with a long brass spike? Then, suddenly, the earth had begun to crumble. A wind blew, a bell sounded, and they were dispersed. There were shrunken old people, timorous and pettish, and a small, heart-stifling town. These and the grown-up children, more strange than strangers. But Hessian Street was over—the great tree was down.

"And Uncle Melrose was a pompous old windbag," thought Tom Carroll. "And yet, if he were alive, I'd be calling him 'Sir.' Oh, Claire's right—the jungle's the jungle—she's saner than I am, always."

It was one of the many maxims Claire found in books. The family was the jungle that you grew up in and, if you did not, somehow, break through to light and air of your own when you were young, you died, quickly or slowly but surely, stifled out, choked down by the overpowering closeness of your own kin. Tom Carroll knew this much—that New York, after Waynesville, had been like passing from the large, squabbling, overheated room of Christmas afternoon into the anonymous peace of a bare and windy street. He had been lonely, often—he had missed Hessian Street and them all. But, oh the endless, intricate, unimportant diplomacy—the feuds and the makings-up—the inflexible machine of the Family, crushing all independence. Not again, not ever again! And yet, here he was, on the train.

Well, nobody could say that he shirked it. He would have to take charge when he got there, like it or not. It wouldn't be easy, straightening everything out—he'd rather handle the Corliss case any day—but he'd done it in other emergencies and he supposed he could do it again. After all, who else was there? Jerry Pye? His mouth narrowed, thinking of Jerry.

The conductor bawled the names of familiar stations, the long, autumnal twilight began beyond the window. If only things could go smoothly just this once! But something always cropped up—something always had to be smoothed over and explained. *Morton Center, Morton Center!* If Aunt Louise had left no will—and she very probably hadn't—there'd be the dickens of a time, securing the estate to Aunt Emmy. But it must be done—he'd ride roughshod over Jerry Pye if necessary. *Brandy Hill! Brandy Hill!* . . . If only nobody would tell him to be sure and notice Mrs. Bache! He could easily fix a pension for Aunt Emmy, but how to do it best? She'd have to leave Hessian Street, of course. Even cutting the old house into apartments hadn't really solved the problem. She could get a small, comfortable, modern flat over in the new section. The silver candlesticks were the only things Claire would have liked, but they would go to Jerry because Jerry had always failed.

Waynesville, next stop! The flowers had been wired from New York. *Waynesville!* We're coming in. There's an A. & P. on Main Street, and Ellerman's Bazaar is gone. *Waynesville!* . . . And God bless Uncle Melrose and Aunt Louise and Aunt Emmy and all my dear relations and friends and Spot and make me a good boy and not afraid of the dark. *Waynesville!*

Right down the middle of Main Street the train clanged till it stopped in front of the bald, new station. Tom Carroll sighed. It was as he had prophesied. Jerry Pye was there to meet him.

He got off the train, and the cousins shook hands.

"Have a good trip, Tom?"

"Not bad. Real fall weather, isn't it?"

"Yes, it's a real fall. You took the limited as far as Bradensburg, I suppose?"

A Death in the Country

"Yes, that seemed the quickest thing for me to do."

"They say she's quite a train," said Jerry Pye. "I was on her once—three years ago, you know. Well, I thought, here's where the old man blows himself for once. Minnie would hardly believe me when I told her. 'Jerry Pye!' she said, 'I don't know what's come over you. You never take me on any limiteds!' 'Well,' I said, 'maybe it is extra-fare, but I just decided the old man could blow himself for once!' Well, you should have seen her expression! Though I guess it wouldn't mean much to you, at that. I guess extra-fare trains don't mean much in people's lives when they come from New York."

"I could have taken a slower train," said Tom Carroll, carefully, "but it wouldn't have saved any time."

This remark seemed to amuse Jerry Pye intensely. His thin, sallow face—the face of a dyspeptic fox—gloated with mirth for an instant. Then he sobered himself, abruptly and pointedly.

"You always were a case, Tom," he said, "always. But this is a sad occasion."

"I didn't mean to be funny," said Tom Carroll. "Had I better get a taxi or is that your car?"

"Oh, we've got the family mistake—a dollar down and a dollar whenever they catch you!" Jerry Pye grinned and sobered himself again with the automatism of a mechanical figure. "I drove up in her night before last," he said, pointedly, as they got in. "Evans is a good man and all that, but he's apt to figure a little close on the cars; and as long as ours is dark blue, it'll look perfectly dignified."

"I telegraphed Aunt Emmy," said Tom Carroll and stopped. There was no possible use in trying to explain oneself to Jerry Pye.

"Yes, indeed," said Jerry, instantly. "Aunt Emmy appreciated it very much. Very much indeed. 'Tom's always very busy,' I told her. 'But don't you worry, Aunt Emmy. Tom may be a big man now, but his heart's in the right place. He'll be here.'"

"I told her," said Tom Carroll, distinctly and in spite of himself, "that in case anything of the sort came up, she had only to—"

"Oh," said Jerry, brightly, "we all knew that. We all knew you couldn't be expected to send one of your big cars all the way from New York to Waynesville. How's Claire?"

"Claire was very sorry indeed not to be able to come," said Tom, his hands gripping his knees. "We have one car," he said. "That's just what I said," said Jerry Pye triumphantly. "I told Aunt Emmy—'you couldn't expect Tom to take the car away from Claire—she'll need it when he's away, shopping and seeing her friends—and naturally she hardly knew Aunt Louise. You wait and see. She'll send handsome flowers,' I said."

"Oh, God, make me a good boy!" prayed Tom Carroll, internally. "It can't last more than ten minutes. Ten minutes isn't really long." He braced himself. "How is Aunt Emmy?" he said.

Their speed instantly dropped to a respectful twenty miles an hour.

"She's wonderful," said Jerry Pye. "Simply wonderful. Of course, Minnie's been a great help to her and then, the end was very peaceful. Just seemed to breathe away." His voice had an obvious relish. "One minute she was there—as bright as a button, considering everything—and the next minute—" He shook his head.

"I'm glad," said Tom Carroll. "I mean——"

"Oh, we wouldn't have wanted her to suffer," said Jerry Pye in a shocked voice, as if he were denying some uncouth suggestion of Tom's. "No, sir, we wouldn't have wanted that. Now when Minnie's mother passed over—I don't know whether I ever told you the whole story, Tom—but from the Friday before—"

He continued, but had only come to the personal idiosyncrasies of the first night nurse when they turned into Hessian Street.

They got out of the car. Jerry Pye was mopping his forehead, though the day was chill. Yes, there was the black wisp on the knocker. But there was a row of bell-pushes where the old name-plate had been. The bricks in the sidewalk were rose-red and old and worn—the long block of quiet houses kept its faded dignity, in spite of a sign, "Pappas' Smoke Shop," a sign, "The Hessian Sergeant—Tea and Antiques." The linden trees had not perished, though their shade was thin.

"If this were a city," thought Tom Carroll, "people would have found out by now that it was quaint and painted the doors green and had studio-parties. Well, anyhow, that hasn't happened."

"Everyone's been very respectful," said Jerry Pye, nodding at the black wisp. "I mean, some people might be touchy when everybody has to use the same front-door. But Mr. Rodman came to me himself—they're the second-floor back. Just leave your bag in the car, Tom. It won't be in the way. I think Minnie's seen us—we figured out if you came today this ought to be the train."

Tom Carroll did not repeat that he had telegraphed or that there was only one afternoon train to Waynesville. He kissed his cousin-in-law's flustered cheek and was kissed by her in return. Minnie was always flustered; she had been a plump, flustered robin of a girl at her wedding; she was unaltered now save for the dust of gray in her abundant, unbecoming hair; they had never exchanged three words, except on family matters; and yet, they always kissed. He wondered if Minnie, too, ever found this circumstance strange. He should not wonder, of course, especially now.

"How's Aunt Emmy?" said Jerry Pye, in the anxious tones of one just returned from a long absence. "There isn't any change?"

"No, dear," said Minnie, solemnly, "she's just the same. She's wonderful. Mrs. Robinson and Mrs. Bache are with her, now. Remember—we must all be very nice to Mrs. Bache, Cousin Tom."

"I did put a tick-tack on her window, once," said Tom Carroll, reflectively. "But I haven't done that for a long time. Not for thirty years."

Minnie, the robin, was shocked for a moment, but brightened.

"That's right," she said. "We must all keep up for Aunt Emmy. Now, if you'll just go in—" She stood aside.

The spare, small, hawk-nosed figure rose from the stiff-backed chair as Tom Carroll entered. "Good evening, Thomas. I am glad you are here," said the unfaltering voice. "I think you know my good neighbors, Mrs. Bache and Mrs. Robinson."

Tom Carroll took the thin, dry, forceful hands. By God, she is wonderful, he thought, in spite of their saying it—it's taken me years to unlearn what she taught me, but she's remarkable. Why don't they let her alone? *Aunt Emmy, Aunt Emmy, you have grown so small! You rapped on my chapped knuckles with a steel thimble when I was cold; you ran me through and through like the emery-bag in your workbox with your sharp and piercing eyes; you let me see that you thought my father a rascal; you made me lie and cheat because of the terror of your name—and now you have grown small and fragile and an old woman, and there is not even injustice left in Hessian Street.*

The moment passed. Tom Carroll found himself mechanically answering Mrs. Bache's questions while his eyes roved about the room. The conch-shell was still on the mantelpiece, but one of the blue vases was gone. This was the front-parlor—the room of reward and punishment, of visitors and chill, the grandest room in the world—this room with the shabby carpet and the huge forbidding pieces of black walnut that never could have come in through a mortal door. What could you do with it all, what could you do? What could be done with a conch-shell and an iron oak-leaf and a set of yellowed pictures for a broken stereopticon? It was incredible that civilized people should ever have cherished such things. It was incredible that he had ever put the conch-shell to his ear and held his breath with wonder, hearing the sea.

"It was just like another home to the Major and myself. Always," said Mrs. Bache. "I can hear your dear grandmother now, before the Major was taken, when he had his trouble. 'Alice, my child, you're young,' she said. 'But, young or old, we all have to bear our cross. The Major is a good man—he'll always be welcome in Hessian Street.' The Major never forgot it. He was very badly treated but he never forgot a kindness. And now, Emmy and I are the last—Emmy and I are the last."

She fumbled for her handkerchief in her vast lap.

"There, there, Mrs. Bache," said Tom Carroll, inadequately, "Grandmother must have been a wonderful woman."

"You never even saw her," said Mrs. Bache, viciously, "Tom Carroll saw to that. Oh, why couldn't it have been me, instead of Louise?" she said. "I've been ready to go so long!"

Tom Carroll's face felt stiff, but he found the handkerchief. After a moment Mrs. Bache arose, enormously yet with a curious dignity.

"Come, Sarah," she said to the dim figure in black that was Mrs. Robinson. "It's time for us to go. I've been making a fool of myself. Good-by, Emma. Frank will take us to the church to-morrow. Try to get some rest."

Minnie was whispering to him that Mrs. Bache was very much broken and that Cousin Tom must not mind. Tom Carroll whispered back at appropriate intervals. He did not mind Mrs. Bache. But there was always so much whispering, and it hurt one's head.

Now they were all standing in the narrow hall, and the others were looking at him.

A Death in the Country

"We can just slip in for a minute before anyone else comes," whispered Minnie, "I know Cousin Tom would rather—"

"Of course," said Tom Carroll. "Thank you, Cousin Minnie." He must have been working too hard, he thought—perhaps he and Claire could go off for a trip together when he got back. Because, after all, it was Aunt Louise who was dead. He knew that perfectly well. And yet, until Minnie had spoken, he hadn't been thinking about her at all.

The statue lay on the walnut bed in the partitioned room that had once been part of the back parlor. Over the head of the bed was a cross of dry, brittle palm-leaves tied with a purple ribbon, and a church-calendar. Against the opposite wall was the highboy that he remembered, with the small china slipper upon it, and above it the ageless engraving of the great Newfoundland dog, head lifted, lying upon the stone blocks of an English quay. "A Member of the Royal Humane Society." There were brown spots on the margin of the engraving now, Tom Carroll noticed. The window was a little open, but everywhere were the massed, triumphant flowers.

A white, transparent veil lay on the face of the statue. The features showed dimly through it, as if Aunt Louise lay in a block of ice. Tom Carroll felt cold. Now Aunt Emmy, putting Minnie aside, went slowly to lift the veil.

Tom Carroll, waking at three o'clock in the morning in his room at the Penniquit House, knew instantly what was in store for him. He might lie on the hillocks of his bed as long as he liked but he would not be allowed to sleep any more.

"You're acting like somebody on the edge of a first-class nervous breakdown," he told himself sternly. "And yet, you haven't been working so hard."

The last year hadn't been easy, but no year was. When times were good, you worked hard to take advantage of them. And when they were bad, you naturally had to work. That was how you got to be somebody, in a city. It was something Waynesville could never understand.

He thought of their life in the city—his and Claire's—for solace. It was cool and glittering and civilized as a cube of bright steel and glass. He thought of the light, pleasant furniture in the apartment, the clean, bright colors, the crisp sunlight on stone and metal, the bright, clean, modern, expensive school where a doctor looked down the boys' throats every morning and they had special blocks of wood to hammer nails in, since apartments were hardly the places to hammer nails. He thought of his office and the things on his desk and the crowded elevators of morning and night. He thought of the crammed red moving vans of October and the spring that bloomed before April in the flowershops and the clever men, putting in the new telephones. He thought of night beside Claire, hearing the dim roar of the city till at last the uneasy lights of the sky were quieted in the breathing-space before dawn.

It was she who had really held their life to its pattern. She had not let them be trapped; she had kept them free as air from the first day. There had been times when he had weakened—he admitted it—but she had kept her level head and never given in.

It had been that way about the old farmhouse in Connecticut and the cooperative apartment in town. He had wanted to buy them both, at different times. It was the Waynesville coming out in him, he supposed. But she had demurred.

"Oh, Tom, let's not tie ourselves up yet!" she had said. "Yes, I know it does seem silly just going on paying rent and having nothing to show for it but a leak in the washstand. But the minute you buy places to live in, they start to own you. You aren't free. You aren't young. You're always worrying. Don't talk to me about just playing with a few acres, not really farming. That was the way Grandfather started. Oh, Tom, don't you see—we're so *right* the way we are! Now, let's go over it sensibly, figures and all."

And she had been right. The old farmhouse, with its lilac hedge, now stood twenty feet away from a four-lane road; the cooperative apartment had failed and crippled its owner-tenants. She had been precisely right. She almost always was.

She had been entirely and unsentimentally right about her mother's coming to live with them for six months out of the year, when that had seemed unescapable.

"It's darling of you, Tom, but, dear old man, it never would work in the world. We've got to be modern and intelligent about the important things. Mother had me, and I'm devoted to her; but, when we're together for more than a week we get on each other's nerves like the very devil. It'll actually be a help to Hattie to have her for the winters—Hattie's always having a fearful time with the children. And we can have her for a long visit in the summer, and in between she can take the trips she's always wanted to take with that terrible Mrs. Tweed. Of course, I don't mean we ought to leave the whole financial end to Hattie and Joe. I'll insist on our doing our share. But I do think people ought to have *some* independence even when they are old and not just be shipped around from one relative to another like parcels, the way they did with Aunt Vi! It's more than sweet of you, Tom, darling. But you see how it is."

Tom Carroll had seen, with some relief, that they were not likely to have Mrs. Fanshawe as a permanent addition to their household, and he had acquiesced. Not that he disliked Mrs. Fanshawe. He got on very well with the rather nervous little lady—which was strange, considering how unlike she was to Claire. It struck him at times that Mrs. Fanshawe, from what he knew of her, had never been a remarkably independent person, and that to begin one's complete independence at the age of sixty-seven might be something of a task. But Claire must know her mother better than he did.

She did get on Claire's nerves and she did spoil the children—he could see that plainly enough. But, then, her visits were seldom very long. Claire would hardly have time to decline three or four invitations because mother was with them for a quiet little time before something would happen to call Mrs. Fanshawe away. And yet she seemed to like his calling her Mother May and pretending he was jealous of Hattie and Joe for stealing away his best girl. She'd laugh her brisk, nervous laugh and say he'd better look out or sometime she'd take him at his word and stay forever. And Claire would be saying, patiently, "Now, mother, are you sure that you have your ticket? And Tom will get you some magazines to read on the train." Afterwards Claire would say, "Oh, Tom, how can you? But she adores it!" and he would mumble something and feel rather pleased. Then Claire would kiss him and go to the telephone.

Only one of the visits had been in the least unfortunate. Claire had been tired that evening, and it was a pity that the conversation had happened to run on the future of the children. "But, of course, you and Tom are planning to make a real home for them sometime?" Mrs. Fanshawe had said. Well, naturally, she could hardly be expected to understand the way he and Claire happened to feel about "homes" in the Waynesville sense. And it had all come right the following morning—had not Mrs. Fanshawe nervously stayed an extra two days in proof? But the evening had carried him back to the hurt feelings of Hessian Street. Tom Carroll was glad there had been another visit before Mrs. Fanshawe died.

She had died in the waiting room of the Auburndale Station, on her way back to Hattie's, after a pleasant month with her old friend, Mrs. Tweed. Even so, she had been considerate; for the station agent knew her and got hold of the Morrises at once—there had been some mix-up about her telegram. Later, they had found out that she had known about her heart trouble for some time.

He had expected to take Claire on to the funeral, but Claire had been adamant. "I will not have you do it, Tom. It'll be bad enough by myself. But I will not have you mixed up in it—it isn't fair. We can have bad memories separately, but I won't have us have them together." She had grown almost hysterical about it—Claire! And so she had gone alone.

He had been very much worried till she returned, with a white changed face that refused to give any details of those three days. "Don't ask me, Tom. I've told you everything I can—oh, yes, everybody was kind and they had her hymns . . . but, oh Tom, it's so terrible. Terrible. The most barbarous, the most humiliating custom I know! I'll tell you this right now, I'm not going to wear mourning. I don't believe in it and I won't submit to it. All the black dresses—mother didn't really like black. Oh, Tom, Tom, when I die don't dare wear mourning for me!"

He had got her to bed and quieted at last. But she had not been herself—the true Claire—for months afterward, though, as soon as she could, she had taken up the strands of their life again and woven the pattern even more deftly and swiftly, as if each new thread were precious and each second not to be recalled.

Naturally, then, it was only right for him to come to this death in his own country alone. Any other course would have been a monstrous selfishness. And yet he wished that he could go to sleep.

Perhaps, if he thought once more of that shining cube of steel and glass that was their planned security, sleep would come.

A Death in the Country

Even death in New York was different and impersonal. Except for the very mighty, it was an anonymous affair. The man in 10B died and, the next fall, they redecorated the apartment for other tenants. In a month or so even the doorman had forgotten; the newsdealer wrote another name on the morning papers. A name dropped out of the 'phone book . . . you had moved again, with October . . . moved to another city—the city at the sprawling edge of town where lie the streets and avenues of the number-less, quickly buried dead. There, too, you would be part of the crowd, and your neighbors would be strangers, as it had been in life. Your dwelling would be well kept-up, for that was written in the contract. No ghosts could ever arise from that suburban earth. For this, John Merritt and Samuel Pye had built a house in the wilderness to be a shelter and a refuge for them and their seed to the generations of generations. It was just.

Something cracked in the shining cube of glass and steel. The girders crunched on one another, wrenching apart; the glass tumbled into nothingness, falling a long way. There was nothing left but the perplexed, forgotten spirit, roused out of long sleep at last to strive, unprepared, against its immortal adversary.

Claire was all right, but she was afraid of death. He was all right, but he was afraid of death. The clever people they knew were entirely right, but most of them were deadly afraid of death.

If the life they led was rich—if it was the good life—why were they so afraid? It was not because they so joyed in all things under the sun that it was bitter to leave them. That was mortal and understandable, that had always been. But this was a blinder fear.

It had not been in sorrow or remorse that Claire had grieved for her mother. She had grieved the most because she had been afraid. And that made Claire a monster, which she was not. But there was something in it, all the same. He could admit it in her because he could admit it in himself. He lay sleepless, dreading the morrow. And yet he was not a coward so far as he knew.

They had won, but where was the victory? They had escaped from Waynesville and Hessian Street, from Fanshawe and Pye and Merritt, but where was the escape? If they were afraid in these years, how were they to deal with the years to come? Tom Carroll heard the clock in the courthouse strike five strokes.

And then, when it seemed to him he could never sleep again, he fell asleep.

They drove at the slow pace down Hessian Street into Main, through the bright, morning sunlight. Tom Carroll felt ashamed of the dreams and waking of the night. He had never felt more solid and confident and assured than he did now, sitting beside Aunt Emmy, his tact and his shoulder ready for her the moment the inevitable breakdown came. Thank God! Jerry Pye was driving his own car. Jerry muddled things so. As for what was to come, that would merely be pathetic—the few old people painfully come together to mourn not only one of their own but a glory that had departed, the Waynesville of their youth. He hoped Aunt Emmy would not notice how few they were. But she, too, was old; and the old lived in the past. She could people the empty pews with the faces that once had been there. It was better so. The lords of Hessian and Bounty Streets had ruled the town with a high hand, even as they sank into poverty, but that was ended. You had only to look along Main to see the new names on the shop-fronts. They knew not Hessian Street, these Caprellos and Szukalskis, but they thrived and inherited the land. Even Waynesville was growing up—there was little charm left in it, but it was alive. And here was the old brick church of the memories.

He helped Aunt Emmy expertly from the car, but she would not take his arm. Well, he respected her courage. He stood tactfully to shield her from the sight of the coffin, just being lifted down from that other, windowless car. But before he knew it Jerry Pye was beside them.

"Aunt Emmy," said Jerry Pye incredibly, "did Aunt Louise really want old Zenas to be one of the coffin-bearers? Because he's there now, and it'll be too late unless somebody tells him . . ."

He actually made a gesture with his hand. Tom Carroll would have been glad to strangle his cousin. But miraculously Aunt Emmy did not break.

She even walked past Tom Carroll to look deliberately at the six black-suited Negroes who now had their burden ready to carry into the church. Tom Carroll looked as well. They were none of them under forty, and their faces were grave and sober,

A Death in the Country

but there was something ceremonial in their attitude that struck Tom Carroll strangely. They were sad but they were not constrained—they were doing something they felt to be right and they did it naturally and with ceremony. They would remember the ceremony always when the sadness had passed.

"Zenas, Joram, Joseph, William, Henry, Devout," said Aunt Emmy, in a half-whisper. "Yes, that's right. That's right. Zenas should be there. Louise would have missed Zenas. No, Tommy, we will let them pass, please."

When the coffin had passed, to the sway of the easy shoulders, they followed it in. It was the beginning of Tom Carroll's astonishment. The astonishment did not lessen when he found the church half full, and not only with the old.

He had always thought of Aunt Louise as Aunt Emmy's shadow—in his boyhood as someone always hurried but vaguely sweet whose peppermint-drops took away the taste of Aunt Emmy's wrath; in his manhood as a responsibility at the back of his mind. But the minister was a young man, and neither Pye nor Merritt, and he spoke of the Louise Pye, whose singlehanded effort had turned the ramshackle old School For The Instruction Of Freed Negroes into an institution model for its time, in terms that assumed his hearers knew and appreciated the difficulties of that task.

Phrases came to Tom Carroll's ears. They were the conventional phrases of oratory, yet the speaker meant them. "Unsparing of time or labor." "The rare gift of personality." "The quiet achievement of many years." "We can say today, in all truth, a light has gone from among us. . . ." But this was Aunt Louise!

And after the service, and on the way to the grave, and after the service there, the astonishment continued. He was by Aunt Emmy's side, and the people spoke to him. Nearly everyone who spoke to him knew his name. They did not find it odd or kind or a favor that he should be there—he was Julia Merritt's son, who was working in New York. You didn't hear as much about him as you did about Jerry Pye, but it was natural that he should return. Not only Mrs. Bache was under the impression that he had come principally to hear the reading of Aunt Louise's will. They did not think ill of him for it, merely prudent. He could explain nothing, even if he had wished to. There was nothing to explain.

He could not count the number of times he was told that the cross of yellow roses was beautiful—did they know by telepathy that it was from him and Claire? He had thought it garish and out of place beside the other flowers, the late asters and first chrysanthemums, the zinnias and snapdragons, the bronzes and reds and golds of the country fall. But that he could not say.

The Negroes who had borne the coffin knew him. They spoke to him gravely in their rich voices when all was done. Aunt Emmy had a curious phrase for each of them. "Thank you, Devout. Thank you, Joram. Miss Louise will be pleased." It would seem macabre, telling it to Claire. It was not; it was only simple. But that she would not believe.

He remembered, as if in a dream, his plans for succor and comfort when Aunt Emmy should collapse. But it was he who felt physically exhausted when they got back to the house.

This, too, was the moment that he had dreaded the most. Last night he had been able to have dinner at the hotel, but this time there was no escaping the cold meal laid in the basement dining room, the haunted and undue fragrance of flowers that had filled the house for a while. But, when the food was in front of him he was hungry and ate. They all ate, even Aunt Emmy. Minnie did what waiting was necessary and did it, for once, without fluster. Jerry Pye seemed tired and subdued. Once Tom Carroll caught himself feeling sorry for him, once he tried to help him out in a story that was meant to be cheerful and fell flat.

"You know," said Minnie, in a flat voice, pouring coffee, "it seems as if Aunt Louise hadn't gone away so far as before it happened."

Tom Carroll knew what she meant. He felt it too—that presence of the dead, but not grimly nor as a ghost. The presence was as real as the October sky, and as removed from flesh. It did not have to mean that all tired souls were immortal—it had its own peace.

After the meal was over, Tom Carroll walked in the back yard and smoked with Jerry Pye. Now and then he remembered from childhood the fear that had walked there with him, with the scent of the overpowering flowers. But, search as he would, he could not find that fear. The few flowers left in the beds were bronze and scentless; there was no fear where they bloomed.

It was time to go in for the reading of Aunt Louise's will. Tom

A Death in the Country

Carroll listened obediently. He did not even mention the names of Norman, Buckstone, and Carroll. Once, when Mr. Dabney, the lawyer, looked at him and said, "You are a member of the New York Bar, I believe, Mr. Carroll?" he felt surprised at being able to say "yes."

It was a long and personal will made up of many small bequests. He could see Aunt Louise going through her innumerable boxes, trying hard to be fair.

"To my nephew, Thomas Carroll, and his wife, Claire Fanshawe Carroll, the pair of silver candlesticks belonging to my dear Father."

Tom Carroll felt the slow red creeping into his face.

They shook hands with Mr. Dabney. They spoke of what was to be done. Tom Carroll did not proffer assistance. There was no need.

Jerry Pye was offering him a lift as far as Bradensburg—Minnie would be staying with Aunt Emmy for the next week or so, but he must get back to work. But Tom Carroll thought he had better wait till the morning.

"Well, I guess you'll be more comfortable here at that," said Jerry Pye. "I'll have to hit her up if I want to get home before 3 G.M. So long, Tom. You see Minnie doesn't step out with a handsomer fellow now the old man's away. And take care of the Pye candlesticks—at that, I guess they'll look better in your place than they would in ours. Our kids might use 'em for baseball bats. Say, give my best to Claire."

He was gone. "Now, Tommy," said Aunt Emmy in her tired, indomitable voice, "you go back to the hotel and get a rest—you look tuckered out. Nelly Jervis is coming in here to get the supper. Half-past six."

They were sitting in the front parlor again that evening, he and she. It wasn't late, but Minnie had been sent to bed, unwilling. She wouldn't close an eye, she said; but they knew she was already asleep.

"It's queer what a good nurse Minnie is," said Aunt Emmy reflectively. "Seems as if it was the only thing that ever got her shut of her fussiness—taking care of sick people. You'd think she'd drop crumbs in the bed, but she never does. I don't know what we'd have done without her. Well, she's a right to be tired."

"How about you, Aunt Emmy?"

"Oh," said Aunt Emmy, "they used to say there'd be some people the Fool Killer would still be looking for on Judgment Day. I guess I'm one of them. Of course I'm tired, Tommy. When I'm tired enough, I'll tell you and go to bed."

"Look here, Aunt Emmy," said Tom Carroll, "if there's anything I can do——"

"And what could you do, Tommy?"

"Well, wouldn't you like a car?" he said, awkwardly, "or somebody to stay with you—or another place. They say those apartments over by the——"

"I was born here," said Aunt Emmy, with a snap of her lips, "and now Louise has gone, I've got just enough money to die here. It isn't the same, but I'm suited. And, of all the horrors of age, deliver me from a paid companion. If I need anything like that I'll get Susan Bache to move in here. She's a fool and she's a tattler," said Aunt Emmy, clearly, "but I'm used to her. And Minnie'll come up, every now and then. Don't worry about me, Tom Carroll. We've all of us been on your back long enough."

"On my back?" said Tom Carroll, astounded.

"Well, I'd like to know where else it was," said Aunt Emmy. "You got Louise's money back from that rascal that bamboozled her, and I know twice you pulled Jerry Pye out of the mudhole, and then there was Cousin Edna all those years. Not to speak of what you did for Melrose. Melrose was my own brother, but he ought to have been ashamed of himself, the way he hindered you. Oh, don't you worry about Waynesville, Tommy—you've no call. You did right to get out when you did and as you did, and Waynesville knows it, too. Not that Waynesville would ever admit George Washington was any great shakes, once he'd moved away. But you wait till you die, Tom Carroll"—and she actually chuckled—"and you see what the *Waynesville Blade* says about her distinguished son. They told Louise for twenty years she was crazy, teaching Negroes to read and write. But they've got two columns about her this evening and an editorial. I've cut it out and I'm going to paste it under her picture. Louise was always the loving one, and I never grudged her that. But I did grudge her forgiving where I didn't see cause to forgive. But that's all done." She rustled the paper in her lap.

"How are your boys, Tommy?" she said. "They look smart enough in their pictures."

A Death in the Country

"We think they are," said Tom Carroll. "I hope you're right."

"They ought to be," said Aunt Emmy. "The Fanshawes never lacked smartness, whatever else they lacked, and your father was a bright man. Well, I've seen Jeremiah's and Minnie's. Boy and girl. Don't laugh at me, because it doesn't seem possible, but Jeremiah makes a good father. I never could get on with children —you ought to know that if anyone does—but I think they'll amount to something. Well, it's time the family was getting some sense again."

"Aunt Emmy!" said Tom Carroll, protestingly.

"Was this a happy house?" said Aunt Emmy, fiercely. "For me it was—yes—because I grew up in it. And I always had Louise and I don't regret anything. But was it happy for your mother and you? You know it wasn't, and a good thing your father took her out of it, adventurer or no adventurer, and a bad thing she had to come back. Well, we did our duty according to our lights. But that wasn't enough. There's no real reason, you know, why families have to get that way, except they seem to. But they will get to thinking they're God Almighty, and, after a while, that gets taken notice of. I'll say this—it wasn't the money with us. We held up our heads with it or without it. But maybe we held them too stiff."

She sank into a brooding silence. Behind her in the corner the vague shadows of innumerable Pyes and Merritts seemed to gather and mingle and wait. After a while she roused herself.

"Where are you going to live, Tommy?" she said.

"I've been thinking about a place in the country sometime," said Tom Carroll. "If Waynesville were a little different——"

Aunt Emmy shook her head.

"You couldn't come back here, Tommy," she said. "It's finished here. And that's just as well. But, if you're going to build your own house, you'd better do it soon. You won't be happy without it—you've got too much Merritt in you. The Merritts made their own places. It was the Pyes that sat on the eggs till finally they tried to hatch chickens out of a doorknob, because it was easier than looking for a new roost. But you haven't much Pye. All the same, you won't be contented till you've got some roots put down. The Fanshawes, they could live in a wagon and like it, but the Bouverins were like the Merritts—when they'd rambled

377

Stephen Vincent Benét

enough, they cleared ground. And Claire looks a lot more Bouverin than Fanshawe to me, whether she likes it or not."

"I didn't know you knew Claire's family," said Tom Carroll.

"She probably wouldn't tell you," said Aunt Emmy. "Well,
that's natural enough. Good Goshen! I remember Claire Fanshawe, a peaked little slip of a child, at Anna Bouverin's funeral,
just before they left Bradensburg. The coffin was still open, and
some ignoramus or other thought it would be fitting for all the
grandchildren to come and kiss their grandma good-by. Mind
you, after they'd said good-by to her once already, before she
died. I could have told them better, little as I know children.
Well, it didn't make much difference to Hattie; she always had
the nerves of an ox. But Claire was just over typhoid and after
they made her do it she had what I'd call a shaking chill, in a
grown person. And yet, they made her get up and recite the
Twenty-Third Psalm in front of everybody—just because she
was smart for her age, and a little child shall lead them. Her
mother didn't stop them—too proud of her knowing it, I guess.
But that was the Fanshawe of it—they had to play-act whatever
happened."

Tom Carroll had his head in his hands.

"She never told me," he said. "She never told me at all."

"No?" said Aunt Emmy, looking at him sharply. "Well, she
was young and maybe she forgot it. I imagine Hattie did."

"Claire never has," said Tom Carroll.

"Well," said Aunt Emmy, "I'll tell you something, Tommy.
When you get to my age you've seen life and death. And there's
just one thing about death, once you start running away from
the thought of it, it runs after you. Till finally you're scared even
to talk about it and, even if your best friend dies, you'll forget
him as quick as you can because the thought's always waiting.
But once you can make yourself turn around and look at it—it's
different. Oh, you can't help the grief. But you can get a child
so it isn't afraid of the dark—though if you scared it first it'll take
a longer while."

"Tell me," said Tom Carroll in a low voice, "were there—very
sweet flowers—when my mother died?"

"It was just before Easter," said Aunt Emmy softly. "You
could smell the flowers all through the house. But we didn't have
any play-acting," she added, quickly. "Not with you. Melrose

378

had that bee in his bonnet, but Louise put her foot down. But it's hard to explain to a child."

"It's hard to explain anyway," said Tom Carroll.

"That's true," said Aunt Emmy. "It's a queer thing," she said. "I never smell lilac without thinking of Lucy Marshall. She was a friend of mine, and then we fell out, and when we were young we used to play by a lilac bush in her yard. It used to trouble me for a long time before I put the two things together. But the pain went out of it then."

"Yes. The pain goes out when you know," said Tom Carroll. "It's not knowing that makes you afraid."

"If Hattie was closer to her, she could do it," said Aunt Emmy. "But the way things are——"

"It'll have to be me," said Tom Carroll. "And I don't know how."

"Well, you're fond of her," said Aunt Emmy. "They say that helps." She rose. "I'll give you the candlesticks in the morning, Tom."

"Can't I leave them with you, Aunt Emmy?"

"What's the use?" said Aunt Emmy practically. "To tell you the truth, Tommy, I'd got right tired of shining them. Besides, they'll look well in your house, when you get your house."

FANTASIES AND PROPHECIES

Fantasies and Prophecies

THE CURFEW TOLLS

"IT IS not enough to be the possessor of genius—the time and the man must conjoin. An Alexander the Great, born into an age of profound peace, might scarce have troubled the world—a Newton, grown up in a thieves' den, might have devised little but a new and ingenious picklock. . . ."

Diversions of Historical Thought by
John Cleveland Cotton.

(The following extracts have been made from the letters of General Sir Charles William Geoffrey Estcourt, C.B., to his sister Harriet, Countess of Stokely, by permission of the Stokely family. Omissions are indicated by triple dots, thus . . .)

St. Philippe-des-Bains, September 3d, 1788.

My Dear Sister: . . . I could wish that my excellent Paris physician had selected some other spot for my convalescence. But he swears by the waters of St. Philip and I swear by him, so I must resign myself to a couple of yawning months ere my constitution mends. Nevertheless, you will get long letters from me, though I fear they may be dull ones. I cannot bring you the gossip of Baden or Aix—except for its baths, St. Philip is but one of a dozen small white towns on this agreeable coast. It has its good inn and its bad inn, its dusty, little square with its dusty, fleabitten beggar, its posting-station and its promenade of scrubby lindens and palms. From the heights one may see Corsica on a clear day, and the Mediterranean is of an unexampled blue. To tell the truth, it is all agreeable enough, and an old Indian campaigner, like myself, should not complain. I am well treated at the Cheval Blanc—am I not an English milord?—and my excellent Gaston looks after me devotedly. But there is a blue-bottle drowsiness about small watering places out of season, and our gallant enemies, the French, know how to bore themselves more exquisitely in their provinces than any nation on earth. Would you think that the daily arrival of the diligence from Toulon would be an excitement? Yet it is to me, I assure you, and to all St. Philip. I walk, I take the waters, I read Ossian, I play piquet with Gaston, and yet I seem to myself but half-alive. . . .

. . . You will smile and say to me, "Dear brother, you have always plumed yourself on being a student of human nature. Is there no society, no character for you to study, even in St. Philippe-des-Bains?" My dear sister, I bend myself earnestly to that end, yet so far with little result. I have talked to my doctor —a good man but unpolished; I have talked to the curé—a good man but dull. I have even attempted the society of the baths, beginning with Monsieur le Marquis de la Percedragon, who has ninety-six quarterings, soiled wristbands, and a gloomy interest in my liver, and ending with Mrs. Macgregor Jenkins, a worthy and red-faced lady whose conversation positively cannonades with dukes and duchesses. But, frankly, I prefer my chair in the garden and my Ossian to any of them, even at the risk of being considered a bear. A witty scoundrel would be the veriest godsend to me, but do such exist in St. Philip? I trow not. As it is, in my weakened condition, I am positively agog when Gaston comes in every morning with his budget of village scandal. A pretty pass to come to, you will say, for a man who has served with Eyre Coote and but for the mutabilities of fortune, not to speak of a most damnable cabal . . . (A long passage dealing with General Estcourt's East Indian services and his personal and unfavorable opinion of Warren Hastings is here omitted from the manuscript.) . . . But, at fifty, a man is either a fool or a philosopher. Nevertheless, unless Gaston provides me with a character to try my wits on, shortly, I shall begin to believe that they too have deteriorated with Indian suns. . . .

September 21st, 1788.

My Dear Sister: . . . Believe me, there is little soundness in the views of your friend, Lord Martindale. The French monarchy is not to be compared with our own, but King Louis is an excellent and well-beloved prince, and the proposed summoning of the States-General cannot but have the most salutary effect. . . .

The Curfew Tolls

(Three pages upon French politics and the possibility of cultivating sugar-cane in Southern France are here omitted.) . . . As for news of myself, I continue my yawning course, and feel a decided improvement from the waters. . . . So I shall continue them though the process is slow. . . .

You ask me, I fear a trifle mockingly, how my studies in human nature proceed?

Not so ill, my dear sister—I have, at least, scraped acquaintance with one odd fish, and that, in St. Philip, is a triumph. For some time, from my chair in the promenade, I have observed a pursy little fellow, of my age or thereabouts, stalking up and down between the lindens. His company seems avoided by such notables of the place as Mrs. Macgregor Jenkins and at first I put him down as a retired actor, for there is something a little theatrical in his dress and walk. He wears a wide-brimmed hat of straw, loose nankeen trousers and a quasi-military coat, and takes his waters with as much ceremony as Monsieur le Marquis, though not quite with the same *ton*. I should put him down as a Meridional, for he has the quick, dark eye, the sallow skin, the corpulence and the rodomontish airs that mark your true son of the Midi, once he has passed his lean and hungry youth.

And yet, there is some sort of unsuccessful oddity about him, which sets him off from your successful bourgeois. I cannot put my finger on it yet, but it interests me.

At any rate, I was sitting in my accustomed chair, reading Ossian, this morning, as he made his solitary rounds of the promenade. Doubtless I was more than usually absorbed in my author, for I must have pronounced some lines aloud as he passed. He gave me a quick glance at the time, but nothing more. But on his next round, as he was about to pass me, he hesitated for a moment, stopped, and then, removing his straw hat, saluted me very civilly.

"Monsieur will pardon me," he said, with a dumpy hauteur, "but surely monsieur is English? And surely the lines that monsieur just repeated are from the great poet, Ossian?"

I admitted both charges, with a smile, and he bowed again.

"Monsieur will excuse the interruption," he said, "but I myself have long admired the poetry of Ossian"—and with that he continued my quotation to the end of the passage, in very fair English, too, though with a strong accent. I complimented him, of

385

course, effusively—after all, it is not every day that one runs across a fellow-admirer of Ossian on the promenade of a small French watering place—and after that, he sat down in the chair beside me and we fell into talk. He seems, astonishingly for a Frenchman, to have an excellent acquaintance with our English poets—perhaps he has been a tutor in some English family. I did not press him with questions on this first encounter, though I noted that he spoke French with a slight accent also, which seems odd.

There is something a little rascally about him, to tell you the truth, though his conversation with me was both forceful and elevated. An ill man, too, and a disappointed one, or I miss my mark, yet his eyes, when he talks, are strangely animating. I fancy I would not care to meet him in a *guet-apens*, and yet, he may be the most harmless of broken pedagogues. We took a glass of waters together, to the great disgust of Mrs. Macgregor Jenkins, who ostentatiously drew her skirts aside. She let me know, afterward, in so many words, that my acquaintance was a noted bandit, though, when pressed, she could give no better reason than that he lives a little removed from the town, that "nobody knows where he comes from" and that his wife is "no better than she should be," whatever that portentous phrase entails. Well, one would hardly call him a gentleman, even by Mrs. Macgregor's somewhat easy standards, but he has given me better conversation than I have had in a month—and if he is a bandit, we might discuss thuggee together. But I hope for nothing so stimulating, though I must question Gaston about him. . . .

October 11th.

. . . But Gaston could tell me little, except that my acquaintance comes from Sardinia or some such island originally, has served in the French army and is popularly supposed to possess the evil eye. About Madame he hinted that he could tell me a great deal, but I did not labor the point. After all, if my friend has been c-ck-ld-d—do not blush, my dear sister!—that, too, is the portion of a philosopher, and I find his wide range of conversation much more palatable than Mrs. Macgregor Jenkins' re-warmed London gossip. Nor has he tried to borrow money from me yet, something which, I am frank to say, I expected and was prepared to refuse. . . .

The Curfew Tolls

. . . Triumph! My character is found—and a character of the first water, I assure you! I have dined with him in his house, and a very bad dinner it was. Madame is not a good housekeeper, whatever else she may be. And what she has been, one can see at a glance—she has all the little faded coquetries of the garrison coquette. Good-tempered, of course, as such women often are, and must have been pretty in her best days, though with shocking bad teeth. I suspect her of a touch of the tarbrush, though there I may be wrong. No doubt she caught my friend young— I have seen the same thing happen in India often enough—the experienced woman and the youngster fresh from England. Well, 'tis an old story—an old one with him, too—and no doubt Madame has her charms, though she is obviously one reason why he has not risen.

After dinner, Madame departed, not very willingly, and he took me into his study for a chat. He had even procured a bottle of port, saying he knew the Englishman's taste for it, and while it was hardly the right Cockburn, I felt touched by the attention. The man is desperately lonely—one reads that in his big eyes. He is also desperately proud, with the quick, touchy sensitiveness of the failure, and I quite exerted myself to draw him out.

And indeed, the effort repaid me. His own story is simple enough. He is neither bandit nor pedagogue, but, like myself, a broken soldier—a major of the French Royal Artillery, retired on half pay for some years. I think it creditable of him to have reached so respectable a rank, for he is of foreign birth—Sardinian, I think I told you—and the French service is by no means as partial to foreigners as they were in the days of the first Irish Brigade. Moreover, one simply does not rise in that service, unless one is a gentleman of quarterings, and that he could hardly claim. But the passion of his life has been India, and that is what interests me. And, 'pon my honor, he was rather astonishing about it.

As soon as, by a lucky chance, I hit upon the subject, his eyes lit up and his sickness dropped away. Pretty soon he began to take maps from a cabinet in the wall and ply me with questions about my own small experiences. And very soon indeed, I am abashed to state, I found myself stumbling in my answers. It was all book knowledge on his part, of course, but where the devil he could have got some of it, I do not know. Indeed, he would even correct me, now and then, as cool as you please. "Eight twelve pounders, I think, on the north wall of the old fortifications of Madras——" and the deuce of it is, he would be right. Finally, I could contain myself no longer.

"But, major, this is incredible," I said. "I have served twenty years with John Company and thought that I had some knowledge. But one would say you had fought over every inch of Bengal!"

He gave me a quick look, almost of anger, and began to roll up his maps.

"So I have, in my mind," he said, shortly, "but, as my superiors have often informed me, my hobby is a tedious one."

"It is not tedious to me," I said boldly. "Indeed, I have often marveled at your government's neglect of their opportunities in India. True, the issue is settled now——"

"It is by no means settled," he said, interrupting me rudely. I stared at him.

"It was settled, I believe, by Baron Clive, at a spot named Plassey," I said frigidly. "And afterward, by my own old general, Eyre Coote, at another spot named Wandewash."

"Oh, yes—yes—yes," he said impatiently, "I grant you Clive—Clive was a genius and met the fate of geniuses. He steals an empire for you, and your virtuous English Parliament holds up its hands in horror because he steals a few lakhs of rupees for himself as well. So he blows out his brains in disgrace—you inexplicable English!—and you lose your genius. A great pity. I would not have treated Clive so. But then, if I had been Milord Clive, I would not have blown out my brains."

"And what would you have done, had you been Clive?" I said, for the man's calm, staring conceit amused me.

His eyes were dangerous for a moment and I saw why the worthy Mrs. Macgregor Jenkins had called him a bandit.

"Oh," he said coolly, "I would have sent a file of grenadiers to your English Parliament and told it to hold its tongue. As Cromwell did. Now there was a man. But your Clive—faugh!—he had the ball at his feet and he refused to kick it. I withdraw the word genius. He was a nincompoop. At the least, he might have made himself a rajah."

This was a little too much, as you may imagine. "General Clive had his faults," I said icily, "but he was a true Briton and a patriot."

"He was a fool," said my puffy little major, flatly, his lower lip stuck out. "As big a fool as Dupleix, and that is saying much. Oh, some military skill, some talent for organization, yes. But a genius would have brushed him into the sea! It was possible to hold Arcot, it was possible to win Plassey—look!" and, with that, he ripped another map from his cabinet and began to expound to me eagerly exactly what he would have done in command of the French forces in India, in 1757, when he must have been but a lad in his twenties. He thumped the paper, he strewed corks along the table for his troops—corks taken from a supply in a tin box, so it must be an old game with him. And, as I listened, my irritation faded, for the man's monomania was obvious. Nor was it, to tell the truth, an ill-designed plan of campaign, for corks on a map. Of course these things are different, in the field.

I could say, with honesty, that his plan had features of novelty, and he gulped the words down hungrily—he has a great appetite for flattery.

"Yes, yes," he said. "That is how it should be done—the thickest skull can see it. And, ill as I am, with a fleet and ten thousand picked men——" He dreamed, obviously, the sweat of his exertions on his waxy face—it was absurd and yet touching to see him dream.

"You would find a certain amount of opposition," I said, in an amused voice.

"Oh, yes, yes," he said quickly, "I do not underrate the English. Excellent horse, solid foot. But no true knowledge of cannon, and I am a gunner——"

I hated to bring him down to earth and yet I felt that I must.

"Of course, major," I said, "you have had great experience in the field."

He looked at me for a moment, his arrogance quite unshaken.

"I have had very little," he said, quietly, "but one knows how the thing should be done or one does not know. And that is enough."

He stared at me for an instant with his big eyes. A little mad, of course. And yet I found myself saying, "But surely, major—what happened?"

"Why," he said, still quietly, "what happens to folk who have naught but their brains to sell? I staked my all on India when I was young—I thought that my star shone over it. I ate dirty puddings—*corpo di Baccho!*—to get there—I was no De Rohan or Soubise to win the king's favor! And I reached there indeed, in my youth, just in time to be included in the surrender of Pondicherry." He laughed, rather terribly, and sipped at his glass.

"You English were very courteous captors," he said. "But I was not released till the Seven Years War had ended—that was in '63. Who asks for the special exchange of an unknown artillery lieutenant? And then ten years odd of garrison duty at Mauritius. It was there that I met Madame—she is a Creole. A pleasant spot, Mauritius. We used to fire the cannon at the sea birds when we had enough ammunition for target practice," and he chuckled drearily. "By then I was thirty-seven. They had to make me a captain—they even brought me back to France. To garrison duty. I have been on garrison duty, at Toulon, at Brest, at——" He ticked off the names on his fingers but I did not like his voice.

"But surely," I said, "the American war, though a small affair—there were opportunities——"

"And who did they send?" he said quickly. "Lafayette—Rochambeau—De Grasse—the sprigs of the nobility. Oh, at Lafayette's age, I would have volunteered like Lafayette. But one should be successful in youth—after that, the spring is broken. And when one is over forty, one has responsibilities. I have a large family, you see, though not of my own begetting," and he chuckled as if at a secret joke. "Oh, I wrote the Continental Congress," he said reflectively, "but they preferred a dolt like Von Steuben. A good dolt, an honest dolt, but there you have it. I also wrote your British War Office," he said in an even voice. "I must show you that plan of campaign—sometime—they could have crushed General Washington with it in three weeks."

I stared at him, a little appalled.

"For an officer who has taken his king's shilling to send to an enemy nation a plan for crushing his own country's ally," I said, stiffly—"well, in England, we would call that treason."

"And what is treason?" he said lightly. "If we call it unsuccessful ambition we shall be nearer the truth." He looked at me, keenly. "You are shocked, General Estcourt," he said. "I am sorry for that. But have you never known the curse"—and his voice vibrated—"the curse of not being employed when you should be employed? The curse of being a hammer with no nail to drive? The curse—the curse of sitting in a dusty garrison town with dreams that would split the brain of a Caesar, and no room on earth for those dreams?"

"Yes," I said, unwillingly, for there was something in him that demanded the truth, "I have known that."

"Then you know hells undreamed of by the Christian," he said, with a sigh, "and if I committed treason—well, I have been punished for it. I might have been a brigadier, otherwise—I had Choiseul's ear for a few weeks, after great labor. As it is, I am here on half pay, and there will not be another war in my time. Moreover, M. de Ségur has proclaimed that all officers now must show sixteen quarterings. Well, I wish them joy of those officers, in the next conflict. Meanwhile, I have my corks, my maps and my family ailment." He smiled and tapped his side. "It killed my father at thirty-nine—it has not treated me quite so ill, but it will come for me soon enough."

And indeed, when I looked at him, I could well believe it, for the light had gone from his eyes and his cheeks were flabby. We chatted a little on indifferent subjects after that, then I left him, wondering whether to pursue the acquaintance. He is indubitably a character, but some of his speeches leave a taste in my mouth. Yet he can be greatly attractive—even now, with his mountainous failure like a cloak upon him. And yet why should I call it mountainous? His conceit is mountainous enough, but what else could he have expected of his career? Yet I wish I could forget his eyes. . . . To tell the truth, he puzzles me and I mean to get to the bottom of him. . . .

February 12th, 1789.
. . . I have another sidelight on the character of my friend, the major. As I told you, I was half of a mind to break off the acquaintance entirely, but he came up to me so civilly, the following day, that I could find no excuse. And since then, he has made me no embarrassingly treasonable confidences, though whenever we discuss the art of war, his arrogance is unbelievable. He even informed me, the other day, that while Frederick of Prussia was a fair general, his tactics might have been improved upon. I merely laughed and turned the question. Now and then I play a war game with him, with his corks and maps, and when I

let him win, he is as pleased as a child. . . . His illness increases visibly, despite the waters, and he shows an eagerness for my company which I cannot but find touching. . . . After all, he is a man of intelligence, and the company he has had to keep must have galled him at times. . . .

Now and then I amuse myself by speculating what might have happened to him, had he chosen some other profession than that of arms. He has, as I have told you, certain gifts of the actor, yet his stature and figure must have debarred him from tragic parts, while he certainly does not possess the humors of the comedian. Perhaps his best choice would have been the Romish church, for there, the veriest fisherman may hope, at least, to succeed to the keys of St. Peter. . . . And yet, Heaven knows, he would have made a very bad priest! . . .

But, to my tale. I had missed him from our accustomed walks for some days and went to his house—St. Helen's it is called; we live in a pother of saints' names hereabouts—one evening to inquire. I did not hear the quarreling voices till the tousle-haired servant had admitted me and then it was too late to retreat. Then my friend bounced down the corridor, his sallow face bored and angry.

"Ah, General Estcourt!" he said, with a complete change of expression as soon as he saw me. "What fortune! I was hoping you would pay us a call—I wish to introduce you to my family!"

He had told me previously of his pair of stepchildren by Madame's first marriage, and I must confess I felt curious to see them. But it was not of them he spoke, as I soon gathered.

"Yes," he said. "My brothers and sisters, or most of them, are here for a family council. You come in the nick of time!" He pinched my arm and his face glowed with the malicious naïveté of a child. "They do not believe that I really know an English general—it will be a great blow to them!" he whispered as we passed down the corridor. "Ah, if you had only worn your uniform and your Garters! But one cannot have everything in life!"

Well, my dear sister, what a group, when we entered the salon! It is a small room, tawdrily furnished in the worst French taste, with a jumble of Madame's femininities and souvenirs from the Island of Mauritius, and they were all sitting about in the French after-dinner fashion, drinking tisane and quarreling. And, indeed, had the room been as long as the nave of St. Peter's, it would yet have seemed too small for such a crew! An old mother, straight as a ramrod and as forbidding, with the burning eyes and the bitter dignity one sees on the faces of certain Italian peasants— you could see that they were all a little afraid of her except my friend, and he, I must say, treated her with a filial courtesy that was greatly to his credit. Two sisters, one fattish, swarthy and spiteful, the other with the wreck of great beauty and the evident marks of a certain profession on her shabby-fine *toilette* and her pinkened cheeks. An innkeeper brother-in-law called Buras or Durat, with a jowlish, heavily handsome face and the manners of a cavalry sergeant—he is married to the spiteful sister. And two brothers, one sheep-like, one fox-like, yet both bearing a certain resemblance to my friend.

The sheep-like brother is at least respectable, I gathered—a provincial lawyer in a small way of business whose great pride is that he has actually appeared before the Court of Appeals at Marseilles. The other, the fox-like one, makes his living more dubiously—he seems the sort of fellow who orates windily in taprooms about the Rights of Man, and other nonsense of M. Rousseau's. I would certainly not trust him with my watch, though he is trying to get himself elected to the States-General. And, as regards family concord, it was obvious at first glance that not one of them trusted the others. And yet, that is not all of the tribe. There are, if you will believe me, two other brothers living, and this family council was called to deal with the affairs of the next to-youngest, who seems, even in this mélange, to be a black sheep.

I can assure you, my head swam, and when my friend introduced me, proudly, as a Knight of the Garters, I did not even bother to contradict him. For they admitted me to their intimate circle at once—there was no doubt about that. Only the old lady remained aloof, saying little and sipping her camomile tea as if it were the blood of her enemies. But, one by one, the others related to me, with an unasked-for frankness, the most intimate and scandalous details of their brothers' and sisters' lives. They seemed united only on two points, jealousy of my friend, the major, because he is his mother's favorite, and dislike of Madame Josephine because she gives herself airs. Except for the haggard beauty—I must say, that, while her remarks anent her sister-in-law were not such as I would care to repeat, she seemed genuinely fond of her brother, the major, and expounded his virtues to me through an overpowering cloud of scent.

It was like being in a nest of Italian smugglers, or a den of quarrelsome foxes, for they all talked, or rather barked at once, even the brother-in-law, and only Madame Mère could bring silence among them. And yet, my friend enjoyed it. It was obvious he showed them off before me as he might have displayed the tricks of a set of performing animals. And yet with a certain fondness, too—that is the inexplicable part of it. I do not know which sentiment was upmost in my mind—respect for this family feeling or pity for his being burdened with such a clan.

For though not the eldest, he is the strongest among them, and they know it. They rebel, but he rules their family conclaves like a petty despot. I could have laughed at the farce of it, and yet, it was nearer tears. For here, at least, my friend was a personage.

I got away as soon as I could, despite some pressing looks from the haggard beauty. My friend accompanied me to the door.

"Well, well," he said, chuckling and rubbing his hands, "I am infinitely obliged to you, general. They will not forget this in a hurry. Before you entered, Joseph"—Joseph is the sheep-like one —"was boasting about his acquaintance with a *sous-intendant*, but an English general, bah! Joseph will have green eyes for a fortnight!" And he rubbed his hands again in a perfect paroxysm of delight.

It was too childlike to make me angry. "I am glad, of course, to have been of any service," I said.

"Oh, you have been a great service," he said. "They will not plague my poor Josie for at least half an hour. Ah, this is a bad business of Louis'—a bad business!"—Louis is the black sheep— "but we will patch it up somehow. Hortense is worth three of him—he must go back to Hortense!"

"You have a numerous family, major," I said, for want of something better to say.

"Oh, yes," he said, cheerfully. "Pretty numerous—I am sorry you could not meet the others. Though Louis is a fool—I pampered him in his youth. Well! He was a baby—and Jerome a mule. Still, we haven't done so badly for ourselves; not badly. Joseph makes a go of his law practice—there are fools enough in the world to be impressed by Joseph—and if Lucien gets to the States-

The Curfew Tolls

General, you may trust Lucien to feather his nest! And there are the grandchildren, and a little money—not much," he said, quickly. "They mustn't expect that from me. But it's a step up from where we started—if papa had lived, he wouldn't have been so ill-pleased. Poor Elisa's gone, but the rest of us have stuck together, and, while we may seem a little rough, to strangers, our hearts are in the right place. When I was a boy," and he chuckled again, "I had other ambitions for them. I thought, with luck on my side, I could make them all kings and queens. Funny, isn't it, to think of a numskull like Joseph as a king! Well, that was the boy of it. But, even so, they'd all be eating chestnuts back on the island without me, and that's something."

He said it rather defiantly, and I did not know which to marvel at most—his preposterous pride in the group or his cool contempt of them. So I said nothing but shook his hand instead. I could not help doing the latter. For surely, if anyone started in life with a millstone about his neck . . . and yet they are none of them ordinary people. . . .

March 13th, 1789.
. . . My friend's complaint has taken a turn for the worse and it is I who pay him visits now. It is the act of a Christian to do so and, to tell the truth, I have become oddly attached to him, though I can give no just reason for the attachment. He makes a bad patient, by the way, and is often abominably rude to both myself and Madame, who nurses him devotedly though unskillfully. I told him yesterday that I could have no more of it and he looked at me with his strangely luminous eyes. "So," he said, "even the English desert the dying." . . . Well, I stayed; after that, what else might a gentleman do? . . . Yet I cannot feel that he bears me any real affection—he exerts himself to charm, on occasion, but one feels he is playing a game . . . yes, even upon his deathbed, he plays a game . . . a complex character. . . .

April 28th, 1789.
. . . My friend the major's malady approaches its term—the last few days find him fearfully enfeebled. He knows that the end draws nigh; indeed he speaks of it often, with remarkable calmness. I had thought it might turn his mind toward religion, but while he has accepted the ministrations of his Church, I fear it is

without the sincere repentance of a Christian. When the priest had left him, yesterday, he summoned me, remarking, "Well, all that is over with," rather more in the tone of a man who has just reserved a place in a coach than one who will shortly stand before his Maker.

"It does no harm," he said, reflectively. "And, after all, it might be true. Why not?" and he chuckled in a way that repelled me. Then he asked me to read to him—not the Bible, as I had expected, but some verses of the poet Gray. He listened attentively, and when I came to the passage, "Hands, that the rod of empire might have swayed," and its successor, "Some mute inglorious Milton here may rest," he asked me to repeat them. When I had done so, he said, "Yes, yes. That is true, very true. I did not think so in boyhood—I thought genius must force its own way. But your poet is right about it."

I found this painful, for I had hoped that his illness had brought him to a juster, if less arrogant, estimate of his own abilities.

"Come, major," I said, soothingly, "we cannot all be great men, you know. And you have no need to repine. After all, as you say, you have risen in the world——"

"Risen?" he said, and his eyes flashed. "Risen? Oh, God, that I should die alone with my one companion an Englishman with a soul of suet! Fool, if I had had Alexander's chance, I would have bettered Alexander! And it will come, too, that is the worst of it. Already Europe is shaking with a new birth. If I had been born under the Sun-King, I would be a Marshal of France; if I had been born twenty years ago, I would mold a new Europe with my fists in the next half-dozen years. Why did they put my soul in my body at this infernal time? Do you not understand, imbecile? Is there no one who understands?"

I called Madame at this, as he was obviously delirious, and, after some trouble, we got him quieted.

May 8th, 1789.
. . . My poor friend is gone, and peacefully enough at the last. His death, oddly enough, coincided with the date of the opening of the States-General at Versailles. The last moments of life are always painful for the observer, but his end was as relatively serene as might be hoped for, considering his character. I was watching at one side of the bed and a thunderstorm was

raging at the time. No doubt, to his expiring consciousness, the cracks of the thunder sounded like artillery, for, while we were waiting the death-struggle, he suddenly raised himself in the bed and listened intently. His eyes glowed, a beatific expression passed over his features. "The army! Head of the army!" he whispered ecstatically, and, when we caught him, he was lifeless . . . I must say that, while it may not be very Christian, I am glad that death brought him what life could not, and that, in the very article of it, he saw himself at the head of victorious troops. Ah, Fame— delusive spectre . . . (A page of disquisition by General Est- court on the vanities of human ambition is here omitted.) . . . The face, after death, was composed, with a certain majesty, even . . . one could see that he might have been handsome as a youth. . . .

                                                        May 26th, 1789.

. . . I shall return to Paris by easy stages and reach Stokely sometime in June. My health is quite restored and all that has kept me here this long has been the difficulty I have met with in attempting to settle my poor friend, the major's affairs. For one thing, he appears to have been originally a native of Corsica, not of Sardinia as I had thought, and while that explains much in his character, it has also given occupation to the lawyers. I have met his rapacious family, individually and in conclave, and, if there are further gray hairs on my head, you may put it down to them. . . . However, I have finally assured the major's relict of her legitimate rights in his estate, and that is something—my one ray of comfort in the matter being the behavior of her son by the former marriage, who seems an excellent and virtuous young man. . . .

. . . You will think me a very soft fellow, no doubt, for wast- ing so much time upon a chance acquaintance who was neither, in our English sense, a gentleman nor a man whose Christian virtues counterbalanced his lack of true breeding. Yet there was a tragedy about him beyond his station, and that verse of Gray's rings in my head. I wish I could forget the expression on his face when he spoke of it. Suppose a genius born in circumstances that made the development of that genius impossible—well, all this is the merest moonshine. . . .

. . . To revert to more practical matters, I discover that the major has left me his military memoirs, papers and commentaries, including his maps. Heaven knows what I shall do with them! I cannot, in courtesy, burn them *sur-le-champ*, and yet they fill two huge packing cases and the cost of transporting them to Stokely will be considerable. Perhaps I will take them to Paris and quietly dispose of them there to some waste-paper merchant. . . . In return for this unsought legacy, Madame has consulted me in regard to a stone and epitaph for her late husband, and, knowing that otherwise the family would squabble over the affair for weeks, I have drawn up a design which I hope meets with their approval. It appears that he particularly desired that the epitaph should be writ in English, saying that France had had enough of him, living—a freak of dying vanity for which one must pardon him. However, I have produced the following, which I hope will answer.

Here lies
NAPOLEONE BUONAPARTE
Major of the Royal Artillery
of France.
Born August 15th, 1737
at Ajaccio, Corsica.
Died May 5th, 1789
at St. Philippe-des-Bains
"Rest, perturbed spirit . . ."

. . . I had thought, for some hours, of excerpting the lines of Gray's—the ones that still ring in my head. But, on reflection, though they suit well enough, they yet seem too cruel to the dust.

THE KING OF THE CATS

"But, my *dear*," said Mrs. Culverin, with a tiny gasp, "you can't actually mean—a *tail!*"

Mrs. Dingle nodded impressively. "Exactly. I've seen him. Twice. Paris, of course, and then, a command appearance at Rome—we were in the Royal box. He conducted—my dear,

The King of the Cats

you've never heard such effects from an orchestra—and, my dear," she hesitated slightly, "he conducted *with it.*"

"How perfectly, fascinatingly too horrid for words!" said Mrs. Culverin in a dazed but greedy voice. "We *must* have him to dinner as soon as he comes over—he is coming over, isn't he?"

"The twelfth," said Mrs. Dingle with a gleam in her eyes. "The New Symphony people have asked him to be guest-conductor for three special concerts—I do hope you can dine with *us* some night while he's here—he'll be very busy, of course—but he's promised to give us what time he can spare——"

"Oh, thank you, dear," said Mrs. Culverin, abstractedly, her last raid upon Mrs. Dingle's pet British novelist still fresh in her mind. "You're always so delightfully hospitable—but you mustn't wear yourself out—the rest of us must do *our* part—I know Henry and myself would be only too glad to——"

"That's very sweet of you, darling." Mrs. Dingle also remembered the larceny of the British novelist. "But we're just going to give Monsieur Tibault—sweet name, isn't it! They say he's descended from the Tybalt in 'Romeo and Juliet' and that's why he doesn't like Shakespeare—we're just going to give Monsieur Tibault the simplest sort of time—a little reception after his first concert, perhaps. He hates," she looked around the table, "large, mixed parties. And then, of course, his—er—little idiosyncrasy——" she coughed delicately. "It makes him feel a trifle shy with strangers."

"But I don't understand yet, Aunt Emily," said Tommy Brooks, Mrs. Dingle's nephew. "Do you really mean this Tibault bozo has a tail? Like a monkey and everything?"

"Tommy dear," said Mrs. Culverin, crushingly, "in the first place Monsieur Tibault is not a bozo—he is a very distinguished musician—the finest conductor in Europe. And in the second place——"

"He has," Mrs. Dingle was firm. "He has a tail. He conducts with it."

"Oh, but honestly!" said Tommy, his ears pinkening. "I mean —of course, if you say so, Aunt Emily, I'm sure he has—but still, it sounds pretty steep, if you know what I mean! How about it, Professor Tatto?"

Professor Tatto cleared his throat. "Tck," he said, putting his

399

fingertips together cautiously, "I shall be very anxious to see this Monsieur Tibault. For myself, I have never observed a genuine specimen of *homo caudatus*, so I should be inclined to doubt, and yet . . . In the Middle Ages, for instance, the belief in men—er —tailed or with caudal appendages of some sort, was both widespread and, as far as we can gather, well-founded. As late as the Eighteenth Century, a Dutch sea-captain with some character for veracity recounts the discovery of a pair of such creatures in the island of Formosa. They were in a low state of civilization, I believe, but the appendages in question were quite distinct. And in 1860, Dr. Grimbrook, the English surgeon, claims to have treated no less than three African natives with short but evident tails—though his testimony rests upon his unsupported word. After all, the thing is not impossible, though doubtless unusual. Web feet—rudimentary gills—these occur with some frequency. The appendix we have with us always. The chain of our descent from the ape-like form is by no means complete. For that matter," he beamed around the table, "what can we call the last few vertebrae of the normal spine but the beginnings of a concealed and rudimentary tail? Oh, yes—yes—it's possible—quite—that in an extraordinary case—a reversion to type—a survival—though, of course——"

"I told you so," said Mrs. Dingle triumphantly. "*Isn't* it fascinating? Isn't it, Princess?"

The Princess Vivrakanarda's eyes, blue as a field of larkspur, fathomless as the centre of heaven, rested lightly for a moment on Mrs. Dingle's excited countenance.

"Ve-ry fascinating," she said, in a voice like stroked, golden velvet. "I should like—I should like ve-ry much to meet this Monsieur Tibault."

"Well, *I* hope he breaks his neck!" said Tommy Brooks, under his breath—but nobody ever paid much attention to Tommy.

Nevertheless as the time for Mr. Tibault's arrival in these States drew nearer and nearer, people in general began to wonder whether the Princess had spoken quite truthfully—for there was no doubt of the fact that, up till then, she had been the unique sensation of the season—and you know what social lions and lionesses are.

It was, if you remember, a Siamese season, and genuine Siamese were at quite as much of a premium as Russian accents had been

The King of the Cats

in the quaint old days when the Chauve-Souris was a novelty. The Siamese Art Theatre, imported at terrific expense, was playing to packed houses. "Gushuptzgu," an epic novel of Siamese farm life, in nineteen closely-printed volumes, had just been awarded the Nobel prize. Prominent pet-and-newt dealers reported no cessation in the appalling demand for Siamese cats. And upon the crest of this wave of interest in things Siamese, the Princess Vivrakanarda poised with the elegant nonchalance of a Hawaiian water-baby upon its surfboard. She was indispensable. She was incomparable. She was everywhere.

Youthful, enormously wealthy, allied on one hand to the Royal Family of Siam and on the other to the Cabots (and yet with the first eighteen of her twenty-one years shrouded from speculation in a golden zone of mystery), the mingling of races in her had produced an exotic beauty as distinguished as it was strange. She moved with a feline, effortless grace, and her skin was as if it had been gently powdered with tiny grains of the purest gold—yet the blueness of her eyes, set just a trifle slantingly, was as pure and startling as the sea on the rocks of Maine. Her brown hair fell to her knees—she had been offered extraordinary sums by the Master Barbers' Protective Association to have it shingled. Straight as a waterfall tumbling over brown rocks, it had a vague perfume of sandalwood and suave spices and held tints of rust and the sun. She did not talk very much—but then she did not have to—her voice had an odd, small, melodious huskiness that haunted the mind. She lived alone and was reputed to be very lazy—at least it was known that she slept during most of the day—but at night she bloomed like a moon-flower and a depth came into her eyes.

It was no wonder that Tommy Brooks fell in love with her. The wonder was that she let him. There was nothing exotic or distinguished about Tommy—he was just one of those pleasant, normal young men who seem created to carry on the bond business by reading the newspapers in the University Club during most of the day, and can always be relied upon at night to fill an unexpected hole in a dinner-party. It is true that the Princess could hardly be said to do more than tolerate any of her suitors —no one had ever seen those aloofly arrogant eyes enliven at the entrance of any male. But she seemed to be able to tolerate Tommy a little more than the rest—and that young man's infatuated day-dreams were beginning to be beset by smart solitaires

401

and imaginary apartments on Park Avenue, when the famous M. Tibault conducted his first concert at Carnegie Hall.

Tommy Brooks sat beside the Princess. The eyes he turned upon her were eyes of longing and love, but her face was as impassive as a mask, and the only remark she made during the preliminary bustlings was that there seemed to be a number of people in the audience. But Tommy was relieved, if anything, to find her even a little more aloof than usual, for, ever since Mrs. Culverin's dinner-party, a vague disquiet as to the possible impression which this Tibault creature might make upon her had been growing in his mind. It shows his devotion that he was present at all. To a man whose simple Princetonian nature found in "Just a Little Love, a Little Kiss," the quintessence of musical art, the average symphony was a positive torture, and he looked forward to the evening's programme itself with a grim, brave smile.

"Ssh!" said Mrs. Dingle, breathlessly. "He's coming!" It seemed to the startled Tommy as if he were suddenly back in the trenches under a heavy barrage, as M. Tibault made his entrance to a perfect bombardment of applause.

Then the enthusiastic noise was sliced off in the middle and a gasp took its place—a vast, windy sigh, as if every person in that multitude had suddenly said, "Ah." For the papers had not lied about him. The tail was there.

They called him theatric—but how well he understood the uses of theatricalism! Dressed in unrelieved black from head to foot (the black dress-shirt had been a special token of Mussolini's esteem), he did not walk on, he strolled, leisurely, easily, aloofly, the famous tail curled nonchalantly about one wrist—a suave, black panther lounging through a summer garden with that little mysterious weave of the head that panthers have when they pad behind bars—the glittering darkness of his eyes unmoved by any surprise or elation. He nodded, twice, in regal acknowledgment, as the clapping reached an apogee of frenzy. To Tommy there was something dreadfully reminiscent of the Princess in the way he nodded. Then he turned to his orchestra.

A second and louder gasp went up from the audience at this point, for, as he turned, the tip of that incredible tail twined with dainty carelessness into some hidden pocket and produced a black baton. But Tommy did not even notice. He was looking at the Princess instead.

She had not even bothered to clap, at first, but now—He had never seen her moved like this, never. She was not applauding, her hands were clenched in her lap, but her whole body was rigid, rigid as a steel bar, and the blue flowers of her eyes were bent upon the figure of M. Tibault in a terrible concentration. The pose of her entire figure was so still and intense that for an instant Tommy had the lunatic idea that any moment she might leap from her seat beside him as lightly as a moth, and land, with no sound, at M. Tibault's side to—yes—to rub her proud head against his coat in worship. Even Mrs. Dingle would notice in a moment.

"Princess——" he said, in a horrified whisper, "Princess——"

Slowly the tenseness of her body relaxed, her eyes veiled again, she grew calm.

"Yes, Tommy?" she said, in her usual voice, but there was still something about her . . .

"Nothing, only—oh, hang—he's starting!" said Tommy, as M. Tibault, his hands loosely clasped before him, turned and *faced* the audience. His eyes dropped, his tail switched once impressively, then gave three little preliminary taps with his baton on the floor.

Seldom has Gluck's overture to "Iphigenie in Aulis" received such an ovation. But it was not until the Eighth Symphony that the hysteria of the audience reached its climax. Never before had the New Symphony played so superbly—and certainly never before had it been led with such genius. Three prominent conductors in the audience were sobbing with the despairing admiration of envious children toward the close, and one at least was heard to offer wildly ten thousand dollars to a well-known facial surgeon there present for a shred of evidence that tails of some variety could by any stretch of science be grafted upon a normally decaudate form. There was no doubt about it—no mortal hand and arm, be they ever so dexterous, could combine the delicate élan and powerful grace displayed in every gesture of M. Tibault's tail.

A sable staff, it dominated the brasses like a flicker of black lightning; an ebon, elusive whip, it drew the last exquisite breath of melody from the woodwinds and ruled the stormy strings like a magician's rod. M. Tibault bowed and bowed again—roar after roar of frenzied admiration shook the hall to its foundations— and when he finally staggered, exhausted, from the platform, the president of the Wednesday Sonata Club was only restrained by force from flinging her ninety-thousand-dollar string of pearls after him in an excess of aesthetic appreciation. New York had come and seen—and New York was conquered. Mrs. Dingle was immediately besieged by reporters, and Tommy Brooks looked forward to the "little party" at which he was to meet the new hero of the hour with feelings only a little less lugubrious than those that would have come to him just before taking his seat in the electric chair.

The meeting between his Princess and M. Tibault was worse and better than he expected. Better because, after all, they did not say much to each other—and worse because it seemed to him, somehow, that some curious kinship of mind between them made words unnecessary. They were certainly the most distinguished-looking couple in the room, as he bent over her hand. "So darlingly foreign, both of them, and yet so different," babbled Mrs. Dingle—but Tommy couldn't agree.

They were different, yes—the dark, lithe stranger with the bizarre appendage tucked carelessly in his pocket, and the blue-eyed, brown-haired girl. But that difference only accentuated what they had in common—something in the way they moved, in the suavity of their gestures, in the set of their eyes. Something deeper, even, than race. He tried to puzzle it out—then, looking around at the others, he had a flash of revelation. It was as if that couple were foreign, indeed—not only to New York but to all common humanity. As if they were polite guests from a different star.

Tommy did not have a very happy evening, on the whole. But his mind worked slowly, and it was not until much later that the mad suspicion came upon him in full force.

Perhaps he is not to be blamed for his lack of immediate comprehension. The next few weeks were weeks of bewildered misery for him. It was not that the Princess's attitude toward him had changed—she was just as tolerant of him as before, but M.

Tibault was always there. He had a faculty of appearing as out of thin air—he walked, for all his height, as lightly as a butterfly—and Tommy grew to hate that faintest shuffle on the carpet that announced his presence.

And then, hang it all, the man was so smooth, so infernally, unrufflably smooth! He was never out of temper, never embarrassed. He treated Tommy with the extreme of urbanity, and yet his eyes mocked, deep-down, and Tommy could do nothing. And, gradually, the Princess became more and more drawn to this stranger, in a soundless communion that found little need for speech—and that, too, Tommy saw and hated, and that, too, he could not mend.

He began to be haunted not only by M. Tibault in the flesh, but by M. Tibault in the spirit. He slept badly, and when he slept, he dreamed—of M. Tibault, a man no longer, but a shadow, a spectre, the limber ghost of an animal whose words came purringly between sharp little pointed teeth. There was certainly something odd about the whole shape of the fellow—his fluid ease, the mould of his head, even the cut of his fingernails—but just what it was escaped Tommy's intensest cogitation. And when he did put his finger on it at length, at first he refused to believe.

A pair of petty incidents decided him, finally, against all reason. He had gone to Mrs. Dingle's, one winter afternoon, hoping to find the Princess. She was out with his aunt, but was expected back for tea, and he wandered idly into the library to wait. He was just about to switch on the lights, for the library was always dark even in summer, when he heard a sound of light breathing that seemed to come from the leather couch in the corner. He approached it cautiously and dimly made out the form of M. Tibault, curled up on the couch, peacefully asleep.

The sight annoyed Tommy so that he swore under his breath and was back near the door on his way out, when the feeling we all know and hate, the feeling that eyes we cannot see are watching us, arrested him. He turned back—M. Tibault had not moved a muscle of his body to all appearance—but his eyes were open now. And those eyes were black and human no longer. They were green—Tommy could have sworn it—and he could have sworn that they had no bottom and gleamed like little emeralds in the dark. It only lasted a moment, for Tommy pressed the light-button automatically—and there was M. Tibault, his normal self, yawning a little but urbanely apologetic, but it gave Tommy time to think. Nor did what happened a trifle later increase his peace of mind.

They had lit a fire and were talking in front of it—by now Tommy hated M. Tibault so thoroughly that he felt that odd yearning for his company that often occurs in such cases. M. Tibault was telling some anecdote and Tommy was hating him worse than ever for basking with such obvious enjoyment in the heat of the flames and the ripple of his own voice.

Then they heard the street-door open, and M. Tibault jumped up—and jumping, caught one sock on a sharp corner of the brass fire-rail and tore it open in a jagged flap. Tommy looked down mechanically at the tear—a second's glance, but enough—for M. Tibault, for the first time in Tommy's experience, lost his temper completely. He swore violently in some spitting, foreign tongue —his face distorted suddenly—he clapped his hand over his sock. Then, glaring furiously at Tommy, he fairly sprang from the room, and Tommy could hear him scaling the stairs in long, agile bounds.

Tommy sank into a chair, careless for once of the fact that he heard the Princess's light laugh in the hall. He didn't want to see the Princess. He didn't want to see anybody. There had been something revealed when M. Tibault had torn that hole in his sock—and it was not the skin of a man. Tommy had caught a glimpse of—black plush. Black velvet. And then had come M. Tibault's sudden explosion of fury. Good *Lord*—did the man wear black velvet stockings under his ordinary socks? Or could he— could he—but here Tommy held his fevered head in his hands.

He went to Professor Tatto that evening with a series of hypo-thetical questions, but as he did not dare confide his real suspicions to the Professor, the hypothetical answers he received served only to confuse him the more. Then he thought of Billy Strange. Billy was a good sort, and his mind had a turn for the bizarre. Billy might be able to help.

He couldn't get hold of Billy for three days and lived through the interval in a fever of impatience. But finally they had dinner together at Billy's apartment, where his queer books were, and Tommy was able to blurt out the whole disordered jumble of his suspicions.

The King of the Cats

Billy listened without interrupting until Tommy was quite through. Then he pulled at his pipe. "But, my dear *man*——" he said, protestingly.

"Oh, I know—I know——" said Tommy, and waved his hands, "I know I'm crazy—you needn't tell me that—but I tell you, the man's a cat all the same—no, I don't see how he could be, but he is—why, hang it, in the first place, everybody knows he's got a tail!"

"Even so," said Billy, puffing. "Oh, my dear Tommy, I don't doubt you saw, or think you saw, everything you say. But, even so——" He shook his head.

"But what about those other birds, werwolves and things?" said Tommy.

Billy looked dubious. "We-ll," he admitted, "you've got me there, of course. At least—a tailed man *is* possible. And the yarns about werwolves go back far enough, so that—well, I wouldn't say there aren't or haven't been werwolves—but then I'm willing to believe more things than most people. But a wer-cat—or a man that's a cat and a cat that's a man—honestly, Tommy——"

"If I don't get some real advice I'll go clean off my hinge. For Heaven's sake, tell me something to *do!*"

"Lemme think," said Billy. "First, you're pizen-sure this man is——"

"A cat. Yeah," and Tommy nodded violently.

"Check. And second—if it doesn't hurt your feelings, Tommy —you're afraid this girl you're in love with has—er—at least a streak of—felinity—in her—and so she's drawn to him?"

"Oh, Lord, Billy, if I only knew!"

"Well—er—suppose she really is, too, you know—would you still be keen on her?"

"I'd marry her if she turned into a dragon every Wednesday!" said Tommy, fervently.

Billy smiled. "H'm," he said, "then the obvious thing to do is to get rid of this M. Tibault. Lemme think."

He thought about two pipes full, while Tommy sat on pins and needles. Then, finally, he burst out laughing.

"What's so darn funny?" said Tommy, aggrievedly.

"Nothing, Tommy, only I've just thought of a stunt—something so blooming crazy—but if he is—h'm—what you think he is

—it *might* work——" And, going to the bookcase, he took down a book.

"If you think you're going to quiet my nerves by reading me a bedtime story——"

"Shut up, Tommy, and listen to this—if you really want to get rid of your feline friend."

"What is it?"

"Book of Agnes Repplier's. About cats. Listen.

" 'There is also a Scandinavian version of the ever famous story which Sir Walter Scott told to Washington Irving, which Monk Lewis told to Shelley and which, in one form or another, we find embodied in the folklore of every land'—now, Tommy, pay attention—'the story of the traveller who saw within a ruined abbey, a procession of cats, lowering into a grave a little coffin with a crown upon it. Filled with horror, he hastened from the spot; but when he had reached his destination, he could not forbear relating to a friend the wonder he had seen. Scarcely had the tale been told when his friend's cat, who lay curled up tranquilly by the fire, sprang to its feet, cried out, "Then I am the King of the Cats!" and disappeared in a flash up the chimney.'

"Well?" said Billy, shutting the book.

"By gum!" said Tommy, staring. "By gum! Do you think there's a chance?"

"*I* think we're both in the booby-hatch. But if you want to try it——"

"Try it! I'll spring it on him the next time I see him. But—listen—I can't make it a ruined abbey——"

"Oh, use your imagination! Make it Central Park—anywhere. Tell it as if it happened to you—seeing the funeral procession and all that. You can lead into it somehow—let's see—some general line—oh, yes—'Strange, isn't it, how fact so often copies fiction. Why, only yesterday——' See?"

"Strange, isn't it, how fact so often copies fiction," repeated Tommy dutifully. "Why, only yesterday——"

"I happened to be strolling through Central Park when I saw something very odd."

"I happened to be strolling through—here, gimme that book!" said Tommy, "I want to learn the rest of it by heart!"

Mrs. Dingle's farewell dinner to the famous Monsieur Tibault, on the occasion of his departure for his Western tour, was looked forward to with the greatest expectations. Not only would everybody be there, including the Princess Vivrakanarda, but Mrs. Dingle, a hinter if there ever was one, had let it be known that at this dinner an announcement of very unusual interest to Society might be made. So everyone, for once, was almost on time, except for Tommy. He was at least fifteen minutes early, for he wanted to have speech with his aunt alone. Unfortunately, however, he had hardly taken off his overcoat when she was whispering some news in his ear so rapidly that he found it difficult to understand a word of it.

"And you mustn't breathe it to a soul!" she ended, beaming. "That is, not before the announcement—I think we'll have *that* with the salad—people never pay very much attention to salad——"

"Breathe what, Aunt Emily?" said Tommy, confused.

"The Princess, darling—the dear Princess and Monsieur Tibault —they just got engaged this afternoon, dear things! Isn't it *fascinating?*"

"Yeah," said Tommy, and started to walk blindly through the nearest door. His aunt restrained him.

"Not there, dear—not in the library. You can congratulate them later. They're just having a sweet little moment alone there now——" And she turned away to harry the butler, leaving Tommy stunned.

But his chin came up after a moment. He wasn't beaten yet.

"Strange, isn't it, how often fact copies fiction?" he repeated to himself in dull mnemonics, and, as he did so, he shook his fist at the library door.

Mrs. Dingle was wrong, as usual. The Princess and M. Tibault were not in the library—they were in the conservatory, as Tommy discovered when he wandered aimlessly past the glass doors.

He didn't mean to look, and after a second he turned away. But that second was enough.

Tibault was seated in a chair and she was crouched on a stool at his side, while his hand, softly, smoothly, stroked her brown hair. Black cat and Siamese kitten. Her face was hidden from Tommy, but he could see Tibault's face. And he could hear.

They were not talking, but there was a sound between them. A warm and contented sound like the murmur of giant bees in

409

a hollow tree—a golden, musical rumble, deep-throated, that came from Tibault's lips and was answered by hers—a golden purr.

Tommy found himself back in the drawing-room, shaking hands with Mrs. Culverin, who said, frankly, that she had seldom seen him look so pale.

The first two courses of the dinner passed Tommy like dreams, but Mrs. Dingle's cellar was notable, and by the middle of the meat course, he began to come to himself. He had only one resolve now.

For the next few moments he tried desperately to break into the conversation, but Mrs. Dingle was talking, and even Gabriel will have a time interrupting Mrs. Dingle. At last, though, she paused for breath and Tommy saw his chance.

"Speaking of that," said Tommy, piercingly, without knowing in the least what he was referring to, "Speaking of that——"

"As I was saying," said Professor Tatto. But Tommy would not yield. The plates were being taken away. It was time for salad.

"Speaking of that," he said again, so loudly and strangely that Mrs. Culverin jumped and an awkward hush fell over the table. "Strange, isn't it, how often fact copies fiction?" There, he was started. His voice rose even higher. "Why, only today I was strolling through——" and, word for word, he repeated his lesson. He could see Tibault's eyes glowing at him, as he described the funeral. He could see the Princess, tense.

He could not have said what he had expected might happen when he came to the end; but it was not bored silence, everywhere, to be followed by Mrs. Dingle's acrid, "Well, Tommy, is that *quite* all?"

He slumped back in his chair, sick at heart. He was a fool and his last resource had failed. Dimly he heard his aunt's voice, saying, " Well, then——" and realized that she was about to make the fatal announcement.

But just then Monsieur Tibault spoke.

"One moment, Mrs. Dingle," he said, with extreme politeness, and she was silent. He turned to Tommy.

"You are—positive, I suppose, of what you saw this afternoon, Brooks?" he said, in tones of light mockery.

"Absolutely," said Tommy sullenly. "Do you think I'd——"

"Oh, no, no, no," Monsieur Tibault waved the implication aside, "but—such an interesting story—one likes to be sure of the details—and, of course, you *are* sure—*quite* sure—that the kind of crown you describe was on the coffin?"

"Of course," said Tommy, wondering, "but——"

"Then I'm the King of the Cats!" cried Monsieur Tibault in a voice of thunder, and, even as he cried it, the house-lights blinked—there was the soft thud of an explosion that seemed muffled in cotton-wool from the minstrel gallery—and the scene was lit for a second by an obliterating and painful burst of light that vanished in an instant and was succeeded by heavy, blinding clouds of white, pungent smoke.

"Oh, those *horrid* photographers," came Mrs. Dingle's voice in a melodious wail. "I *told* them not to take the flashlight picture till dinner was over, and now they've taken it *just* as I was nibbling lettuce!"

Someone tittered a little nervously. Someone coughed. Then, gradually the veils of smoke dislimned and the green-and-black spots in front of Tommy's eyes died away.

They were blinking at each other like people who have just come out of a cave into brilliant sun. Even yet their eyes stung with the fierceness of that abrupt illumination and Tommy found it hard to make out the faces across the table from him.

Mrs. Dingle took command of the half-blinded company with her accustomed poise. She rose, glass in hand. "And now, dear friends," she said in a clear voice, "I'm sure all of us are very happy to——" Then she stopped, open-mouthed, an expression of incredulous horror on her features. The lifted glass began to spill its contents on the tablecloth in a little stream of amber. As she spoke, she had turned directly to Monsieur Tibault's place at the table—and Monsieur Tibault was no longer there.

Some say there was a bursting flash of fire that disappeared up the chimney—some say it was a giant cat that leaped through the window at a bound, without breaking the glass. Professor Tatto puts it down to a mysterious chemical disturbance operating only over M. Tibault's chair. The butler, who is pious, believes the devil in person flew away with him, and Mrs. Dingle hesitates between witchcraft and a malicious ectoplasm dematerializing on the wrong cosmic plane. But be that as it may, one thing is certain—in the instant of fictive darkness which followed the glare of the flashlight, Monsieur Tibault, the great conductor, disappeared forever from mortal sight, tail and all.

Mrs. Culverin swears he was an international burglar and that she was just about to unmask him, when he slipped away under cover of the flashlight smoke, but no one else who sat at that historic dinner-table believes her. No, there are no sound explanations, but Tommy thinks he knows, and he will never be able to pass a cat again without wondering.

Mrs. Tommy is quite of her husband's mind regarding cats—she was Gretchen Woolwine, of Chicago—for Tommy told her his whole story, and while she doesn't believe a great deal of it, there is no doubt in her heart that one person concerned in the affair was a *perfect* cat. Doubtless it would have been more romantic to relate how Tommy's daring finally won him his Princess —but, unfortunately, it would not be veracious. For the Princess Vivrakanarda, also, is with us no longer. Her nerves, shattered by the spectacular denouement of Mrs. Dingle's dinner, required a sea-voyage, and from that voyage she has never returned to America.

Of course, there are the usual stories—one hears of her, a nun in a Siamese convent, or a masked dancer at Le Jardin de ma Soeur—one hears that she has been murdered in Patagonia or married in Trebizond—but, as far as can be ascertained, not one of these gaudy fables has the slightest basis of fact. I believe that Tommy, in his heart of hearts, is quite convinced that the sea-voyage was only a pretext, and that by some unheard-of means, she has managed to rejoin the formidable Monsieur Tibault, wherever in the world of the visible or the invisible he may be—in fact, that in some ruined city or subterranean palace they reign together now, King and Queen of all the mysterious Kingdom of Cats. But that, of course, is quite impossible.

DOC MELLHORN AND THE PEARLY GATES

Doc Mellhorn had never expected to go anywhere at all when he died. So, when he found himself on the road again, it surprised him. But perhaps I'd better explain a little about Doc Mellhorn first. He was seventy-odd when he left our town; but when he came, he was as young as Bates or Filsinger or any of the boys at the hospital. Only there wasn't any hospital when he came. He came with a young man's beard and a brand-new bag and a lot of newfangled ideas about medicine that we didn't take to much. And he left, forty-odd years later, with a first-class county health record and a lot of people alive that wouldn't have been alive if he hadn't been there. Yes, a country doctor. And nobody ever called him a man in white or a death grappler that I know of, though they did think of giving him a degree at Pewauket College once. But then the board met again and decided they needed a new gymnasium, so they gave the degree to J. Prentiss Parmalee instead.

They say he was a thin young man when he first came, a thin young man with an Eastern accent who'd wanted to study in Vienna. But most of us remember him chunky and solid, with white hair and a little bald spot that always got burned bright red in the first hot weather. He had about four card tricks that he'd do for you, if you were a youngster—they were always the same ones—and now and then, if he felt like it, he'd take a silver half dollar out of the back of your neck. And that worked as well with the youngsters who were going to build rocket ships as it had with the youngsters who were going to be railway engineers. It always worked. I guess it was Doc Mellhorn more than the trick.

But there wasn't anything unusual about him, except maybe the card tricks. Or, anyway, he didn't think so. He was just a good doctor and he knew us inside out. I've heard people call him a pigheaded, obstinate old mule—that was in the fight about the water supply. And I've heard a weepy old lady call him a saint. I took the tale to him once, and he looked at me over his glasses and said, "Well, I've always respected a mule. Got ten times the sense of a—horse." Then he took a silver half dollar out of my ear.

Well, how do you describe a man like that? You don't—you call him up at three in the morning. And when he sends in his bill, you think it's a little steep.

All the same, when it came to it, there were people who drove a hundred and fifty miles to the funeral. And the Masons came down from Bluff City, and the Poles came from across the tracks, with a wreath the size of a house, and you saw cars in town that you didn't often see there. But it was after the funeral that the queer things began for Doc Mellhorn.

The last thing he remembered, he'd been lying in bed, feeling pretty sick, on the whole, but glad for the rest. And now he was driving his Model T down a long straight road between rolling, misty prairies that seemed to go from nowhere to nowhere.

It didn't seem funny to him to be driving the Model T again. That was the car he'd learned on, and he kept to it till his family made him change. And it didn't seem funny to him not to be sick any more. He hadn't had much time to be sick in his life—the patients usually attended to that. He looked around for his bag, first thing, but it was there on the seat beside him. It was the old bag, not the presentation one they'd given him at the hospital, but that was all right too. It meant he was out on a call and, if he couldn't quite recollect at the moment just where the call was, it was certain to come to him. He'd wakened up often enough in his buggy, in the old days, and found the horse was taking him home, without his doing much about it. A doctor gets used to things like that.

All the same, when he'd driven and driven for some time without raising so much as a traffic light, just the same rolling prairies on either hand, he began to get a little suspicious. He thought, for a while, of stopping the car and getting out, just to take a look around, but he'd always hated to lose time on a call. Then he noticed something else. He was driving without his glasses. And yet he hadn't driven without his glasses in fifteen years.

"H'm," said Doc Mellhorn. "I'm crazy as a June bug. Or else— Well, it might be so, I suppose."

But this time he did stop the car. He opened his bag and looked inside it, but everything seemed to be in order. He opened his wallet and looked at that, but there were his own initials, half rubbed away, and he recognized them. He took his pulse, but it felt perfectly steady.

"H'm," said Doc Mellhorn. "Well."

Then, just to prove that everything was perfectly normal, he took a silver half dollar out of the steering wheel of the car.

"Never did it smoother," said Doc Mellhorn. "Well, all the same, if this is the new highway, it's longer than I remember it."

But just then a motorcycle came roaring down the road and stopped with a flourish, the way motor cops do.

Doc Mellhorn and the Pearly Gates

"Any trouble?" said the motor cop. Doc Mellhorn couldn't see his face for his goggles, but the goggles looked normal.

"I am a physician," said Doc Mellhorn, as he'd said a thousand times before to all sorts of people, "on my way to an urgent case." He passed his hand across his forehead. "Is this the right road?" he said.

"Straight ahead to the traffic light," said the cop. "They're expecting you, Doctor Mellhorn. Shall I give you an escort?"

"No; thanks all the same," said Doc Mellhorn, and the motor cop roared away. The Model T ground as Doc Mellhorn gassed her. "Well, they've got a new breed of traffic cop," said Doc Mellhorn, "or else—"

But when he got to the light, it was just like any light at a crossroads. He waited till it changed and the officer waved him on. There seemed to be a good deal of traffic going the other way, but he didn't get a chance to notice it much, because Lizzie bucked a little, as she usually did when you kept her waiting. Still, the sight of traffic relieved him, though he hadn't passed anybody on his own road yet.

Pretty soon he noticed the look of the country had changed. It was parkway now and very nicely landscaped. There was dogwood in bloom on the little hills, white and pink against the green; though, as Doc Mellhorn remembered it, it had been August when he left his house. And every now and then there'd be a nice little white-painted sign that said TO THE GATES.

"H'm," said Doc Mellhorn. "New State Parkway, I guess. Well, they've fixed it up pretty. But I wonder where they got the dogwood. Haven't seen it bloom like that since I was East."

Then he drove along in a sort of dream for a while, for the dogwood reminded him of the days when he was a young man in an Eastern college. He remembered the look of that college and the girls who'd come to dances, the girls who wore white gloves and had rolls of hair. They were pretty girls, too, and he wondered what had become of them. "Had babies, I guess," thought Doc Mellhorn. "Or some of them, anyway." But he liked to think of them as the way they had been when they were just pretty, and excited at being at a dance.

He remembered other things too—the hacked desks in the lecture rooms, and the trees on the campus, and the first pipe he'd ever broken in, and a fellow called Paisley Grew that he hadn't thought of in years—a rawboned fellow with a gift for tall stories and playing the jew's-harp.

"Ought to have looked up Paisley," he said. "Yes, I ought. Didn't amount to a hill of beans, I guess, but I always liked him. I wonder if he still plays the jew's-harp. Pshaw, I know he's been dead twenty years."

He was passing other cars now and other cars were passing him, but he didn't pay much attention, except when he happened to notice a license you didn't often see in the state, like Rhode Island or Mississippi. He was too full of his own thoughts. There were foot passengers, too, plenty of them—and once he passed a man driving a load of hay. He wondered what the man would do with the hay when he got to the Gates. But probably there were arrangements for that.

"Not that I believe a word of it," he said, "but it'll surprise Father Kelly. Or maybe it won't. I used to have some handsome arguments with that man, but I always knew I could count on him, in spite of me being a heretic."

Then he saw the Wall and the Gates, right across the valley. He saw them, and they reached to the top of the sky. He rubbed his eyes for a while, but they kept on being there.

"Quite a sight," said Doc Mellhorn.

No one told him just where to go or how to act, but it seemed to him that he knew. If he'd thought about it, he'd have said that you waited in line, but there wasn't any waiting in line. He just went where he was expected to go and the reception clerk knew his name right away.

"Yes, Doctor Mellhorn," he said. "And now, what would you like to do first?"

"I think I'd like to sit down," said Doc Mellhorn. So he sat, and it was a comfortable chair. He even bounced the springs of it once or twice, till he caught the reception clerk's eye on him.

"Is there anything I can get you?" said the reception clerk. He was young and brisk and neat as a pin, and you could see he aimed to give service and studied about it. Doc Mellhorn thought, "He's the kind that wipes off your windshield no matter how clean it is."

"No," said Doc Mellhorn. "You see, I don't believe this. I don't believe any of it. I'm sorry if that sounds cranky, but I don't."

"That's quite all right, sir," said the reception clerk. "It often

416

takes a while." And he smiled as if Doc Mellhorn had done him a favor.

"Young man, I'm a physician," said Doc Mellhorn, "and do you mean to tell me—"

Then he stopped, for he suddenly saw there was no use arguing. He was either there or he wasn't. And it felt as if he were there.

"Well," said Doc Mellhorn, with a sigh, "how do I begin?"

"That's entirely at your own volition, sir," said the reception clerk briskly. "Any meetings with relatives, of course. Or if you would prefer to get yourself settled first. Or take a tour, alone or conducted. Perhaps these will offer suggestions," and he started to hand over a handful of leaflets. But Doc Mellhorn put them aside.

"Wait a minute," he said. "I want to think. Well, naturally, there's Mother and Dad. But I couldn't see them just yet. I wouldn't believe it. And Grandma—well, now, if I saw Grandma —and me older than she is—was—used to be—well, I don't know what it would do to me. You've got to let me get my breath. Well, of course, there's Uncle Frank—he'd be easier." He paused. "Is he here?" he said.

The reception clerk looked in a file. "I am happy to say that Mr. Francis V. Mellhorn arrived July 12, 1907," he said. He smiled winningly.

"Well!" said Doc Mellhorn. "Uncle Frank! Well, I'll be—well! But it must have been a great consolation to Mother. We heard —well, never mind what we heard—I guess it wasn't so. . . . No, don't reach for that phone just yet, or whatever it is. I'm still thinking."

"We sometimes find," said the reception clerk eagerly, "that a person not a relative may be the best introduction. Even a stranger sometimes—a distinguished stranger connected with one's own profession—"

"Well, now, that's an idea," said Doc Mellhorn heartily, trying to keep his mind off how much he disliked the reception clerk. He couldn't just say why he disliked him, but he knew he did.

It reminded him of the time he'd had to have his gall bladder out in the city hospital and the young, brisk interns had come to see him and called him "Doctor" every other word.

"Yes, that's an idea," he said. He reflected. "Well, of course, I'd like to see Koch," he said. "And Semmelweiss. Not to speak of Walter Reed. But, shucks, they'd be busy men. But there is one fellow—only he lived pretty far back—"

"Hippocrates, please," said the reception clerk into the telephone or whatever it was. "*H* for horse—"

"No!" said Doc Mellhorn quite violently. "Excuse me, but you just wait a minute. I mean if you can wait. I mean, if Hippocrates wants to come, I've no objection. But I never took much of a fancy to him, in spite of his oath. It's Aesculapius I'm thinking about. George W. Oh, glory!" he said. "But he won't talk English. I forgot."

"I shall be happy to act as interpreter," said the reception clerk, smiling brilliantly.

"I haven't a doubt," said Doc Mellhorn. "But just wait a shake." In a minute, by the way the clerk was acting, he was going to be talking to Aesculapius. "And what in time am I going to say to the man?" he thought. "It's too much." He gazed wildly around the neat reception room—distempered, as he noticed, in a warm shade of golden tan. Then his eyes fell on the worn black bag at his feet and a sudden warm wave of relief flooded over him.

"Wait a minute," he said, and his voice gathered force and authority. "Where's my patient?"

"Patient?" said the reception clerk, looking puzzled for the first time.

"Patient," said Doc Mellhorn. "*P* for phlebitis." He tapped his bag.

"I'm afraid you don't quite understand, sir," said the reception clerk.

"I understand this," said Doc Mellhorn. "I was called here. And if I wasn't called professionally, why have I got my bag?"

"But, my dear Doctor Mellhorn—" said the reception clerk.

"I'm not your dear doctor," said Doc Mellhorn. "I was called here, I tell you. I'm sorry not to give you the patient's name, but the call must have come in my absence and the girl doesn't spell very well. But in any well-regulated hospital—"

"But I tell you," said the reception clerk, and his hair wasn't slick any more, "nobody's ill here. Nobody can be ill. If they could, it wouldn't be He—"

"Humph," said Doc Mellhorn. He thought it over, and felt worse. "Then what does a fellow like Koch do?" he said. "Or

Pasteur?" He raised a hand. "Oh, don't tell me," he said. "I can see they'd be busy. Yes, I guess it'd be all right for a research man. But I never was . . . Oh, well, shucks, I've published a few papers. And there's that clamp of mine—always meant to do something about it. But they've got better ones now. Mean to say there isn't so much as a case of mumps in the whole place?"

"I assure you," said the reception clerk, in a weary voice. "And now, once you see Doctor Aesculapius—"

"Funny," said Doc Mellhorn. "Lord knows there's plenty of times you'd be glad to be quit of the whole thing. And don't talk to me about the healer's art or grateful patients. Well, I've known a few . . . a few. But I've known others. All the same, it's different, being told there isn't any need for what you can do."

"*A* for Ararát," said the reception clerk into his instrument. "*E* for Eden."

"Should think you'd have a dial," said Doc Mellhorn desperately. "We've got 'em down below." He thought hard and frantically. "Wait a shake. It's coming back to me," he said. "Got anybody named Grew here? Paisley Grew?"

"*S* for serpent . . ." said the reception clerk. "What was that?"

"Fellow that called me," said Doc Mellhorn. "G-r-e-w. First name, Paisley."

"I will consult the index," said the reception clerk.

He did so, and Doc Mellhorn waited, hoping against hope.

"We have 94,183 Grews, including 83 Prescotts and one Penobscot," the reception clerk said at last. "But I fail to find Paisley Grew. Are you quite sure of the name?"

"Of course," said Doc Mellhorn briskly. "Paisley Grew. Chronic indigestion. Might be appendix—can't say—have to see. But anyhow, he's called." He picked up his bag. "Well, thanks for the information," he said, liking the reception clerk better than he had yet. "Not your fault, anyway."

"But—but where are you going?" said the reception clerk.

"Well, there's another establishment, isn't there?" said Doc Mellhorn. "Always heard there was. Call probably came from there. Crossed wires, I expect."

"But you can't go there!" said the reception clerk. "I mean—"

"Can't go?" said Doc Mellhorn. "I'm a physician. A patient's called me."

419

"But if you'll only wait and see Aesculapius!" said the reception clerk, running his hands wildly through his hair. "He'll be here almost any moment."

"Please give him my apologies," said Doc Mellhorn. "He's a doctor. He'll understand. And if any messages come for me, just stick them on the spike. Do I need a road map? Noticed the road I came was all one way."

"There is, I believe, a back road in rather bad repair," said the reception clerk icily. "I can call Information if you wish."

"Oh, don't bother," said Doc Mellhorn. "I'll find it. And I never saw a road beat Lizzie yet." He took a silver half dollar from the doorknob of the door. "See that?" he said. "Slick as a whistle. Well, good-by, young man."

But it wasn't till he'd cranked up Lizzie and was on his way that Doc Mellhorn really felt safe. He found the back road and it was all the reception clerk had said it was and more. But he didn't mind—in fact, after one particularly bad rut, he grinned.

"I suppose I ought to have seen the folks," he said. "Yes, I know I ought. But—not so much as a case of mumps in the whole abiding dominion! Well, it's lucky I took a chance on Paisley Grew."

After another mile or so, he grinned again.

"And I'd like to see old Aesculapius' face. Probably rang him in the middle of dinner—they always do. But shucks, it's happened to all of us."

Well, the road got worse and worse and the sky above it darker and darker, and what with one thing and another, Doc Mellhorn was glad enough when he got to the other gates. They were pretty impressive gates, too, though of course in a different way, and reminded Doc Mellhorn a little of the furnaces outside Steeltown, where he'd practiced for a year when he was young.

This time Doc Mellhorn wasn't going to take any advice from reception clerks and he had his story all ready. All the same, he wasn't either registered or expected, so there was a little fuss. Finally they tried to scare him by saying he came at his own risk and that there were some pretty tough characters about. But Doc Mellhorn remarked that he'd practiced in Steeltown. So, after he'd told them what seemed to him a million times that he was a physician on a case, they finally let him in and directed him to Paisley Grew. Paisley was on Level 346 in Pit 68,953, and Doc Mellhorn recognized him the minute he saw him. He even had the jew's-harp, stuck in the back of his overalls.

"Well, Doc," said Paisley finally, when the first greetings were over, "you certainly are a sight for sore eyes! Though, of course, I'm sorry to see you here," and he grinned.

"Well, I can't see that it's so different from a lot of places," said Doc Mellhorn, wiping his forehead. "Warmish, though."

"It's the humidity, really," said Paisley Grew. "That's what it really is."

"Yes, I know," said Doc Mellhorn. "And now tell me, Paisley, how's that indigestion of yours?"

"Well, I'll tell you, Doc," said Paisley. "When I first came here, I thought the climate was doing it good. I did for a fact. But now I'm not so sure. I've tried all sorts of things for it—I've even tried being transferred to the boiling asphalt lakes. But it just seems to hang on, and every now and then, when I least expect it, it catches me. Take last night. I didn't have a thing to eat that I don't generally eat—well, maybe I did have one little snort of hot sulphur, but it wasn't the sulphur that did it. All the same, I woke up at four, and it was just like a knife. Now . . ."

He went on from there and it took him some time. And Doc Mellhorn listened, happy as a clam. He never thought he'd be glad to listen to a hypochondriac, but he was. And when Paisley was all through, he examined him and prescribed for him. It was just a little soda bicarb and pepsin, but Paisley said it took hold something wonderful. And they had a fine time that evening, talking over the old days.

Finally, of course, the talk got around to how Paisley liked it where he was. And Paisley was honest enough about that.

"Well, Doc," he said, "of course this isn't the place for you, and I can see you're just visiting. But I haven't many real complaints. It's hot, to be sure, and they work you, and some of the boys here are rough. But they've had some pretty interesting experiences, too, when you get them talking—yes, sir. And anyhow, it isn't Peabodyville, New Jersey," he said with vehemence. "I spent five years in Peabodyville, trying to work up in the leather business. After that I bust out, and I guess that's what landed me here. But it's an improvement on Peabodyville." He looked at Doc Mellhorn sidewise. "Say, Doc," he said, "I know this is a vacation for you, but all the same there's a couple of the boys—nothing really wrong with them of course—but—well, if you could just look them over—"

"I was thinking the office hours would be nine to one," said Doc Mellhorn.

So Paisley took him around and they found a nice little place for an office in one of the abandoned mine galleries, and Doc Mellhorn hung out his shingle. And right away patients started coming around. They didn't get many doctors there, in the first place, and the ones they did get weren't exactly the cream of the profession, so Doc Mellhorn had it all to himself. It was mostly sprains, fractures, bruises and dislocations, of course, with occasional burns and scalds—and, on the whole, it reminded Doc Mellhorn a good deal of his practice in Steeltown, especially when it came to foreign bodies in the eye. Now and then Doc Mellhorn ran into a more unusual case—for instance, there was one of the guards that got part of himself pretty badly damaged in a rock slide. Well, Doc Mellhorn had never set a tail before, but he managed it all right, and got a beautiful primary union, too, in spite of the fact that he had no X-ray facilities. He thought of writing up the case for the State Medical Journal, but then he couldn't figure out any way to send it to them, so he had to let it slide. And then there was an advanced carcinoma of the liver —a Greek named Papadoupolous or Prometheus or something. Doc Mellhorn couldn't do much for him, considering the circumstances, but he did what he could, and he and the Greek used to have long conversations. The rest was just everyday practice— run of the mine—but he enjoyed it.

Now and then it would cross his mind that he ought to get out Lizzie and run back to the other place for a visit with the folks. But that was just like going back East had been on earth— he'd think he had everything pretty well cleared up, and then a new flock of patients would come in. And it wasn't that he didn't miss his wife and children and grandchildren—he did. But there wasn't any way to get back to them, and he knew it. And there was the work in front of him and the office crowded every day. So he just went along, hardly noticing the time.

Now and then, to be sure, he'd get a suspicion that he wasn't too popular with the authorities of the place. But he was used to not being popular with authorities and he didn't pay much

Doc Mellhorn and the Pearly Gates

attention. But finally they sent an inspector around. The minute Doc Mellhorn saw him, he knew there was going to be trouble. Not that the inspector was uncivil. In fact, he was a pretty high-up official—you could tell by his antlers. And Doc Mellhorn was just as polite, showing him around. He showed him the free dispensary and the clinic and the nurse—Scotch girl named Smith, she was—and the dental chair he'd rigged up with the help of a fellow named Ferguson, who used to be an engineer before he was sentenced. And the inspector looked them all over, and finally he came back to Doc Mellhorn's office. The girl named Smith had put up curtains in the office, and with that and a couple of potted gas plants it looked more homelike than it had. The inspector looked around it and sighed.

"I'm sorry, Doctor Mellhorn," he said at last, "but you can see for yourself, it won't do."

"What won't do?" said Doc Mellhorn, stoutly. But, all the same, he felt afraid.

"Any of it," said the inspector. "We could overlook the alleviation of minor suffering—I'd be inclined to do so myself—though these people are here to suffer, and there's no changing that. But you're playing merry Hades with the whole system."

"I'm a physician in practice," said Doc Mellhorn.

"Yes," said the inspector. "That's just the trouble. Now, take these reports you've been sending," and he took out a sheaf of papers. "What have you to say about that?"

"Well, seeing as there's no county health officer, or at least I couldn't find one—" said Doc Mellhorn.

"Precisely," said the inspector. "And what have you done? You've condemned fourteen levels of this pit as unsanitary nuisances. You've recommended 2136 lost souls for special diet, remedial exercise, hospitalization—Well—I won't go through the list."

"I'll stand back of every one of those recommendations," said Doc Mellhorn. "And now we've got the chair working, we can handle most of the dental work on the spot. Only Ferguson needs more amalgam."

"I know," said the inspector patiently, "but the money has to come from somewhere—you must realize that. We're not a rich community, in spite of what people think. And these unauthorized requests—oh, we fill them, of course, but—"

423

"Ferguson needs more amalgam," said Doc Mellhorn. "And that last batch wasn't standard. I wouldn't use it on a dog."

"He's always needing more amalgam!" said the inspector bitterly, making a note. "Is he going to fill every tooth in Hades? By the way, my wife tells me I need a little work done myself—but we won't go into that. We'll take just one thing—your entirely unauthorized employment of Miss Smith. Miss Smith has no business working for you. She's supposed to be gnawed by a never-dying worm every Monday, Wednesday and Friday."

"Sounds silly to me," said Doc Mellhorn.

"I don't care how silly it sounds," said the inspector. "It's regulations. And, besides, she isn't even a registered nurse."

"She's a practical one," said Doc Mellhorn. "Of course, back on earth a lot of her patients died. But that was because when she didn't like a patient, she poisoned him. Well, she can't poison anybody here and I've kind of got her out of the notion of it anyway. She's been doing A-1 work for me and I'd like to recommend her for—"

"Please!" said the inspector. "Please! And as if that wasn't enough, you've even been meddling with the staff. I've a note here on young Asmodeus—Asmodeus XIV—"

"Oh, you mean Mickey!" said Doc Mellhorn, with a chuckle. "Short for Mickey Mouse. We call him that in the clinic. And he's a young imp if I ever saw one."

"The original Asmodeus is one of our most prominent citizens," said the inspector severely. "How do you suppose he felt when we got your report that his fourteenth great-grandson had rickets?"

"Well," said Doc Mellhorn, "I know rickets. And he had 'em. And you're going to have rickets in these youngsters as long as you keep feeding 'em low-grade coke. I put Mickey on the best Pennsylvania anthracite, and look at him now!"

"I admit the success of your treatment," said the inspector, "but, naturally—well, since then we've been deluged with demands for anthracite from as far south as Sheol. We'll have to float a new bond issue. And what will the taxpayers say?"

"He was just cutting his first horns when he came to us," said Doc Mellhorn reminiscently, "and they were coming in crooked. Now, I ask you, did you ever see a straighter pair? Of course,

if I'd had cod liver oil—My gracious, you ought to have somebody here that can fill a prescription; I can't do it all."

The inspector shut his papers together with a snap. "I'm sorry,
Doctor Mellhorn," he said, "but this is final. You have no right
here, in the first place; no local license to practice in the second—"

"Yes, that's a little irregular," said Doc Mellhorn, "but I'm a
registered member of four different medical associations—you
might take that into account. And I'll take any examination that's
required."

"No," said the inspector violently. "No, no, no! You can't stay
here! You've got to go away! It isn't possible!"

Doc Mellhorn drew a long breath. "Well," he said, "there
wasn't any work for me at the other place. And here you won't
let me practice. So what's a man to do?"

The inspector was silent.

"Tell me," said Doc Mellhorn presently. "Suppose you do
throw me out? What happens to Miss Smith and Paisley and the
rest of them?"

"Oh, what's done is done," said the inspector impatiently, "here
as well as anywhere else. We'll have to keep on with the anthracite and the rest of it. And Hades only knows what'll happen in
the future. If it's any satisfaction to you, you've started something."

"Well, I guess Smith and Ferguson between them can handle
the practice," said Doc Mellhorn. "But that's got to be a promise."

"It's a promise," said the inspector.

"Then there's Mickey—I mean Asmodeus," said Doc Mellhorn.
"He's a smart youngster—smart as a whip—if he is a hellion. Well,
you know how a youngster gets. Well, it seems he wants to be a
doctor. But I don't know what sort of training he'd get—"

"He'll get it," said the inspector feverishly. "We'll found the
finest medical college you ever saw, right here in West Baal.
We'll build a hospital that'll knock your eye out. You'll be satisfied. But now, if you don't mind—"

"All right," said Doc Mellhorn, and rose.

The inspector looked surprised. "But don't you want to—" he
said. "I mean my instructions are we're to give you a banquet, if
necessary—after all, the community appreciates—"

"Thanks," said Doc Mellhorn, with a shudder, "but if I've got to go, I'd rather get out of town. You hang around and announce your retirement, and pretty soon folks start thinking they ought to give you a testimonial. And I never did like testimonials."

All the same, before he left he took a silver half dollar out of Mickey Asmodeus' chin.

When he was back on the road again and the lights of the gates had faded into a low ruddy glow behind him, Doc Mellhorn felt alone for the first time. He'd been lonely at times during his life, but he'd never felt alone like this before. Because, as far as he could see, there was only him and Lizzie now.

"Now, maybe if I'd talked to Aesculapius—" he said. "But pshaw, I always was pigheaded."

He didn't pay much attention to the way he was driving and it seemed to him that the road wasn't quite the same. But he felt tired for a wonder—bone-tired and beaten—and he didn't much care about the road. He hadn't felt tired since he left earth, but now the loneliness tired him.

"Active—always been active," he said to himself. "I can't just lay down on the job. But what's a man to do?

"What's a man to do?" he said. "I'm a doctor. I can't work miracles."

Then the black fit came over him and he remembered all the times he'd been wrong and all the people he couldn't do anything for. "Never was much of a doctor, I guess," he said. "Maybe, if I'd gone to Vienna. Well, the right kind of man would have gone. And about that Bigelow kid," he said. "How was I to know he'd hemorrhage? But I should have known.

"I've diagnosed walking typhoid as appendicitis. Just the once, but that's enough. And I still don't know what held me back when I was all ready to operate. I used to wake up in a sweat, six months afterward, thinking I had.

"I could have saved those premature twins, if I'd known as much then as I do now. I guess that guy Dafoe would have done it anyway—look at what he had to work with. But I didn't. And that finished the Gorhams' having children. That's a dandy doctor, isn't it? Makes you feel fine.

"I could have pulled Old Man Halsey through. And Edna Biggs. And the little Lauriat girl. No, I couldn't have done it with her. That was before insulin. I couldn't have cured Ted Allen. No, I'm clear on that. But I've never been satisfied about the Collins woman. Bates is all right—good as they come. But I knew her, inside and out—ought to, too—she was the biggest nuisance that ever came into the office. And if I hadn't been down with the flu . . .

"Then there's the flu epidemic. I didn't take my clothes off, four days and nights. But what's the good of that, when you lose them? Oh, sure, the statistics looked good. You can have the statistics.

"Should have started raising hell about the water supply two years before I did.

"Oh, yes, it makes you feel fine, pulling babies into the world. Makes you feel you're doing something. And just fine when you see a few of them, twenty-thirty years later, not worth two toots on a cow's horn. Can't say I ever delivered a Dillinger. But there's one or two in state's prison. And more that ought to be. Don't mind even that so much as a few of the fools. Makes you wonder.

"And then, there's incurable cancer. That's a daisy. What can you do about it, Doctor? Well, Doctor, we can alleviate the pain in the last stages. Some. Ever been in a cancer ward, Doctor? Yes, Doctor, I have.

"What do you do for the common cold, Doctor? Two dozen clean linen handkerchiefs. Yes, it's a good joke—I'll laugh. And what do you do for a boy when you know he's dying, Doctor? Take a silver half dollar out of his ear. But it kept the Lane kid quiet and his fever went down that night. I took the credit, but I don't know why it went down.

"I've only got one brain. And one pair of hands.

"I could have saved. I could have done. I could have.

"Guess it's just as well you can't live forever. You make fewer mistakes. And sometimes I'd see Bates looking at me as if he wondered why I ever thought I could practice.

"Pigheaded, opinionated, ineffective old imbecile! And yet, Lord, Lord, I'd do it all over again."

He lifted his eyes from the pattern of the road in front of him. There were white markers on it now and Lizzie seemed to be bouncing down a residential street. There were trees in the street and it reminded him of town. He rubbed his eyes for a second and Lizzie rolled on by herself—she often did. It didn't seem strange to him to stop at the right house.

"Well, Mother," he said rather gruffly to the group on the

lawn. "Well, Dad. . . . Well, Uncle Frank." He beheld a small, stern figure advancing, hands outstretched. "Well, Grandma," he said meekly.

Later on he was walking up and down in the grape arbor with Uncle Frank. Now and then he picked a grape and ate it. They'd always been good grapes, those Catawbas, as he remembered them.

"What beats me," he said, not for the first time, "is why I didn't notice the Gates. The second time, I mean."

"Oh, that Gate," said Uncle Frank, with the easy, unctuous roll in his voice that Doc Mellhorn so well remembered. He smoothed his handle-bar moustaches. "That Gate, my dear Edward—well, of course it has to be there in the first place. Literature, you know. And then, it's a choice," he said richly.

"I'll draw cards," said Doc Mellhorn. He ate another grape.

"Fact is," said Uncle Frank, "that Gate's for one kind of person. You pass it and then you can rest for all eternity. Just fold your hands. It suits some."

"I can see that it would," said Doc Mellhorn.

"Yes," said Uncle Frank, "but it wouldn't suit a Mellhorn. I'm happy to say that very few of our family remain permanently on that side. I spent some time there myself." He said, rather self-consciously, "Well, my last years had been somewhat stormy. So few people cared for refined impersonations of our feathered songsters, including lightning sketches. I felt that I'd earned a rest. But after a while—well, I got tired of being at liberty."

"And what happens when you get tired?" said Doc Mellhorn.

"You find out what you want to do," said Uncle Frank.

"My kind of work?" said Doc Mellhorn.

"Your kind of work," said his uncle. "Been busy, haven't you?"

"Well," said Doc Mellhorn. "But here. If there isn't so much as a case of mumps in—"

"Would it have to be mumps?" said his uncle. "Of course, if you're aching for mumps, I guess it could be arranged. But how many new souls do you suppose we get here a day?"

"Sizable lot, I expect."

"And how many of them get here in first-class condition?" said Uncle Frank triumphantly. "Why, I've seen Doctor Rush—Benjamin Rush—come back so tired from a day's round he could hardly flap one pinion against the other. Oh, if it's work you want—And then, of course, there's the earth."

"Hold on," said Doc Mellhorn. "I'm not going to appear to any young intern in wings and a harp. Not at my time of life. And anyway, he'd laugh himself sick."

" 'Tain't that," said Uncle Frank. "Look here. You've left children and grandchildren behind you, haven't you? And they're going on?"

"Yes," said Doc Mellhorn.

"Same with what you did," said Uncle Frank. "I mean the inside part of it—that stays. I don't mean any funny business—voices in your ear and all that. But haven't you ever got clean tuckered out, and been able to draw on something you didn't know was there?"

"Pshaw, any man's done that," said Doc Mellhorn. "But you take the adrenal—"

"Take anything you like," said Uncle Frank placidly. "I'm not going to argue with you. Not my department. But you'll find it isn't all adrenalin. Like it here?" he said abruptly. "Feel satisfied?"

"Why, yes," said Doc Mellhorn surprisedly, "I do." He looked around the grape arbor and suddenly realized that he felt happy.

"No, they wouldn't all arrive in first-class shape," he said to himself. "So there'd be a place." He turned to Uncle Frank. "By the way," he said diffidently, "I mean, I got back so quick—there wouldn't be a chance of my visiting the other establishment now and then? Where I just came from? Smith and Ferguson are all right, but I'd like to keep in touch."

"Well," said Uncle Frank, "you can take that up with the delegation." He arranged the handkerchief in his breast pocket. "They ought to be along any minute now," he said. "Sister's been in a stew about it all day. She says there won't be enough chairs, but she always says that."

"Delegation?" said Doc Mellhorn. "But—"

"You don't realize," said Uncle Frank, with his rich chuckle. "You're a famous man. You've broken pretty near every regulation except the fire laws, and refused the Gate first crack. They've got to do something about it."

"But—" said Doc Mellhorn, looking wildly around for a place of escape.

"Sh-h!" hissed Uncle Frank. "Hold up your head and look as though money were bid for you. It won't take long—just a welcome." He shaded his eyes with his hand. "My," he said with frank admiration, "you've certainly brought them out. There's Rush, by the way."

"Where?" said Doc Mellhorn.

"Second from the left, third row, in a wig," said Uncle Frank. "And there's—"

Then he stopped, and stepped aside. A tall grave figure was advancing down the grape arbor—a bearded man with a wise, majestic face who wore robes as if they belonged to him, not as Doc Mellhorn had seen them worn in college commencements. There was a small fillet of gold about his head and in his left hand, Doc Mellhorn noticed without astonishment, was a winged staff entwined with two fangless serpents. Behind him were many others. Doc Mellhorn stood straighter.

The bearded figure stopped in front of Doc Mellhorn. "Welcome, Brother," said Aesculapius.

"It's an honor to meet you, Doctor," said Doc Mellhorn. He shook the outstretched hand. Then he took a silver half dollar from the mouth of the left-hand snake.

THE LAST OF THE LEGIONS

The governor wanted to have everything go off as quietly as possible, but he couldn't keep the people from the windows or off the streets. After all, the legion had been at Deva ever since there was a town to speak of, and now we were going away. I don't want to say anything against the Sixth or the Second—there are good men under all the eagles. But we're not called the Valeria Victrix for nothing, and we've had the name some few centuries. It takes a legion with men in it to hold the northwest.

I think, at first, they intended to keep the news secret, but how could you do that, in a town? There's always someone who tells his girl in strict confidence, and then there are all the peddlers and astrologers and riffraff, and the sharp-faced boys with tips on the races or the games. I tell you, they knew about it as soon as the general or the governor—not to speak of the rumors before. As a matter of fact, there had been so many rumors that, when the orders came at last, it was rather a relief. You get tired of telling women that nothing will happen to them even if the legion does go, and being stopped five times in ten minutes whenever you go into town.

All the same, I had to sit up half the night with one recruit of ours. He had a girl in the town he was mad about, and a crazy notion of deserting. I had to point out to the young imbecile that even if the legion goes, Rome stays, and describe the two men I'd happened to see flogged to death, before he changed his mind. The girl was a pretty little weak-mouthed thing—she was crying in the crowd when we marched by, and he bit his lips to keep steady. But I couldn't have him deserting out of our cohort—we haven't had a thing like that happen in twenty years.

It was queer, their not making more noise. They tried to cheer —governor's orders—when we turned the camp over to the native auxiliaries in the morning, but it wasn't much of a success. And yet, the auxiliaries looked well enough, for auxiliaries. I wouldn't give two cohorts of Egyptians for them myself, but they had their breastplates shined and kept a fairly straight front. I imagined they'd dirty up our quarters—auxiliaries always do—and that wasn't pleasant to think of. But the next legion that came to Deva —us or another—would put things straight again. And it couldn't be long.

Then we had our own march past—through the town—and, as I say, it was queer. I'm a child of the camp—I was brought up in the legion. The tale is that the first of us came with Caesar—I don't put much stock in that—and of course we've married British ever since. Still, I know what I know, and I know what a crowd sounds like, on most occasions. There's the mutter of a hostile one, and the shouts when they throw flowers, and the sharp, fierce cheering when they know you're going out to fight for them. But this was different. There wasn't any heart or pith in it—just a queer sort of sobbing wail that went with us all the way to the gates. Oh, here and there, people shouted, "Come back with their heads!" or "Bring us a Goth for a pet!" the way they do, but not as if they believed what they were saying. Too many of them were silent, and that queer sort of sobbing wail went with us all the way.

I march with the first cohort; it wasn't so bad for me. Though here and there, I saw faces in the crowd—old Elfrida, who kept the wine shop, with the tears running down her fat cheeks, shouting like a good one, and Parmesius, the usurer, biting his nails and not saying anything at all. He might have given us a cheer; he'd had enough of our money. But he stood there, looking scared. I expect he was thinking of his money bags and wondering if somebody would slip a knife in his ribs at night. We'd kept good order in the town.

It took a long time, at the gates, for the governor had to make a speech—like all that old British stock, he tries to be more Roman than the Romans. Our general listened to him, sitting his horse like a bear. He's a new general, one of Stilicho's men, and a good one in spite of his hairiness and his Vandal accent. I don't think he cared very much for the governor's speech—it was the usual one. The glorious Twentieth, you know, and our gallant deeds, and how glad they'd be to have us back again. Well, we knew that without his telling—we could read it in the white faces along the walls. They were very still, but you could feel them, looking. The whole town must have been at the walls. Then the speech ended, and our general nodded his bear head and we marched. I don't know how long they stayed at the walls—I couldn't look back.

But my recruit got away, after all, at the second halt, and that bothered me. He was a likely looking young fellow, though I'd always thought his neck was too long. Still, he was one of the children of the camp—you wouldn't have picked him to desert. After that, half a dozen others tried it—those things are like a disease—but our general caught two and made an example, and that stopped the rest. I don't care for torture, myself—it leaves a bad taste in your mouth—but there are times when you have to use a firm hand. They were talking too much about Deva and remembering too many things. Well, I could see, myself, that if we had to be marched half across Britain to take ship at Anderida, that meant the Northmen were strong again. And I wouldn't like to hold the northwest against Northmen and Scots with nothing but auxiliaries. But that was the empire's business—it wasn't mine.

After it was over, I was having a cup of wine and chatting with Agathocles—he's a small man, but clever with the legion accounts and very proud that his father was a Greek. He has special privileges, and that's apt to get a man disliked, but I always got along well with him. If you're senior centurion, you have your own rights, and he didn't often try the nasty side of his tongue on me.

"Well, Death's-Head," I said—we call him that because of his bony face—"were you present at the ceremonies?"

"Oh, I was present," he said. He shivered a little. "I suppose you liked hearing them squeal," he said, with his black eyes full of malice.

"Can't say that I did," I said, "but it'll keep the recruits in order."

"For a while," he said, and laughed softly. But I wasn't really thinking of the men who had been caught—I was thinking of my own recruit who'd gotten away. I could see him, you know, quite plainly, with his long neck and his bright blue Northern eyes— a tiny, running figure, hiding in ditches and traveling by night. He'd started in full marching order, too, like an idiot. Pretty soon, he'd be throwing pieces of equipment away. And what would he do when he did get back to Deva—hide on one of the outlying farms? Our farmers were a rough lot—they'd turn him over to the governor, if they didn't cut his throat for the price of his armor. It's a bad feeling, being hunted—I've had it myself. You begin to hear noises in the bracken and feel the joints in your armor where an arrow could go through. He'd scream, too, if he were caught—scream like a hare. And all for a weak-faced girl and because he felt homesick! I couldn't understand it.

"Worried about your recruit?" said Agathocles, though I hadn't said a word.

"The young fool!" I said. "He should have known better."

"Perhaps he was wiser than you think," said Agathocles. "Perhaps he's a soothsayer and reads omens."

"Soothsayer!" I said. "He'll make a pretty-looking soothsayer if the governor catches him! Though I suppose he has friends in the town."

"Why, doubtless," said Agathocles. "And, after all, why should they waste a trained man? He might even change his name and join the auxiliaries. He might have a good story, you know."

I thought, for a moment. Of course they'd be slack, now we'd left, but I couldn't believe they'd be as slack as that.

433

"I should hope not, I'm sure," I said, rather stiffly. "After all, the man's a deserter."

"Old Faithful," said Agathocles, laughing softly. "Always Old Faithful. You like the boy, but you'd rather see him cut to ribbons like our friends today. Now, I'm a Greek and a philosopher —I look for causes and effects."

"All Greeks are eaters of wind," I said, not insultingly, you know, but just to show him where he stood. But he didn't seem to hear me.

"Yes," he said, "I look for causes and effects. You think the man a deserter, I think him a soothsayer—that is the difference between us. Would a child of the camp have deserted the legion a century ago, or two centuries ago, Old Faithful?"

"How can I tell what anyone would do a century ago?" I said, for it was a foolish question.

"Exactly," he said. "And a century ago they would not have withdrawn the Twentieth—not from that border—not unless Rome fell." He clapped me on the back with an odious familiarity. "Do not worry about your recruit, Old Faithful," he said. "Perhaps he will even go over to the other side, and, indeed, that might be wise of him."

"Talk treason to your accounts, Greek," I growled, "and take your hand off my shoulder. I am a Roman."

He looked at me with sad eyes.

"After three hundred years in Britain," he said. "And yet he says he is a Roman. Yes, it is a very strong law. And yet we had a law and states once, too, we Greeks. Be comforted, my British Roman. I am not talking treason. After all, I, too, have spent my life with the eagles. But I look for causes and effects."

He sighed in his wine cup and, in spite of his nonsense, I could not help but feel sorry for him. He was not a healthy man and his chest troubled him at night.

"Forget them," I said, "and attend to your accounts. You'll feel better when we're really on the march."

He sighed again. "Unfortunately, I am a philosopher," he said. "It takes more than exercise to cure that. I can even hear a world cracking, when it is under my nose. But you are not a philosopher, Old Faithful—do not let it give you bad dreams."

I manage to get my sleep without dreams, as a rule, so I told him that and left him. But, all the same, some of his nonsense must have stuck in my head. For, all the way down to Anderida, I kept noticing little things. Usually, on a long march, once you get into the swing of it, you live in that swing. There's the back of the neck of the man in front of you, and the weather, fine or wet, and the hairy general, riding his horse like a bear, and the dust kicked up by the column and the business of billets for the night. The town life drops away from you like a cloak you left behind in the pawnshop and, pretty soon, you've never led any other kind of life. You have to take care of your men and see the cooks are up to their work and tell from the look on a man's face whether he's the sort of fool who rubs his feet raw before he complains. And all that's pleasant enough and so is the change in the country, and the villages you go through, likely never to see again, but there was good wine in one, and a landlord's daughter in another, and perhaps you washed your feet in a third and joked with the old girl who came down by the stream and told you you were a fine-looking soldier. It's all there, and nothing to remember, but pleasant while it lasts. And, toward the end, there's the little tightness at the back of the mind that makes you know you're coming near the fighting. But, before that, you hardly think at all.

This wasn't any different and yet I kept looking at the country. I'd been south before, as far as Londinium, but not for years, and there's no denying that it's a pleasant land. A little soft, as the people are, but very green, very smiling, between the forests. You could see they took care of their fields; you could see it was a rich place, compared to the north. There were sheep in the pastures, whole flocks of them, fat and baaing, and the baths in the towns we passed through got better all the way. And yet I kept looking for places where a cohort or two could make a stand without being cut off completely—now, why should I do that? You can say it was my business, but Mid-Britain has been safe for years. You have only to look at the villas—we've got nothing like them in the northwest. I couldn't help wondering what a crew of wild Scots or long-haired Northmen would do to some of them. We'd have blocked up half those windows where I come from—once they start shooting fire arrows, big windows are a nuisance, even in a fortified town.

And yet, in spite of the way Agathocles rode along like a death's-head, it was reassuring too. For it showed you how solid the empire was, a big solid block of empire, green and smiling, with its magistrates and fine special ladies and theaters and country houses, all the way from Mid-Britain to Rome, and getting richer all the way. I didn't feel jealous about it or particularly proud, but there it was, and it meant civilized things. That's the difference between us and the barbarians—you may not think of it often, but, when you see it, you know. I remember a young boy, oh, eight or nine. He'd been sent down from the big house on his fat pony with his tutor, to look at the soldiers, and there he sat, perfectly safe, while his pony cropped the grass and the old man had a hand in the pony's mane. He was clean out of bowshot of the big house, and the hedges could have held a hundred men, but you could see he'd never been afraid in his life, or lived in disputed ground. Not even the old tutor was afraid—he must have been a slave, but he grinned at us like anything. Well, that shows you. I thought the worse of Agathocles, after that.

And yet, there were other things—oh, normal enough. But, naturally, you can't move a legion without people asking questions, and civilians are like hens when they start to panic. Well, we knew there was trouble in Gaul—that was all we could say. Still, they'd follow you out of the town, and that would be unpleasant. But that didn't impress me nearly as much as the one old man.

We'd halted for half an hour and he came down from his fields, a countryman and a farmer. He had a speckled straw hat on, but it takes more than a dozen years' farming to get the look out of a man's back.

"The Twentieth," he said slowly, when he saw our badge of the boar, "the Valeria Victrix. Welcome, comrade!" so I knew at once that he'd served. I gave him the regulation salute and asked him a question, and his eyes glowed.

"Marcus Hostus," he said. "Centurion of the Third Cohort of the Second, twenty years ago." He pulled his tunic aside to show me the seamed scar.

"That was fighting the Welsh tribesmen," he said. "They were good fighters. After that, they gave me my land. But I still remember the taste of black beans in a helmet," and he laughed a high old man's laugh.

"Well," I said, "I wouldn't regret them. You've got a nice little place here." For he had.

He looked around at his fields. The woman had come to the door of the hut by then, with a half-grown girl beside her, and a couple of recruits were asking her for water.

"Yes," he said, "it's a nice little place and my sons are strong. There are two of them in the upper field. Are you halting for long, Centurion? I should like them to see the eagles before I die."

"Not for long," I said. "As a matter of fact, we're on our way to the seacoast. They seem to need us in Gaul."

"Oh," he said, "they need you in Gaul. But you'll be coming back."

"As Caesar wills it," I said. "You know what orders are, Centurion."

He looked at the eagles again.

"Yes," he said. "I know what orders are. The Valeria Victrix, the bulwark of the northwest. And you are marching to the ships—Oh, do not look at me, Centurion—I have been a centurion too. It must be a very great war that calls the Valeria Victrix from Britain."

"We have heard of such a war," I said, for he, too, had served with the eagles.

He nodded his old head once or twice. "Yes," he said, "a very great war. Even greater than the wars of Theodosius, for he did not take the Twentieth. Well, I can still use a sword."

I wanted to tell him that he would not have to use one, for there was the hut and the fields and the half-grown girl. But, looking at him, the words stuck in my throat. He nodded again.

"When the eagles go, Britain falls," he said, very quietly. "If I were twenty years younger, I would go back to the Second—that would be good fighting. Or, perhaps, to the Sixth, at Eboracum—they will not withdraw the Sixth till the last of all. As it is, I die here, with my sons." He straightened himself. "Hail, Centurion of the Valeria Victrix—and farewell," he said.

"Hail, Marcus Hostus, Centurion," I said, and they raised the eagles. I know that he watched us out of sight; though, again, I

437

could not look back. It is true that he was an old man, and old men dream, but I was as glad that Agathocles had not heard his words.

For it seemed to me that Agathocles was always at my elbow and I grew very weary indeed of his company and his cough and what he called his philosophy. The march had done him no good—he was bonier than ever and his cheeks burned—but that did not stop his talkativeness. He was always pointing out to me little things I would hardly have noticed by myself—where a plowland had been left fallow or where a house or a barn still showed the scars of old burnings. By Hercules! As if a man couldn't plant wheat for a year without the empire's falling—but he'd point and nod his head. And then he'd keep talking—oh, about the states and the law they'd had in Greece, long before the city was founded. Well, I never argue with a man about the deeds of his ancestors—it only makes bad feeling. But I told him once, to shut him up, that I knew about Athens. A friend of mine had been stationed there once and said they had quite decent games for a provincial capital. His eyes flashed at that and he muttered something in his own tongue.

"Yes," he said. "They have decent games there. And buildings that make the sacred Forum at Rome—which I have seen, by the way, and which you have not seen—look like a child's playing with mud and rubble. That was when we had states and a law. Then we fought with each other, and it went—yes, even before the man from Macedon. And then you came and now, at last, it is your turn. Am I sorry or glad? I do not know. Sorry, I think, for the life is out of my people—they are clever and will always be clever, but the life is out of them. And I am not philosopher enough not to grieve when an end comes."

"Oh, talk as you like, Agathocles," I said, for I was resolved he shouldn't anger me again. "But you'd better not talk like that in front of the general."

"Thank you, Old Faithful," he said, and coughed till he nearly fell from his mule. "But I do not talk like that to the general—only to persons of rare intelligence, like yourself. The general does not like me very well, as it is, but I am still useful with the accounts. Perhaps, when we get to Gaul—if we go to Gaul—he will have me flayed or impaled. I believe those are Vandal customs. Yes, that is very probable, I think, if my cough does not kill me before. But, meanwhile, I must observe—we Greeks are so curious."

"Observe all you like," I said, "but the legion's shaking down very nicely, it seems to me."

"Yes, shaking down very nicely," he said. "Do you ever think of your deserter, who went back to Deva? No, I thought not. And yet he was the first effect of the cause I seek, and there have been others since." He chuckled quite cheerfully at that and went along reciting Greek poetry to himself till the cough took him again. The poetry was all about the fall of a city called Troy— he translated some of it to me, and it sounded quite well, if you care for that sort of thing, though, as I pointed out to him, our own Vergil had covered the same subjects, as I understand it.

We had turned toward the seacoast by then—we weren't going through Londinium after all. That disappointed our recruits, but of course the general was right about it. We'd kept excellent discipline so far, but it's a very different thing, letting the men loose in a capital. I was sorry not to see it again myself. I told the men that when they complained. This was southern country we passed through, very soft and gentle; though, on the coasts, there is danger. But, when we halted for the night, there had been no danger for years—it was a wide pocket of peace.

I remember the look of the big painted rooms of the villa, when I was summoned there. A very fine villa it was—it belonged to a rich man. They'd had Roman names so long, they'd forgotten their own stock, though the master looked British enough when you looked him full in the face. They had winged cupids painted on the walls of the dining room—they were sharpening arrows and driving little cars with doves—very pretty and bright. It must have been imported work—no Briton could paint like that. And the courtyard had orange trees in it, growing in tubs—I know what an orange tree costs, for my cousin was a gardener. A swarm of servants, too, better trained than our northern ones and sneakingly insolent, as rich men's servants are apt to be. But they were all honey to me, and sticky speeches—they knew better than to mock an officer on duty.

Well, I went into the room, and there was my general and the master of the house, both with wreaths around their heads in the old-fashioned way, and Agathocles making notes on his tablets in a corner and hiding his cough with his hand. My general had his

439

wreath on crooked and he looked like a baited bear, though they must have had a good feed, and he liked wine. There were other people in the room—some sons and sons-in-law—all very well dressed, but a little shrill in their conversation, as that sort is apt to be, but the master of the house and my general were the ones I noticed.

My general called me in and told them who I was, while I stood at attention and Agathocles coughed. Then he said: "This is my senior centurion. . . . And how many leagues does the legion cover in a day, Centurion?"

I told him, though he knew well enough.

"Good," he said, in his thick Vandal accent. "And how many leagues would we cover in a day—let me see—accompanied by civilians, with litters and baggage?"

I told him; though, of course, he knew. It was less, of course; it made a decided difference. A legion does not march like the wind—that is not its business—but civilians slow everything up. Especially when there are women.

"As I thought," he said to the master of the villa. "As you see, it is quite impossible," and, in spite of his crooked wreath, his eyes were bleak and shrewd. Then arose a babble of talk and expostulation from the sons and the sons-in-law. I have heard such talk before—it is always the same. As I say, rich men are apt to think that all government, including the army, exists for their personal convenience. I stood at attention, waiting to be dismissed.

The master of the villa waited till the others had had their say. He was a strong man with a beaky nose, much stronger than his sons. He waited till the babble had ceased, his eyes calm, regarding our general. Then he said, in the smooth, careless voice of such men:

"The general forgets, perhaps, that I am a cousin of the legate. I merely ask protection for myself and my household. And we would be ready to move—well, within twenty-four hours. Yes, I can promise you, within twenty-four hours." There was such perfect assurance in his voice that I could have admired the man.

"I am sorry not to oblige a cousin of the legate," said my general, with his bear's eyes gleaming dully. "Unfortunately, I have my orders."

The Last of the Legions

"And yet," said the master of the villa, charmingly, "a certain laxity—a certain interpretation, let us say . . ."

He left his words in the air—you could see he had done this sort of thing before, and always successfully. You could see that, all his life, he had been accustomed to rules being broken for him because of his place and name. I have liked other generals better than this general—after all, the Vandals are different from us—but I liked the way he shook his head now.

"I have my orders," he said, and lay hunched like a bear on his couch.

"Let us hope you will never regret your strict interpretation of them, General," the master of the villa said without rancor, and a cool wind blew through the room. I felt the cool wind on my own cheek, though I am a senior centurion and my appeal is to Caesar. The man was strong enough for that.

"Let us hope not," said my general gruffly, and rose. "Your hospitality has been very enjoyable." I must say, for a Vandal, he made his manners well. On the way out, the master of the villa stopped me unobtrusively.

"And what would it be worth, Centurion," he said in a low voice, "to carry a single man on your rolls who was not on your rolls before? A single man—I do not ask for more."

"It would be worth my head," I said; for though my general did not seem to be looking at me, I knew that he was looking.

The master of the villa nodded, and a curious, dazed look came over his strong face. "I thought so," he said, as if to himself. "And, after all, what then? My nephew in Gaul writes me that Gaul is not safe; my bankers in Rome write me that Rome itself is not safe. Will you tell me what place is safe if Rome is not safe any more?" he said in a stronger voice, and caught at my arm. I did not know how to answer him, so I kept silent. He looked, suddenly, very much older than he had when I entered the room.

"A king's ransom out at loan and the interest of the interest," he muttered. "And yet, how is a man to be safe? And my cousin is the legate, too—I have first-hand information. They will not bring back the legions—blood does not flow back, once it is spilt. And yet, how can I leave my house here, with everything so uncertain?"

It seemed a fine house to me, though not very defensible; but, even as he spoke, I could see the rain beating through the walls. I could see the walls fallen, and the naked people, the barbarians, huddled around a dim fire. I had not believed that possible before, but now I believed it. There was ruin in the face of that man. I could feel Agathocles tugging at my elbow and I went away —out through the courtyard where the orange trees stood in their tubs, and the bright fish played in the pool.

When we were back in our billets, Agathocles spoke to me.

"The general is pleased with you," he said. "He saw that they tried to bribe you, but you were not bribed. If you had been bribed, he would have had your head."

"Do I care for that?" I said, a little wildly. "What matters one head or another? But if Rome falls, something ends."

He nodded soberly, without coughing. "It is true," he said. "You had nothing but an arch, a road, an army and a law. And yet a man might walk from the east to the west because of it— yes, and speak the same tongue all the way. I do not admire you, but you were a great people."

"But tell me," I said, "why does it end?"

He shook his head. "I do not know," he said. "Men build and they go on building. And then the dream is shaken—it is shaken to bits by the storm. Afterwards, there follow darkness and the howling peoples. I think that will be for a long time. I meant to be a historian, when I first joined the eagles. I meant to write of the later wars of Rome as Thucydides wrote of the Greek wars. But now my ink is dry and I have nothing to say."

"But," I said, "it is there—it is solid—it will last," for I thought of the country we had marched through, and the boy, unafraid, on his pony.

"Oh," said Agathocles, "it takes time for the night to fall— that is what people forget. Yes, even the master of your villa may die in peace. But there are still the two spirits in man—the spirit of building and the spirit of destruction. And when the second drives the faster horse, then the night comes on."

"You said you had a state and a law," I said. "Could you not have kept them?"

"Why, we could," said Agathocles, "but we did not. We had Pericles, but we shamed him. And now you and I—both Romans" —and he laughed and coughed—"we follow a hairy general to an unknown battle. And, beyond that, there is nothing."

The Last of the Legions

"They say it is Alaric, the Goth," I said. "They say he marches on Rome," for, till then, except in jest, we had not spoken of these wars.

"Alaric, or another, what matters?" said Agathocles. "Who was that western chieftain—he called himself Niall of the Hundred Battles, did he not? And we put him down, in the end, but there were more behind him. Always more. It is time itself we fight, and no man wins against time. How long has the legion been in Britain, Centurion?"

"Three hundred and fifty years and eight," I said, for that is something that even children know.

"Yes," said Agathocles, "the Valeria Victrix. And who remembers the legions that were lost in Parthia and Germany? Who remembers their names?"

But by then I had come back to myself and did not wish to talk to him.

"All Greeks are eaters of wind," I said. "Caw like a crow, if you like; I do not listen."

"It does not matter to me," he said, with a shrug, and a cough. "I tell you, I shall be flayed before the ending, unless my cough ends it. No sensible general would let me live, after the notes I have taken tonight. But have it your own way."

I did not mean to let him see that he had shaken me, but he had. And when, six days later, we came to Anderida and the sea, I was shaken again. The ships should have been ready for us, but they were not, though our general raged like a bear, and we had to wait four days at Anderida. That was hard, for, in four days you get to know the look of a town. They had felt the strength of the sea pirates; they were not like Mid-Britain. I thought of my man at the villa and how he might die in peace, even as Agathocles had said. But all the time, the moss would be creeping on the stone and the rain beating at the door. Till, finally, the naked people gathered there, without knowledge—they would have forgotten the use of the furnace that kept the house warm in winter and the baths that made men clean. And the fields of my veteran centurion of the Second, would go back to witch grass and cockleburs because they were too busy with killing to plant the wheat in the field. I even thought back to my deserter and saw him living, on one side or the other, but with memory of order and law and civilized things. Then that, too, would go, and his

443

children would not remember it, except as a tale. I wanted to ask Agathocles what a race should leave to its kind, but I did not, for I knew he would talk of Greece, and I am a Roman.

Then we sailed, on a very clear day, with little wind, but enough to get us out of harbor. It came suddenly, as those things do, and we did not have time to think. I was very busy—it was only when we were ready to embark that I thought at all. I am a child of the camp and the legion is my hearth. But I knew, as we stood there, waiting, what we were leaving—the whole green, rainy, smoky, windy island, with its seas on either hand and its deep graves in the earth. We had been there three hundred and fifty and eight—we had been the Valeria Victrix. Now we followed a hairy general to an unknown battle, over the rim of the world, and we would win fights and lose them, but our time was over.

I heard the speech for the last time—the British Latin. After that, it would only be the legion, wherever we went. Our general stood like a bear—he would take care of us as long as he could. Agathocles looked seasick already—his face was pinched and thin, and he coughed behind his hand. Before us lay the wide channel and the great darkness. And the Sixth still held Eboracum —I wished, for a moment, that I had been with the Sixth.

"Get your packs on board, you sons!" I shouted to the men.

As the crowd began to cheer, a little, I wanted to say to somebody, "Remember the Valeria Victrix! Remember our name!" But I could not have said it to anyone, and there was no time for those things.

THE BLOOD OF THE MARTYRS

The man who expected to be shot lay with his eyes open, staring at the upper left-hand corner of his cell. He was fairly well over his last beating, and they might come for him any time now. There was a yellow stain in the cell corner near the ceiling; he had liked it at first, then disliked it; now he was coming back to liking it again.

He could see it more clearly with his glasses on, but he only put on his glasses for special occasions now—the first thing in

The Blood of the Martyrs

the morning, and when they brought the food in, and for interviews with the General. The lenses of the glasses had been cracked in a beating some months before, and it strained his eyes to wear them too long. Fortunately, in his present life he had very few occasions demanding clear vision. But, nevertheless, the accident to his glasses worried him, as it worries all near-sighted people. You put your glasses on the first thing in the morning and the world leaps into proportion; if it does not do so, something is wrong with the world.

The man did not believe greatly in symbols, but his chief nightmare, nowadays, was an endless one in which, suddenly and without warning, a large piece of glass would drop out of one of the lenses and he would grope around the cell, trying to find it. He would grope very carefully and gingerly, for hours of darkness, but the end was always the same—the small, unmistakable crunch of irreplaceable glass beneath his heel or his knee. Then he would wake up sweating, with his hands cold. This dream alternated with the one of being shot, but he found no great benefit in the change.

As he lay there, you could see that he had an intellectual head—the head of a thinker or a scholar, old and bald, with the big, domed brow. It was, as a matter of fact, a well-known head; it had often appeared in the columns of newspapers and journals, sometimes when the surrounding text was in a language Professor Malzius could not read. The body, though stooped and worn, was still a strong peasant body and capable of surviving a good deal of ill-treatment, as his captors had found out. He had fewer teeth than when he came to prison, and both the ribs and the knee had been badly set, but these were minor matters. It also occurred to him that his blood count was probably poor. However, if he could ever get out and to a first-class hospital, he was probably good for at least ten years more of work. But, of course, he would not get out. They would shoot him before that, and it would be over.

Sometimes he wished passionately that it would be over—tonight—this moment; at other times he was shaken by the mere blind fear of death. The latter he tried to treat as he would have treated an attack of malaria, knowing that it was an attack, but not always with success. He should have been able to face it better than most—he was Gregor Malzius, the scientist—but that

445

did not always help. The fear of death persisted, even when one had noted and classified it as a purely physical reaction. When he was out of here, he would be able to write a very instructive little paper on the fear of death. He could even do it here, if he had writing materials, but there was no use asking for those. Once they had been given him and he had spent two days quite happily. But they had torn up the work and spat upon it in front of his face. It was a childish thing to do, but it discouraged a man from working.

It seemed odd that he had never seen anybody shot, but he never had. During the war, his reputation and his bad eyesight had exempted him from active service. He had been bombed a couple of times when his reserve battalion was guarding the railway bridge, but that was quite different. You were not tied to a stake, and the airplanes were not trying to kill you as an individual. He knew the place where it was done here, of course. But prisoners did not see the executions, they merely heard, if the wind was from the right quarter.

He had tried again and again to visualize how it would be, but it always kept mixing with an old steel engraving he had seen in boyhood—the execution of William Walker, the American filibuster, in Honduras. William Walker was a small man with a white semi-Napoleonic face. He was standing, very correctly dressed, in front of an open grave, and before him a ragged line of picturesque natives were raising their muskets. When he was shot he would instantly and tidily fall into the grave, like a man dropping through a trap door; as a boy, the extreme neatness of the arrangement had greatly impressed Gregor Malzius. Behind the wall there were palm trees, and, somewhere off to the right, blue and warm, the Caribbean Sea. It would not be like that at all, for his own execution; and yet, whenever he thought of it, he thought of it as being like that.

Well, it was his own fault. He could have accepted the new regime; some respectable people had done that. He could have fled the country; many honorable people had. A scientist should be concerned with the eternal, not with transient political phenomena; and a scientist should be able to live anywhere. But thirty years at the university were thirty years, and, after all, he was Malzius, one of the first biochemists in the world. To the last, he had not believed that they would touch him. Well, he had been wrong about that.

The truth, of course, was the truth. One taught it or one did not teach it. If one did not teach it, it hardly mattered what one did. But he had no quarrel with any established government; he was willing to run up a flag every Tuesday, as long as they let him alone. Most people were fools, and one government was as good as another for them—it had taken them twenty years to accept his theory of cell mutation. Now, if he'd been like his friend Bonnard—a fellow who signed protests, attended meetings for the cause of world peace, and generally played the fool in public—they'd have had some reason to complain. An excellent man in his field, Bonnard—none better—but outside of it, how deplorably like an actor, with his short gray beard, his pink cheeks and his impulsive enthusiasm! Any government could put a fellow like Bonnard in prison—though it would be an injury to science and, therefore, wrong. For that matter, he thought grimly, Bonnard would enjoy being a martyr. He'd walk gracefully to the execution post with a begged cigarette in his mouth, and some theatrical last quip. But Bonnard was safe in his own land—doubtless writing heated and generous articles on The Case of Professor Malzius—and he, Malzius, was the man who was going to be shot. He would like a cigarette, too, on his way to execution; he had not smoked in five months. But he certainly didn't intend to ask for one, and they wouldn't think of offering him any. That was the difference between him and Bonnard.

His mind went back with longing to the stuffy laboratory and stuffier lecture hall at the university; his feet yearned for the worn steps he had climbed ten thousand times, and his eyes for the long steady look through the truthful lens into worlds too tiny for the unaided eye. They had called him "The Bear" and "Old Prickly," but they had fought to work under him, the best of the young men. They said he would explain the Last Judgment in terms of cellular phenomena, but they had crowded to his lectures. It was Williams, the Englishman, who had made up the legend that he carried a chocolate éclair and a set of improper post cards in his battered brief case. Quite untrue, of course—chocolate always made him ill, and he had never looked at an improper post card in his life. And Williams would never know that he knew the legend, too; for Williams had been killed long ago in the war. For a moment, Professor Malzius felt blind hate at the thought of an excellent scientific machine like Williams being smashed in a war. But blind hate was an improper emotion for a scientist, and he put it aside.

He smiled grimly again; they hadn't been able to break up his classes—lucky he was The Bear! He'd seen one colleague hooted from his desk by a band of determined young hoodlums —too bad, but if a man couldn't keep order in his own classroom, he'd better get out. They'd wrecked his own laboratory, but not while he was there.

It was so senseless, so silly. "In God's name," he said reasonably, to no one, "what sort of conspirator do you think I would make? A man of my age and habits! I am interested in cellular phenomena!" And yet they were beating him because he would not tell about the boys. As if he had even paid attention to half the nonsense! There were certain passwords and greetings—a bar of music you whistled, entering a restaurant; the address of a firm that specialized, ostensibly, in vacuum cleaners. But they were not his own property. They belonged to the young men who had trusted The Bear. He did not know what half of them meant, and the one time he had gone to a meeting, he had felt like a fool. For they were fools and childish—playing the childish games of conspiracy that people like Bonnard enjoyed. Could they even make a better world than the present? He doubted it extremely. And yet, he could not betray them; they had come to him, looking over their shoulders, with darkness in their eyes.

A horrible, an appalling thing—to be trusted. He had no wish to be a guide and counselor of young men. He wanted to do his work. Suppose they were poor and ragged and oppressed; he had been a peasant himself, he had eaten black bread. It was by his own efforts that he was Professor Malzius. He did not wish the confidences of boys like Gregopolous and the others—for, after all, what was Gregopolous? An excellent and untiring laboratory assistant—and a laboratory assistant he would remain to the end of his days. He had pattered about the laboratory like a fox terrier, with a fox terrier's quick bright eyes. Like a devoted dog, he had made a god of Professor Malzius. "I don't want your problems, man. I don't want to know what you are doing outside

The Blood of the Martyrs

the laboratory." But Gregopolous had brought his problems and his terrible trust none the less, humbly and proudly, like a fox terrier with a bone. After that—well, what was a man to do?

He hoped they would get it over with, and quickly. The world should be like a chemical formula, full of reason and logic. Instead, there were all these young men, and their eyes. They conspired, hopelessly and childishly, for what they called freedom against the new regime. They wore no overcoats in winter and were often hunted and killed. Even if they did not conspire, they had miserable little love affairs and ate the wrong food—yes, even before, at the university, they had been the same. Why the devil would they not accept? Then they could do their work. Of course, a great many of them would not be allowed to accept —they had the wrong ideas or the wrong politics—but then they could run away. If Malzius, at twenty, had had to run from his country, he would still have been a scientist. To talk of a free world was a delusion; men were not free in the world. Those who wished got a space of time to get their work done. That was all. And yet, he had not accepted—he did not know why.

Now he heard the sound of steps along the corridor. His body began to quiver and the places where he had been beaten hurt him. He noted it as an interesting reflex. Sometimes they merely flashed the light in the cell and passed by. On the other hand, it might be death. It was a hard question to decide.

The lock creaked, the door opened. "Get up, Malzius!" said the hard, bright voice of the guard. Gregor Malzius got up, a little stiffly, but quickly.

"Put on your glasses, you old fool!" said the guard, with a laugh. "You are going to the General."

Professor Malzius found the stone floors of the corridor uneven, though he knew them well enough. Once or twice the guard struck him, lightly and without malice, as one strikes an old horse with a whip. The blows were familiar and did not register on Professor Malzius' consciousness; he merely felt proud of not stumbling. He was apt to stumble; once he had hurt his knee.

He noticed, it seemed to him, an unusual tenseness and officiousness about his guard. Once, even, in a brightly lighted corridor the guard moved to strike him, but refrained. However, that, too,

449

happened occasionally, with one guard or another, and Professor Malzius merely noted the fact. It was a small fact, but an important one in the economy in which he lived.

But there could be no doubt that something unusual was going on in the castle. There were more guards than usual, many of them strangers. He tried to think, carefully, as he walked, if it could be one of the new national holidays. It was hard to keep track of them all. The General might be in a good humor. Then they would merely have a cat-and-mouse conversation for half an hour and nothing really bad would happen. Once, even, there had been a cigar. Professor Malzius, the scientist, licked his lips at the thought.

Now he was being turned over to a squad of other guards, with salutings. This was really unusual; Professor Malzius bit his mouth, inconspicuously. He had the poignant distrust of a monk or an old prisoner at any break in routine. Old prisoners are your true conservatives; they only demand that the order around them remains exactly the same.

It alarmed him as well that the new guards did not laugh at him. New guards almost always laughed when they saw him for the first time. He was used to the laughter and missed it— his throat felt dry. He would have liked, just once, to eat at the university restaurant before he died. It was bad food, ill cooked and starchy, food good enough for poor students and professors, but he would have liked to be there, in the big smoky room that smelt of copper boilers and cabbage, with a small cup of bitter coffee before him and a cheap cigarette. He did not ask for his dog or his notebooks, the old photographs in his bedroom, his incomplete experiments or his freedom. Just to lunch once more at the university restaurant and have people point out The Bear. It seemed a small thing to ask, but of course it was quite impossible.

"Halt!" said a voice, and he halted. There were, for the third time, salutings. Then the door of the General's office opened and he was told to go in.

He stood, just inside the door, in the posture of attention, as he had been taught. The crack in the left lens of his glasses made a crack across the room, and his eyes were paining him already, but he paid no attention to that. There was the familiar figure of the General, with his air of a well-fed and extremely healthy tomcat, and there was another man, seated at the General's desk. He could not see the other man very well—the crack made him bulge and waver—but he did not like his being there.

"Well, professor," said the General, in an easy, purring voice. Malzius' entire body jerked. He had made a fearful, an unpardonable omission. He must remedy it at once. "Long live the state," he shouted in a loud thick voice, and saluted. He knew, bitterly, that his salute was ridiculous and that he looked ridiculous, making it. But perhaps the General would laugh—he had done so before. Then everything would be all right, for it was not quite as easy to beat a man after you had laughed at him.

The General did not laugh. He made a half turn instead, toward the man at the desk. The gesture said, "You see, he is well trained." It was the gesture of a man of the world, accustomed to deal with unruly peasants and animals—the gesture of a man fitted to be General.

The man at the desk paid no attention to the General's gesture. He lifted his head, and Malzius saw him more clearly and with complete unbelief. It was not a man but a picture come alive. Professor Malzius had seen the picture a hundred times; they had made him salute and take off his hat in front of it, when he had had a hat. Indeed, the picture had presided over his beatings. The man himself was a little smaller, but the picture was a good picture. There were many dictators in the world, and this was one type. The face was white, beaky and semi-Napoleonic; the lean, military body sat squarely in its chair. The eyes dominated the face, and the mouth was rigid. I remember also a hypnotist, and a woman Charcot showed me, at his clinic in Paris, thought Professor Malzius. But there is also, obviously, an endocrine unbalance. Then his thoughts stopped.

"Tell the man to come closer," said the man at the desk. "Can he hear me? Is he deaf?"

"No, Your Excellency," said the General, with enormous, purring respect. "But he is a little old, though perfectly healthy. . . . Are you not, Professor Malzius?"

"Yes, I am perfectly healthy. I am very well treated here," said Professor Malzius, in his loud thick voice. They were not going to catch him with traps like that, not even by dressing up somebody as the Dictator. He fixed his eyes on the big old-fashioned inkwell on the General's desk—that, at least, was perfectly sane.

Stephen Vincent Benét

"Come closer," said the man at the desk to Professor Malzius, and the latter advanced till he could almost touch the inkwell with his fingers. Then he stopped with a jerk, hoping he had done right. The movement removed the man at the desk from the crack in his lenses, and Professor Malzius knew suddenly that it was true. This was, indeed, the Dictator, this man with the rigid mouth. He began to talk.

"I have been very well treated here and the General has acted with the greatest consideration," he said. "But I am Professor Gregor Malzius—professor of biochemistry. For thirty years I have lectured at the university; I am a fellow of the Royal Society, a corresponding member of the Academy of Sciences at Berlin, at Rome, at Boston, at Paris and Stockholm. I have received the Nottingham Medal, the Lamarck Medal, the Order of St. John of Portugal and the Nobel Prize. I think my blood count is low, but I have received a great many degrees and my experiments on the migratory cells are not finished. I do not wish to complain of my treatment, but I must continue my experiments."

He stopped, like a clock that has run down, surprised to hear the sound of his own voice. He noted, in one part of his mind, that the General had made a move to silence him, but had himself been silenced by the Dictator.

"Yes, Professor Malzius," said the man at the desk, in a harsh, toneless voice. "There has been a regrettable error." The rigid face stared at Professor Malzius. Professor Malzius stared back. He did not say anything.

"In these days," said the Dictator, his voice rising, "the nation demands the submission of every citizen. Encircled by jealous foes, our reborn land yet steps forward toward her magnificent destiny." The words continued for some time, the voice rose and fell. Professor Malzius listened respectfully; he had heard the words many times before and they had ceased to have meaning to him. He was thinking of certain cells of the body that rebel against the intricate processes of Nature and set up their own bellicose state. Doubtless they, too, have a destiny, he thought, but in medicine it is called cancer.

"Jealous and spiteful tongues in other countries have declared that it is our purpose to wipe out learning and science," concluded the Dictator. "That is not our purpose. After the cleansing, the rebirth. We mean to move forward to the greatest science in the world—our own science, based on the enduring principles of our nationhood." He ceased abruptly, his eyes fell into their dream. Very like the girl Charcot showed me in my young days, thought Professor Malzius; there was first the ebullition, then the calm. "I was part of the cleansing? You did not mean to hurt me?" he asked timidly.

"Yes, Professor Malzius," said the General, smiling, "you were part of the cleansing. Now that is over. His Excellency has spoken."

"I do not understand," said Professor Malzius, gazing at the fixed face of the man behind the desk.

"It is very simple," said the General. He spoke in a slow careful voice, as one speaks to a deaf man or a child. "You are a distinguished man of science—you have received the Nobel Prize. That was a service to the state. You became, however, infected by the wrong political ideas. That was treachery to the state. You had, therefore, as decreed by His Excellency, to pass through a certain period for probation and rehabilitation. But that, we believe, is finished."

"You do not wish to know the names of the young men any more?" said Professor Malzius. "You do not want the addresses?"

"That is no longer of importance," said the General patiently. "There is no longer opposition. The leaders were caught and executed three weeks ago."

"There is no longer opposition," repeated Professor Malzius. "At the trial, you were not even involved."

"I was not even involved," said Professor Malzius. "Yes."

"Now," said the General, with a look at the Dictator, "we come to the future. I will be frank—the new state is frank with its citizens."

"It is so," said the Dictator, his eyes still sunk in his dream.

"There has been—let us say—a certain agitation in foreign countries regarding Professor Malzius," said the General, his eyes still fixed on the Dictator. "That means nothing, of course. Nevertheless, your acquaintance, Professor Bonnard, and others have meddled in matters that do not concern them."

"They asked after me?" said Professor Malzius, with surprise. "It is true, my experiments were reaching a point that——"

"No foreign influence could turn us from our firm purpose," said the Dictator. "But it is our firm purpose to show our nation first in science and culture as we have already shown her first in manliness and statehood. For that reason, you are here, Professor Malzius." He smiled.

Professor Malzius stared. His cheeks began to tremble.

"I do not understand," said Professor Malzius. "You will give me my laboratory back?"

"Yes," said the Dictator, and the General nodded as one nods to a stupid child.

Professor Malzius passed a hand across his brow.

"My post at the university?" he said. "My experiments?"

"It is the purpose of our regime to offer the fullest encouragement to our loyal sons of science," said the Dictator.

"First of all," said Professor Malzius, "I must go to a hospital. My blood count is poor. But that will not take long." His voice had become impatient and his eyes glowed. "Then—my notebooks were burned, I suppose. That was silly, but we can start in again. I have a very good memory, an excellent memory. The theories are in my head, you know," and he tapped it. "I must have assistants, of course; little Gregopolous was my best one——"

"The man Gregopolous has been executed," said the General, in a stern voice. "You had best forget him."

"Oh," said Professor Malzius. "Well, then, I must have someone else. You see, these are important experiments. There must be some young men—clever ones—they cannot all be dead. I will know them." He laughed a little, nervously. "The Bear always got the pick of the crop," he said. "They used to call me The Bear, you know." He stopped and looked at them for a moment with ghastly eyes. "You are not fooling me?" he said. He burst into tears.

When he recovered he was alone in the room with the General. The General was looking at him as he himself had looked once at strange forms of life under the microscope, with neither disgust nor attraction, but with great interest.

"His Excellency forgives your unworthy suggestion," he said. "He knows you are overwrought."

"Yes," said Professor Malzius. He sobbed once and dried his glasses.

"Come, come," said the General, with a certain bluff heartiness. "We mustn't have our new president of the National Academy crying. It would look badly in the photographs."

The Blood of the Martyrs

"President of the Academy?" said Professor Malzius quickly. "Oh, no; I mustn't be that. They make speeches; they have administrative work. But I am a scientist, a teacher."

"I'm afraid you can't very well avoid it," said the General, still heartily, though he looked at Professor Malzius. "Your induction will be quite a ceremony. His Excellency himself will preside. And you will speak on the new glories of our science. It will be a magnificent answer to the petty and jealous criticisms of our neighbors. Oh, you needn't worry about the speech," he added quickly. "It will be prepared; you will only have to read it. His Excellency thinks of everything."

"Very well," said Professor Malzius; "and then may I go back to my work?"

"Oh, don't worry about that," said the General, smiling. "I'm only a simple soldier; I don't know about those things. But you'll have plenty of work."

"The more the better," said Malzius eagerly. "I still have ten good years."

He opened his mouth to smile, and a shade of dismay crossed the General's face.

"Yes," he said, as if to himself. "The teeth must be attended to. At once. And a rest, undoubtedly, before the photographs are taken. Milk. You are feeling sufficiently well, Professor Malzius?"

"I am very happy," said Professor Malzius. "I have been very well treated and I come of peasant stock."

"Good," said the General. He paused for a moment, and spoke in a more official voice.

"Of course, it is understood, Professor Malzius——" he said.

"Yes?" said Professor Malzius. "I beg your pardon. I was thinking of something else."

"It is understood, Professor Malzius," repeated the General, "that your—er—rehabilitation in the service of the state is a permanent matter. Naturally, you will be under observation, but, even so, there must be no mistake."

"I am a scientist," said Professor Malzius impatiently. "What have I to do with politics? If you wish me to take oaths of loyalty, I will take as many as you wish."

"I am glad you take that attitude," said the General, though he looked at Professor Malzius curiously. "I may say that I regret the unpleasant side of our interviews. I trust you bear no ill will."

"Why should I be angry?" said Professor Malzius. "You were told to do one thing. Now you are told to do another. That is all."

"It is not quite so simple as that," said the General rather stiffly. He looked at Professor Malzius for a third time. "And I'd have sworn you were one of the stiff-necked ones," he said. "Well, well, every man has his breaking point, I suppose. In a few moments you will receive the final commands of His Excellency. Tonight you will go to the capitol and speak over the radio. You will have no difficulty there—the speech is written. But it will put a quietus on the activities of our friend Bonnard and the question that has been raised in the British Parliament. Then a few weeks of rest by the sea and the dental work, and then, my dear president of the National Academy, you will be ready to undertake your new duties. I congratulate you and hope we shall meet often under pleasant auspices." He bowed from the waist to Malzius, the bow of a man of the world, though there was still something feline in his moustaches. Then he stood to attention, and Malzius, too, for the Dictator had come into the room.

"It is settled?" said the Dictator. "Good. Gregor Malzius, I welcome you to the service of the new state. You have cast your errors aside and are part of our destiny."

"Yes," said Professor Malzius, "I will be able to do my work now."

The Dictator frowned a little.

"You will not only be able to continue your invaluable researches," he said, "but you will also be able—and it will be part of your duty—to further our national ideals. Our reborn nation must rule the world for the world's good. There is a fire within us that is not in other stocks. Our civilization must be extended everywhere. The future wills it. It will furnish the subject of your first discourse as president of the Academy."

"But," said Professor Malzius, in a low voice, "I am not a soldier. I am a biochemist. I have no experience in these matters you speak of."

The Dictator nodded. "You are a distinguished man of science," he said. "You will prove that our women must bear soldiers, our men abandon this nonsense of republics and democracies for trust in those born to rule them. You will prove by scientific law that certain races—our race in particular—are destined to rule the world. You will prove they are destined to rule by the virtues of war, and that war is part of our heritage."

"But," said Professor Malzius, "it is not like that. I mean," he said, "one looks and watches in the laboratory. One waits for a long time. It is a long process, very long. And then, if the theory is not proved, one discards the theory. That is the way it is done. I probably do not explain it well. But I am a biochemist; I do not know how to look for the virtues of one race against another, and I can prove nothing about war, except that it kills. If I said anything else, the whole world would laugh at me."

"Not one in this nation would laugh at you," said the Dictator.

"But if they do not laugh at me when I am wrong, there is no science," said Professor Malzius, knotting his brows. He paused. "Do not misunderstand me," he said earnestly. "I have ten years of good work left; I want to get back to my laboratory. But, you see, there are the young men—if I am to teach the young men."

He paused again, seeing their faces before him. There were many. There was Williams, the Englishman, who had died in the war, and little Gregopolous with the fox-terrier eyes. There were all who had passed through his classrooms, from the stupidest to the best. They had shot little Gregopolous for treason, but that did not alter the case. From all over the world they had come—he remembered the Indian student and the Chinese. They wore cheap overcoats, they were hungry for knowledge, they ate the bad, starchy food of the poor restaurants, they had miserable little love affairs and played childish games of politics, instead of doing their work. Nevertheless, a few were promising—all must be given the truth. It did not matter if they died, but they must be given the truth. Otherwise there could be no continuity and no science.

He looked at the Dictator before him—yes, it was a hysteric face. He would know how to deal with it in his classroom—but such faces should not rule countries or young men. One was willing to go through a great many meaningless ceremonies in order to do one's work—wear a uniform or salute or be president of the Academy. That did not matter; it was part of the due to Caesar. But not to tell lies to young men on one's own subject. After all, they had called him The Bear and said he carried improper post cards in his brief case. They had given him their terrible confidence—not for love or kindness, but because they had found him honest. It was too late to change.

The Dictator looked sharply at the General. "I thought this had been explained to Professor Malzius," he said.

"Why, yes," said Professor Malzius. "I will sign any papers. I assure you I am not interested in politics—a man like myself, imagine! One state is as good as another. And I miss my tobacco —I have not smoked in five months. But, you see, one cannot be a scientist and tell lies."

He looked at the two men.

"What happens if I do not?" he said, in a low voice. But, looking at the Dictator, he had his answer. It was a fanatic face.

"Why, we shall resume our conversations, Professor Malzius," said the General, with a simper.

"Then I shall be beaten again," said Professor Malzius. He stated what he knew to be a fact.

"The process of rehabilitation is obviously not quite complete," said the General, "but perhaps, in time——"

"It will not be necessary," said Professor Malzius. "I cannot be beaten again." He stared wearily around the room. His shoulders straightened—it was so he had looked in the classroom when they had called him The Bear. "Call your other officers in," he said in a clear voice. "There are papers for me to sign. I should like them all to witness."

"Why——" said the General. "Why——" He looked doubtfully at the Dictator.

An expression of gratification appeared on the lean, semi-Napoleonic face. A white hand, curiously limp, touched the hand of Professor Malzius.

"You will feel so much better, Gregor," said the hoarse, tense voice. "I am so very glad you have given in."

"Why, of course, I give in," said Gregor Malzius. "Are you not the Dictator? And besides, if I do not, I shall be beaten again. And I cannot—you understand?—I cannot be beaten again."

He paused, breathing a little. But already the room was full of other faces. He knew them well, the hard faces of the new regime. But youthful some of them too.

The Dictator was saying something with regard to receiving the distinguished scientist, Professor Gregor Malzius, into the service of the state.

"Take the pen," said the General in an undertone. "The inkwell is there, Professor Malzius. Now you may sign."

The Blood of the Martyrs

Professor Malzius stood, his fingers gripping the big, old-fashioned inkwell. It was full of ink—the servants of the Dictator were very efficient. They could shoot small people with the eyes of fox terriers for treason, but their trains arrived on time and their inkwells did not run dry.

"The state," he said, breathing. "Yes. But science does not know about states. And you are a little man—a little, unimportant man."

Then, before the General could stop him, he had picked up the inkwell and thrown it in the Dictator's face. The next moment the General's fist caught him on the side of the head and he fell behind the desk to the floor. But lying there, through his cracked glasses, he could still see the grotesque splashes of ink on the Dictator's face and uniform, and the small cut above his eye where the blood was gathering. They had not fired; he had thought he would be too close to the Dictator for them to fire in time.

"Take that man out and shoot him. At once," said the Dictator in a dry voice. He did not move to wipe the stains from his uniform—and for that Professor Malzius admired him. They rushed then, each anxious to be first. But Professor Malzius made no resistance.

As he was being hustled along the corridors, he fell now and then. On the second fall, his glasses were broken completely, but that did not matter to him. They were in a great hurry, he thought, but all the better—one did not have to think while one could not see.

Now and then he heard his voice make sounds of discomfort, but his voice was detached from himself. There was little Gregopolous—he could see him very plainly—and Williams, with his fresh English coloring—and all the men whom he had taught.

He had given them nothing but work and the truth; they had given him their terrible trust. If he had been beaten again, he might have betrayed them. But he had avoided that.

He felt a last weakness—a wish that someone might know. They would not, of course; he would have died of typhoid in the castle and there would be regretful notices in the newspapers. And then he would be forgotten, except for his work, and that was as it should be. He had never thought much of martyrs—hysterical people in the main. Though he'd like Bonnard to have known about the ink; it was in the coarse vein of humor that Bonnard

459

could not appreciate. But then, he was a peasant; Bonnard had often told him so.

They were coming out into an open courtyard now; he felt the fresh air of outdoors. "Gently," he said. "A little gently. What's the haste?" But already they were tying him to the post. Someone struck him in the face and his eyes watered. "A schoolboy covered with ink," he muttered through his lost teeth. "A hysterical schoolboy too. But you cannot kill truth."

They were not good last words, and he knew that they were not. He must try to think of better ones—not shame Bonnard. But now they had a gag in his mouth; just as well; it saved him the trouble.

His body ached, bound against the post, but his sight and his mind were clearer. He could make out the evening sky, gray with fog, the sky that belonged to no country, but to all the world.

He could make out the gray high buttress of the castle. They had made it a jail, but it would not always be a jail. Perhaps in time it would not even exist. But if a little bit of truth were gathered, that would always exist, while there were men to remember and rediscover it. It was only the liars and the cruel who always failed.

Sixty years ago, he had been a little boy, eating black bread and thin cabbage soup in a poor house. It had been a bitter life, but he could not complain of it. He had had some good teachers and they had called him The Bear.

The gag hurt his mouth—they were getting ready now. There had been a girl called Anna once; he had almost forgotten her. And his rooms had smelt a certain way and he had had a dog. It did not matter what they did with the medals. He raised his head and looked once more at the gray foggy sky. In a moment there would be no thought, but, while there was thought, one must remember and note. His pulse rate was lower than he would have expected and his breathing oddly even, but those were not the important things. The important thing was beyond, in the gray sky that had no country, in the stones of the earth and the feeble human spirit. The important thing was truth.

"Ready!" called the officer. "Aim! Fire!" But Professor Malzius did not hear the three commands of the officer. He was thinking about the young men.

INTO EGYPT

It had finally been decided to let them go and now, for three days, they had been passing. The dust on the road to the frontier had not settled for three days or nights. But the strictest orders had been given and there were very few incidents. There could easily have been more.

Even the concentration camps had been swept clean, for this thing was to be final. After it, the State could say "How fearless we are—we let even known conspirators depart." It is true that, in the case of those in the concentration camps, there had been a preliminary rectification—a weeding, so to speak. But the news of that would not be officially published for some time and the numbers could always be disputed. If you kill a few people, they remain persons with names and identities, but, if you kill in the hundreds, there is simply a number for most of those who read the newspapers. And, once you start arguing about numbers, you begin to wonder if the thing ever happened at all. This too had been foreseen.

In fact, everything had been foreseen—and with great acuteness. There had been the usual diplomatic tension, solved, finally, by the usual firm stand. At the last moment, the other Powers had decided to co-operate. They had done so unwillingly, grudgingly, and with many representations, but they had done so. It was another great victory. And everywhere the trains rolled and the dust rose on the roads, for, at last and at length, the Accursed People were going. Every one of them, man, woman and child, to the third and the fourth generation—every one of them with a drop of that blood in his veins. And this was the end of it all and, by sunset on the third day, the land would know them no more. It was another great victory—perhaps the greatest. There would be a week of celebration after it, with appropriate cere-monies and speeches, and the date would be marked in the new calendar, with the date of the founding of the State and other dates.

Nevertheless, and even with the noteworthy efficiency of which the State was so proud, any mass evacuation is bound to be a complicated and fatiguing affair. The lieutenant stationed at the crossroads found it so—he was young and in the best of health but the strain was beginning to tell on him, though he would never have admitted it. He had been a little nervous at first—

a little nervous and exceedingly anxious that everything should go according to plan. After all, it was an important post, the last crossroads before the frontier. A minor road, of course—they'd be busier on the main highways and at the ports of embarkation —but a last crossroads, nevertheless. He couldn't flatter himself it was worth a decoration—the bigwigs would get those. But, all the same, he was expected to evacuate so many thousands—he knew the figures by heart. Easy enough to say one had only to follow the plan! That might do for civilians—an officer was an officer. Would he show himself enough of an officer, would he make a fool of himself in front of his men? Would he even, perhaps, by some horrible, unforeseen mischance, get his road clogged with fleeing humanity till they had to send somebody over from Staff to straighten the tangle out? The thought was appalling.

He could see it happening in his mind—as a boy, he had been imaginative. He could hear the staff officer's words while he stood at attention, eyes front. One's first real command and a black mark on one's record! Yes, even if it was only police work —that didn't matter—a citizen of the State, a member of the Party must be held to an unflinching standard. If one failed to meet that standard there was nothing left in life. His throat had been dry and his movements a little jerky as he made his last dispositions and saw the first black specks begin to straggle toward the crossroads.

He could afford to laugh at that now, if he had had time. He could even afford to remember old Franz, his orderly, trying to put the brandy in his coffee, that first morning. "It's a chilly morning, Lieutenant," but there had been a question in Franz's eyes. He'd refused the brandy, of course, and told Franz off properly, too. The new State did not depend on Dutch courage but on the racial valor of its citizens. And the telling-off had helped—it had made his own voice firmer and given a little fillip of anger to his pulse. But Franz was an old soldier and imperturbable. What was it he had said, later? "The lieutenant must not worry. Civilians are always sheep—it is merely a matter of herding them." An improper remark, of course, to one's lieutenant, but it had helped settle his mind and make it cooler. Yes, an orderly like Franz was worth something, once one learned the knack of keeping him in his place.

Then they had begun to come, slowly, stragglingly, not like soldiers. He couldn't remember who had been the first. It was strange but he could not—he had been sure that he would remember. Perhaps a plodding family, with the scared children looking at him—perhaps one of the old men with long beards and burning eyes. But, after three days, they all mixed, the individual faces. As Franz had said, they became civilian sheep—sheep that one must herd and keep moving, keep moving always through day and night, moving on to the frontier. As they went, they wailed. When the wailing grew too loud, one took measures; but, sooner or later it always began again. It would break out down the road, die down as it came toward the post. It seemed to come out of their mouths without their knowledge—the sound of broken wood, of wheat ground between stones. He had tried to stop it completely at first, now he no longer bothered. And yet there were many—a great many—who did not wail.

At first, it had been interesting to see how many different types there were. He had not thought to find such variety among the Accursed People—one had one's own mental picture, reinforced by the pictures in the newspapers. But, seeing them was different. They were not at all like the picture. They were tall and short, plump and lean, black-haired, yellow-haired, red-haired. It was obvious, even under the film of dust, that some had been rich, others poor, some thoughtful, others active. Indeed, it was often hard to tell them, by the looks. But that was not his affair—his affair was to keep them moving. All the same, it gave you a shock, sometimes, at first.

Perhaps the queerest thing was that they all looked so ordinary, so much a part of everyday. That was because one had been used to seeing them—it could be no more than that. But, under the film of dust and heat, one would look at a face. And then one would think, unconsciously, "Why, what is that fellow doing, so far from where he lives? Why, for heaven's sake, is he straggling along this road? He doesn't look happy." Then the mind would resume control and one would remember. But the thought would come, now and then, without orders from the mind.

He had seen very few that he knew. That was natural—he came from the South. He had seen Willi Schneider, to be sure —that had been the second day and it was very dusty. When he was a little boy, very young, he had played in Willi's garden with

Willi, in the summers, and, as they had played, there had come
to them, through the open window, the ripple of a piano and
the clear, rippling flow of Willi's mother's voice. It was not a
great voice—not a Brunhild voice—but beautiful in *lieder* and
beautifully sure. She had sung at their own house; that was odd
to remember. Of course, her husband had not been one of them
—a councilor, in fact. Needless to say, that had been long before
the discovery that even the faintest trace of that blood tainted.
As for Willi and himself, they had been friends—yes, even
through the first year or so at school. Both of them had meant
to run away and be cowboys, and they had had a secret password. Naturally, things had changed, later on.

For a horrible moment, he had thought that Willi would speak
to him—recall the warm air of summer and the smell of linden
and those young, unmanly days. But Willi did not. Their eyes
met, for an instant, then both had looked away. Willi was helping
an old woman along, an old woman who muttered fretfully as she
walked, like a cat with sore paws. They were both of them covered with dust and the old woman went slowly. Willi's mother
had walked with a quick step and her voice had not been cracked
or fretful. After play, she had given them both cream buns,
laughing and moving her hands, in a bright green dress. It was not
permitted to think further of Willi Schneider.

That was the only real acquaintance but there were other,
recognizable faces. There was the woman who had kept the news-
stand, the brisk little waiter at the summer hotel, the taxi chauffeur with the squint and the heart specialist. Then there was the
former scientist—one could still tell him from his pictures—and
the actor one had often seen. That was all that one knew and
not all on the same day. That was enough. He had not imagined
the taxi chauffeur with a wife and children and that the youngest
child should be lame. That had surprised him—surprised him almost as much as seeing the heart specialist walking along the road
like any man. It had surprised him, also, to see the scientist led
along between two others and to recognize the fact that he was
mad.

But that also mixed with the dust—the endless, stifling cloud
of the dust, the endless, moving current. The dust got in one's
throat and one's eyes—it was hard to cut, even with brandy, from

one's throat. It lay on the endless bundles people carried; queer bundles, bulging out at the ends, with here a ticking clock, and there a green bunch of carrots. It lay on the handcarts a few of them pushed—the handcarts bearing the sort of goods that one would snatch, haphazard, from a burning house. It rose and whirled and penetrated—it was never still. At night, slashed by the efficient searchlights that made the night bright as day, it was still a mist above the road. As for sleep—well, one slept when one could, for a couple of hours after midnight, when they too slept, ungracefully, in heaps and clumps by the road. But, except for the first night, he could not even remember Franz pulling his boots off.

His men had been excellent, admirable, indefatigable. That was, of course, due to the Leader and the State, but still, he would put it in his report. They had kept the stream moving, always. The attitude had been the newly prescribed one—not that of punishment, richly as that was deserved, but of complete aloofness, as if the Accursed People did not even exist. Naturally, now and then, the men had had their fun. One could not blame them for that—some of the incidents had been extremely comic. There had been the old woman with the hen—a comedy character. Of course, she had not been permitted to keep the hen. They should have taken it away from her at the inspection point. But she had looked very funny, holding on to the squawking chicken by the tail feathers, with the tears running down her face.

Yes, the attitude of the men would certainly go in his report. He would devote a special paragraph to the musicians also—they had been indefatigable. They had played the prescribed tunes continually, in spite of the dust and the heat. One would hope that those tunes would sink into the hearts of the Accursed People, to be forever a warning and a memory. Particularly if they happened to know the words. But one could never be sure about people like that.

Staff cars had come four times, the first morning, and once there had been a general. He had felt nervous, when they came, but there had been no complaint. After that, they had let him alone, except for an occasional visit—that must mean they thought him up to his work. Once, even, the road had been almost clear, for a few minutes—he was moving them along faster than they did at the inspection point. The thought had gone to his head for an instant, but he kept cool—and, soon enough, the road had been crowded again.

As regarded casualties—he could not keep the exact figure in his head, but it was a minor one. A couple of heart attacks—one of the man who had been a judge, or so the others said. Unpleasant but valuable to see the life drain out of a face like that. He had made himself watch it—one must harden oneself. They had wanted to remove the body—of course, that had not been allowed. The women taken in childbirth had been adequately dealt with—one could do nothing to assist. But he had insisted, for decency's sake, on a screen, and Franz had been very clever at rigging one up. Only two of those had died, the rest had gone on—they showed a remarkable tenacity. Then there were the five executions, including the man suddenly gone crazy, who had roared and foamed. A nasty moment, that—for a second the whole current had stopped flowing. But his men had jumped in at once—he himself had acted quickly. The others were merely incorrigible stragglers and of no account.

And now, it was almost over and soon the homeland would be free. Free as it never had been—for, without the Accursed People, it would be unlike any other country on earth. They were gone, with their books and their music, their false, delusive science and their quick way of thinking. They were gone, all the people like Willi Schneider and his mother, who had spent so much time in talking and being friendly. They were gone, the willful people, who clung close together and yet so willfully supported the new and the untried. The men who haggled over pennies, and the others who gave—the sweater, the mimic, the philosopher, the discoverer—all were gone. Yes, and with them went their slaves' religion, the religion of the weak and the humble, the religion that fought so bitterly and yet exalted the prophet above the armed man.

One could be a whole man, with them gone, without their doubts and their mockery and their bitter, self-accusing laughter, their melancholy, deep as a well, and their endless aspiration for something that could not be touched with the hand. One could be solid and virile and untroubled, virile and huge as the old, thunderous gods. It was so that the Leader had spoken, so it must be true. And the countries who weakly received them would be themselves corrupted into warm unmanliness and mockery, into a desire for peace and a search for things not tangible. But the homeland would stand still and listen to the beat of its own heart —not even listen, but stand like a proud fierce animal, a perfect, living machine. To get children, to conquer others, to die gloriously in battle—that was the end of man. It had been a long time forgotten, but the Leader had remembered it. And, naturally, one could not do that completely with them in the land, for they had other ideas.

He thought of these things dutifully because it was right to think of them. They had been repeated and repeated in his ears till they had occupied his mind. But, meanwhile, he was very tired and the dust still rose. They were coming by clumps and groups, now—the last stragglers—they were no longer a solid, flowing current. The afternoon had turned hot—unseasonably hot. He didn't want any more brandy—the thought of it sickened his stomach. He wanted a glass of beer—iced beer, cold and dark, with foam on it—and a chance to unbutton his collar. He wanted to have the thing done and sit down and have Franz pull off his boots. If it were only a little cooler, a little quieter—if even these last would not wail so, now and then—if only the dust would not rise! He found himself humming, for comfort, a Christmas hymn—it brought a little, frail coolness to his mind.

> "Silent night, holy night,
> All is calm, all is bright. . . ."

The old gods were virile and thunderous, but, down in the South, they would still deck the tree, in kindliness. Call it a custom—call it anything you like—it still came out of the heart. And it was a custom of the homeland—it could not be wrong. Oh, the beautiful, crisp snow of Christmas Day, the greetings between friends, the bright, lighted tree! Well, there'd be a Christmas to come. Perhaps he'd be married, by then—he had thought of it, often. If he were, they would have a tree—young couples were sentimental, in the South. A tree and a small manger beneath it, with the animals and the child. They carved the figures out of wood, in his country, with loving care—the thought of them was very peaceful and cool. In the old days, he had always given Willi Schneider part of his almond cake—one knew it was not Willi's festival but one was friendly, for all that. And that must be forgotten. He had had no right to give Willi part of his almond cake—it was the tree that mattered, the tree and the tiny candles, the smell of the fresh pine and the clear, frosty sweetness of the day. They would keep that, he and his wife, keep it with rejoicing, and Willi would not look in through the window, with his old face or his new face. He would not look in at all, ever any more. For now the homeland was released, after many years.

Now the dust was beginning to settle—the current in the road had dwindled to a straggling trickle. He was able to think, for the first time, of the land to which that trickle was going—a hungry land, the papers said, in spite of its boastful ways. The road led blankly into it, beyond the rise of ground—hard to tell what it was like. But they would be dispersed, not only here, but over many lands. Of course, the situation was not comparable—all the same, it must be a queer feeling. A queer feeling, yes, to start out anew, with nothing but the clothes on your back and what you could push in a handcart, if you had a handcart. For an instant the thought came, unbidden, "It must be a great people that can bear such things." But they were the Accursed People—the thought should not have come.

He sighed and turned back to his duty. It was really wonderful—even on the third day there was such order, such precision. It was something to be proud of—something to remember long. The Leader would speak of it, undoubtedly. The ones who came now were the very last stragglers, the weakest, but they were being moved along as promptly as if they were strong. The dust actually no longer rose in a cloud—it was settling, slowly but surely.

He did not quite remember when he had last eaten. It did not matter, for the sun was sinking fast, in a red warm glow. In a moment, in an hour, it would be done—he could rest and undo his collar, have some beer. There was nobody on the road now—nobody at all. He stood rigidly at his post—the picture of an officer, though somewhat dusty—but he knew that his eyes were closing. Nobody on the road—nobody for a whole five minutes . . . for eight . . . for ten.

He was roused by Franz's voice in his ear—he must have gone to sleep, standing up. He had heard of that happening to soldiers on the march—he felt rather proud that, now, it had happened to him. But there seemed to be a little trouble on the road—he walked forward to it, stiffly, trying to clear his throat.

It was a commonplace grouping—he had seen dozens like it in the course of the three days—an older man, a young woman, and, of course, the child that she held. No doubt about them, either —the man's features were strongly marked, the woman had the liquid eyes. As for the child, that was merely a wrapped bundle. They should have started before—stupid people—the man looked strong enough. Their belongings were done up like all poor people's belongings.

He stood in front of them, now, erect and a soldier. "Well," he said. "Don't you know the orders? No livestock to be taken. Didn't they examine you, down the road?" ("And a pretty fool I'll look like, reporting one confiscated donkey to Headquarters," he thought, with irritation. "We've been able to manage, with the chickens, but this is really too much! What can they be thinking of at the inspection point? Oh, well, they're tired too, I suppose, but it's my responsibility.")

He put a rasp in his voice—he had to, they looked at him so stupidly. "Well?" he said. "Answer me! Don't you know an officer when you see one?"

"We have come a long way," said the man, in a low voice. "We heard there was danger to the child. So we are going. May we pass?" The voice was civil enough, but the eyes were dark and large, the face tired and worn. He was resting one hand on his staff, in a peasant gesture. The woman said nothing at all and one felt that she would say nothing. She sat on the back of the gray donkey and the child in her arms, too, was silent, though it moved.

The lieutenant tried to think rapidly. After all, these were the last. But the thoughts buzzed around his head and would not come out of his mouth. That was fatigue. It should be easy enough for a lieutenant to give an order.

He found himself saying, conversationally, "There are just the three of you?"

"That is all," said the man and looked at him with great simplicity. "But we heard there was danger to the child. So we could not stay any more. We could not stay at all."

"Indeed," said the lieutenant and then said again, "indeed."

469

"Yes," said the man. "But we shall do well enough—we have been in exile before." He spoke patiently and yet with a certain authority. When the lieutenant did not answer, he laid his other hand on the rein of the gray donkey. It moved forward a step and with it, also, the child stirred and moved. The lieutenant, turning, saw the child's face now, and its hands, as it turned and moved its small hands to the glow of the sunset.

"If the lieutenant pleases—" said an eager voice, the voice of the Northern corporal.

"The lieutenant does not please," said the lieutenant. He nodded at the man. "You may proceed."

"But Lieutenant—" said the eager voice.

"Swine and dog," said the lieutenant, feeling something snap in his mind, "are we to hinder the Leader's plans because of one gray donkey? The order says—all out of the country by sunset. Let them go. You will report to me, Corporal, in the morning."

He turned on his heel and walked a straight line to the field hut, not looking back. When Franz, the orderly, came in a little later, he found him sitting in a chair.

"If the lieutenant would take some brandy—" he said, respectfully.

"The lieutenant has had enough brandy," said the lieutenant, in a hoarse, dusty voice. "Have my orders been obeyed?"

"Yes, Lieutenant."

"They are gone—the very last of them?"

"Yes, Lieutenant."

"They did not look back?"

"No, Lieutenant."

The lieutenant said nothing, for a while, and Franz busied himself with boots. After some time, he spoke.

"The lieutenant should try to sleep," he said. "We have carried out our orders. And now, they are gone."

"Yes," said the lieutenant, and, suddenly, he saw them again, the whole multitude, dispersed among every country—the ones who had walked his road, the ones at the points of embarkation. There were a great many of them, and that he had expected. But they were not dispersed as he had thought. They were not dispersed as he had thought, for, with each one went shame, like a visible burden. And the shame was not theirs, though they carried it—the shame belonged to the land that had driven them forth—his own land. He could see it growing and spreading like a black blot—the shame of his country spread over the whole earth.

"The lieutenant will have some brandy," he said. "Quickly, Franz."

When the brandy was brought, he stared at it for a moment, in the cup.

"Tell me, Franz," he said. "Did you know them well? Any of them? Before?"

"Oh yes, Lieutenant," said Franz, in his smooth, orderly's voice. "In the last war, I was billeted—well, the name of the town does not matter, but the woman was one of them. Of course that was before we knew about them," he said, respectfully. "That was more than twenty years ago. But she was very kind to me—I used to make toys for her children. I have often wondered what happened to her—she was very considerate and kind. Doubtless I was wrong, Lieutenant? But that was in another country."

"Yes, Franz," said the lieutenant. "There were children, you say?"

"Yes, Lieutenant."

"You saw the child today? The last one?"

"Yes, Lieutenant."

"Its hands had been hurt," said the lieutenant. "In the middle. Right through. I saw them. I wish I had not seen that. I wish I had not seen its hands."

BY THE WATERS OF BABYLON

The north and the west and the south are good hunting ground, but it is forbidden to go east. It is forbidden to go to any of the Dead Places except to search for metal and then he who touches the metal must be a priest or the son of a priest. Afterwards, both the man and the metal must be purified. These are the rules and the laws; they are well made. It is forbidden to cross the great river and look upon the place that was the Place of the Gods—this is most strictly forbidden. We do not even say its name though we know its name. It is there that spirits live, and demons—it is there that there are the ashes of the Great

Burning. These things are forbidden—they have been forbidden since the beginning of time.

My father is a priest; I am the son of a priest. I have been in the Dead Places near us, with my father—at first, I was afraid. When my father went into the house to search for the metal, I stood by the door and my heart felt small and weak. It was a dead man's house, a spirit house. It did not have the smell of man, though there were old bones in a corner. But it is not fitting that a priest's son should show fear. I looked at the bones in the shadow and kept my voice still.

Then my father came out with the metal—a good, strong piece. He looked at me with both eyes but I had not run away. He gave me the metal to hold—I took it and did not die. So he knew that I was truly his son and would be a priest in my time. That was when I was very young—nevertheless, my brothers would not have done it, though they are good hunters. After that, they gave me the good piece of meat and the warm corner by the fire. My father watched over me—he was glad that I should be a priest. But when I boasted or wept without a reason, he punished me more strictly than my brothers. That was right.

After a time, I myself was allowed to go into the dead houses and search for metal. So I learned the ways of those houses— and if I saw bones, I was no longer afraid. The bones are light and old—sometimes they will fall into dust if you touch them. But that is a great sin.

I was taught the chants and the spells—I was taught how to stop the running of blood from a wound and many secrets. A priest must know many secrets—that was what my father said. If the hunters think we do all things by chants and spells, they may believe so—it does not hurt them. I was taught how to read in the old books and how to make the old writings—that was hard and took a long time. My knowledge made me happy—it was like a fire in my heart. Most of all, I liked to hear of the Old Days and the stories of the gods. I asked myself many questions that I could not answer, but it was good to ask them. At night, I would lie awake and listen to the wind—it seemed to me that it was the voice of the gods as they flew through the air.

We are not ignorant like the Forest People—our women spin wool on the wheel, our priests wear a white robe. We do not eat grubs from the tree, we have not forgotten the old writings,

By the Waters of Babylon

although they are hard to understand. Nevertheless, my knowledge and my lack of knowledge burned in me—I wished to know more. When I was a man at last, I came to my father and said, "It is time for me to go on my journey. Give me your leave."

He looked at me for a long time, stroking his beard, then he said at last, "Yes. It is time." That night, in the house of the priesthood, I asked for and received purification. My body hurt but my spirit was a cool stone. It was my father himself who questioned me about my dreams.

He bade me look into the smoke of the fire and see—I saw and told what I saw. It was what I have always seen—a river, and, beyond it, a great Dead Place and in it the gods walking. I have always thought about that. His eyes were stern when I told him—he was no longer my father but a priest. He said, "This is a strong dream."

"It is mine," I said, while the smoke waved and my head felt light. They were singing the Star song in the outer chamber and it was like the buzzing of bees in my head.

He asked me how the gods were dressed and I told him how they were dressed. We know how they were dressed from the book, but I saw them as if they were before me. When I had finished, he threw the sticks three times and studied them as they fell.

"This is a very strong dream," he said. "It may eat you up."

"I am not afraid," I said and looked at him with both eyes. My voice sounded thin in my ears but that was because of the smoke.

He touched me on the breast and the forehead. He gave me the bow and the three arrows.

"Take them," he said. "It is forbidden to travel east. It is forbidden to cross the river. It is forbidden to go to the Place of the Gods. All these things are forbidden."

"All these things are forbidden," I said, but it was my voice that spoke and not my spirit. He looked at me again.

"My son," he said. "Once I had young dreams. If your dreams do not eat you up, you may be a great priest. If they eat you, you are still my son. Now go on your journey."

I went fasting, as is the law. My body hurt but not my heart. When the dawn came, I was out of sight of the village. I prayed and purified myself, waiting for a sign. The sign was an eagle. It flew east.

473

Sometimes signs are sent by bad spirits. I waited again on the flat rock, fasting, taking no food. I was very still—I could feel the sky above me and the earth beneath. I waited till the sun was beginning to sink. Then three deer passed in the valley, going east—they did not wind me or see me. There was a white fawn with them—a very great sign.

I followed them, at a distance, waiting for what would happen. My heart was troubled about going east, yet I knew that I must go. My head hummed with my fasting—I did not even see the panther spring upon the white fawn. But, before I knew it, the bow was in my hand. I shouted and the panther lifted his head from the fawn. It is not easy to kill a panther with one arrow but the arrow went through his eye and into his brain. He died as he tried to spring—he rolled over, tearing at the ground. Then I knew I was meant to go east—I knew that was my journey. When the night came, I made my fire and roasted meat.

It is eight suns' journey to the east and a man passes by many Dead Places. The Forest People are afraid of them but I am not. Once I made my fire on the edge of a Dead Place at night and, next morning, in the dead house, I found a good knife, little rusted. That was small to what came afterward but it made my heart feel big. Always when I looked for game, it was in front of my arrow, and twice I passed hunting parties of the Forest People without their knowing. So I knew my magic was strong and my journey clean, in spite of the law.

Toward the setting of the eighth sun, I came to the banks of the great river. It was half-a-day's journey after I had left the god-road—we do not use the god-roads now for they are falling apart into great blocks of stone, and the forest is safer going. A long way off, I had seen the water through trees but the trees were thick. At last, I came out upon an open place at the top of a cliff. There was the great river below, like a giant in the sun. It is very long, very wide. It could eat all the streams we know and still be thirsty. Its name is Ou-dis-sun, the Sacred, the Long. No man of my tribe had seen it, not even my father, the priest. It was magic and I prayed.

Then I raised my eyes and looked south. It was there, the Place of the Gods.

How can I tell what it was like—you do not know. It was there, in the red light, and they were too big to be houses. It was there with the red light upon it, mighty and ruined. I knew that in another moment the gods would see me. I covered my eyes with my hands and crept back into the forest.

Surely, that was enough to do, and live. Surely it was enough to spend the night upon the cliff. The Forest People themselves do not come near. Yet, all through the night, I knew that I should have to cross the river and walk in the places of the gods, although the gods ate me up. My magic did not help me at all and yet there was a fire in my bowels, a fire in my mind. When the sun rose, I thought, "My journey has been clean. Now I will go home from my journey." But, even as I thought so, I knew I could not. If I went to the Place of the Gods, I would surely die, but, if I did not go, I could never be at peace with my spirit again. It is better to lose one's life than one's spirit, if one is a priest and the son of a priest.

Nevertheless, as I made the raft, the tears ran out of my eyes. The Forest People could have killed me without fight, if they had come upon me then, but they did not come. When the raft was made, I said the sayings for the dead and painted myself for death. My heart was cold as a frog and my knees like water, but the burning in my mind would not let me have peace. As I pushed the raft from the shore, I began my death song—I had the right. It was a fine song.

"I am John, son of John," I sang. "My people are the Hill People.
   They are the men.
I go into the Dead Places but I am not slain.
I take the metal from the Dead Places but I am not blasted.
I travel upon the god-roads and am not afraid. E-yah! I have
   killed the panther, I have killed the fawn!
E-yah! I have come to the great river. No man has come there
   before.
It is forbidden to go east, but I have gone, forbidden to go on
   the great river, but I am there.
Open your hearts, you spirits, and hear my song.
   Now I go to the Place of the Gods, I shall not return.
My body is painted for death and my limbs weak, but my heart
   is big as I go to the Place of the Gods!"

All the same, when I came to the Place of the Gods, I was

afraid, afraid. The current of the great river is very strong—
it gripped my raft with its hands. That was magic, for the
river itself is wide and calm. I could feel evil spirits about me,
in the bright morning; I could feel their breath on my neck as
I was swept down the stream. Never have I been so much alone—
I tried to think of my knowledge, but it was a squirrel's heap of
winter nuts. There was no strength in my knowledge any more
and I felt small and naked as a new-hatched bird—alone upon the
great river, the servant of the gods.

Yet, after a while, my eyes were opened and I saw. I saw both
banks of the river—I saw that once there had been god-roads
across it, though now they were broken and fallen like broken
vines. Very great they were, and wonderful and broken—broken
in the time of the Great Burning when the fire fell out of the
sky. And always the current took me nearer to the Place of the
Gods, and the huge ruins rose before my eyes.

I do not know the customs of rivers—we are the People of
the Hills. I tried to guide my raft with the pole but it spun
around. I thought the river meant to take me past the Place of the
Gods and out into the Bitter Water of the legends. I grew angry
then—my heart felt strong. I said aloud, "I am a priest and the
son of a priest!" The gods heard me—they showed me how to
paddle with the pole on one side of the raft. The current changed
itself—I drew near to the Place of the Gods.

When I was very near, my raft struck and turned over. I can
swim in our lakes—I swam to the shore. There was a great
spike of rusted metal sticking out into the river—I hauled myself
up upon it and sat there, panting. I had saved my bow and two
arrows and the knife I found in the Dead Place but that was all.
My raft went whirling downstream toward the Bitter Water.
I looked after it, and thought if it had trod me under, at least
I would be safely dead. Nevertheless, when I had dried my bow-
string and re-strung it, I walked forward to the Place of the
Gods.

It felt like ground underfoot; it did not burn me. It is not
true what some of the tales say, that the ground there burns
forever, for I have been there. Here and there were the marks
and stains of the Great Burning, on the ruins, that is true. But
they were old marks and old stains. It is not true either, what
some of our priests say, that it is an island covered with fogs and

enchantments. It is not. It is a great Dead Place—greater than any Dead Place we know. Everywhere in it there are god-roads, though most are cracked and broken. Everywhere there are the ruins of the high towers of the gods.

How shall I tell what I saw? I went carefully, my strung bow in my hand, my skin ready for danger. There should have been the wailings of spirits and the shrieks of demons, but there were not. It was very silent and sunny where I had landed—the wind and the rain and the birds that drop seeds had done their work —the grass grew in the cracks of the broken stone. It is a fair island—no wonder the gods built there. If I had come there, a god, I also would have built.

How shall I tell what I saw? The towers are not all broken— here and there one still stands, like a great tree in a forest, and the birds nest high. But the towers themselves look blind, for the gods are gone. I saw a fish-hawk, catching fish in the river. I saw a little dance of white butterflies over a great heap of broken stones and columns. I went there and looked about me—there was a carved stone with cut-letters, broken in half. I can read letters but I could not understand these. They said UBTREAS. There was also the shattered image of a man or a god. It had been made of white stone and he wore his hair tied back like a woman's. His name was ASHING, as I read on the cracked half of a stone. I thought it wise to pray to ASHING, though I do not know that god.

How shall I tell what I saw? There was no smell of man left, on stone or metal. Nor were there many trees in that wilderness of stone. There are many pigeons, nesting and dropping in the towers—the gods must have loved them, or, perhaps, they used them for sacrifices. There are wild cats that roam the god-roads, green-eyed, unafraid of man. At night they wail like demons but they are not demons. The wild dogs are more dangerous, for they hunt in a pack, but them I did not meet till later. Everywhere there are the carved stones, carved with magical numbers or words.

I went North—I did not try to hide myself. When a god or a demon saw me, then I would die, but meanwhile I was no longer afraid. My hunger for knowledge burned in me—there was so much that I could not understand. After awhile, I knew that my belly was hungry. I could have hunted for my meat, but I

477

did not hunt. It is known that the gods did not hunt as we do —they got their food from enchanted boxes and jars. Sometimes these are still found in the Dead Places—once, when I was a child and foolish, I opened such a jar and tasted it and found the food sweet. But my father found out and punished me for it strictly, for, often, that food is death. Now, though, I had long gone past what was forbidden, and I entered the likeliest towers, looking for the food of the gods.

I found it at last in the ruins of a great temple in the mid-city. A mighty temple it must have been, for the roof was painted like the sky at night with its stars—that much I could see, though the colors were faint and dim. It went down into great caves and tunnels—perhaps they kept their slaves there. But when I started to climb down, I heard the squeaking of rats, so I did not go —rats are unclean, and there must have been many tribes of them, from the squeaking. But near there, I found food, in the heart of a ruin, behind a door that still opened. I ate only the fruits from the jars—they had a very sweet taste. There was drink, too, in bottles of glass—the drink of the gods was strong and made my head swim. After I had eaten and drunk, I slept on the top of a stone, my bow at my side.

When I woke, the sun was low. Looking down from where I lay, I saw a dog sitting on his haunches. His tongue was hanging out of his mouth; he looked as if he were laughing. He was a big dog, with a gray-brown coat, as big as a wolf. I sprang up and shouted at him but he did not move—he just sat there as if he were laughing. I did not like that. When I reached for a stone to throw, he moved swiftly out of the way of the stone. He was not afraid of me; he looked at me as if I were meat. No doubt I could have killed him with an arrow, but I did not know if there were others. Moreover, night was falling.

I looked about me—not far away there was a great, broken god-road, leading North. The towers were high enough, but not so high, and while many of the dead-houses were wrecked, there were some that stood. I went toward this god-road, keeping to the heights of the ruins, while the dog followed. When I had reached the god-road, I saw that there were others behind him. If I had slept later, they would have come upon me asleep and torn out my throat. As it was, they were sure enough of me; they did not hurry. When I went into the dead-house, they kept watch at the entrance—doubtless they thought they would have a fine hunt. But a dog cannot open a door and I knew, from the books, that the gods did not like to live on the ground but on high.

I had just found a door I could open when the dogs decided to rush. Ha! They were surprised when I shut the door in their faces—it was a good door, of strong metal. I could hear their foolish baying beyond it but I did not stop to answer them. I was in darkness—I found stairs and climbed. There were many stairs, turning around till my head was dizzy. At the top was another door—I found the knob and opened it. I was in a long small chamber—on one side of it was a bronze door that could not be opened, for it had no handle. Perhaps there was a magic word to open it but I did not have the word. I turned to the door in the opposite side of the wall. The lock of it was broken and I opened it and went in.

Within, there was a place of great riches. The god who lived there must have been a powerful god. The first room was a small ante-room—I waited there for some time, telling the spirits of the place that I came in peace and not as a robber. When it seemed to me that they had had time to hear me, I went on. Ah, what riches! Few, even, of the windows had been broken —it was all as it had been. The great windows that looked over the city had not been broken at all though they were dusty and streaked with many years. There were coverings on the floors, the colors not greatly faded, and the chairs were soft and deep. There were pictures upon the walls, very strange, very wonderful—I remember one of a bunch of flowers in a jar—if you came close to it, you could see nothing but bits of color, but if you stood away from it, the flowers might have been picked yesterday. It made my heart feel strange to look at this picture—and to look at the figure of a bird, in some hard clay, on a table and see it so like our birds. Everywhere there were books and writings, many in tongues that I could not read. The god who lived there must have been a wise god and full of knowledge. I felt I had right there, as I sought knowledge also.

Nevertheless, it was strange. There was a washing-place but no water—perhaps the gods washed in air. There was a cooking-place but no wood, and though there was a machine to cook food, there was no place to put fire in it. Nor were there candles or lamps—there were things that looked like lamps but they had neither oil nor wick. All these things were magic, but I touched them and lived—the magic had gone out of them. Let me tell one thing to show. In the washing-place, a thing said "Hot" but it was not hot to the touch—another thing said "Cold" but it was not cold. This must have been a strong magic but the magic was gone. I do not understand—they had ways—I wish that I knew.

It was close and dry and dusty in their house of the gods. I have said the magic was gone but that is not true—it had gone from the magic things but it had not gone from the place. I felt the spirits about me, weighing upon me. Nor had I ever slept in a Dead Place before—and yet, tonight, I must sleep there. When I thought of it, my tongue felt dry in my throat, in spite of my wish for knowledge. Almost I would have gone down again and faced the dogs, but I did not.

I had not gone through all the rooms when the darkness fell. When it fell, I went back to the big room looking over the city and made fire. There was a place to make fire and a box with wood in it, though I do not think they cooked there. I wrapped myself in a floor-covering and slept in front of the fire—I was very tired.

Now I tell what is very strong magic. I woke in the midst of the night. When I woke, the fire had gone out and I was cold. It seemed to me that all around me there were whisperings and voices. I closed my eyes to shut them out. Some will say that I slept again, but I do not think that I slept. I could feel the spirits drawing my spirit out of my body as a fish is drawn on a line.

Why should I lie about it? I am a priest and the son of a priest. If there are spirits, as they say, in the small Dead Places near us, what spirits must there not be in that great Place of the Gods? And would not they wish to speak? After such long years? I know that I felt myself drawn as a fish is drawn on a line. I had stepped out of my body—I could see my body asleep in front of the cold fire, but it was not I. I was drawn to look out upon the city of the gods.

It should have been dark, for it was night, but it was not dark. Everywhere there were lights—lines of light—circles and blurs of light—ten thousand torches would not have been the same. The sky itself was alight—you could barely see the stars for the glow in the sky. I thought to myself "This is strong magic" and trembled. There was a roaring in my ears like the rushing of rivers. Then my eyes grew used to the light and my ears to the sound. I knew that I was seeing the city as it had been when the gods were alive.

That was a sight indeed—yes, that was a sight: I could not have seen it in the body—my body would have died. Everywhere went the gods, on foot and in chariots—there were gods beyond number and counting and their chariots blocked the streets. They had turned night to day for their pleasure—they did not sleep with the sun. The noise of their coming and going was the noise of many waters. It was magic what they could do—it was magic what they did.

I looked out of another window—the great vines of their bridges were mended and the god-roads went East and West. Restless, restless, were the gods and always in motion! They burrowed tunnels under rivers—they flew in the air. With unbelievable tools they did giant works—no part of the earth was safe from them, for, if they wished for a thing, they summoned it from the other side of the world. And always, as they labored and rested, as they feasted and made love, there was a drum in their ears—the pulse of the giant city, beating and beating like a man's heart.

Were they happy? What is happiness to the gods? They were great, they were mighty, they were wonderful and terrible. As I looked upon them and their magic, I felt like a child—but a little more, it seemed to me, and they would pull down the moon from the sky. I saw them with wisdom beyond wisdom and knowledge beyond knowledge. And yet not all they did was well done—even I could see that—and yet their wisdom could not but grow until all was peace.

Then I saw their fate come upon them and that was terrible past speech. It came upon them as they walked the streets of their city. I have been in the fights with the Forest People—I have seen men die. But this was not like that. When gods war with gods, they use weapons we do not know. It was fire falling out of the sky and a mist that poisoned. It was the time of the Great Burning and the Destruction. They ran about like ants in the streets of their city—poor gods, poor gods! Then the towers began to fall. A few escaped—yes, a few. The legends tell it. But, even after the city had become a Dead Place, for many years the poison was still in the ground. I saw it happen, I saw the last of them die. It was darkness over the broken city and I wept.

All this, I saw. I saw it as I have told it, though not in the body. When I woke in the morning, I was hungry, but I did not think first of my hunger for my heart was perplexed and confused. I knew the reason for the Dead Places but I did not see why it had happened. It seemed to me it should not have happened, with all the magic they had. I went through the house looking for an answer. There was so much in the house I could not understand—and yet I am a priest and the son of a priest. It was like being on one side of the great river, at night, with no light to show the way.

Then I saw the dead god. He was sitting in his chair, by the window, in a room I had not entered before and, for the first moment, I thought that he was alive. Then I saw the skin on the back of his hand—it was like dry leather. The room was shut, hot and dry—no doubt that had kept him as he was. At first I was afraid to approach him—then the fear left me. He was sitting looking out over the city—he was dressed in the clothes of the gods. His age was neither young nor old—I could not tell his age. But there was wisdom in his face and great sadness. You could see that he would have not run away. He had sat at his window, watching his city die—then he himself had died. But it is better to lose one's life than one's spirit—and you could see from the face that his spirit had not been lost. I knew, that, if I touched him, he would fall into dust—and yet, there was something unconquered in the face.

That is all of my story, for then I knew he was a man—I knew then that they had been men, neither gods nor demons. It is a great knowledge, hard to tell and believe. They were men —they went a dark road, but they were men. I had no fear after that—I had no fear going home, though twice I fought off the dogs and once I was hunted for two days by the Forest People. When I saw my father again, I prayed and was purified. He touched my lips and my breast, he said, "You went away a boy. You come back a man and a priest." I said, "Father, they were men! I have been in the Place of the Gods and seen it! Now slay me, if it is the law—but still I know they were men."

He looked at me out of both eyes. He said, "The law is not

always the same shape—you have done what you have done. I could not have done it my time, but you come after me. Tell!"

I told and he listened. After that, I wished to tell all the people but he showed me otherwise. He said, "Truth is a hard deer to hunt. If you eat too much truth at once, you may die of the truth. It was not idly that our fathers forbade the Dead Places." He was right—it is better the truth should come little by little. I have learned that, being a priest. Perhaps, in the old days, they ate knowledge too fast.

Nevertheless, we make a beginning. It is not for the metal alone we go to the Dead Places now—there are the books and the writings. They are hard to learn. And the magic tools are broken —but we can look at them and wonder. At least, we make a beginning. And, when I am chief priest we shall go beyond the great river. We shall go to the Place of the Gods—the place newyork—not one man but a company. We shall look for the images of the gods and find the god ASHING and the others— the gods Licoln and Biltmore and Moses. But they were men who built the city, not gods or demons. They were men. I remember the dead man's face. They were men who were here before us. We must build again.